READINGS IN TECHNOLOGY AND AMERICAN LIFE

READINGS
IN TECHNOLOGY
AND AMERICAN
LIFE

CARROLL W. PURSELL, JR.

OXFORD UNIVERSITY PRESS   NEW YORK   LONDON   TORONTO
1969

Contents

READINGS IN TECHNOLOGY AND AMERICAN LIFE

Introduction

Technology holds a special place in both the hearts and history of Americans. Although tools have always played an important role in the history of man, it is commonly admitted that they have played a special and magnified role in the New World. Whether we are envied for our refrigerators, despised for our transistor radios, or feared for our nuclear weapons, the American Way of Life is viewed throughout the world as one in which gadgets, tools, and machines play a dominant part.

Americans have long been aware of this difference. One of the earliest and most provocative images of America was that of a Garden, carved out of the wilderness by machines. The first settlers came here as invaders, determined to conquer nature, not to live in harmony with it. The vast distances, severe winters, and thick forests, no less than the native Indians, were their enemies. This handful of invaders, alone in a hostile environment, needed all the mechanical advantage they could command to help even the odds.

Once survival was assured, the same technology was turned to the task of improvement. As Americans gained self-consciousness as a people with a mission, they turned gratefully to technology to accomplish their great national purposes. If this was to be a land of economic opportunity, then machines were needed to convert the land's resources into actual wealth. If it was to be a land of equality, then the machines and tools must be available to all, and used to eliminate degrading and servile tasks. If the American empire was to rival those of Europe, then the far reaches of the nation must be tied together with the cords of transport, communications must be improved, and manufactures encouraged. If Americans had a civilizing purpose in God's plan, then our superior arms and entrepreneurial skill must be imposed upon inferior peoples for their own good.

Not surprisingly, technology—the means to progress—came eventually to be the measure of progress. When nineteenth-century Americans (and English-

3

men, too, for that matter) sought to describe the rapid improvement of mankind they could do no better than to point to the legion of new and improved devices which appeared almost daily. Within the lifetime of a single man this nation moved from horseback and sailing ship, through steamboat and railroad, to automobile and airplane. During these same years the continent was populated, our national industries challenged and then bettered those of Great Britain, and we became a world power, one to be reckoned with. It was a proud record, and one which could be told in terms of improved technologies.

There were always critics, of course—men who warned that the machine would destroy the very garden it had created. It was not a dominant theme, however. Even in our own time, when our incredibly sophisticated and powerful technology seems capable of serving only the policies of great military and corporate mandarins, we persist in the deadly folly of substituting technology for purpose. Americans, by and large, believe that technology is rational, benign, and not only compatible with but indispensable for the fulfillment of the American dream.

Strangely enough, aside from a folk cult gathered around such figures as Henry Ford and Thomas Edison, Americans have shown little curiosity about the historic role of technology in the development of their nation. Such interest is usually limited to a catalogue of "firsts," which speaks more of pride than of understanding. The history of invention, of course, even when accurate, is not the same thing as the history of technology. While the latter defies precise definition, it certainly includes the development of both machines and method, both invention and innovation.

Defined in this way, technology has always been an important and integral factor in the development of the nation. Indeed, to properly appreciate the role of technology in our history it must be looked at as Americans have always looked at it—as a way of getting the job done. Americans needed guns to kill Indians and overthrow the British colonial government. They needed steamboats and factories to build an empire of their own. They needed mass production and scientific management to convert natural resources into consumer goods for a democratic society. If technology is not the Hamlet of the American drama, it is at least the Claudius. Our story would hardly be the same without it.

PART I COLONIAL TECHNOLOGY

Colonial American technology was essentially medieval in character. The Europeans who came to the new land across the Atlantic brought with them a strong tradition of technology—plows and muskets, windmills and sailing ships. The Middle Ages had been rich in technical innovation, and it was largely the technical superiority these innovations gave to the colonists that allowed them to destroy or subdue the native peoples they found already occupying the land. Gradually, the somewhat different demands of the new environment and the colonists' increasing exposure to the technology of the American Indians brought about changes in their European technology. Some of these changes were improvements, such as the American axe, but some were retrogressive, such as the virtual abandonment of the medieval three-field system of cultivation.

In whatever area, tools and machines in America shared certain characteristics. First, they were primarily hand tools. There were mills, of course, some of very ancient design, but for the most part power was supplied by human hands rather than by animals, wind, or water. Second, colonial technology was based upon the use of wood rather than iron. Third, devices were made by craftsmen either in the home or in small shops. Fourth, science had yet to offer much to technology in the way of better understanding or improved techniques. And finally, technology was a comparatively conservative activity, slow to change, and when it took new forms was usually resisted.

An estimated 18 per cent of the colonial population were craftsmen; 80 per cent were farmers. But whether the colonist handcrafted objects for a living or only for his own use, whether he lived in a busy seaport or on the rawest frontier, he brought his technical background to bear upon the problems of life in a new country, using what he could of traditional knowledge and tools, but innovating where he had to. It was a technical system that remained virtually unchallenged until the end of the eighteenth century, when the

Americans—after winning their political independence—discovered that, while they had been fighting one revolution, another had taken place in the industry of the mother country.

1. Migration of Craftsmen, 1654

EDWARD JOHNSON, *Wonder-Working Providence*

Captain Edward Johnson (d. 1672), though he was unlettered, was a man of substance, both in the Old World and in New England, to which he came in 1630. Being a farmer and ship carpenter by trade, he knew from experience the fate of the crafts in New England. Disturbed by rumors that all was not well in the New World, Johnson wrote a book, *The Wonder-Working Providence of Zion's Saviour in New England*, to confound her detractors and paint a true—and optimistic—picture of colonial life. The book was first published in London in 1654. In it Johnson described the attempts that had been made to initiate industrial activity on a large scale as well as the opportunities that awaited craftsmen of every description.

Of the Lords wonder-working Providence, in fitting this people with all kind of Manufactures, and the bringing of them into the order of a commonwealth.

On the day of Election for Governor and Magistrates, (which are new chosen every year) the honored John Winthrope Esquire was chosen Governor, and the like honored Thomas Dudly Esquire Deputy Governor, John Endicut Esquire was chosen Major-General, which is an Officer the Freemen make a yearly choice of, all other Military Officers stand for term of life, unless any be out for misdemeanour; the number of freemen added this year were about 85. The Land affording very good iron stone, divers persons of good rank and quality in England were stirred up by the provident hand of the Lord to venture their estates upon an iron work, which they began at Braintree, and profited the owners little, but rather wasted their stock, which caused some of them to sell away the remainder, the chief reason being the high price of labour, which ordinarily was as much more as in England, and in many things treble; the way of going on with such a work here, was not suddainly to be discerned, although the Steward had a very able eye, yet experience hath out-stript learning here, and the most quick-sighted in the Theory of things, have been forced to pay prety roundly to Lady Experience for filling their heads with a little of her active after-wit; much hope there is now, that the owners may pick up their crums again, if they be but made partakers of the gain, in putting off England commodities at N. E. price, it will take off one third of the great price they gave for labour, and the price of their iron; it is supposed another third is taken of the abundance of wood had for little, will surely take off the residue, besides land at easie rates, and common land

From *Johnson's Wonder-Working Providence*, J. Franklin Jamison, ed. (New York, 1910), pp. 245-48.

free for their use; it were to be desired that those Gentlemen who have undertaken the work, would consider the place where their works are, namely in N. E. where the Lord Christ hath chosen to plant his Churches in, to hide his people under the covert of his wings, till the tyranny of Antichrist be overpassed, and any that have disbursed pence for the furthering of his work, shall be repayed with thousands: Besides, the Gentlemen that govern this Colony are very desirous to be helpful in what they may, and had rather take any burthens upon themselves and the Inhabitants, that in justice they ought, then that those Gentlemen should be any wayes damnified. The Lord is pleased also to compleat this Commonwealth abundantly beyond all expectation in all sorts of needful occupations, it being for a long time the great fear of many, and those that were endued with grace from above also, that this would be no place of continued habitation, for want of a staple-commodity, but the Lord, whose promises are large to his Sion, hath blest his peoples provision, and satisfied her poor with bread, in a very little space, every thing in the country proved a staple-commodity, wheat, rye, oats, peas, barley, beef, pork, fish, butter, cheese, timber, mast, tar, sope, plank-board, frames of houses, clabboard, and pipestaves, iron and lead is like to be also; and those who were formerly forced to fetch most of the bread they eat, and beer they drink, a hundred leagues by Sea, are through the blessing of the Lord so encreased, that they have not only fed their Elder Sisters, Virginia, Barbados, and many of the Summer Islands that were prefer'd before her for fruitfulness, but also the Grandmother of us all, even the firtil Isle of Great Britain, beside Portugal

hath had many a mouthful of bread and fish from us, in exchange of their Madeara liquor, and also Spain; nor could it be imagined, that this Wilderness should turn a mart for Merchants in so short a space, Holland, France, Spain, and Portugal coming hither for trade, shipping going on gallantly, till the Seas became so troublesome, and England restrain'd our trade, forbidding it with Barbados, etc. and Portugal stopt and took our ships; many a fair ship had her framing and finishing here, besides lesser vessels, barques, and ketches, many a Master, beside common Seamen, had their first learning in this Colony. Boston, Charles-Town, Salem, and Ipswitch, our Maritan Towns began to encrease roundly, especially Boston, the which of a poor country village, in twice seven years is become like unto a small City, and is in election to be Mayor Town suddainly, chiefly increased by trade by Sea, yet of late the Lord hath given a check to our traffique, but the reason may be rendred hereafter; nor hath this Colony alone been actors in this trade of venturing by Sea, but New-haven also, who were many of them well experienced in traffique, and had good estates to manage it. Canectico did not linger behind, but put forth to Sea with the other; all other trades have here fallen into their ranks and places, to their great advantage; especially Coopers and Shomakers, who had either of them a Corporation granted, inriching themselves by their trades very much, Coopers having their plenty of stuff at a cheap rate, and by reason of trade with forraign parts abundance of work; as for Tanners and Shomakers, it being naturalized into these occupations, to have a higher reach in mannaging their manifactures, then other men in N. E. are, having not chang'd their nature in this, between them both they have kept men to their stander hitherto, almost doubling the price of their commodities, according to the rate they were sold for in England, and yet the plenty of Leather is beyond what they had their [there], counting the number of the people, but the transportation of Boots and Shoes into forraign parts hath vented all however: as for Tailors, they have not come behind the former, their advantage being in the nurture of new-fashions, all one with England; Carpenters, Joyners, Glaziers, Painters, follow their trades only; Gun-smiths, Lock-smiths, Blacksmiths, Naylers, Cutlers, have left the husbandmen to follow the Plow and Cart, and they their trades; Weavers, Brewers, Bakers, Costermongers, Felt-makers, Braziers, Pewterers, and Tinkers, Ropemakers, Masons, Lime, Brick, and Tilemakers, Cardmakers to work, and not to play, Turners, Pumpmakers, and Wheelers, Glovers, Fellmungers, and Furriers, are orderly turn'd to their trades, besides divers sorts of Shopkeepers, and some who have a mystery beyond others, as have the Vintners.

Thus hath the Lord been pleased to turn one of the most hideous, boundless, and unknown Wildernesses in the world in an instant, as 'twere (in comparison of other work) to a well-ordered Commonwealth, and all to serve his Churches, of which the Author intends to speak of three more, which came to be gathered in the compass of these years.

2. Farming a New Land, 1747

JARED ELIOT, *Essays Upon Field-Husbandry*

No technology was of more critical importance to the colonists than agriculture. Most Americans were farmers, and their success with the soil determined their prosperity. In the century after Englishmen began to populate America, changes in agriculture in the old country began to take on the appearance of a revolution in this ancient occupation. Indeed, scholars have spoken of these changes as the Agricultural Revolution—one which preceded and laid the groundwork for the later Industrial Revolution. New crops (such as turnips), new machines (such as the seed drill), new regimens (such as crop rotations), and other changes (such as the famous enclosure movement) were introduced by gentlemen farmers whose example gradually filtered down to their less prosperous, less progressive, less well-placed neighbors.

From Jared Eliot, *Essays upon Field-Husbandry in New-England and Other Papers, 1748-1762*, Harry J. Carman and Rexford G. Tugwell, eds. (New York, 1967), pp. 102-11, 116-21.

One of the great figures of the Agricultural Revolution in England was Jethro Tull, who, in 1731, wrote his influential book *Horse Hoeing Husbandry*. In 1747, the Connecticut clergyman and natural philosopher Jared Eliot (1685-1763) undertook to write a series of essays explaining Tull's innovations in farming, which he had tested against the American environment, and put forth such changes as occurred to him as a result of his experiments. He published six essays in 1760 under the title *Essays upon Field-Husbandry in New-England, As it is or may be Ordered* (Boston, 1760).

In the fifth of these essays Eliot directed particular attention to the importance of adequate plowing, and the implements necessary for correct planting. Here he displayed those qualities which made him such a remarkable student of agriculture: his rational approach to the subject, his willingness to accept innovation, and his careful insistence on collecting evidence from many sources—the Bible, his own experience, that of his correspondents in other colonies, and the writings of technical experts in England.

I purpose to proceed in the same plain simple Manner, to set before the Reader the Way of mending our poor Land, and raising Crops, either without any Dung at all, or if any be applied, it shall be in such a small Quantity, that the Expence will be but little compared with the common Way of Husbandry.

In this Undertaking, I pretend to no other Merit than that,

I. To explain the Doctrine or Principles of Mr. *Tull* in such a Manner as to be open to any common Understanding.

II. To offer such Reasons and Proofs for the Support of these Principles, as will naturally occur.

III. To direct to the Performance of the Work with Instruments less intricate, more plain, cheap and commodious, than those used and described by Mr. *Tull*.

Under these three Heads may, I think, be comprehended all that I design at present to say of this Method of Husbandry, 'till Time and Experience shall enable me to write farther upon this important Subject: For if I succeed

according to my Expectation and Desire, I apprehend Husbandry, in the Tillage of Land, will stand upon a good Footing.

The only Way we have to inrich the Land, is by Dung, or by Tillage separately, or by both of them together: It is performed by dividing the Earth into many Parts, or as the common Way of speaking, it is done by making the Ground mellow and soft, so that the Roots may freely pass and find their proper Nourishment. The more mellow and fine the Earth is made, the more Roots will be sent out, from Corn or whatever is sowed or planted in such mellow Land; and the more soft and mellow the Ground is made, there will be not only more Roots, but they will be longer and extend farther: so that the Corn, Turnip, Carrot, or whatever Plant it is, will receive so much the more Nourishment, and consequently grow so much the bigger and better. Dung, or any other Measure, divides the Ground, sets the Parts at a Distance, and so gives a free Passage to the Roots of Plants. In this Action the Salts in

Dung hath much the same Operation and Effect as Leaven, or Emptyings hath on Dough; it makes it rise, makes it light, that is, sets the Parts at a Distance. If nothing be done to divide the Parts, and make the Ground mellow by ploughing, or Dung, or both, no Crop can be expected. Sow or plant upon untill'd Land, which is hard and uncultivated, no Corn will grow. If the Earth can be as well divided, and made as mellow by ploughing, digging or howing, why should not Tillage do without Dung; provided the Tillage be equal, or in Proportion to Dung? To do this in the common Way of repeated plain Ploughing and Harrowing, would be too much Charge and Labour: For Mr. *Tull* said, that three Times plain ploughing did only prepare the Land for Tillage. There is a Way of Tillage alone, without Dung, to make the Ground fine and mellow; and this Way is cheap and effectual; is done in the following manner,

First plough your Ground plain, and plough it deep; if you have no Dung, you must have the more loose mellow Earth: When it is thus ploughed, harrow it well with an Iron-Tooth Harrow; let it lye a Fortnight exposed to the Sun, Air and Dews, then plough it into Ridges; to every Ridge there must be eight Furrows of the Plain-ploughing, two Furrows covered, four ploughed, and two left open; so that in Ridge-ploughing the Team and Plough travels but half so far as in Plain-ploughing: Ridge-ploughing will cost but half so much as Plain-ploughing.

I suppose I need not give any particular Directions concerning ploughing the Land into Ridges, every Ploughman understands this, or if he doth not, he may soon learn it of them that do. When it is thus ploughed into Ridges, it is pre-pared to plant with Wheat, or Cabbages, Carrots, or what else you see fit to plant. In what Manner, and with what Instruments the Seeds of Wheat, Turnips, or Cabbages are to be planted, I shall describe under the third Head, when I come to speak of the Instruments by which it is performed. I shall only add in this Place that the Wheat is to be planted in two Rows on the Middle of the Ridge, the Rows to be at ten Inches Distance; the Cabbages and Turnips in one Row on the Middle of the Ridge, the Turnips at six Inches Distance from each other, Cabbages at a Foot and Half, or two Foot Distance; Carrots are to be planted in two Rows at ten Inches distance, that is, the Space between the Rows is to be ten Inches, the Carrots to be planted at six Inches Distance one from the other, as they stand in the Line or Row.

The Reader will observe, that as yet there is no more Tillage applied to the Land than what is common and usual in our ordinary Way of Husbandry. Now, what follows, is that in which the Art and Mistery doth consist and when it is described and set before you, will appear so simple, so little, so mean, that it will be to you as *go wash in Jordan* was to *Naaman* the Syrian. Suppose it be Turnips, Cabbages or Carrots planted in the Spring, (for as to what relates to Wheat the golden Grain, I purpose to treat of that distinctly by itself) as soon as your Cabbages and Turnips can be seen, weed them with a small hand Hoe. The Carrots for the first Time must be weeded with the Fingers; this is tedious Work: When this is done, and the Plants a little grown so as to be plainly seen, then take one Yoke of Oxen, a long Yoke so long that one Ox may go in one Furrow, and the other Ox in the other, and the Ridge between, in the same Manner as we plough Indian Corn: and with a common Ox Plow, turn of a Furrow from the Ridge, coming as close to the Plants as you can, and not plough them up; you may come within two or three Inches, if the Oxen and Plough are good. Thus take off a Furrow from each Side of every Ridge till all is ploughed; let it lye in this State a Fortnight or three Weeks, then with the Plough turn up the two Furrows to the Ridge; stay about as long as before, and turn the two Furrows off from the Ridge again; the oftner this is repeated so much the better: We ordinarily do it but four Times; but seven times will do better. When the Plants grow larger, you must keep the Plough at a greater Distance; for if you plough as near the Plants as when they are small, you will cut off too many Roots.

You must hoe between the Rows of Carrots with a narrow hand Hoe, to kill the Weeds; and to till the Ground between the Rows, you must mind to dig deep.

Turnips, and whatever is planted in a single Line or Row, must be tended with a hand Hoe, while the Plants are young, and 'till all the Weeds are destroyed so that you may use the Plough. I have been obliged to enter into the practical Part of this Sort of Husbandry, without which I should not be able to explain the Principles, or doctrinal Part, as I proposed under the first Head.

1. This Way of tilling Land makes it exceeding fine, soft and mellow, beyond what you would imagine: This, we have shewed already, is one Thing requisite and needful.

2. By this Tillage we open such Clods and Parts of Earth as never were opened before, and consequently never was touched by any Root; its whole nourishing Virtue remains intire: In short it is new Land. Every one knows what new Land will do before its native and original Strength and Vigour is consumed and exhausted by the Roots of Corn and other Plants. Thus this Sort of Tillage doth, in a Degree furnish us with new Land. In this Way old Things become new.

3. In this Way of Tillage we intirely destroy and extirpate all Weeds and Grass yea, even that stubborn Grass called *Blue Grass*, which is so hurtful to Corn; by which a whole Crop is frequently almost destroyed. This Grass by many is called *Dutch Grass;* and probably that Grass in *England* there called *Couch Grass*, may be the same, and miscalled here *Dutch*, from a Resemblance or Likeness of Sound; their Farmers making the same Complaint of it as ours do here. The Destruction of Weeds and Grass is of great Advantage in Tillage. Weeds very much exhaust the Land, hinder and damnify the Crop: The more these Robbers are destroyed, the more Nourishment there is for Corn.

This Method not only destroys the Weeds for the present, but for the future also; for ploughing stirs up the latent Seeds of Weeds, sets them a growing, and then destroys them when they are come up. The Seeds of Weeds are numerous and hardy, they will lye many Years in the Ground, and when by the Plough are properly situated for Growth, they will come up very plentifully: *Charlock*, commonly called *Terrify*, which cannot be subdued in the common Way of Tillage, I suppose in this Way, may be effectually conquered.

That the Destruction of Weeds is one Design we have in View when we till Land, is what is allowed by all; nay, many think that this is the only End, and at least they act and conduct as if they thought so: If it were not so, why do they neglect to hoe and plough if there be no Weeds? And why do they aim at going no deeper than just to cut up the Weeds? But there are other great Advantages to be had by Tillage, besides killing Weeds, as has been said already, and will further appear.

4. This Way of repeated ploughing keeps the Land from going out of Tillage. If Land be never so much ploughed and harrowed, and made ever so light and mellow, yet in a Year's Time the Tillage is spent in a great Degree. The Weight of great Rains, and the natural Weight of the Earth, settles it down so that it is daily growing closer and harder; there is less and less Room for the Roots to extend and spread, find their Food and get Nourishment; for the Roots in Plants are as the Mouth is to Man and Beast; the more Roots the more growth. When Land, by the Law of Gravitation, is thus continually sinking down, closeing together, and so going out of Tillage, we then plough it once in a Month, or oftener, if there be need. Thus the Tillage is kept up in the same State as at first. I find that a great heavy Rain if it fall soon after the Land has been ploughed, it will need ploughing again: In dry Weather it will continue in a State of Tillage much longer. Our Indian Corn has this repeated Tillage; but our Wheat suffers much for Want of after Tillage: We sow one Year and reap the next, so that from sowing Time 'till Harvest, is ten or eleven Months.

5. There is in Land a twofold and opposite State which renders Tillage absolutely necessary: This repeated plowing answers for both. In the common and ordinary State of Land, it is too hard and close, the parts are so nigh that there are no Holes or Passages left

for the Roots to spread downwards, and side ways; or at least these Pores, Holes or Passages, are too small and too few to give Room for the Roots: Often and repeated ploughing sets the Particles of Earth at such a Distance, and so enlargeth these Pores or Holes in the Earth, that the Growth of Plants is by this Means greatly promoted.

Although this be the ordinary State of Land which makes Tillage necessary; yet there is some Land in a State just the Reverse: it is too light, its Parts are at too great a Distance, the Pores and Passages are too wide, so that the Roots are not big enough to fill the Pores, or Holes. If the Roots do not touch the Earth it cannot get Nourishment: The Root should be inclosed on all Sides by the Earth. Every one knows that Roots above Ground in the open Air, can do the Plant no good. All the Difference between Roots under Ground, which do not touch the Earth, and some Roots above Ground, is, that one is shaded, and the other is exposed to the Sun and Wind: But as Roots in the most hollow and light Land, touch the Earth in some Places, so they get some Nourishment and keep alive, yet the Plant makes but a poor Progress.

I have a Piece of Summer Wheat in a drained Swamp, that almost died of this Disease: The Land was so new that it would not bear a Team, so that it could not be ploughed; the Top Earth was exceeding light and puffy; the Seed was howed in, it came up and grew well, so long as the Blade could live upon the Milk of the Wheat Kernel; but when that Store was spent, and the Time was come that it must live by Nourishment obtained by the Roots, it turned yellow, and the Tops died: One of my Sons told me the Wheat would all die; but an heavy Rain fell, which so closed and pressed this light Earth to-gether, and so lessened the Pores, that the Roots were inclosed on all Sides, the Corn recovered its Colour, grew vig-orously and well, and put up good large Ears. This Land as much required ploughing as hard heavy Land would have done. Repeated ploughing in Land that is too light, and the Pores too large, will settle it down and close it together, contract and lessen the Pores, as well as raise the heavy Land, and enlarge its Pores. This seeming Contradiction, this blowing Hot and Cold out the same Mouth, may be well enough reconciled, and accounted for in a philosophical Manner: but so long as Experience shews that all this is true, it will be to no Advantage to the Farmer to say any more about it: Nor should I have en-tered so far into the Philosophy of Till-age as I have done, were it not neces-sary for a practical Farmer to understand it so far as to make a Judgment, and see into the Reason of this new Kind of Tillage and Farming: And this is the more needful, as there is a Prejudice in Men's Minds against what is new, or at least what Men suppose to be new.

6. This Method or Way of repeated ploughing, fits and prepares the Land to receive and retain all the Benefits of the Atmosphere: It is now open to re-ceive the floating Particles of Sulphur, and the nitrous Salts of the Air, the Ben-efit of the Sun's Rays, which, when ac-companied with a sufficient Degree of Moisture, enlivens and invigorates all Nature. When the Winter hath brought a universal Gloom upon the Face of the vegitable Creation, Paleness and Death appears on all Sides: The Psalmist saith of it, *Thou hidest thy Face they are troubled.* Then speaking of the Sun, *thou sendest forth thy Spirit they are created, and thou renewest the Face of the Earth.*

But above all this, we are hereby put in Possession of the Dews, which is one of the rich Treasures of the *Atmosphere;* when Land is made fine a good Depth, it is prepared with open Mouth, to drink in and retain the Dews: When the Dew falls upon Land that is untilled, or but poorly tilled, the Ground being hard it doth not sink deep, so the next Day's Sun carries it all off again. It is the same if Land be too light and loose; there is not a sufficient Connection of Parts to convey the Dew from one Particle of Earth to another: I apprehend, that the Moisture of the Dew passeth down in well prepared Land as Water is con-veyed through a Rag in Filtration, if the Rag hath large Holes in it the Water will stop: But let this be as it will, it is certain, and known to every observing Farmer, that the best tilled Land in a dry Time, always is moister, and bears the Drought much better than the same Sort of Land which is but poorly tilled; that *Indian* Corn, which is the best ploughed and hoed, will always bear the Drought best. And what is the Reason? Because the Land is prepared to receive and retain the Dew. Mr. *Eve-lin* made the following Experiment: he dug a Hole in the Ground a good Depth, reduced the Earth to fine Pow-der, and filled up the Hole with it: a Drought came on, this powdered Earth was moist to the Bottom, when the ad-joining Land was exceeding hard and dry. Another Experiment was made thus, a Gallon of Rain-Water was put into a Bowl, and a Gallon of Dew-Water in another Vessel, and set them to dry away in the Sun; the Conse-quence was, the Sediment or Settlings of the Dew-Water was more in Quan-tity, blacker and richer than that of the Rain-Water. The Dews and the Salts of the Air, is all by which the Land is inriched; for the other Advantages of Ploughing are but transient. The Advantage this Way is so much, that Mr. *Tull* saith, that Land he hath improved this Way, by this kind of Husbandry, going into another Hand, who used it in the common Way of Husbandry, that Part of the Field was so much inriched by the new Tillage, that there was a visible Difference for the better seven Years after. I suppose, that it is this alone which changed the Colour of my Land in six Months; for having ploughed very deep, and turned up much Foxcolour'd dead Earth, it soon became of a good brown Colour; so that this Kind of Tillage seems likely to put us in Possession of *Joseph's* Blessing: of which we have an Account, *Deut.* xxxiii. 13, 14, and of Joseph he said; Blessed of the Lord be his Land, for the precious Things of Heaven, for the Dew, and for the Deep that coucheth beneath; and for the precious Fruits brought forth by the Sun, and for the precious Things put forth by the Moon. Some understand by the Deep that coucheth beneath, to be the Springs and subterraneous Waters: but it seems more likely, to intend the Riches of the under Earth which coucheth beneath; which, like a couching Lion, must be roused and raised up by a proper Tillage, in order to exert its full Strength.

Thus I have explained the Principles of this kind of Husbandry, the Foundation and Reason of it, in as plain and easy a Manner as I can.

Before I took any Step or Pace towards this Sort of Tillage, I read all I could find upon the Subject with Care, thought and studied on it with Attention; wrote to my good Friend, Mr. *John Bartram,* a Farmer in *Pennsylvania,* a Man of Worth, to know his Opinion of it. He judiciously observ'd, that

England, where it had been practised with Success, was an Island, having the Sea on all Sides, the Air must be filled with more Vapours and larger Dews, than what we enjoy upon the Continent; their *Atmosphere* being much more replete with Riches for the Earth, than what is to be expected in our dry thin Air. Notwithstanding all this, it ran strongly in my Head to try; for I considered, that, *as God had not left himself without Witness, in that he had given us Rain and fruitful Seasons,* so, in some Degree, he hath given us the other Benefits of the Atmosphere, *to fill our Hearts with Food and Gladness;* therefore thought it our Duty to take all the Advantage of it that we can; and that we would try the Method as far as we could, without the proper Instruments, how much there was of Truth in the Doctrine or Principles, if used and applied in this Climate; and so proceed, or forbear to get the Drill Plough, and other Instruments, as we should find Encouragement. . . .

I come now to direct the Performance of the Work with Instruments less intricate, more plain, cheap and commodious, than those directed to and described by Mr. *Tull.*

Having found by Experience the Advantage of planting Seeds in Rows, and also finding that to plant by Hand is a slow and chargeable Way; therefore I designed to use it no longer than was necessary to find, that it was likely the Method would answer the Design proposed: Being satisfied in that Point, the next Thing was to get Instruments suitable to the Work.

The Instruments peculiar to this Husbandry, are Drill Ploughs. By a Drill I mean an Instrument that will make one Channel or more, upon a Ridge, and drop in the Seed at due Distances, and in a just Proportion: This is what it will do in better Order than Men can possibly do it with their Fingers, and will do more in one Day, than One Hundred Men can do by Hand. There is not much Reason to call it a Plough, for there is no Affinity or Likeness between them but only in this, the Drill has two Coulters by which the Channels are cut.

There are in Use several Sorts of Drills; there is the Wheat Drill, the Turnip Drill, and divers others; but these named are the Chief; to which I have added a Dung Drill, by which Dung, Ashes, or any other Manure, may be conveyed into the Channels where the Seed is to be dropped. Mr. *Tull's* Wheat Drill is a wonderful Invention, but it being the first invented of that Kind, no Wonder if it be intricate, as indeed it is, and consists of more Wheels, and other Parts, than there is really any Need of. This I was very sensible of all along, but knew not how to mend it, therefore applied myself to the Reverend Mr. *Clap,* President of *Yale* College, and desired him for the Regard which he had to the Publick and to me, that he would apply his mathematical Learning, and mechanical Genius, in that Affair; which he did to so good Purpose, that this new modelled Drill can be made with a fourth Part of what Mr. *Tull's* will cost. This [I] look upon as a great Improvement, and take this Opportunity to make my Acknowledgements for the Favour. When this Drill came home, I found the Wheels were too low for our Ridges, therefore it must be mounted upon new Wheels. The next Thing I wanted in order to compass my Design, was a Dung Drill; this is an Invention intirely new, for which there was no Precedent or Model. For this I applied myself to *Benoni Hylliard,* a very ingenious Man of this

Town, a Wheel-Wright by Trade. I told him what I wanted, and desired him to make one. At first we could think of no Way but to make it as a distinct Instrument: But at length his Ingenuity led him to set this and the Wheat Drill upon one Frame, so that it became one Instrument. Mr. *Tull,* it is 'true, might think this Drill not to be needful; for he tells us, that he tried applying of Dung by Hand to the Channels, but found that this Assistance of Dung was not necessary: For he writes, that, to his great Surprize, he found that the Want of Dung might be supplied by repeated Horse-ploughings, and that Two Shillings in Horse-ploughing would do more than *Forty Shillings* in Dung. I should be glad, if in our Climate the One-half of this would prove true. The Land which I design to make use of, is so low and poor, that I shall have need enough of my Dung-Drill, at least, when I first begin with this kind of Husbandry. I hope that in Time, the Land may be so inriched by Tillage, that this may prove needless.

The Dung-Drill, exhibits or sheds into the Channel eighty Bushels of Dung to the Acre, which is about two Cart Loads; the Board on the Fore-side of the Drill-Box, is made fast only by a Spring, so that if any Clod, Lump or Stone, cannot pass through the Drill, the Foreboard opens and lets it out, and the Spring shuts it again: Thus the Danger of stopping or breaking the Drill is prevented.

Wheat is planted in two Rows, but Turnips in one Row on the Middle of the Ridge. The Engine is so contrived, that the Wheat-Drill may be taken off, and a Turnip-Drill be put on; and then the Dung-Drill can be so ordered, that the Dung shall be conveyed into that one Channel, either so much Dung as was shed into the two Channels, or half so much more or less as we please.

The Hopper of the Wheat-Drill, holds about a Peck, and the Dung-Hopper two Bushels and an half. Before we plant either Wheat or Turnips, the Tops of the Ridges must be harrowed and made smooth; to do this, Mr. *Tull* used two Harrows at once, one upon one Ridge, and the other upon the next Ridge; a Pole from the Out-side of each Harrow held them together, an Horse made fast to the Middle of the Pole, drew both Harrows: But instead of all this, we have a small Harrow on the Fore-part of the Frame, which first harrows the Ridge; after the Harrow comes two Coulters, which makes the two Channels at ten Inches Distance; The Dung-Drill fills these Channels with Dung; then comes the two Coulters belonging to the Wheat-Drill, and opens the two Channels, and the Wheat-Drill drops in the Wheat Seed, half a Bushel to an Acre; after this follows a small Harrow, which covers the Seed. There is a Tongue or Neb to go between the Oxen; a long Yoak is used for this Work, so that one Ox travels in one Furrow, and the other in the next, with the Ridge between: One Horse might draw it with Ease, could we find any Way to do it, and the Horse travel in the Furrow; if the Horse walk upon the Ridge it would be hurtful. Mr. *Tull's* Wheat-Drill, required two Pair of Wheels: We have two Drills fastened upon a Frame two Foot eight Inches square, and two Harrows, each performing its respective Part of Work at one Movement; and to the Whole but one Pair of Wheels: The Shaft of the Dung-Drill carries round the Shaft of the Wheat-Drill by a Cogg-Wheel; the several Parts are all plain Work, open and easy to the Understanding; this I esteem a compendious

Instrument. It has cost me a great deal more than it will to make another, Imitation being so much more easy than Invention.

The next Instrument that was thought necessary for this Kind of Husbandry, is the Hoe-Plough, of which Mr. *Tull* has given us a Draught, which I shewed to our best Plough-Wrights, but they could not understand it, so that I was almost discouraged: But at length I found a Way to do well enough, without any such strange-built Hoe-Plough: Nor is there any Manner of Difficulty about it, for the Furrows may be ploughed from, and up to the Ridges, with a common Plough, a Yoak of Oxen in a long Yoak, so that one Ox may go in one Furrow, and the other Ox in the other Furrow, and the Ridge between. Let the Plants be what they will, we can come as near to them as is needful; or it may be done with one Horse, with an Horse-Plough; but the Way with Oxen I like best, because there is sufficient Strength to plough deep, which is of great Importance, in order to raise a great deal of Mould, for the Purposes above-mentioned. What will be the Success of raising Wheat in this Method, will be left to Experience, and the History of that Trial to be communicated in another Essay. It is high Time something were done; our old Towns raising very little Wheat, it is purchased at the new Towns, and these new Towns will be old in Time; and then what shall we do unless some better Way can be found to manage our old Land which is plain and smooth? For any Man's Reason will tell him, that stony, rocky, rough Land, is by no Means fit for this Sort of drilling Husbandry; there is enough of such plain Land to produce a vast deal of Corn, could there be found any Way to make it bring forth good Crops.

Mr. *Tull* saith, that the Wheat planted in this Manner is not subject to blast, therefore it is a Method that may enable those Parts of *New-England*, to raise Wheat, who never could, in ordinary, attain to it; of this we can have no Certainty but by Trial.

Another Instrument necessary in this Sort of Husbandry, is the *Turnip-Drill:* This is an Instrument which drops a single Turnip-Seed into a Channel cut for that Purpose on the Middle of the Ridge, at six inches Distance; but mine is made to drop one at three Inches Distance, lest the Fly should destroy any of them, or any Seeds should fail coming up; They should be six Inches Distance; if they should be too thick, it is easy to cut them out. They raise Turnips in Abundance in *England* to feed Cattle; some do it in the random Way of sowing, then where they are too thick hoe them up, till they are thinned to a proper Proportion; but then they grow so close together, that it might be difficult and chargeable Work to do it:

It is found by Experience, that this Way of Drilling, and tending them with the Horse-Plough, is, by far, the cheapest and most profitable Way.

Mr. *Tull* saith, that his Turnips drilled and well ploughed, weighed from six Pounds to fourteen, did produce Six Hundred and Forty Bushels to the Acre: I should be very glad of half that Quantity: As to the Ease in raising them in this Method, by ploughing the Furrows off and on, I am satisfied by Experience, and that they will grow larger; what I tried were Spring Turnips.

The Usefulness of Turnips for Cows when they calve, for Winter Milch-Cows, is known to all those who have tried.

To make a Turnip-Drill that will drop a single Seed and no more, is a nice Piece of Work. Any Thing farther relating to drilling and ploughing of Wheat and Turnips, must be referred to another Essay, when Time and Experience shall enable me.

3. Ironworks, 1732

WILLIAM BYRD, *A Progress to the Mines*

Colonel William Byrd, of Westover in Virginia, was as much the product of his colony as Johnson and Eliot were of theirs. An eighteenth-century gentleman in the best sense of the word, Byrd embraced the world with a hearty and humane enthusiasm which made the best of his comfortable position. He was the owner of vast lands in Virginia; his enterprises included not only farming and the breeding of slaves, but such industrial pursuits as milling as well.

From William Byrd, *A Progress to the Mines,* ed. John Spencer Bassett, in *The Writing of "Colonel William Byrd of Westover in Virginia Esqr"* (New York, 1901), pp. 333-55.

Ironworks were fairly common all along the coast from Massachusetts to the Carolinas, and in 1732 Colonel Byrd set out on a tour of the countryside to learn the state of the business in Virginia and assess his own chances of establishing a furnace. From mid-September until early October he visited mines and ironworks, and inquired into their prosperity and method of operation.

Sept. 18. For the Pleasure of the good Company of Mrs. Byrd, and her little Governour, my Son, I went about half way to the Falls in the Chariot. There we halted, not far from a purling Stream, and upon the Stump of a prop-agate Oak picket the Bones of a piece of Roast Beef. By the Spirit which that gave me, I was the better able to part with the dear Companions of my Trav-els, and to perform the rest of my Jour-ney on Horseback by myself. I reacht Shaccoa's before 2 a'clock, and crost the River to the Mills. I had the Grief to find them both stand as still for the want of Water, as a dead Woman's Tongue, for want of Breath. It had rain'd so little for many Weeks above the Falls, that the Naides had hardly Water enough left to wash their Faces. However, as we ought to turn all our Misfortunes to the best Advantage, I directed Mr. Booker, my first Minister there, to make use of the lowness of the Water for blowing up the Rocks at the Mouth of the Canal. For that purpose I order'd Iron Drills to be made about 2 foot long, pointed with Steel, Chizzel fashion, in order to make holes, into which we put our Cartridges of Powder, containing each about 3 Ounces. There wanted Skill among my Engineers to chuse the best parts of the Stone for boring, that we might blow to the most advantage. They made all their Holes quite perpendicular, whereas they should have humour'd the Grain of the Stone for the more effectual Execution. I order'd the points of the Drills to be made Chizzel way, rather than the Dia-mond, that they might need to be Sel-domer repair'd, tho' in Stone the Dia-mond points would make the most despatch. The Water now flow'd out of the River so slowly, that the Miller was oblig'd to pond it up in the Canal, by setting open the Flood-gates at the Mouth, and shutting those close at the Mill. By this contrivance, he was able at any time to grind two or three Bush-els, either for his choice Customers, or for the use of my Plantations. Then I walkt to the place where they broke the Flax, which is wrought with much greater ease than the Hemp, and is much better for Spinning. From thence I paid a Visit to the Weaver, who needed a little of Minerva's Inspiration to make the most of a piece of fine Cloth. Then I lookt in upon my Caledonian Spinster, who was mended more in her looks than in her Humour. However, she promised much, tho' at the same time intended to per-form little. She is too high-Spirited for Mr. Booker, who hates to have his sweet Temper ruffled, and will rather suffer matters to go a little wrong sometimes, than give his righteous Spirit any un-easiness. He is very honest, and would make an admirable Overseer where Servants will do as they are bid. But Eye-Servants, who want abundance of overlooking, are not so proper to be committed to his Care. I found myself out of order, and for that reason retir'd Early; yet with all this precaution had a gentle feaver in the Night, but towards morning Nature sat open all her Gates, and drove it out in a plentiful perspiration.

Sept. 19. The worst of this feaver was, that it put me to the Necessity of taking another Ounce of Bark. I moisten'd every dose with a little Brandy, and fill'd the Glass up with Water, which is the least Nauseous way of taking this Popish Medicine, and besides hinders it from Purging. After I had swallow'd a few Poacht Eggs, we rode down to the Mouth of the Canal, and from thence crost over to the broad Rock Island in a Canoe. Our errand was to view some Iron Ore, which we dug up in two places. That on the Surface seem'd very spongy and poor, which gave us no great Encouragement to search deeper, nor did the Quantity appear to be very great. However, for my greater Satisfaction, I order'd a hand to dig there for some time this Winter. . . .

Sept. 23. After this, I had 8 Miles to Mr. Chiswell's, where I arriv'd at about 2 a'Clock, and sav'd my Dinner. I was very handsomely entertain'd, finding every thing very clean, and very Good. I had not seen Mrs. Chiswell in 24 Years, which, alas! had made great Havoc with her pretty Face, and plow'd very deep Furrows in her fair Skin. It was impossible to know her again, so much the flower was faded. However, tho' she was grown an Old Woman, yet she was one of those absolute Rarities, a very good old Woman. I found Mr. Chiswell a sensible, well-bred Man, and very frank in communicating his knowledge in the Mystery of making Iron, wherein he has had long Experience. I told him I was come to Spy the Land,

and inform myself of the Expence of carrying on an Iron work with Effect. That I sought my Instruction from Him, who understood the whole Mystery, having gain'd full Experience in every part of it; Only I was very sorry he had bought that Experience so dear. He answer'd that he would, with great Sincerity, let me into the little knowledge he had, and so we immediately entered upon the Business. He assured me the first step I was to take was to acquaint myself fully with the Quantity and Quality of my Oar. For that reason I ought to keep a good Pick-ax Man at work a whole Year to search if there be a Sufficient Quantity, without which it would be a very rash undertaking. That I shou'd also have a Skilful person to try the richness of the oar. Nor is it great Advantage to have it exceeding rich, because then it will yield Brittle Iron, which is not valuable. But the way to have it tough is to mix poor Oar and Rich together, which makes the poorer sort extremely necessary for the production of the best Iron. Then he shew'd me a Sample of the Richest Oar they have in England, which yields a full Moiety of Iron. It was of a Pale red Colour, smooth and greasy, and not exceedingly heavy; but it produced so brittle a Metal, that they were oblig'd to melt a poorer Oar along with it. He told me, after I was certain my Oar was good and plentiful enough, my next inquiry ought to be, how far it lyes from a Stream proper to build a furnace upon, and again what distance that Furnace will be from Water Carriage; Because the Charge of Carting a great way is very heavy, and eats out a great part of the Profit. That this was the Misfortune of the Mines of Fredericksville, where they were oblig'd to Cart the Oar a Mile to the Furnace, and after twas run into Iron, to carry that 24 Miles, over an uneven Road to Rappahannock River, about a Mile below Fredericksburgh, to a Plantation the Company rented of Colo. Page. If I were satisfy'd with the Situation, I was in the next place to consider whether I had Woodland enough near the Furnace to Supply it with Charcoal, whereof it wou'd require a prodigious Quantity. That the properest Wood for that purpose was that of Oyly kind, such as Pine, Walnut, Hiccory, Oak, and in short all that yields Cones, Nuts, or Acorns. That 2 Miles Square of Wood, wou'd supply a Moderate furnace; so that what you fell first may have time to grow up again to a proper bigness (which must be 4 Inches over) by that time the rest is cut down. He told me farther, that 120 Slaves, including Women, were necessary to carry on all the Business of an Iron Work, and the more Virginians amongst them the better; Tho' in that number he comprehended Carters, Colliers, and those that planted the Corn. That if there should be much Carting, it would require 1600 Barrels of Corn Yearly to Support the People, & the Cattle employ'd; nor dos even that Quantity suffice at Fredericksville. That if all these Circumstances shou'd happily concur, and you cou'd procure honest Colliers and Firemen, which will be difficult to do, you may easily run 800 Tuns of Sow Iron a Year. The whole charge of Freight, Custom, Commission, and other Expences in England, will not exceed 30 Shillings a Tun, and twill commonly sell for £6, and then the clear profit will amount to £4, , 10. So that allowing the ten Shillings for Accidents, you may reasonably expect a clear Profit of £4, which being multiplied by 800, will amount to £3200 a year, to pay you for your Land and Negroes. But

then it behooved me to be fully inform'd of the whole Matter myself, to prevent being imposed upon; and if any offer'd to put tricks upon me, to punish them as they deserve. Thus ended our Conversation for this day, and I retir'd to a very clean Lodging in another House, and took my Bark, but was forced to take it in Water, by reason a light finger'd Damsel had ransackt my Baggage, and drunk up my Brandy. This unhappy Girl, it seems, is a Baronet's Daughter; but her Complexion, being red hair'd, inclin'd her so much to Lewdness, that her Father sent her, under the Care of the virtuous Mr. Cheep, to seek her fortune on this Side the Globe. . . .

Sept. 25. After saying some very civil things to Mrs. Chiswell, for my handsome Entertainment, I mounted my Horse, and Mr. Chiswell his Phaeton, in order to go to the Mines at Fredericksville. We cou'd converse very little by the way, by reason of our different Voitures. The Road was very Straight and level the whole Journey, which was 25 Miles, the last ten whereof I rode in the Chair, and my Friend on my Horse, to ease ourselves by that Variety of Motion. About a Mile before we got to Fredericksville, we forded over the North Branch of Pomunky, about 60 Yards over. Neither this nor the South Branch run up near so high as the Mountains, but many Miles below them spread out into a kind of Morass, like Chickahominy. When we approacht the Mines, there open'd to our View a large Space of clear'd Ground, whose Wood had been cut down for coaling. We Arriv'd here about 2 A'Clock, and Mr. Chiswell had been so provident as to bring a Cold Venison Pasty, with which we appeased our Appetites, without the Impatience of waiting. When our

Tongues were at leizure for discourse, my Friend told me there was one Mr. Harison, in England, who is so universal a dealer in all Sorts of Iron, that he cou'd govern the Market just as he pleas'd. That it was by his artful Management that our Iron from the Plantations sold for less than that made in England, tho' it was generally reckon'd much better. That Ours wou'd hardly fetch 6£ a Tun, when theirs fetcht 7 or 8, purely to serve that Man's Interest. Then he explain'd the Several Charges upon our Sow Iron, after it was put on Board the Ships. That in the first place it paid 7ʃ6 a Tun for Freight, being just so much clear gain to the Ships, which carry it as Ballast, or wedge it in among the Hogsheads. When it gets Home, it pays 3ʃ9 custome. These Articles together make no more than 11ʃ3, and yet the Merchants, by their great Skill in Multiplying Charges, Swell the account up to near 30ʃ a Tun by that time it gets out of their Hands, and they are continually adding more and more, as they serve us in our Accounts of Tobacco. He told me a strange thing about Steel, that the making of the best remains at this day a profound Secret in the breast of a very few, and therefore is in danger of being lost, as the Art of Staining of Glass, and many others, have been. He cou'd only tell me they us'd Beech Wood in the making of it in Europe, & burn it a Considerable time in powder of Charcoal; but the Mystery lies in the Liquor they quench it in. After dinner we took a walk to the Furnace, which is elegantly built of Brick, tho' the Hearth be of Fire-Stone. There we saw the Founder, Mr. Derham, who is paid 4 Shillings for every Tun of Sow Iron that he runs, which is a Shilling cheaper than the last Workman had. This Operator lookt a little Melancholy,

because he had nothing to do, the Furnace having been Cold ever since May, for want of Corn to Support the Cattle. This was however no neglect of Mr. Chiswell, because all the Persons he had contracted with had basely disappointed him. But having receiv'd a small Supply, they intended to blow very soon. With that view they began to heat the Furnace, which is 6 Weeks before it comes to that intense heat required to run the Metal in perfection. Nevertheless, they commonly begin to blow when the Fire has been kindled a Week or ten days. Close by the Furnace stood a very spacious House full of Charcoal, holding at least 400 Loads, which will be burnt out in 3 Months. The Company has contracted with Mr. Harry Willis to fall the Wood, and then maul it and cut it into pieces of 4 feet in length, and bring it to the Pits where it is to be coal'd. All this he has undertaken to do for 2 Shillings a Cord, which must be 4 foot broad, 4 foot high, and 8 foot long. Being thus carry'd to the Pits, the Collier has contracted to Coal it for 5 Shillings a Load, consisting of 160 Bushels. The Fire in the Furnace is blown by 2 Mighty pair of Bellows, that cost one Hundred pounds each, and these Bellows are mov'd by a great Wheel of 26 foot diameter. The Wheel again is carry'd round by a small Stream of Water, conveyed about 350 Yards over Land in a Trough, from a Pond made by a wooden Dam. But there is great want of Water in a dry Season, which makes the Furnace often blow out, to the great prejudice of the Works. Having thus fill'd my Head with all these Particulars, we return'd to the House, where, after talking of Colo. Spotswood, and his Strategems to shake off his Partners, and secure all his Mines to himself, I retired to a homely Lodging, which, like a homespun Mistress, had been more tolerable, if it had been sweet.

Sept. 26. Over our Tea, Mr. Chiswell told me the expence which the Company had been already at amounted to near Twelve Thousand Pounds: But then the Land, Negroes, and Cattle were all included in that Charge. However, the Money began now to come in, they having run 1200 Tuns of Iron, and all their heavy disbursements were over. Only they were stil forct to buy great Quantitys of Corn, because they had not strength of their own to make it. That they had not more than 80 Negroes, and few of those Virginia born. That they need 40 Negroes more to carry on all the Business with their own Force. They have 15000 Acres of Land, tho' little of it rich except in Iron, and of that they have a great Quantity. Mr. FitzWilliams took up the mine tract, and had the address to draw in the Governor, Capt. Pearse, Dr. Nicolas and Mr. Chiswell to be jointly concern'd with him, by which contrivance he first got a good price for the Land, and then, when he had been very little out of Pocket, sold his Share to Mr. Nelson for 500 £; and of these Gentlemen the Company at present consists. And Mr. Chiswell is the only person amongst them that knows any thing of the matter, and has 100 £ a year for looking after the Works, and richly deserves it. After breaking our Fast we took a walk to the principal Mine, about a Mile from the Furnace, where they had sunk in some places about 15 or 20 foot deep. The Operator, Mr. Gordon, rais'd the Oar, for which he was to have by contract 1ʃ6p Cart-Load of 26 Hundred Weight. This man was oblig'd to hire all the Laborers he wanted for this Work of the Company, after the rate

of 25ʃ a Month, and for all that was able to clear 40 £ a-year for himself. We saw here several large Heaps of oar of 2 sorts, one of rich, and the other Spongy and poor, which they melted together to make the Metal more tough. The way of raising the oar was by blowing it up, which Operation I saw here from beginning to End. They first drill'd a hole in the Mine, either upright or Slopeing, as the grain of it required. This hole they cleansed with a Rag fastene'd to the End of an Iron with a Worm at the end of it. Then they put in a Cartridge of Powder containing about 3 Ounces, and at the same time a Reed full of fuse that reacht to the Powder. Then they ramn'd dry Clay, or soft Stone very hard into the Hole, and lastly they fired the fuse with a Paper that had been dipt in a Solution of Saltpetre and dry'd, which burning Slow and Sure, gave leizure to the Engineer to retire to a proper distance before the Explosion. This in the Miner's Language is call'd making a Blast, which will losen several hundred Weight of Oar at once; and afterwards the Laborers easily separate it with Pick-axes and carry it away in Baskets up to the Heap. At our return we saw near the Furnace large Heaps of Mine with Charcoal mixet with it, a Stratum of each alternately, beginning first with a layer of Charcoal at the Bottom. To this they put Fire, which in a little time spreads thro' the whole Heap, and calcines the Oar, which afterwards easily crumbles into small pieces fit for the Furnace. Then was likewise a mighty Quantity of Limestone, brought from Bristol, by way of ballast, at 2ʃ6 a Tun, which they are at the Trouble to Cart hither from Rappahanock River, but contrive to do it when the Carts return from carrying of Iron. They put this into the

Furnace with the Iron Oare, in the proportion of one Tun of Stone to ten of Oar, with design to absorb the Sulphur out of the Iron, which wou'd otherwise make it brittle. And if that be the use of it, Oyster Shells wou'd certainly do as well as LimeStone, being altogether as strong an Alkali, if not Stronger. Nor can their being taken out of Salt water be any Objection, because tis pretty certain the West India LimeStone, which is thrown up by the Sea, is even better than that imported from Bristol. But the founders who never try'd either of these will by no means be perswaded to go out of their way, tho' the Reason of the thing be never so evident. I observ'd the richer Sort of Mine, being of a dark Colour Mixt with rust, was laid in a heap by itself, and so was the poor, which was of a Liver or Brick Colour. The Sow Iron is in the Figure of a half-round, about two feet and a half-long, weighing 60 or 70 Pounds, whereof 3000 weight make a Cart-load drawn by 8 Oxen, which are commonly shod to save their Hoofs in those Stony ways. When the Furnace blows, it runs about 20 Tuns of Iron a Week. The founders find it very hot work to tend the Furnace, especially in Summer, and are oblig'd to spend no small part of their Earnings in strong Drink, to recruit their Spirits. Besides the Founder, the Collier, and Miner, who are paid in proportion to their Work, the Company have several other Officers upon Wages, a Stock-taker, who weighs and measures every thing, a Clerk, who keeps an Account of all Receipts and Disbursements, a Smith to Shoe their Cattle, and keep all their Iron work in repair, a

wheel-Wright, Cartwright, Carpenter, and Several Carters. The Wages of all these Persons amount to one Hundred Pounds a Year; so that including Mr. Chiswell's Salary, they disburse 200 £ p Annum in standing Wages. The Provisions too are a heavy Article, which their Plantations dont yet produce in a Sufficient Quantity, tho' they are at the Charge of a general Overseer. But while Corn is so short with them, there can be no great Increase of Stock of any kind.

Sept. 27. Having now pretty well exhausted the Subject of Sow Iron, I askt my Friend some Questions about Bar-Iron. He told me we had as yet no Forge erected in Virginia, tho' we had 4 Furnaces. But there was a very good one set up at the head of the Bay in Maryland, that made exceeding good Work. He let me know that the duty in England upon Bar Iron was 24ʄ a Tun, and that it sold there from Ten to 16 pounds a Tun. This wou'd pay the Charge of Forging abundantly, but he doubted the Parliament of England would soon forbid us that Improvement, lest after that we shou'd go farther, and manufacture Our Bars into all Sorts of Iron Ware, as they already do in New England & Pennsylvania. Nay, he question'd whether we shou'd be suffer'd to cast any Iron, which they can do themselves at their Furnaces. Thus ended our Conversation, and I thankt my Friend for being so free in communicating everything to me. Then, after tipping a Pistole to the Clerk, to drink prosperity to the Mines with all the Workmen, I accepted the kind offer of going part of my Journey in the Phaeton.

4. A Colonial Gristmill, 1764

Pennsylvania Gazette, Advertisement

The technology of the colonial years was best characterized by the many gristmills. These water-powered mills, which used wooden machinery, were usually found in the countryside, grinding for a local trade. Some, however, like those in Wilmington, Delaware, were very large and ground grain for an extensive export trade. Gristmills were technically very like a number of othr types of mills—those used to grind powder, chocolate, spices, bark, and so forth. The millwrights who designed and built these mills were among the founders of the engineering profession. The mill described below was typical of its kind, although since it was located in the very heart of the wheat-producing colonies it was larger than most.

To be sold by the Subscriber, at the Mouth of Redclay Creek, New-Castle County, near Newport, one of the best watered Mills on the Continent, and is perhaps the largest and most commodious of any in America, being in a pleasant and healthy Situation, having all necessary Conveniences in good Order, has a good new Dam, two Water Wheels, three Pair of good Mill Stones, one of which are excellent French Burrs, one Screen, a Dutch Fan, two Setts of Boulting Gears with good Cloths, etc. It is in a fine Part of the Country for Wheat, either by Land or Water, as the Tide comes up to the Mill, and is about 12 Miles from the Head of Elk, where large Quantities of Wheat may be had at almost all Times of the Year, on the easiest Terms, and the Flour can be sent up to Philadelphia at Six-pence a Cask; and as there is a good Landing Place on the Premises, the Buyer may have Advantage of not only importing and exporting his own Commodities, but may have the Benefit of shalloping Flour to Philadelphia for the back Country People, it being the nearest Landing Place to all the Mills between it and Lancaster; a good well finished Brick Dwelling-house and Kitchen, two Storey high, three Rooms on each Floor, a Cellar under the whole, in three Divisions; a good Spring and Spring-house, fitting for a Cooper, or a Miller, both quite convenient to the Mill, with about 115 Acres of very good Land, about 20 Acres whereof extraordinary good Meadow, and more may be easily made; a good Orchard in its Prime; also a good Saw-Mill, contiguous to said Grist Mill, with a new Flutter Wheel; excellently situated for Plenty of good Timber, which can be had on very reasonable Terms. Also a smart healthy Negroe Lad, about 19 Years old, that understands Milling and Farming, and has had the Small-Pox. Any Person inclining to purchase, by applying to the Subscriber on the Prem-

From *Pennsylvania Gazette,* August 23, 1764.

ises, may know the Terms, which will be as easy as is consistent with Reason, he being desirous to remove to Philadelphia as soon as possible.

N. B. There is likewise a fine Place for fishing for Rock, Perch, Shad, and Herring in great Plenty. The Title indisputable.

Richard Jacobs

PART II THE INDUSTRIAL REVOLUTION

The most fundamental fact about the history of early American technology—perhaps the most important fact about all our early history—is that the American Revolution and the Industrial Revolution took place at the same time. Between 1763 and 1787, the years of political turmoil in North America, James Watt perfected his steam engine; Arkwright, Cartwright, Crompton, and others mechanized the textile industry; the first canal was built, the first steamboats were constructed; and the iron industry was fundamentally changed by the introduction of coal, puddling furnaces, and rolling mills. This burst of technical innovation was so widespread and so fundamental that the term "Revolution" is always used to describe it.

It was during these same years that the American colonists began and perfected their political revolution against the British Empire and set out to erect an empire of their own. The Americans confidently expected that the United States would settle the West, create her own literature, preserve her liberty, increase her foreign trade, encourage a flowering of science, support a rising standard of living for her citizens, and in every other way prove the wisdom of independence and the power of free institutions.

The basic material fact in America, at this point in her history, was that the nation controlled immeasurable natural resources scattered over a vast area that was, at the same time, thinly populated. The Americans thus began the wholesale importation of the Industrial Revolution—the new transportation methods to overcome the great distances and the new machines to overcome the want of workmen. While numbers of "Yankee" inventors struggled to reinvent the basic machines at work in Britain, the easier path proved to be the importation of drawings, models, descriptions, in some cases the actual machines—but most importantly, the technical experts themselves. American governments, both federal and state, gave broad encouragement to this effort at innovation. A patent law was provided for in the Constitution itself,

27

a protective tariff was soon erected, bounties were provided for, and transportation companies were incorporated and their stock was bought by the government.

By 1860 the transformation was virtually complete. Iron had replaced wood as the universal material. The original medieval technology, brought to America and slowly modified in the face of environmental necessity, was replaced by the new industrial technology. Machines were replacing hand methods. Technical processes were carried on in factories or large shops, far from the home workshop of the earlier period. The beginnings of a connection with science were made, although only in certain areas such as civil engineering. Technology, traditionally one of the most conservative of human activities, was beginning to change so rapidly that innovation was becoming the ordinary and accepted condition of things. So necessary was this new technology to the creation of an American empire that Americans began to identify themselves and their progress with the technology itself.

1. British Skills at Work, 1794

HENRY WANSEY, *An Excursion to the United States*

The winning of political independence for the United States by no means ended this country's technological dependence on Europe, and especially its dependence on Great Britain. In the years after the Revolutionary War many Britishers came to America—some to apply their skills in the new environment, and others, like the woolen manufacturer Henry Wansey, merely to observe and report upon the progress of the new nation. His pessimism over the chances for success of most of the small textile mills he saw was well-founded. It was not uncommon during these years for such mills to be under-financed, operated by unskilled workers, and equipped with machines that were not of sufficient quality (even when the design was adequate) to permit profitable operation. Nonetheless, it was through such emigrant technicians as Wansey met that the new technology of textile production was transferred to this country.

From Henry Wansey, *An Excursion to the United States of North America, in the Summer of 1794* (2nd ed., Salisbury, 1798), pp. 52-53, 68-70, 260-61.

[Connecticut]

We dined at a very good tavern there. We had on our table, mutton, veal, plenty of garden stuff, with cucumbers, a good sallad, with cyder and brandy, for all which we paid only half a dollar, or two and three-pence sterling. One of my companions in the coach, was a Mr. M'Intosh, originally from Bocking, in Essex. He took me in a one-horse chair to see his large manufactory, which he had lately established at a head of water, about three miles from Newhaven. It is patronised by the State, which has already advanced him ten thousand dollars, and engaged to go as far as sixty thousand; they being very anxious to establish the woollen and cotton manufactory in that district. But from what I saw of the undertaking, I am convinced, a great deal of money will be sunk to very little purpose. The building is one hundred feet long, thirty-eight feet wide, and four story high. There is not a single window placed on the north side, which is the best of all lights for a manufactory. There were two carding engines finished and at work, but both were very much warped and cracked, by the heat and dryness of the room, as well as from being made of unseasoned wood. Two slubbing and two spinning machines of good and complete workmanship, but the cotton yarn, which was then spinning, was not better than candlewick yarn. He has a water wheel of thirty feet diameter, and eight feet wide, but I think they will often be in want of water to drive it: the cards were very badly made. He has erected forges on the spot, and is making the heavy wrought and cast iron wheels, brasses, screws, spindles, &c. at a vast expence. The coal for working and smelting is brought from Virginia. A vast number of workmen are employed in this department at a very heavy expence. He has many English workmen engaged at great wages, particularly one from Sir George Young's manufactory at Ottery, in Devonshire, who engages to undertake the spinning worsted by water; a promise I do not think he will ever perform. . . .

[New York]

May 31. Went with a party to see Dickson's cotton manufactory at Hell Gates, about five miles from New York. It is worked by a breast water wheel, twenty feet diameter. There are two large buildings four story high, and eighty feet long. In one shop I saw twenty-six looms at work, weaving fustians, calicoes, nankeens, nankinets, dimities, &c. and there are ten other looms in the neighbourhood. They have the new-invented spring shuttle. They also spin by water, using all the new improvements of Arkwright and others. Twelve or fourteen workmen from Manchester. All the machinery in wood, steel, and brass, were made on the spot from models brought from England and Scotland. They are training up women and children to the business, of whom I saw twenty or thirty at work; they give the women two dollars a week, and find them in board and lodging; the children are bound apprentice till twenty-one years of age, with an engagement to board, clothe and educate them. They have the machine called the mule, at which they have spun cotton yarn so fine as twenty-one hundred scains to the pound, and they purpose making muslins. My observations on the undertaking are;—the situation is not well chosen; they have sunk a vast deal of money in buildings and machinery unnecessarily, which is a heavy tax on the undertaking, so that the interest of the money will eat up almost all the profit; they are so deficient in water in summer time to keep the wheel going, that to remedy this, a thousand pounds more is to be laid out, to erect in the sea another large wheel to work by the ebb and flow of the tide, to raise water into the reservoir, to supply this deficiency. The English workmen are dissatisfied, and ready to leave the factory as soon as they have saved up a few pounds, in order to become landholders up the country, and arrive at independence. The company also try at too many things, and the goods they make are very inferior to what they get from us.

The famous cotton manufactory for fustians, corderoys, and jeans, at Beverley, in Massachusetts, of which such favorable hopes were entertained for five years past, does not answer; so says Mr. C. V. of Boston, who belongs to a society for encouraging undertakings of this kind. They had a capital lent them at three per cent. and workshops built for them, and yet they are gone behind hand.

I saw another cotton manufactory at Brooklyn, in Long Island;—a double carding engine worked by a horse; a slubbing, and two spinning machines, all of very good workmanship. This was a small concern, where they make yarn for sale, and employ no weavers; and it *seems* to answer well.

The general error of all their large undertakings has been, their laying out their capital in large buildings and an unnecessary stock of machinery, &c. which brings a heavy mortgage on the concern, before they actually begin. They also put the whole business under the care of a chief workman (being ignorant themselves) who has no interest in an œconomical management of the concern. The large cotton manufac-

tory at Paterson, fifteen miles west of New York, has almost been ruined twice by such men. . . .

[Connecticut]

The carding and scribbling engines, at Hartford, were of the oldest fashion. Two large center cylinders in each, with two doffers, and only two working cylinders, of the breadth of bare sixteen inches, said to be invented by some person there. They had no spinning jennies, the yarn being all spun by hand. They were scribbling deep blue wool, of the quality of Wiltshire running fine, for making coarse broad cloth; the spinning was very bad, the wool not being half worked. I saw in the weaving shop, five looms, two on broad cloth, two on coarse cassimeres, with worsted chains, and one on narrow or forest cloth. They gave the weavers nine-pence per yard currency, for the cassimeres, i. e. sixpence three-farthings sterling; dear enough, considering the largeness of the spinning. They could weave six yards of broad cloth in a day. I saw there some very good well-combed worsted. They sort a fleece into seven sorts. I observed some very fine wool there, which, they told me, came from Georgia, but it was in bad condition. The concern is carried on by a company; nine thousand three hundred dollars have been lent towards the undertaking, by the State. None of the partners understand any thing about it, and all depends on an Englishman, who is the sorter of the wool. Mr. Elisha Colt, a store-keeper, or woollen-draper, has the present direction of it, but he is going to settle in another place very shortly. He shewed me every part of the manufactory, and afterwards, at his own store, twenty or thirty pieces of cassimere, broad cloth, elastics, and narrow cloths, of the Hartford manufacture. He could sell them at about the same price, I found, as our English goods would cost, when delivered into the stores there, but the fabric was very poor, and hard in the spinning, and very badly dressed, and therefore very inferior to, and dearer than the British. . . .

2. Steam Power, 1812

OLIVER EVANS, "Account of the Steam Engines of Oliver Evans"

One of the key factors in the Industrial Revolution was the substitution of water power for human or animal power in the operation of machines and mills. Water power, however, was severely limited by location and amount. When it was fully exploited in any area, no further growth was possible; where it was not available at all, only hand industry could flourish.

The great breakthrough came with the introduction of steam engines into manufactures. In Great Britain James Watt's low-pressure engine was the leader, but in the United States most preferred the high-pressure engines of Oliver Evans (1755-1819), the early Republic's premier inventor. Although his engines became most famous for driving steamboats and railroads, they were widely used in mills and shops. As was the custom, Evans used testimonials from satisfied customers to advertise his engines.

Mars Works, Feb. 22d, 1812.

SIR,

In answer to your several queries of yesterday, viz.

1. What are the principles and structure of your improved steam engines, and how do they differ from the well known English engine of Bolton and Watt?

2. How many are in use, where situated, for what purpose are they used, and by whom owned?

3. How many are you making, for what purpose, and by whom engaged, and where are they to be used? I reply:

My improvement consists, 1st, in the application of a principle in nature, viz. every addition of 30 degrees of heat by Fahrenheit's thermometer, to the temperature of water, doubles the elasticity or power of the steam; so that doubling the heat of the water, increases the power of the steam about 100 times.

2d. In the construction of my engines, of such forms, as to generate steam rapidly, and at the same time be capable of holding steam of high elastic power, which enables me to make my small en-

From Oliver Evans, "Account of the Steam Engines of Oliver Evans," *Archives of Useful Knowledge,* II (April 1812), 362-69.

gines as powerful as the great ones formerly used.

My engines are wrought with high elastic steam. The temperature of the water being 302 degrees; the power of the steam 120 lbs. to the inch area of the piston, will carry a load from fifty to one hundred lbs. to the inch area, as we choose to work: doubling the consumption of fuel in a given time, gives us about sixteen times the power. The higher the elasticity of the steam, the less fuel is required to obtain a given power. Any given power can be obtained with one-third the fuel, and one-fourth the weight of engines; therefore they will excel more for propelling boats and land carriages, than they have already excelled for mills. They require not more than one-fortieth of the usual quantity of water, while we do not condense to take off the resistance of the atmosphere, and when we do condense, less condensing water is required. Therefore they can be set any where on a common water well.

If the water proves impregnated with limestone or salt, then I make my boilers inexhaustible, so that not more than one cubic foot of fresh water will be used in 24 hours, producing a twenty horse power. This is done by using the salt or limestone water to condense the steam to water again, to supply the boiler; and none is wasted, except the small quantity that is decomposed and changed into air, by which means no sediment can accumulate to cause the boilers to burn out.

3d. My engines are simple in their structure, having but one valve rotatory in its motion, answering all the purposes of four, used in other engines; and they will last as long as the cylinder, say 100 years.

They are safer from accidents; the boilers being cylindrical, will hold steam ten times as powerful as we ever wish to use it.

See my book, explaining the principles fully, page 60, where I shew the difference of the costs and expense of keeping one on the old principles, and one on the new, at work 10 years, to be $40,000.

Yet this great improvement is strongly opposed by many who ought to know better; and would have been with great difficulty brought into use, had not Congress enabled me to stem the torrent of opposition, by their act for my relief.

There are of my engines now at work,

1st. One of twenty horse power, began in 1803, by M'Keever and Valcourt, at New Orleans, to propel a boat; but they were burnt out by incendiaries, before they had the opportunity of trying the engine to the boat. The engine was repaired, and is applied to saw timber in Florida.

2d. One of twenty horse power, applied to saw timber, at Mansihak, in Louisiana; the weekly task has been 18,000 feet boards, besides grinding all the corn wanted for use, driving four saws and a pair mill stones. The property of William Donaldson, esq. **New** Orleans. (a)

3d. One ten horse power, first set up at Lexington, Kentucky, by Luther Stephens, the inventor of the improved rotatory valve, now used. It was made inexhaustible, as the water was impregnated with limestone, and applied to grind grain, but now removed to Natchez, and applied to sawing timber. The property of Messrs. Foster and Withers.

4th. One for manufacturing flour, at Pittsburgh, twenty or twenty-four horse power, doing the work of 60 or 72 horses, grinding 20 bushels grain per hour. The property of Owen Evans and Son, and Oliver Evans and Son.

5th. One at Middletown, Connecticut; the property of the Middletown Woollen Manufacturing Company; twenty-four horse power, driving all the machinery for carding, spinning, reeling, weaving, washing, fulling, dyeing, shearing, dressing, and finishing. The steam, after doing all this, warms the house, heats water, &c. and serves instead of oil, in dressing the cloth. It is preferred by the artist, Mr. J. Sandford, who directs the establishment, to all he had seen in England, after remaining there thirteen years, and seeing all the best British steam engines. (b)

6th. One in Pittsburgh, ten horse power. The property of Mr. Eichbaum and Son; and applied to draw iron wire, grind glass, turn wood and metals, &c.; it works very well. This engine was first set up in Philadelphia, to saw timber, by a steam engineer, instructed in the old principles; but he could not make it work above one minute at a time, nor would he suffer me to correct his errors, but took it down and sold it, and set up one on old principles, which he thought he could make work better; and cautioned the public against the errors of my principles; but he has taken his last engine down also.

7th. One at Lexington, Kentucky, twenty or twenty-four horse power, set up by Mr. Luther Stephens, instead of the one he sold; it is inexhaustible also; applied to grind grain and manufacture flour. The property of the Lexington Steam Mill Company.

8th. One at Marietta, Ohio, twenty horse power; grinding grain and manufacturing flour. The property of the Marietta Mill Company: David Putnam, esq. president. (c)

9th. One at Vidalia, opposite Natchez, on the Mississippi, now setting up, to saw timber; twenty-four horse power. The property of Joseph Vidalls, esq.

10th. One at Mars Iron Works, Philadelphia, five or six horse power, applied to turn and bore iron, in aid of manufacturing steam engines, and other machinery. This, though last mentioned, was first made, and applied to grind plaster and saw marble, to show the principles in operation.

I have made, at my works, ready for setting up, the following engines:

One thirty horse power, will do the work of ninety horses; it is to be applied to a variety of purposes, for manufacturing, &c. &c. The property of Doctor George Hunter.

One twenty-four horse power, to be applied to saw 5,000 feet boards in 12 hours day, and grind 220 bushels grain in 12 hours night. The property of Hunter and Evans.

One twenty horse power, to be applied to propel a boat in Merimack canal and Merimack river.

One I am making for a boat to run in the Mississippi; the weight of this engine will not exceed one-third that of a common twenty horse power; and its greatest power when wanted, will perhaps exceed 40 horses. The property of Vidall and Evans. The boat loaded with the engine, 100 passengers, with fuel and provisions, will displace by sinking, a column of water about 14 inches deep by 15 wide. How fast may we expect her to run through still water?

One twenty-four horse power, to be set on a wharf, to drive three pair of six feet millstones, and grind and manufacture into flour 20 bushels of wheat per hour, in competition with many of the best water mills, situated near the same place. Of this I am to own one-fourth part.

One making at Pittsburgh, by Stackhouse & Rogers, 70 horse power, intended to roll iron, &c.

One engaged, do. twenty horse power, for a paper mill.

One do. do. twenty-four horse power, to grind grain, &c. at Cincinnati, Kentucky.

One making at Mars Works, Philadelphia, to saw 5,000 feet boards in 12 hours; of which I am to own one-third part.

One do. for a steam boat.

Making in all, 10 in use; and 10 made, making and engaged.

I discovered the principles of these engines, when an apprentice boy, 36 years ago, and have been labouring all my life to get them introduced into use, for propelling boats, wagons, and mills, &c.; you may perceive, that as soon as I had the power, they began to progress rapidly. All I receive for licenses to use my other improvements, I am laying out to bring my engines into use; and I am clearly of opinion, the time is not far distant, when the old principles will be abandoned as useless, as certainly as, that those millers who first opposed my improvements in the manufacture of flour, now adopt and use them.

I am, Sir, your most obedient servant,
OLIVER EVANS.
DR. J. MEASE.

Notes.

(a) With respect to the second engine mentioned, Mr. Evans published the following statement in 1808:

Mark Stackhouse, steam engineer, one of the three workmen who went to set up one of my improved steam engines, in Louisiana, for sawing timber, has returned, and makes the following report, viz.

"That he and the other two, with others to assist them, were engaged for the first six months in a cypress swamp, in building houses, bridges, making roads, preparing timber for the saw-mill, &c. That from the day they began to frame the saw-mill, until the day he left the works, was 12 months and 15 days; during which time, they built the saw-mill in the most permanent manner, 51 by 40 feet, calculated for four saws in separate frames, set up the engine and three saws, and found it to possess power to drive four; but as three sawed as fast as they could conveniently supply the timber for, and remove the lumber, they intended to set up a pair of mill-stones instead of the fourth saw. That they had sawed 367,000 feet of boards and scantling, (chiefly boards,) French measure; which, owing to the high price of lumber in that country, had (in his opinion,) already defrayed the whole expense of his establishment, viz. of the engine, saw-mill, buildings, wages, and expenses of every kind. That nothing relating to the engine had broke, or went out of order so as to stop the mill one hour. They sawed by day only, and the three saws cut from twenty-five hundred to three thousand feet French measure, per day of 12 hours; and the engine consumed about one and an half cords wood per day."—Here ends his report.

The working cylinder of this engine, is only nine inches diameter, and the stroke of the piston three feet, making thirty-six strokes per minute, and works without a condenser; the fire is applied to the outside of the boiler, yet possesses power equal to twenty horses, and will do the work of sixty horses, if kept going day and night; this simple form will suit most situations; but where fuel is dear, the fire flue may be passed through the centre of the boiler; a larger cylinder, with a condenser to take off the resistance of the atmosphere, may be used with advantage, and by thus putting the whole of my improvements into operation, I have reason to expect, to produce effects equal to the best English engines, with one-third part of the fuel, because it appears that doubling the consumption of fuel on my new simple principle, gives the engine sixteen times the power.

(b) Mr. Sanford says, in a letter to Mr. Evans, "as to the engine we had from you, it continues to perform with increasing credit, and thus far exceeds any thing of the kind I ever saw. It is my opinion, that it will continue superior to all other modes of constructing steam engines; as to all former constructions for that purpose, they are so far inferior, in my opinion, that I would not take them as a gift, could I obtain yours at your price."

ISAAC SANDFORD.

Middletown, (Conn.)
June 16, 1811.

The following additional testimony in favour of this machine, has been received recently:

Middletown, Feb. 27, 1812.

MR. O. EVANS,

Sir—It is now nine months since we have had your improved steam engine in operation at our woollen manufactory; during which period, we have been gradually loading it with machinery of different kinds, and having now got all that we intend for the present at work, it is with much pleasure we make known to you our high opinion respecting it. We consider it in every respect superior to Watt and Bolton's improved engines. Its simplicity is such, that any lad of common parts can take care of it, with a day's instruction. Very little sediment collect in the boilers, and an examination of them twice a year is sufficient—the piston requires packing once a month—the rotatory valve, through which the steam is admitted and discharged from the working cylinder, is an important improvement, and answers the most sanguine expectations we had formed of it. Your method of applying the steam as the prime mover of the piston in the working cylinder, both up and down, is so obviously preferable to the English method of using it only as the best means of forming a vacuum, that your engines must, before long, be universally adopted. The prejudices and erroneous opinions which have existed with some respecting them, will be dissipated—and when they get generally into use, you will have the satisfaction of knowing that you have done your country great service, by a saving of vast sums of money in this one article. Mr. Morrison, of Boston, came here last summer to see your engine, and was so highly pleased with it, that I understand he has engaged one from you for propelling boats on the principle of an endless chain. I hope it will be ready, as he expects it to be sent as soon as the Delaware is navigable.

Our engine requires about 96 feet of oak wood, or three-fourths of a cord, to work 12 hours with our present machinery. We derive great advantages in using your steam engine in preference to a water power, in our woollen manufactory—the heat that escapes from under the boilers, and the steam that has done its work, enable us to warm our rooms in winter, so that the risque from fire is greatly lessened—and we have a temperature that is very advantageous to us in working wool in winter. Our factory is not liable to be carried away by freshets; and in using steam, we have an agent always at command, that will neither freeze up in winter, nor be affected by a drought in summer.

I remain, dear sir, respectfully yours,

ARTHUR W. MAGILL,
Superintendant for the Middletown
Manufacturing Company.

(c) The following notice of the mill at Marietta, appeared in the newspapers lately:

"On Tuesday, the 7th instant, (January,) the steam mill at Marietta, was put in operation for the first time, and its success met the most sanguine expectation of the proprietors. It was built by William Green, of Zanesville, and is universally allowed, by good judges, to be of superior workmanship. The house is capacious, well constructed, and built altogether of hewn stone. It stands on the west bank of the Muskingum, about thirty rods from its confluence with the Ohio, and is easy of access by water, at all seasons of the year. There is yet but one pair of stones in operation, which were taken from the banks of Racoon creek, in the state of Ohio, and are said to be equal if not superior to the celebrated burrs. They will grind a bushel of grain in three minutes. The proprietors, Messrs. Gilman, Barber, Skinner, Fearing, and Putnam, contemplate to attach to the mill a carding, spinning, and woollen factory.

3. Advantages of Manufactures, 1815

E. I. DU PONT to Isaac Briggs, December 30, 1815

For many Americans, independence meant the opportunity to develop in the New World an empire that would rival those of the Old. These men, many of whom identified themselves with the Jeffersonian faction in politics, dreamed of building a country that was economically as well as politically independent, one that fostered manufactures and transportation as well as commerce and agriculture. They believed that industry, borrowing the new technology of the Industrial Revolution, was not only a necessary component of imperial prosperity, but also a force that would fructify all the other elements of the nation's economy.

When Isaac Briggs, a surveyor, teacher, inventor, and office holder under President Thomas Jefferson, asked the French émigré and powder-maker E. I. du Pont what influence the coming of the Industrial Revolution had had in the area of Wilmington, Delaware, the latter drew a glowing but accurate picture of a dying eighteenth-century town that had become a vigorous, nineteenth-century manufacturing city.

Letter from E. I. du Pont to Isaac Briggs, December 30, 1815, Eleutherian Mills Historical Library, Greenville, Delaware. Reprinted by permission.

Your letter of the 22d inst. is received, requesting Wm. Young, Joseph Bringhurst and I to communicate our ideas on the influence that the establishment of manufactures has upon agriculture, and the particular effect that their introduction in this neighbourhood has had on the value of land, and the general wellfare of this part of the country.

Few places in the United States can give more striking proof of the advantages of manufactures than those which have been displayed these few years past in Wilmington and its vicinity. About twelve years ago Wilmington, which was formerly a small port of enport, not being able from the want of capital to carry on commercial business in competition with the wealth of Philadelphia, had nearly abandoned every pretension to foreign trade; from Seventeen vessels employed in that line of business and which once belonged to the place, only one remained.—Wilmington was visibly decreasing, and shewed the evident marks of decay which are yet to be seen in Newcastle, Christiana Bridge and other places too far distant to have been much benefited by the establishment of manufactures on the Brandywine.—From this period the aspect of our village and of the country around has improved in an astonishing degree.—New houses, new wharves, are built in town every year; two fine bridges have been constructed; the rate of rent in town is more than doubled; five turnpikes, leading in every direction from our town to the boundry of the State, have been undertaken and compleated at the expense of the inhabitants mostly the farmers; in the course of four or five years the price of land has more than trebled.—I myself purchased five years ago at the rate of $21 pr. acre a farm of 200 acres a great portion of which was

excellent wood land; the plantation adjoining to it, but still farther from town, has been sold last Thursday at public sale, some lots of wood land divided from it, as high as from $100 to $151 pr. acre, and the main body of the farm with no other improvements than some old log houses, at the rate of $65-50 pr. acre.

The face of the country is changed, old fields formerly covered with what is called here poverty grass are now in rich clover; the farms are well fenced; new barns and new Stone houses are rapidly rising.—The price of produce has increased in proportion with the wants of the new consumers.—The farmers have found a market and ready sale, not only for their principal productions but also for a number of articles, as wood, porc, mutton, veal, poultries, butter, potatoes, &c., which formerly they could not carry to the Philadelphia market, on account of the distance, and were obliged to sell at a low price on the then small Wilmington market.— This new way of selling at home, has enabled the farmers to increase those kind of productions that were before of very little advantage to them, and which on a well managed farm will bring more to the pocket of the industrious farmer than even his best crop of wheat.

The new consumers, who have been the cause of this new outlet for produce, and who are scattering their wages daily among the farmers, are not, as the opposers to manufactures have advanced, *hands taken from the plough*, but mostly artificers imported from europe to employ their industry for the benefit of the United States, or poor women and children unable till then to avoid scarcity and want.

That a new source of wealth has been created here is well demonstrated by its effects.—This wealth, which is now earned by American industry, is nothing else but a small portion of that immense capital yearly exported from this country to england for the payment of british goods; which capital accomplishes there the same magic effects on a larger scale, enriches the country and the farmers, and enables british subjects to pay their enormous taxes.—Let our infant manufactories be destroyed by the policy of England, or by our own want of discernment, and the money which we have seen distributed here for a few years, and which rendered this little spot so florishing, will return to its former channel, and vivify some other village *in england.*

4. A Factory and Its Discipline

Hunt's Merchants' Magazine

In the United States, as in Great Britain, textile mills were the cutting edge of the Industrial Revolution. Fulling mills, which finished woolens, were built as early as the seventeenth century, but mills designed for spinning and weaving did not begin to appear until copies of English machines became available in the 1790's. Though at first the textile mills were small in size, few in number, and crude in operation, they gradually grew larger and more sophisticated until, by the 1830's, there were many American mills—and the best of them were as good as any in Britain. This growth greatly increased the demand for textile machinery, and a number of machine-making firms were established to meet this need. Some, like the Matteawan Company, provided a wide range of machines and services.

Those who have sailed up the Hudson River cannot fail to have noticed the grandeur of the scenery around that beautiful expansion of its waters which lies directly opposite the village of Newburgh. If they have landed at that place, and cast a glance at the chain of mountains which bound the horizon on the east, and overlook the flourishing settlement of Fishkill landing, they have scarcely dreamed that the base of that mountain range was watered by a stream which holds its course between bold and rugged shores, and gives employment to a large and industrious population. Yet here is the valley of Fishkill Creek, a small, though important tributary of the Hudson, whose shores, a few years since, were the resort of the Indian, and the haunt of the

From "Manufacturing Industry of the State of New York," *Hunt's Merchants' Magazine,* XV (October 1846), 370-72.

beaver and otter, both of which have now disappeared before the progress of industry and civilization. It was in allusion to the excellent quality of the furs procured in this region, that the aborigines applied the name of Mat-te-a-wan, or "good fur," to the particular locality we are about to describe.

Matteawan manufacturing village is situated on Fishkill Creek, about one mile and a half from the steamboat ferry which plies between the landing of Fishkill and the village of Newburgh. Having ascended the acclivity that overlooks the Hudson, the approach to it is through a beautiful avenue, constructed at the expense of the company, in order to avoid the circuitousness of the ancient route. As you enter the village, the first object that arrests the attention is a mill of venerable aspect, which was probably the earliest attempt to convert the water-power at this place to profitable account. The next instant, your ears are saluted by the noise of the loom and the spindle; and as the eye wanders instinctively over the long vista of tenements which lie on either side of the stream, you cannot avoid paying an involuntary tribute to the air of comfort and neatness which seem everywhere to prevail. As you advance a short distance farther, the next object that arrests the attention is the original cotton factory, which is 80 feet by 40, three stories high, and surmounted by a belfry, whose "brazen tongue" gives warning of the hours devoted to the pursuits of industry. This building was erected in 1814, by the Messrs. Peter A. Schenck, Peter H. Schenck, and Henry Dowling, the latter of whom eventually resigned his interest to his associates. It was the only building appropriated to manufacturing purposes at this place, until 1822, when an additional structure, 138 feet

by 72, and also three stories high, was put up by the Messrs. Schenck, who associated with them Mr. William B. Leonard, so long and favorably known as the efficient agent of the company. In 1832, a machine shop, 150 feet by 30, was erected, which, together with the foundry, employs about 200 hands, and produces annually, in cotton machinery, sugar-mills, steam-engines, &c., to the value of $262,462. The company have also a building, 40 feet by 60, a portion of which is appropriated to storage and the transaction of business, and the balance to the manufacture of cards by machinery. The cotton department runs 6,000 spindles, and gives employment to 300 operatives, including men, women, and children, who turn out annually about 1,296,000 yards of Canton flannels, fustians, mariners' stripes, pantaloon stuffs, &c., valued at $173,692. The entire amount of capital invested, is about $350,000. The average number of hours devoted to labor, are 10 in the machine shop, and 11 hours 35 minutes in the cotton factory. The entire population, directly or indirectly dependent on the company, may be estimated at 1,700. The tenements which they occupy number about 100, and are distributed over an area of as many acres.

The regimen of the establishment is strict, without being severe; moral, without bordering on intolerance. Every facility is afforded to the cause of education and religion, and habits of industry and sobriety are carefully inculcated. The following are the

RULES AND REGULATIONS OF THE MATTEAWAN COMPANY

No person will be admitted into the yard during working hours, except on business, without permission of an agent. At all other times, the watchmen will be invested with full control.

The work bell will be rung three minutes, and tolled five minutes; at the expiration of which, every person is expected to be at their work, and every entrance closed, except through the office, which will at all times be open during the working hours of the factory.

No person employed in the manufacturing departments can be permitted to leave their work without permission from their overseer. All others employed in and about the factory are requested to give notice to the agent or superintendent, if they wish to be absent from their work.

No talking can be permitted among the hands in any of the working departments, except on subjects relating to their work.

No spirituous liquors, smoking, or any kind of amusements, will be allowed in the workshops or yards.

Those who take jobs will be considered as overseers of the persons employed by them, and subject to these rules.

Should there exist among any of the persons employed, an idea of oppression on the part of the company, they are requested to make the same known in an honorable manner, that such grievances, if really existing, may be promptly considered.

To convince the enemies of domestic manufactures that such establishments are not "sinks of vice and immorality," but, on the contrary, nurseries of morality, industry, and intelligence, a strictly moral conduct is required of every one. Self-respect, it is presumed, will induce every one to be as constant in attendance on some place of divine worship as circumstances will permit. Intemperance, or any gross impropriety of conduct, will cause an immediate discharge of the individual.

The agent and other members of the company are desirous of cultivating the most friendly feeling with the workmen in the establishment, believing that they are to rise or fall together. Therefore, to promote the interest and harmony of all, it is necessary there should be a strict observance of these rules and regulations.

5. A Machinist-Inventor

DAVID WILKINSON, "Reminiscences"

Machine making was an important technological key to the spread of the Industrial Revolution in the United States. It was one thing to conceive of a textile mill and know what kind of machinery should go into it. It was quite

From "David Wilkinson's Reminiscences," *Transactions of the Rhode Island Society for the Encouragement of Domestic Industry. In the Year 1861* (Providence, 1862), pp. 100-111.

another matter to actually obtain machinery of sufficient quality to ensure satisfactory results. Even so, it was relatively easy to find men who could build them. The machine industry was important in another way. Skill in making machinery tended to be generally applicable; when a man had mastered the technique of making one type of machine, he could make other types as well. Thus the machine shop became a marketplace of new techniques and methods which, developed for one purpose, could easily be transferred to others. It was also here that the ideas of inventors were translated into iron and steel, and their innovations for one industry were applied to others.

The machinists of early America produced few men of prominence; they were largely an anonymous group. A machinist who did leave a record was David Wilkinson, one of the most versatile and useful of his trade.

Autumn, 1846.

In April, 1776, Eleazer Smith, who had been at work for Jeremiah Wilkinson, junior, a Quaker of Cumberland, came to my father's blacksmith shop, which was making scythes, in the town of Cumberland, Rhode Island, to make a machine to manufacture card teeth, for Daniel Anthony, of Providence, who was going into the card making business. While at work, Smith told my father of Jeremiah Wilkinson's making card tacks of cold iron. In laying the strip of leather around the hand card, he lacked four large tacks to hold the corners in place, while driving the tacks around the outer edge. He took a plate of an old door lock off the floor, cut four points with shears, and made heads in the vice; but afterwards made a steel bow with scores in it, and put it in the vice, and in that way made tacks.

I think in 1777, my father made a small pinch press, with different sized impressions, placed on an oak log, with a stirrup for the foot, and sat me astraddle on the log, to heading nails, which were cut with common shears. He cut the points off of plates drawn by trip hammer. This was the com-

mencement, in the world, of making nails from cold iron.

I think about 1820, I went to Cumberland, with Samuel Greene, my nephew, and purchased of Jeremiah Wilkinson, the old shears, with which he cut the first four nails. He was, I think, ninety years of age at that time. The shears were a pair of tailor's shears, with bows straightened out, and the blades cut off half the length. They were deposited with the Historical Society, in Providence, by Samuel Greene.

My father, Oziel Wilkinson, lived in the town of Smithfield, Rhode Island, in 1775, at the commencement of the war, and owned a blacksmith-shop, with a hammer worked by water. It was here Eleazer Smith made the machine for Daniel Anthony. I was then about five years old, and my curiosity was so great to see the work going on, that my father sat me on Mr. Smith's bench, to look on, while he worked. And at this time, seventy years afterwards, I could make a likeness of nearly every piece of that machine,—so durable are the first impressions on the mind of youth. After Smith had finished the machine, so as to make a perfect card tooth, he told the people in the shop that he could make a machine to make the tooth, prick the leather, and set the tooth, at one operation.

Jeremiah Wilkinson carried on the business of making hand cards for carding sheep's wool, and it being difficult to import wire, he drew the wire out by horse power.

In 1784 or '5, my father put the anchor shop in operation, at Pawtucket Falls, on the Blackstone river, in North Providence, Rhode Island.

About this time, I heard of cotton yarn being made in, or near East Greenwich, in which John Reynolds and James Macarris, who employed a Mr. Mackwire, or Maguire, to make yarn on a jenny, for which I forged and ground spindles. I made a small machine to grind with, which had a roller of wood to roll on the stone, which turned the spindle against the stone, and so ground the steel spindles perfectly. I heard of no machines for carding cotton.

About this time also, a number of gentlemen in the town of Providence, commenced some machinery for working cotton. Andrew Dexter, merchant, the father of S. Newton Dexter, of Orickany, Oneida county, New York; Aaron Mann, father of Samuel F. Mann of Providence; Lewis Peck, merchant; Daniel Anthony, and I think Moses Brown of Providence, were aiding in the work. My father was applied to, to make iron work for a machine for carding cotton, which was done by the help of a carpenter, named Joshua Lindley, and a brass founder, named Daniel Jackson, father of Samuel and John Jackson, of Providence. The card circles, or rims, were made of wrought iron, as there was no furnace near. The card was put in operation in the Market House

chamber, in Providence, and was turned by a colored man, named Prince Hopkins, who had lost one leg, and I think one arm, in Sullivan's expedition at Newport, a few years before. The cotton was taken from the card, in rolls about eighteen inches long, and carried one mile from town to Moses Brown's, where it was made into roping, by a young woman in Mr. Brown's employ, named Amey Lawrence.

About this time, too, Daniel Anthony made a trip to Bridgewater, and returning said he had some parts of a machine, called the Arkwright Water Frame, which was commenced by a European, in the employ of Colonel Orr, of Bridgewater, and given up, or the few parts thrown by. He soon had one under way in Providence, which was made and finished in Pawtucket, and put in operation there, by Anthony's two sons, Joseph and Richard, assisted occasionally, by two other sons, Daniel and William. The rollers were made of half inch wrought iron, with swells of brass cast on, and fluted with files. The bobbin which received the yarn from the spindle was made with a score in the bottom, to receive a cross cat-gut twine, with a tightning wooden thumbscrew, like a violin, to regulate the taking up;— which Mr. Slater performed in his first water frames, by making a wide flat bottom to the bobbin, set on a wooden cloth washer, to regulate the taking up, as the friction would increase by weight as the bobbin filled, and needed more friction. (Mr. Slater run his first machinery by rope bands, for his carding machines, roping and drawing, as the use of belts was not then known in this country. The first leather belts I ever heard of were made by John Blackburn, when he was setting a mule in operation for Mr. Slater. Mr. Slater informed me there had been a new machine for making yarn got up in England, which was a mixture of the Jack and Jenny and the Arkwright Water Frame.)

I assisted the Anthony's in finishing and keeping in order their machine.

Their being no cotton gins at the south, they, (the Providence people above referred to) imported some of the cotton in seed, and picked it off by hand, which being in bad condition, and the machinery imperfect, they made some few tons of yarn, and laid the machinery by. Moses Brown bought the machinery, and advertised in New York which brought Mr. Samuel Slater to Providence.

Mr. Slater came out with Moses Brown, to my father's at Pawtucket, to commence an Arkwright Water Frame, and Breaker, and two Finishers, Carding Machines. I forged the iron work, and turned the rollers and spindles, in part. All the turning was done with hand tools, and by hand power, with crank wheels. When the card rims and wheels were wanting, I went with Slater to Mansfield, Massachusetts, to a furnace owned by a French gentlemen, named Dauby, who came I think with Lafayette's army, who has a son and one daughter now living in Utica and Auburn. The card rims broke in cooling. Mr. Slater said the iron shrunk more than the English iron. I told him we would make a crooked arm, that would let the rim move round,—the arms being carried one way, and when the hub cooled would return, and leave the wheel not divided against itself,—which proves a remedy in all cases, if the arms are made the width the right way, to let the curve spring easy, with sufficient strength of iron. I told him cast iron broke more often by division in its own family, than by labor.

About the year 1786-7, my father bought the machinery for cutting iron screws, called the Fly screw, for pressing paper,—of Israel Wilkinson of Smithfield, the son of Israel who built the Hope furnace for the Browns and others, —and with the help of a Mr. Crabb, who was employed by the Browns, John, Joseph, Nicholas and Moses, in building the sperm candle works, on what is now called India Point. They used a screw of cast iron, about seven inches in diameter, and five or six feet long, which was cut by setting it upright, with a wooden guide screw, which was connected with an iron socket, with a mortice to hold the cutter, which was fastened with an iron wedge.

After Wilkinson had finished the Candle works, with Mr. Crabb, he put in operation works for making screws, in Smithfield, and cut in the same manner as the English plan, brought over by Mr. Crabb. The old man (old Israel Wilkinson,) went to different furnaces in Massachusetts, to mould his screws. There were no moulders who would undertake it. My father had once seen old Israel Wilkinson mould one screw, and, after he had bought these old tools of young Israel, as he was called, and at a time when he wanted some moulding done, he took me—then about fifteen years old—into his chaise and carried me to Hope furnace, about fourteen miles from Providence, in Scituate, to mould a paper mill screw, as they had no moulder at their furnace who would undertake to mould one. I had never seen a furnace in operation, or seen a thing moulded, in my life. I moulded three or four screws before I left for home. I stayed there about a month. The screws weighed about five hundred pounds each—were five inch top, with cross holes seven inches diameter, through a lantern head for a lever seven inches diameter. They were cast in dried-clay moulds, hooped and strapped with iron bands. I took the screws home to Pawtucket and cut and finished them there. They were made for Hudson & Goodwin, of New York, and Lazarus Beach, of Danbury, Connecticut. We made many screws of wrought iron for clothiers' presses, and oil mills; but they were imperfect, and I told my father I wanted to make a machine to cut screws on centers, which would make them more perfect. He told me I might commence one. My father, in 1791, built a small air furnace, or reverbera-tory, for casting iron, in which were cast the first wing-gudgeons known in America, to our knowledge, for Samuel Slater's old factory.

On my way home from Hope fur-nace, I called at the Ore bed, in Crans-ton, and found Mr. Ormsbee, (I think Elijah,) of Providence, repairing the large steam engine, which raised the water seventy-two feet from the bot-tom of the ore pits. The engine was made with the main cylinder open at the top, and the piston raised with a large balance lever, as the news of the cap on the cylinder by Boulton & Watt had not yet come to this country when that engine was built. Mr. Ormsbee told me he had been reading of a boat being put in operation by steam, at the city of Philadelphia, and if I would go home with him and build the engine, he would build a steamboat. I went home and made my patterns, cast and bored the cylinder, and made the wrought iron work, and Ormsbee hired a large boat of John Brown, belonging to one of his large India ships—should think about twelve tons. I told him of two plans of paddles, one I called the flutter wheel and the other, the goose

foot paddle. We made the goose foot, to open and shut with hinges, as the driv-ing power could be much cheaper ap-plied than the paddle wheel. After we had got the boat nearly done, Charles Robbins made a pair of paddle wheels, and attached them to a small skiff, and run about with a crank, by hand power. After having the steamboat in opera-tion, we exhibited it near Providence, between the two bridges; I think, while the bridges were being built. After our frolic was over, being short of funds, we hauled the boat up and gave it over.

About this time, a young man called on me, and wished to see the boat, and remained a day or two examining all the works. He told me his name was Daniel French, from Connecticut. I never knew where he came from, nor where he went.

Some three or four years after we laid our boat by, I was at New York and saw some work commenced at Fulton's Works, for steamboat shafts, and saw a small steamboat in North river, built by Col. John Stevens, of Ho-boken. I went over to his place, and saw his boring mill. I thought he was ahead of Fulton, as an inventor.

In the winter of 1814-15, hearing of a trial which was coming on before the Legislature of New Jersey, between Robert Fulton and Col. Ogden, of New Jersey, I had the curiosity to attend—as I always thought it singular that the idea of the paddle-wheel should strike two persons so, at the same time, at such a distance apart; yet I knew so simple a thing might happen. I learned in Trenton, that Fulton had said he made the draft of the wheel, in Lon-don. The case in court was managed for Ogden, by Hopkinson and Southard; and for Fulton, by Emmet and Samp-son. I, being a stranger there, was in the crowd to learn what I could. After the trial was over,—in company with Emmet, Sampson, Fulton, and others,—I took stage for New York; and, in the midst of an extremely heavy snow-storm, wallowed our way along as far as Jersey City, where we found all the houses full, and no mail had crossed to New York, for two days. Fulton, Emmet and Sampson took a boat, with four oarsmen, and got over by crossing the cakes of floating ice, and launching the boat several times. The boat returned with General Brown and suit. The next boat took me, with several others. Not long after I arrived home, I saw an account of Fulton's death.

About the year 1840, I was on the railroad from Utica to Albany, with an aged gentleman in the cars, and the subject of steam power came up, when I informed him of my early acquaintance with steam power, &c. He was a well informed man, and I think, had been a member of Assembly. He said, he thought more credit had been given to Fulton, than was his due; that Col. John Stevens was more deserving than Fulton. I told him, I never thought Fulton an inventor, but simply a busy collector of other people's inventions. "Well," replied the gentleman, "I always said so, and he would never have succeeded had it not been for Daniel French. "What do you mean by Daniel French?" asked I. "Why a Yankee," said he, "that Fulton kept locked up for six months, making drafts for him."

The name of Daniel French, burst upon my ears for the first time, for forty-nine years, and almost explained some mysteries.

In 1798, when in Philadelphia, I called in at the Museum, and saw an old bald-head eagle walking about the yard. The keeper, who I think was named Peal, told me the eagle was ninety-six years old; that he was taken from the nest, ninety-six years before, at Halifax, or Nova Scotia, and that he would have a new bill in four years,—four years after, I saw mention in a Philadelphia paper, that the old eagle had got a new bill on. I had never seen any other account of the eagle, except in scripture,—of his renewing his age, like the eagle.

In, or about 1794, Col. Noami Baldwin came from Boston to Pawtucket, after machinery for a canal he was going to make, north from Boston. We made the patterns and cast his wheels, racks, &c., and he took them to Charlestown and finished the locks. I was there and saw the operation. It being the first canal in the country, a good deal of curiosity was excited among the people.

About this time, I saw the platform hay scales, at Charlestown Neck, at what was called Page's Tavern. The plan of the scales was brought from Ireland, by a Mr. Cox, of Boston, who built the old Warren Bridge, from Boston to Charlestown, and who was called to Ireland to build a bridge there. On his return to Boston, he brought a three-wheeled carriage, with a Shetland pony, for his son, and the plan of the platform scales, which has been the subject of so many patents in the United States.

We cast at Pawtucket, the iron for the draw for the Cambridge bridge.

A Mr. Mills, who built the South Boston bridge, came to me for the machinery for the bridge. I fixed the patterns, and went to Raynham, got the castings, and carried them to Boston, for the first new bridge.

Jeptha Wilkinson, junior, nephew of Jeremiah Wilkinson, invented a machine for making weavers' steel reeds, by water power.

Gardner Wilkinson invented the rolling axletree in two parts, so useful on rail road curves, &c. He also made the morticing machine, and, I think, he and his brother, made the pivot bridge, used on canals.

About 1794, my father built a rolling and slitting mill, at Pawtucket, On the gudgeon of the wheel of which, I put my new screw machine in operation, which was on the principle of the gauge or sliding lathe now in every workshop almost throughout the world; the perfection of which consists in that most faithful agent *gravity*, making the joint, and that almighty perfect number *three*, which is harmony itself. I was young when I learnt that principle. I had never seen my grandmother putting a chip under a three legged milking stool; but she always had to put a chip under a four legged table, to keep it steady. I cut screws of all dimensions by this machine, and did them perfectly.

I now made a model in miniature, and had thought of trying to procure a patent, but was afraid there might be something somewhere to interfere with me, already in use. So I started off to make inquiries. I went to New York, and found an Englishman, in Greenwich street, on North River, named Barton, making clothiers' screws. He was welding an iron guide on the end of his tap, and forcing it through a socket, with an iron bar, by hand, which was the old imperfection that troubled me always. I could hear of no other in New York. I had heard of one in Canaan, in Connecticut. I went on board a sloop, old Captain Wicks, of Long Island, master, bound for Albany. In five days, I landed at Fishkill, and went ashore, and walked some thirty miles, to Canaan. I

found screws made there by Forbes & Adams, by water power, but they welded on, and forced through a socket in the old way. I heard of screws being made in Canaan, from Abram Burt, of Taunton, Massachusetts. He called at Pawtucket, and looking at the old machine, I was at work with by horse power, said he had been making screws, at Canaan, by water power; that he could "set his cutter in the socket, draw the gate, and then it lathered away like the devil," which I fully believed when I saw the machine. I returned to New York, and from there went to Philadelphia, and found no screws made there except after the same mode as in New York. I heard of screws being made on the Brandywine, but my informant assured me they were made the same way as his and Barton's, at New York. I now returned home, and in the year 1797, went again to Philadelphia, when Congress was in session, and made application for a patent; Mr. Joseph Tillinghast, then a senator from Rhode Island, assisting me. On my return home, my father informed me that Jacob Perkins had been there and wanted to see my machine, and that, when he saw it, he laughed out, and remarked that he could do his engraving on cast steel, for Bank Note plates, with that machine,—that he could make a hair stroke with that, for it would never tremble,—that he could put an oval under the end of the rut, and, with an eccentric, make all his oval figures. I suppose Mr. Perkins afterwards derived great benefit from the thing.

Whilst I was at work on Slater's machinery, the owners were unwilling that I should make a slide lathe, on the principle of my screw machine, which was made for large turning; it was too heavy for cotton machinery. Mr. Slater said he had heard of one being made in England since he left, which would turn rollers. He wrote to Derbyshire, to his brother, John Slater, to come over, and bring a man who could build one. John came, and brought a Mr. John Blackburn, who made a slide lathe, which was on the principle of the old fluting machine, with the slide rest grooved in, in four edges, on two edged bars, forced in towards each other, by wedges, in mortises, behind the tenon. They worked this lathe some few weeks, and then threw it out of doors, and afterwards did their work by the old hand tool, as before.

About that time, my father, brothers, brothers-in-law William Wilkinson and Timothy Greene, and James, William, and Christopher Rhodes, purchased a water power on the Quinnebaug river, Connecticut, at Pomfret, and commenced building a cotton factory. These owners consented that I might build a gauge lathe, like my large one. I then went to work, and made my patterns in Sylvanus Brown's shop in Pawtucket. I left out the three friction rollers from under the rut, as for light work and slow motion, I was willing to risk the friction.

About this time, a Company in Providence got a master machinist from England, named Samuel Ogden, to build a factory at Hope Furnace. He was a man of great experience and good abilities. He advised me as a friend to abandon my new machine, for said he, "you can *ner* do it, for we have tried it out and out at *ome*, and given it up; and don't you think we should have been doing it at *ome*, if it could have been done?"

Mr. Pitkin, of East Hartford, had an Englishman, named Warburton, with him, building a factory. Warburton told me, "*they* could never make our work in Europe,—that Watt & Bolton gave it

to a man for a month's work to finish a piston rod, with hand tools."

When I had finished my patterns for the lathe, and was already to start next morning, for the furnace, in Foxborough, Sylvanus Brown took it into his head to put them into the stove, and burn them up. I made others then, and got them cast, and made my lathe, and it worked to a charm. Mr. Richard Anthony, who was building a factory, in Coventry, with his brother William, paid me ten dollars for the use of my lathe patterns, to cast after. And this is all I ever received for so valuable an invention.

Captain Benjamin Walcott, father of the Walcotts at York Mills, Oneida county, New York, and of Edward Walcott, of Pawtucket, with Nathan J. Sweetland, put the "live centre" arbour, and the rack, in place of the screw for the feeder, to a lathe they built afterwards. But, on long experience, the screw is found best, and the two "dead centres" will make the truest work,—though they are not quite so convenient perhaps as the "live centre" arbour. But the two great principles of my machine can never be improved upon,—that is, *three bearings* to the rest, and *weight* to hold it down, where you may weigh your friction to an ounce.

The slide lathe has bent sent to all parts of the world. A certain mechanic commenced business in this country, but after using one of my slide lathes awhile, he bought one, and returned to England with it; remarking, that with that lathe in England, he could do better than at any business he could get into in this country.

It was unfortunate for me patenting my machine, when the machine making and manufacturing business in this country was only in its infancy. The patent would run out before it could be brought into very extensive use. It certainly did run out without my deriving that benefit from the invention, I was so justly entitled to. One solitary ten dollar note is surely but small recompense for an improvement that is worth all the other tools in use, in any workshop in the world, for finishing brass and iron work.

The weighted slide, the joint made by gravity, applies to planing, turning, and boring of metals of every kind, and every way, as it needs no watching, and, instead of wearing *out* of repair, it is always wearing *into repair.*

I was always too much engaged in various business to look after and make profit out of my inventions. Other people, I hope, gained something by them.

We built machinery to go to almost every part of the country,—to Pomfret and Killingly, Connecticut; to Hartford, Vermont; to Waltham, Norton, Raynham, Plymouth, Halifax, Plympton, Middleboro, and other places in Massachusetts; for Wall & Wells, Trenton, New Jersey; for Union & Gray, on the Patapsco; for the Warren factories, on the Gunpowder, near Baltimore; to Tarboro' and Martinburgh, North Carolina; to two factories in Georgia; to Louisiana; to Pittsburgh; to Delaware; to Virginia, and other places. Indeed, Pawtucket was doing something for almost every part of the Union, and I had my hands too full of business, and was laboring too much for the *general prosperity,* to take proper care of the details, perhaps, and the advancement of my own individual interests.

In 1829, we all broke down; and although I was sixty years of age, and in very bad health, I thought I would move away, and see if I could not earn my own living. I moved with my family to Cohoes Falls, in the State of New York,

and there fixed my new home. I have since recovered my health wonderfully, and, at this moment, being about seventy-six years old, I am hearty and well —enjoy my food as well as any one, and can bear a good deal of fatigue and exposure. Few men, of my age, enjoy their faculties and health better than I do. Have I not much to be thankful for? I have, and am most sincerely thankful to a merciful God, for the many and great blessings.

The prospects at Cohoes were flattering for a time. But Nullification, Locofocory, Jacksonism, Free trade, and such abominations, killed the new village just born. Europeans who were applying for water power at Cohoes, at this time, went away, saying, now we were going to have free trade; they could do our work cheaper at " 'ome" than they could in this Country, and they would build their factories there.

We were compelled, now, to get our living where we could,—to go abroad, if we could not get work at home. I went to work on the Delaware and Raritan Canal, in New Jersey; then on the St. Lawrence improvements, in Canada; then to Ohio, on the Sandy and Beaver Canal; then to the new Wire bridge, on the Ottawa river, at Bytown, Canada, and Virginia. Wherever I could find anything to do, I went; and it is wonderful how I endured exposure to wet and cold, as I did.

In 1835-6, while engaged on the St. Lawrence river, I met a gentleman at Kingston, who advised me to go back of the Rideau lake, to get what I wanted, about seventy miles north of Kingston, to a village named Perth, which was given to the officers and soldiers who served in the late war with the United States. At the hotel at Perth, the landlord showed me a silver clasp, which was taken from the leg of a large eagle, which was shot in the village. The plate, or clasp, was from some place in Connecticut, I do not remember the town, nor the person's name, but directed to Henry Clay. It was after the war, and the bearer of the express probably thought he might safely take a circuitous route through the British provinces. But these Canadians did n't like the name of Henry Clay; his policy had too anti-British a tendency to suit them, so they took the poor express eagle as a spy, I suppose, and refused to sell the clasp, at any price. Perhaps, they wanted to have the story to tell, that our American eagle had been struck to them, at least.

These are the recollections of an old man, and you will please take them for what they are worth. If they are worth anything to any one, I shall be glad. To yourself, I believe, they will be valuable, and be the means of recalling many pleasant incidents of olden times, and of an old friend.

6. Overview of American Manufactures, 1854

JOSEPH WHITWORTH AND GEORGE WALLIS, *The Industry of the United States*

When the United States decided to hold an exhibit of American arts and industry that would rival the British Crystal Palace Exhibition of 1851, the British machinist Joseph Whitworth was among those selected as a delegation to visit this country to report on its progress in the mechanic arts. Touring about the eastern seaboard, the committee was able to visit many manufactories, producing a wide variety of products. Their impressions, reported to Parliament and to the British nation at large, served as an excellent picture of what technology had become in this country in the years since Independence. The differences they found were echoed by other observers and have, in fact, become the traditional judgments upon technology in this country.

The close relation which subsists between the kingdom of Great Britain and the Republic of America, arising from community of origin, of language, of civil and religious freedom, and to a great extent from the similarity of the laws under which both countries are placed, renders it natural that the people of these countries should regard each other with the deepest interest, and maintain a friendly rivalry in all that relates to social progress.

From Joseph Whitworth and George Wallis, *The Industry of the United States in Machinery, Manufactures, and Useful and Ornamental Arts* (London, 1854), pp. iii-ix.

The American citizen is eminently a man of facts and figures, and there is very little in our arts and manufactures which escapes his keen observation. For reasons sufficiently obvious, it is most desirable that the British subject should be furnished with the means of knowing the state of manufacturing industry on the other side of the Atlantic, and of acquiring the lessons of practical value which may be learned from comparing these matters as they are presented in the Old and the New World.

It must be confessed, on all hands, that the means of such comparison which were anticipated from the Exhibition in Hyde Park, were not furnished in such a manner as to lead to any just and satisfactory results. The industry of the United States cannot be properly exhibited under a glass case. To be estimated aright, it must be witnessed *in situ.* It must be inspected in its gigantic manufactories, erected on the banks of rapid rivers; its vast and ingenious machinery must be seen in operation supplying the want of human hands and arms; and for this end, the intelligent traveller must allow himself to be transported for thousands of miles, from State to State, and over rocky mountains, availing himself of the cheap "cars," which are at his service in all directions.

Peculiar facilities for obtaining an adequate acquaintance with the industry of the United States were afforded to the deputation sent out from this country on occasion of the Industrial Exhibition at New York. That deputation consisted of gentlemen eminently qualified in their various departments to appreciate the subject brought under examination, and to report thereon. The delay in completing the arrangements for the Exhibition led to the determination to "visit the various localities in which raw materials were most abundant, mechanical skill most largely applied, manufacturing industry fairly established, and art and science most perfectly developed. . . ."

The industry of the United States has to be estimated by the peculiar circumstances of the country to which it has been devoted. In the States the labour-market is higher than with ourselves, especially as respects skilled labour. It has, therefore, been a principal aim as much as possible to apply machinery for the purpose of supplying this want, and, as the consequence, it will be seen that some of the principal achievements of American inventors have been acquired in this department. To this very want of human skill, and the absolute necessity for supplying it, may be attributed the extraordinary ingenuity displayed in many of their labour-saving machines, where automatic action so completely supplies the place of the more abundant hand-labour of older manufacturing countries.

Of this we have an illustration in the machine for the manufacture of the seamless grain-bags, the loom for which is described as a perfect self-actor, or automaton, commencing the bag, and continuing the process until the work is turned out complete.

For another curious illustration of this automatic action we have the manufacture of ladies' hair-pins at Waterbury. A quantity of wire is coiled upon a drum or cylinder, and turns round upon its axis, as suspended from the ceiling of the workshop. The point of the wire being inserted into the machine, and the power applied, the wire is cut off to the requisite length, carried forward and bent to the proper angle, and then pointed with the necessary blunt points, and finally dropped into a receiver, quite finished, all but the lacquering or japanning. These pins are made at the rate of 180 per minute.

The reader is referred also to the automaton machine for shanking buttons. The blanks being cut in thin brass, are put into a curved feeding-pipe, in which they descend to the level of the machine, by which a hole is stamped in the centre of each. Then the shank is formed by another portion of the machine, from a continuous wire carried along horizontally, the wire being shaped into the shank, and pushed up into its proper place. These operations are completed at the rate of 200 a minute, the only attendance required being that of one person to feed this automaton with the blanks and the wires, which he is so well able to work up to the satisfaction of his masters.

There is, of course, nothing to boast of on the ground of superiority on account of these inventions; but it is much to the credit of the American inventor, that he is able so to meet the necessities of his case, and supply the want of fingers, which are at present so scarce.

Another peculiarity observable in American industry, is the want of that division of labour which is one of the great causes of excellence in the productions of our own and other of the older countries in which art is carried to a high point of perfection. With us, trades and manufactures branch out into a variety of subdivisions, from which, besides the perfection noticed, we have a great economy of time, and, consequently, of expense. The citizen of the United States knows that matters are different with him, and seems really to pride himself in not remaining over long at any particular occupation, and being able to turn his hand to some dozen different pursuits in the course of his life.

This knowledge of two or three departments of one trade, or even the pursuit of several trades, by one individual, does not interfere so much with the systematic division of labour as may be supposed. In most instances the change of employment is made at convenient periods, or as a relief to the workman from the monotony of always doing the same thing. This change and variety of occupation is, in many respects, favourable to the man, as distinguished from the operative or the artist. In many cases our economic laws enhance the work or the value of time, when they degrade the workmen, between whom and the perfection of their works a singular contrast exists. While our American operative is a man and a citizen, he is often found wanting in that perfect skill of hand and marvellous accuracy which distinguish the workmen of this country. So much is there to check the national tendencies of self-gratulation and boasting on either side of the Atlantic, and to promote respect and good-feeling among us all.

The machinery of a country will naturally correspond with its wants, and with the history and state of its people. Testing the machinery of the United States by this rule of adaptation, the mechanical appliances in use must call forth much admiration. A large proportion of the mechanical power of the States has, from its earliest application, been, from the circumstances of the country, directed to wood, this being the material on which it has been requisite to operate for so many purposes, and which is presented in the greatest abundance. Stone, for a similar reason, has been subdued to man's use by the application of machinery, of which we have an instance in the fact that one man is able to perform as much work by machinery in stone-dressing, as twenty persons by hand. In common with our own and other great manufacturing countries, the Union presents remarkable illustrations of the amazingly productive power of machinery, as compared with mere manual operations. Into the details of these triumphs of machinery it is unnecessary here to enter. It may suffice to refer to the improvements effected in spinning-machinery, by which one man can attend to a mule containing 1,088 spindles, each spinning three hanks, or 3,264 hanks a day; so that, as compared with the operations of the most expert spinner in Hindoostan, the American operative can perform the work of 3,000 men.

The Law of Limited Liability, which is now engaging public attention, is an important source of the prosperity which attends the industry of the United States. This law affords the most ample facilities for the investment of capital, and has led to a much greater development of the industrial resources and skill of that country than could have resulted under other circumstances for many years to come. In the United States, the agent or secretary, manager, treasurer, and directors being also shareholders, are held by the law responsible to the extent of their means for the results of the management intrusted to them. The limited responsibility is confined to the non-managing shareholders only. It will be seen from the several illustrations given in the following pages, that this law works well in America; and these facts will strengthen the case of those who advocate its application to our country.

The comparative density of the old and the new countries, differing as they do, will account for the very different feelings with which the increase of machinery has been regarded in many parts of this country and the United States, where the workmen hail with satisfaction all mechanical improvements, the importance and value of which, as releasing them from the drudgery of unskilled labour, they are enabled by education to understand and appreciate. This statement is not intended to disparage the operatives of our own country, who in many respects are placed in a position different from that of their class in the United States, where the principles that ought to regulate the relations between the employer and the employed are thoroughly understood, and where the law of limited liability, to which we have just referred, affords the most ample facilities for the investment of capital in business, and where the skilled labourer is in many respects furnished with many opportunities of advancement which he has not among us. Particularly it should be noticed that no taxation of any kind is suffered to interfere with the free development of the press, and that the humblest labourer can indulge in the luxury of his daily paper, so that everybody reads, and intelligence penetrates through the lowest grades of society.

7. Internal Improvements, 1838

DAVID STEVENSON, *Sketch of the Civil Engineering of North America*

The problem of adequate transportation was central to the economic development of the United States. From earliest colonial times, men and goods moved by water if possible, on horseback or foot if necessary. Roads were the responsibility of local governments, and colonial legislatures merely laid down traditional and general guidelines for their construction.

The vast improvement in transportation that occurred in Great Britain in the last half of the eighteenth century—based primarily upon canals—was slow in coming to America. When it finally did, civil engineering became a distinct profession, and the first to organize itself in voluntary association. At the height of what has come to be called the Transportation Revolution in this country, a Scots engineer, uncle to the novelist Robert Louis Stevenson, toured the United States and commented perceptively upon the civil engineering he found in progress.

Having at various times heard much to interest and surprise me respecting the engineering works of America, and having been unable to meet with any publication containing satisfactory information regarding them, I resolved to take advantage of a short interval of professional leisure, to examine the subject for myself.

In a tour of about three months I visited Upper and Lower Canada, and the most interesting parts of the United States of America, and endeavoured, throughout, to direct my attention to those objects which are of greatest importance to a Civil-Engineer. My observation embraced many of the principal Sea-ports, and navigable Rivers, two of the Great Lakes, the principal Canals, Railroads, Bridges, and other means of communication, and the most remarkable of the works for supplying the cities with water. The Steam-navigation of those countries, and the system of Lighthouses established along their coasts, also came incidentally under my notice, as well as some other points of more or less interest and importance.

I was well aware, before leaving this country, that a field so extensive and varied could not be fully examined in so limited a period; but this rapid tour, though it has not afforded that full measure of information upon many points of inquiry, which, had my time permitted, it would have been my endeavour to procure, has fully answered my purpose, by giving me a general view of the state of Civil-Engineering in America.

Having in the course of this journey

From David Stevenson, *Sketch of the Civil Engineering of North America . . .* (London, 1838), *passim.*

seen a good deal that was entirely new to me, I have been induced to lay before my professional brethren the information thus obtained. It is true that Civil-Engineering, as practised in America, is not always applicable to the circumstances of Europe; but still the modifications to which it is subject in a new country may prove useful, by suggesting various methods of working, adapted to local circumstances or limited funds.

The object, however, of this brief sketch is not to satisfy the curiosity of Engineers in England; but rather to stimulate others, who may have it in their power, not only to examine more thoroughly the ground here gone over, but to extend their researches to other parts of the country, which my limited time did not permit me to visit. Judging from the attentions shewn me by all classes of persons in America, and their readiness to communicate freely every kind of information, I feel certain that any such extended engineering tour would be attended with no less pleasure than interest. . . .

The original founders of the sea-port towns on this coast appear to have been very judicious in their selection of situations for forming their settlements. The towns, if not placed at the mouths of fine navigable rivers, in most cases possess the advantages of sheltered anchorages, with deep water, and accommodation for all classes of vessels. The chief object in founding most of the towns seems to have been the formation of a port for shipping, or the cultivation of a valuable adjacent tract of country watered by a navigable river; in which latter case the harbours do not always possess the same natural advantages, but stand in need of works for their improvement, which would involve a greater expenditure of capital, and occupy more time in their execution, than a country, as yet new in the arts, has been disposed to bestow upon them. Viewing the harbours of America generally, however, no one can fail to be struck with their importance, and, in connection with its inland navigation, convinced of their mighty effect in advancing the prosperity of that enterprising country.

The largest ports of North America are Quebec, Halifax, and Montreal, in the British dominions, and Boston, New York, Philadelphia, Baltimore, Charleston, and New Orleans, in the United States. Besides these ports, there are many towns on the coast, of later origin, having less trade and importance, but nevertheless possessing splendid natural facilities for the formation of harbours.

I was fortunate enough to visit many of the American ports, and in most of them, I found that accommodation for vessels of great burden had been obtained in so satisfactory a manner, and at so small an expense, as could not fail to strike with astonishment all who have seen the enormously costly docks of London and Liverpool, and the stupendous asylum harbours of Plymouth, Kingstown, and Cherbourg. I have little hesitation in saying, that the smallest of the post-office packet stations in the Irish Sea has required a much larger expenditure of capital, than the Americans have invested in the formation of harbour accommodation for trading vessels along a line of coast of no less than 4000 miles, extending from the Gulf of St. Lawrence to the Mississippi.

The American packet-ships trading between New York and the ports of London, Liverpool, and Havre, are generally allowed to be the finest class of merchant-vessels at present navigating the ocean; and for their accommodation we find in England the splendid docks of London and Liverpool, and in France the docks of Havre. An European naturally concludes that a berthage no less commodious and costly awaits their arrival in the ports to which they sail; but great will be his astonishment when, on reaching New York, the same fine vessel which lately graced the solid stone-docks of Europe, is moored by bow and stern to a wooden quay; and, on leaving the vessel, he will not fail to miss the shade of a covered verandah enclosed within high walls, the characteristic of a British dockyard, and will have any thing but pleasant sensations when he is ushered forth upon a hastily constructed wooden jetty, which, in certain states of the weather, is deeply covered with mud, and generally affords a footpath far from agreeable.

This state of things strikes a foreigner, on first landing in America, in a very forcible manner. The high, and in some cases superfluous, finish, which the Americans bestow on many of their vessels employed in trading with this country, lead those who do not know the contrary to expect a corresponding degree of comfort, and an equal display of workmanship, in the works of art connected with their ports; and it strikes one at first sight as a strange inconsistency, that all the works connected with the formation of the harbours in America should be of so rude and temporary a description, that, but for the sheltered situations in which they are placed, and other circumstances of a no less favourable nature, the structures would be unfit to serve the ends for which they were intended. But, when we come to inquire into the reasons for this difference between the construction of the European and American harbours, they

soon become apparent and satisfactory. The difficulties and expense encountered in the formation of most European harbours, have arisen chiefly from the necessity of constructing works of a sufficient strength to withstand the violence of a raging sea to which they are in general exposed, or in obtaining a sufficient depth of water, by the construction of docks or other means, to enable the vessels frequenting them to lie afloat at all times of tide. In Britain, these difficulties in a great measure arise from the narrowness of our country, which necessarily contains but a small extent of inland waters, whose quantity and currents, when compared with the bays and rivers on the American coast, are agents too unimportant and feeble to produce, without recourse to artificial means, the depth or shelter required in a good harbour. The Americans, on the contrary, among the numerous large bays and sounds by which their coasts are indented, have the choice of situations for their harbours, perfectly defended from the surge of the ocean, and requiring no works, like the breakwaters of Plymouth and Cherbourg, for their protection; and the basins formed and scoured by their large navigable rivers afford, without resorting to the construction of docks like those of Liverpool, London, Leith, or Dundee, natural havens, where their largest vessels lie afloat at all times of tide within a few paces of their warehouse doors. . . .

Such is a brief sketch of the construction and capabilities of some of the principal harbours of America, in the formation of which nature has done so much, that little has been left for the labour of man, and works of an extensive and massive description, and operations such as are found to be indispensable in rendering European harbours accessible or commodious, have there been found to be unnecessary. By erections of a temporary description, constructed of the wood produced in the operation of clearing their lands, the inhabitants have been enabled, along the whole line of coast, to afford, at a very small cost, accommodation for an extent and class of shipping, to obtain which, in any other quarter of the globe, would have involved an enormous investment of capital, and a much greater consumption of time. . . .

Whatever differences of opinion may exist as to the actual invention of the steam-boat, there is no doubt that steam navigation was first fully and successfully introduced into real use in the United States of America, and that Fulton, a native of North America, launched a steam-vessel at New York in the year 1807; while the first successful experiment in Europe was made on the Clyde in the year 1812, before which period steam had been, during four years, generally used as a propelling power in the vessels navigating the Hudson.

The steam navigation of the United States is one of the most interesting subjects connected with the history of North America, and it is strange that hitherto we should have received so little information regarding it, especially as there is no class of works, in that comparatively new and still rising country, which bear stronger marks of long continued exertion, successfully directed to the perfection of its object, than are presented by many of the steam-boats which now navigate its rivers, bays, and lakes.

It would be improper to compare the present state of steam navigation in America with that of this country, for the nature of things has established a very important distinction between them. By far the greater number of the American steam-boats ply on the smooth surfaces of rivers, sheltered bays, or arms of the sea, exposed neither to waves nor to wind; whereas most of the steam-boats in this country go out to sea, where they encounter as bad weather and as heavy waves as ordinary sailing vessels. The consequence is, that in America a much more slender built, and a more delicate mould, give the requisite strength to their vessels, and thus a much greater speed, which essentially depends upon these two qualities, is generally obtained. In America the position of the machinery and of the cabins, which are raised above the deck of the vessels, admits of powerful engines, with an enormous length of stroke being employed to propel them; but this arrangement would be wholly inapplicable to the vessels navigating our coasts, at least to the extent to which it has been carried in America.

But perhaps the strongest proof that the American vessels are very differently circumstanced from those of Europe, and therefore admit of a construction more favourable for the attainment of great speed, is the fact that they are not generally, as in Europe, navigated by persons possessed of a knowledge of seamanship. In this country steam navigation produces hardy seamen, and British steamers being exposed to the open sea in all weathers, are furnished with masts and sails, and must be worked by persons who, in the event of any accident happening to the machinery, are capable of sailing the vessel, and who must therefore be experienced seamen. The case is very different in America, where, with the exception of the vessels navigating the Lakes, and one or two of those which ply on the eastern coast, there is not a steamer in the country which has either masts or sails, or is commanded by a professional seaman. These facts forcibly shew the different state of steam navigation in America, a state very favourable for the attainment of great speed, and a high degree of perfection in the locomotive art.

The early introduction of steam navigation into the country, and the rapid increase which has since taken place in the number of steam-boats, have afforded an extensive field for the prosecution of valuable inquiries on this interesting subject; and the builders of steam-boats, by availing themselves of the opportunities held out to them, have been enabled to make constant accessions to their practical knowledge, which have gradually produced important improvements in the construction and action of their vessels. But on minutely examining the most approved American steamers, I found it impossible to trace any *general* principles which seem to have served as guides for their construction. Every American steam-boat builder holds opinions of his own, which are generally founded, not on theoretical principles, but on deductions drawn from a close examination of the practical effects of the different arrangements and proportions adopted in the construction of different steam-boats, and these opinions never fail to influence, in a greater or less degree, the built of his vessel, and the proportions which her several parts are made to bear to each other. . . .

The inferences to be drawn from these facts are, that the great experiment for the improvement of steam navigation, in which the Americans may be said to have been engaged for the last thirty years, is not completed, and the speed at which they have succeeded

in propelling their steam-vessels may yet be increased; and also that, in the construction of their vessels, they have been governed by experience and practice alone, without attempting to introduce theoretical principles, in the application of which, to the practice of propelling vessels, by the action of paddle-wheels on the water, numerous difficulties have hitherto been experienced.

There are local circumstances, connected with the nature of the trade in which the steam-boats are engaged, and the waters which they are intended to navigate, that have given rise to the employment of three distinct classes of vessels in American steam navigation, all of which I had an opportunity of sailing in and particularly examining.

These steam-boats may be ranged under the following classification: First, those navigating the Eastern Waters. This class includes all the vessels plying on the River Hudson, Long Island Sound, Chesapeake and Delaware Bays, and all those which run to and from Boston, New York, Philadelphia, Baltimore, Charleston, Norfolk and the other ports on the eastern coast of the country, or what the Americans call the Seaboard. Second, those navigating the Western Waters, including all the steamers employed on the river Mississippi and its numerous tributaries, including the Missouri and Ohio. Third, the steamers engaged in the Lake navigation. These classes of vessels vary very much in their construction, which has been modified to suit the respective services for which they are intended.

The general characteristics by which the Eastern Water boats are distinguished, are, a small draught of water, great speed and the use of condensing engines of large dimensions, having a great length of stroke. On the Western

Waters, on the other hand, the vessels have a greater draught of water and less speed, and are propelled by high-pressure engines of small size, worked by steam of great elasticity. The steamers on the Lakes, again, have a very strong built and a large draught of water, possessing in a greater degree the character of *sea*-boats than any of those belonging to the other two classes. They also differ in having masts and sails, with which the others are not provided. . . .

I need scarcely mention, that wood is very much used as fuel throughout the greater part of the United States and the British dominions in America, both for domestic purposes and for steam-engines, excepting in the neighbourhood of most of the large towns, where, the surrounding country having been cleared and brought into cultivation, it has now become very scarce, and much too valuable to be made use of in that way. In such situations coal has of course been substituted in its place. Still, however, throughout a large part of the territory of the United States, the forest is looked to for the great supply of fuel. The firewood is cut into pieces about four feet long, and twelve inches in girth, and is sold in piles four feet square, and eight feet in length, containing 128 cubic feet, a measure called by the Americans, a "cord." It varies in price in different parts of the country. In New York, a cord of wood costs about 20s.; in Albany, 14s.; on Lake Champlain, the average price is 9s.; on the St Lawrence, 7s. 3d.; and on Lake Ontario, 5s.; its value gradually decreasing as the country becomes less populous. On the Mississippi and Ohio, the price of wood is from 5s. to 8s. a cord. Many experiments have been made in America to

ascertain the relative values of wood and coal as fuel for steam-engines; the result of which is, that about two and three-fourth cords of wood, and one ton of coal, generate, in well-constructed boilers, an equal quantity of steam. Pine timber is considered to be the best fuel: its texture is more open, and its combustion is more perfect than hardwood, the heart or interior of which, being less affected by the heat, is often left unconsumed. . . .

Bituminous coal occurs in large quantities on the western side of the Alleghany Mountains, and has been extensively worked in the neighbourhood of Pittsburg, where it is much used in the manufacture of iron. This coal occurs in other parts of the United States, particularly in New England and in Rhode Island. In the British dominions of Nova Scotia, a vein has also been opened at the Albion coal-mines, which is said to be fifty feet in thickness. The steam-boats on the Ohio, and also on the St Lawrence, occasionally burn bituminous coal; but the fire-places are all too large for coal, having been constructed for the combustion of wood.

Anthracite coal has been more extensively worked, and is much more generally used in the United States for domestic purposes, than bituminous coal. The most extensive anthracite coal-fields occur in the State of Pennsylvania, on the courses of the rivers Schuylkill and Lehigh, the navigation of which has been improved at a great expense, to facilitate the carriage of the coal from the mines to the sea for shipment. It has also been found on the banks of the Merrimac, in New England.

The Schuylkill and Lehigh coal-fields lie between a mountain called the Blue Ridge and the river Susquehanna, and are situate about 100 miles northeast of

Philadelphia, the port from which the coal is shipped. The most extensive workings are at Pottsville, on the Schuylkill, and Mauch Chunk, on the Lehigh. At Pottsville, the strata of coal dip from N.E. to S.W., at an angle of about 45°, and at Mauch Chunk they are nearly horizontal. They are in general worked by level drifts, carried into the face of a long range of rising ground, which is entirely composed of one vast bed of coal. The quantity of coal brought from the Pennsylvanian mines to Delaware Bay during the year 1836, was no less than 696,526 tons.

The anthracite coal of North America has a strong resemblance to that found in some parts of Wales, and also in Ireland. It is exceedingly close-grained, has a bright lustre, and, when broken, the fracture presents a great variety of fine colours, from which circumstance it has received in America the name of "peacock-tail" coal. It requires a very high temperature for its combustion, and in order to obtain this, it is necessary that the fire-places in which it is used should be lined with a good non-conducting substance. It has been several times tried in the boilers commonly used in steam-boats, but in the fire-places of the common construction it was found that the coal was brought too closely into contact with the bottom of the boiler and flues, and the caloric being too suddenly withdrawn from it, the fire burned languidly and was occasionally extinguished. Dr Nott of New York has bestowed much labour and time in constructing a boiler and fire-place suited for anthracite coal. These have been introduced in one or two steam-boats, and particularly in some of the ferry-boats plying in the bay of New York. This kind of coal is also burned in the locomotive engines on the Baltimore and Washington railway; but its application to the purpose of generating steam, cannot yet be said to have assumed a more permanent character than that of an experiment.

The principle on which the anthracite boilers are constructed is sufficiently simple. The combustion of the fuel is carried on in a chamber lined with a non-conducting substance, which is quite detached from the boiler, and the heated air only is allowed to pass through the flues, so that the disadvantages arising from the rapid abstraction of caloric from the fuel, which takes place in fire-places constructed for the combustion of bituminous coal or wood, are in this boiler completely obviated. The coal is also broken into small pieces about the size of a hen's egg, and in this way a great surface is exposed to the atmospheric air, and a thorough combustion of the fuel is produced.

The anthracite coal is much used for domestic purposes in New York, Philadelphia, Baltimore and Washington. It is burned sometimes in stoves, and sometimes in an open fire-place. The heat given out by it, when burned in either way, being very dry, evaporating pans are generally used to produce that degree of moisture in the apartments which is requisite to counteract the disagreeable effects produced by breathing a dry and close atmosphere.

Brick is the building material uniformly used for dwelling-houses in the large towns in the United States, in most of which wooden structures are not now permitted to be erected. The public edifices, however, are generally built of marble, which is found in great abundance in different parts of the country. . . .

The Americans have not rested satisfied with the natural inland navigation afforded by their rivers and lakes, nor made the bounty of Nature a plea for idleness or want of energy; but, on the contrary, they have been zealously engaged in the work of internal improvement; and their country now numbers, among its many wonderful artificial lines of communication, a mountain railway, which, in boldness of design and difficulty of execution, I can compare to no modern works I have ever seen, excepting, perhaps, the passes of the Simplon, and Mont Cenis in Sardinia; but even these remarkable passes, viewed as engineering works, did not strike me as being more wonderful than the Alleghany Railway in the United States.

The objects to which that enterprising people have chiefly directed their exertions for the advancement of their country in the scale of civilization, are the removal of obstructions in navigable rivers; the junction of different tracts of natural navigation; the connection of large towns, and the formation of lines of communication from the Atlantic Ocean to the great lakes, and the valleys of the Mississippi, Missouri, and Ohio. The number and extent of canals and railways which they have executed in effecting these important objects, sufficiently prove that their exertions, during the short time they have been so engaged, have been neither small nor ill directed. The aggregate length of the canals at present in operation in the United States alone, amounts to upwards of two thousand seven hundred miles, and that of the railways already completed to sixteen hundred miles. Nor are the labours of the people at an end, for even now there are no fewer than thirty-three railways in an unfinished state, whose aggregate length, when completed, will amount to upwards of two thousand five hundred miles.

The zeal with which the Americans undertake, and the rapidity with which they carry on every enterprise, which has the enlargement of their trade for its object, cannot fail to strike all who visit the United States as a characteristic of the nation. Forty years ago, that country was almost without a lighthouse, and now no fewer than two hundred are nightly exhibited on its coast; thirty years ago, it had but one steamer and one short canal, and now its rivers and lakes are navigated by between five and six hundred steamers, and its canals are upwards of two thousand seven hundred miles in length; ten years ago, there were but three miles of railway in the country, and now there are no less than sixteen hundred miles in operation. These facts appear much more wonderful when it is considered, that many of these great lines of communication are carried for miles in a trough, as it were, cut through thick and almost impenetrable forests, where it is no uncommon occurrence to travel for a whole day without encountering a village, or even a house, excepting perhaps a few log-huts inhabited by persons connected with the works. . . .

English and American engineers are guided by the same principles in designing their works; but the different nature of the materials employed in their construction, and the climates and circumstances of the two countries, naturally produce a considerable dissimilarity in the practice of civil-engineers in England and America. At the first view, one is struck with the temporary and apparently unfinished state of many of the American works, and is very apt, before inquiring into the subject, to impute to want of ability what turns out, on investigation, to be a judicious and ingenious arrangement to suit the circumstances of a new country, of which the climate is severe,—a country where stone is scarce and wood is plentiful, and where manual labour is very expensive. It is vain to look to the American works for the finish that characterises those of France, or the stability for which those of Britain are famed. Undressed slopes of cuttings and embankments, roughly built rubble arches, stone parapet-walls coped with timber, and canal-locks wholly constructed of that material, every where offend the eye accustomed to view European workmanship. But it must not be supposed that this arises from want of knowledge of the principles of engineering, or of skill to do them justice in the execution. The use of wood, for example, which may be considered by many as wholly inapplicable to the construction of canal-locks, where it must not only encounter the tear and wear occasioned by the lockage of vessels, but must be subject to the destructive consequences of alternate immersion in water and exposure to the atmosphere, is yet the result of deliberate judgment. The Americans have, in many cases, been induced to use the material of the country, ill adapted though it be in some respects to the purposes to which it is applied, in order to meet the wants of a rising community, by speedily and perhaps superficially completing a work of importance, which would otherwise be delayed, from a want of the means to execute it in a more substantial manner; and although the works are wanting in finish, and even in solidity, they do not fail for many years to serve the purposes for which they were constructed, as efficiently as works of a more lasting description.

When the wooden locks on any of the canals begin to show symptoms of decay, stone structures are generally substituted, and materials suitable for their erection are with ease and expedition conveyed from the part of the country where they are most abundant, by means of the canal itself to which they are to be applied; and thus the less substantial work ultimately becomes the means of facilitating its own improvement, by affording a more easy, cheap, and speedy transport of those durable and expensive materials, without the use of which, perfection is unattainable.

One of the most important advantages of constructing the locks of canals, in new countries such as America, of wood, unquestionably is, that in proportion as improvement advances and greater dimensions or other changes are required, they can be introduced at little cost, and without the mortification of destroying expensive and substantial works of masonry. Some of the locks on the great Erie canal are formed of stone, but had they all been made of wood, it would in all probability have been converted into a ship-canal long ago.

But the locks are not the only parts of the American canals in which wood is used. Aqueducts over ravines or rivers are generally formed of large wooden troughs resting on stone pillars, and even more temporary expedients have been chosen, the ingenuity of which can hardly fail to please those who view them as the means of carrying on improvements, which, but for such contrivances, might be stopped by the want of funds necessary to complete them. . . .

Road-making is a branch of engineering which has been very little cultivated in America, and it was not until the introduction of railways that the Americans entertained the idea of transporting heavy goods by any other means than those afforded by canals and slackwater navigation. Their objection to paved or Macadamized roads such as are used in Europe is founded on the prejudicial effects exerted upon works of that description by the severe and protracted winters by which the country is visited, and also the difficulty and expense of obtaining materials suitable for their construction, and for keeping them in a state of proper repair. Stone fitted for the purposes of road-making is by no means plentiful in America; and as the number of workmen is small in proportion to the quantity of work which is generally going forward in the country, manual labour is very expensive. Under these circumstances, it is evident that roads would have been a very costly means of communication, and as they are not suitable for the transport of heavy goods, the Americans, in commencing their internal improvements, directed their whole attention to the construction of canals, as being much better adapted to supply their wants.

The roads throughout the United States and Canada, are, from these causes, not very numerous, and most of those by which I travelled were in so neglected and wretched a condition, as hardly to deserve the name of highways, being quite unfit for any vehicle but an American stage, and any pilot but an American driver. In many parts of the country, the operation of cutting a track through the forests of a sufficient width to allow vehicles to pass each other, is all that has been done towards the formation of a road. The roots of the felled trees are often not removed, and in marshes, where the ground is wet and soft, the trees themselves are cut in lengths of about ten or twelve feet, and laid close to each other across the road, to prevent vehicles from sinking, forming what is called in America a "Corduroy road," over which the coach advances by a series of leaps and starts, particularly trying to those accustomed to the comforts of European travelling. . . .

On the road leading from Pittsburg on the Ohio to the town of Erie on the lake of that name, I saw all the varieties of forest road-making in great perfection. Sometimes our way lay for miles through extensive marshes, which we crossed by corduroy-roads, formed in the manner shown above; at others the coach stuck fast in mud, from which it could be extricated only by the combined efforts of the coachman and passengers; and at one place we travelled for upwards of a quarter of a mile through a forest flooded with water, which stood to the height of several feet on many of the trees, and occasionally covered the naves of the coachwheels. The distance of the route from Pittsburg to Erie is 128 miles, which was accomplished in forty-six hours, being at the very slow rate of about two miles and three quarters an hour, although the conveyance by which I travelled carried the mail, and stopped only for breakfast, dinner, and tea, but there was considerable delay caused by the coach being once upset and several times "mired."

The best roads in the United States are those of New England, where, in the year 1796, the first American turnpikeact was granted. These roads are made of gravel; a material which, by the way, is much used for road-making in Ireland. The surface of the New England roads is very smooth; but as no attention has been paid to forming or draining them, it is only for a few months during summer that they possess any superiority, or are, in fact, at all tolerable. In Virginia and all the States lying to the south, as well as throughout the whole country to the westward of the Alleghany Mountains, the roads, I believe, are, generally speaking, of the same description as the one already mentioned between Pittsburg and Erie, affording very little comfort or facility to those who have the misfortune to be obliged to travel upon them.

But on the construction of one or two lines of road, the Americans have bestowed a little more attention. The most remarkable of them is that called the "National Road," stretching across the country from Baltimore to the State of Illinois, a distance of no less than 700 miles, an arduous and extensive work, which was constructed at the expense of the government of the United States. The narrow tract of land from which it was necessary to remove the timber and brushwood for the passage of the road, measures eighty feet in breadth; but the breadth of the road itself is only thirty feet. . . . Commencing at Baltimore, it passes through part of the State of Maryland, and entering that of Pennsylvania, crosses the range of the Alleghany Mountains, after which, it passes through the States of Virginia, Ohio and Indiana, to Illinois. It is in contemplation to produce this line of road to the Mississippi at St. Louis, where, the river being crossed by a ferry-boat stationed at that place, the road is ultimately to be extended into the State of Missouri, which lies to the west of the Mississippi.

The "Macadamized road," as it is called, leading from Albany to Troy, is another line which has been formed at some cost, and with some degree of care. This road, as its name implies, is constructed with stone broken, according to Macadam's principle. It is six miles in length, and has been formed of a sufficient breadth to allow three carriages to stand abreast on it at once. It belongs to an incorporated company, who are said to have expended about L.20,000 in constructing and upholding it.

Some interesting experiments have lately been set on foot at New York, for the purpose of obtaining a permanent and durable City Road, for streets over which there is a great thoroughfare. The place chosen for the trial was the Broadway, in which the traffic is constant and extensive.

The specimen of road-making first put to the test was a species of causewaying or pitching but the materials employed are round water-worn stones, of small size; and their only recommendation for such a work appears to be their great abundance in the neighbourhood of the town. The most of the streets in New York, and indeed in all the American towns, are paved with stones of this description; but, owing to their small size and round form, they easily yield to the pressure of carriages passing over them, and produce the large ruts and holes for which American thoroughfares are famed. To form a smooth and durable pavement, the pitching-stones should have a considerable depth, and their opposite sides ought to be as nearly parallel as possible, or, in other words, the stones should have very little taper. The footpaths in most of the towns are paved with bricks set on edge, and bedded in sand, similar to the "clinkers," or small hard-burned bricks so generally used for road-making in Holland.

The second specimen was formed with broken stones, but the materials, owing chiefly no doubt to the high rate of wages, are not broken sufficiently small to entitle it to the name of a "Macadamized Road." It is, however, a wonderful improvement on the ordinary pitched pavement of the country, and the only objections to its general introduction, as already noticed, are the prejudicial effects produced on it by the very intense frost with which the country is visited, and the expense of keeping it in repair.

The third specimen is rather of an original description. It consists of a species of tesselated pavement, formed of hexagonal billets of pine wood measuring six inches on each side, and twelve inches in depth. . . . From the manner in which the timber is arranged, the pressure falls on it parallel to the direction in which its fibres lie, so that the tendency to wear is very small. The blocks are coated with pitch or tar, and are set in sand, forming a smooth surface for carriages, which pass easily and noiselessly over it. There can be no doubt of the suitableness of wood for forming a roadway; and such an improvement is certainly much wanted in all American towns, and in none of them more than in New York. Some, however, have expressed a fear that great difficulty would be experienced in keeping pavements constructed in this manner in a clean state, and that during damp weather a vapour might arise from the timber, which, if it were brought into general use, would prove hurtful to the salubrity of large towns. . . .

The vast rivers, lakes and arms of the sea, spanned by many of the American bridges, are on a scale which far surpasses the comparatively insignificant streams of this country, and, but for the facilities afforded for bridge-building by the great abundance of timber, the only communication across most of the American waters must still have been by means of a ferry or a ford. The bridge over the river Susquehanna at Columbia, and that over the Potomac at Washington, for example, are each one mile and a quarter in length; and in the neighbourhood of Boston there are no less than seven bridges, varying from 1500 feet to one mile and a half in length. The bridge over Lake Cayuga is one mile, and those at Kingston on Lake Ontario, and at St John's on Lake Champlain, are each more than one-third of a mile in length.

The American bridges are in general constructed entirely of wood. Although good building materials had been plentiful in every part of the country, the consumption of time and money attending the construction of stone-bridges of so great extent must, if not in all, at least in most cases, have proved too considerable to warrant their erection. Many of those recently built, however, consist of a wooden superstructure resting on stone-piers, and in general exhibit specimens of good carpentry, and not unfrequently of good engineering. In those bridges which are of considerable extent and importance, the roadway, and the timbers by which it is supported, are generally protected by a roof or covering to preserve the wood from decay. . . . The roadway is lighted by windows, formed at convenient distances in the covering, as shewn in the drawings. The wooden bridges in Switzerland and Germany are generally covered in the same manner as those in America; and by adopting this plan, the objections to wood as a building material, arising from its tendency to decay by exposure to the atmosphere, are in some degree palliated. The planking or flooring of the American bridges is never covered with any composition, as is generally the case in this country, but is left quite bare. . . .

The Quincy Railroad in Massachusetts was the first constructed in America. It was intended for the conveyance of stone from the Quincy granite quarries to a shipping port on the river Neponsett, a distance of about four miles. . . .

In 1837, there were no fewer than fifty-seven railways completed and in full operation, whose aggregate length amounts to upwards of 1600 miles; and also that thirty-three railways were then in progress, which, when completed, will amount to about 2800 miles. In addition to this, upwards of one hundred and fifty railway companies have been incorporated; and the works of many of them will, in all probability, be very soon commenced.

The early American railroads consisted of iron rails and chairs resting on stone blocks, and were constructed on the same principles as those in this country. But the American engineers soon discovered that this construction of road, although it had been to a certain extent successfully applied in England, was not at all capable of withstanding the rigours of an American winter. The intense frost, with which the northern part of the country is visited, was found to split the stone blocks and to affect the ground in which they were embedded, to such a degree, that their positions were materially altered, and the rails were in many cases so much twisted and deranged as to be quite unfit for the passage of carriages. The consequence was, that most of the railroads constructed in the United States after the English system, had actually to be relaid at the close of every winter, and during the continuance of the frost could only be travelled on at a decreased speed. The Americans have put numerous plans to the test of actual experiment, in their endeavours to form a structure for supporting the rails, adapted to the climate and circumstances of the country. There are hardly two railways in the United States which are made exactly in the same way, and few of them are constructed throughout their whole extent on the same principles; but although great improvements have undoubtedly been effected, it is doubtful whether a structure perfectly proof against the detrimental effects of frost has yet been produced. An enumeration of the various schemes which have been proposed for the construction of railways in America, would not be very useful, even if it were possible. . . .

The American railroads are much more cheaply constructed than those in this country, which is owing chiefly to three causes; *first,* they are exempted from the heavy expenses often incurred in the construction of English railways, by the purchase of land and compensation for damages; *second,* the works are not executed in so substantial and costly a style; and, *third,* wood, which is the principal material used in their construction, is got at a very small cost. . . .

On some of the American railways, where the line is short or the traffic small, horse power is employed, but locomotive engines for transporting goods and passengers are in much more general use. In New York, Brooklyn, Philadelphia, Baltimore, and other places which have lines of railway leading from them, the depôt or station for the locomotive engines is generally placed at the outskirts, but the rails are continued through the streets to the heart of the town, and the carriages are dragged over this part of the line by horses, to avoid the inconvenience and danger attending the passage of locomotive engines through crowded thoroughfares. I travelled by horse power on the Mohawk and Hudson Railway, from Schenectady to Albany, a distance of sixteen miles, and the journey was performed in sixty-five minutes, being at the astonishing rate of fifteen miles an hour. The car by which I was conveyed carried twelve passengers, and was drawn by two horses which ran stages of five miles.

The first locomotive engines used in America were of British manufacture, but several very large workshops have lately been established in the country for the construction of these machines, which are now manufactured in great numbers. The largest locomotive engine-works are those of Mr Baldwin, Mr Norris, Mr Long, and Messrs Grant and Eastrick, all in Philadelphia, and the Lowell Engine-work at Lowell. When I visited the work of Mr Baldwin, to whom I am indebted for much attention and information, I found no less than twelve locomotive carriages in different states of progress, and all of substantial and good workmanship. Those parts of the engine, such as the cylinder, piston, valves, journals, and slides, in which good fitting and fine workmanship are indispensable to the

efficient action of the machine, were very highly finished, but the external parts, such as the connecting rods, cranks, framing, and wheels, were left in a much coarser state than in engines of British manufacture. The American engines with their boilers filled, weigh from twelve to fifteen tons, and cost about L.1400 or L.1500, including the tender. This is not much more than the cost of an engine of the same weight in this country. They have six wheels. These are arranged in the following manner, so as to allow the engine to travel on rails having a great curvature; the driving wheels, which are five feet in diameter, are placed in the posterior part of the engine close to the fire-box, and the fore part of the engine rests on a truck running on four wheels of about two feet six inches in diameter: a series of friction-rollers, arranged in a circular form, is placed on the top of the truck, and in the centre, stands a vertical pivot which works in a socket in the framing of the engine. The whole weight of the cylinders and the fore part of the boiler rests on the friction rollers, and the truck turning on the pivot as a centre, has freedom to describe a small arc of a circle; so that when the engine is not running upon a perfectly straight road, its wheels adapt themselves to the curvature of the rails, while the relative positions which the body of the engine, the connecting rods, and other parts of the machinery bear to each other, remain unaltered.

8. The New Age Defended, 1832

TIMOTHY WALKER, "Defense of Mechanical Philosophy"

The Industrial Revolution had its detractors as well as its defenders. In Great Britain especially, some critics saw industrialization as a malignant force, creating false values and alienating man from himself. A classic statement of this pessimistic view, by the British writer Thomas Carlyle, was published in the *Edinburgh Review* in 1829, under the title "Signs of the Times." His attack on the Mechanical Age was answered, appropriately enough, by an American, Timothy Walker, who gave in his turn a classic statement of optimistic belief in the goodness of Progress and the benefits of mechanism. It is doubtful, of course, whether many Americans thought deeply or philosophically about machines at all; but there is no doubt that Walker's "Defense of Mechanical Philosophy" expressed what most Americans instinctively felt to be true about the tendencies of their time.

The article which we have just named raises the grave and solemn question, whether mankind are advancing or not, in moral and intellectual attainments? The writer expresses his opinion, with sufficient distinctness, in the following words; "In whatever respects the pure moral nature, in true dignity of soul and character, we are, *perhaps*, inferior to most civilized ages." If this be true, it is a truth of deep and melancholy import. But is it true? Well may we pause, and ponder the matter carefully. What are the petty controversies which agitate sects, parties, or nations, compared with one which concerns the destinies of the whole human race? When we essay to cast the world's horoscope, and interpret auguries for universal man, it becomes us to approach the task with diffidence. And we do approach it with unfeigned diffidence. We despair of being able to rise to the height of the theme, on which we are to speak. Yet we feel that good may come even from the attempt.

Are we, then, in fact, degenerating? Has the hand been moved backward on the dial-plate of Time? Has the human race, comet-like, after centuries of advancement, swept suddenly round its perihelion of intelligence, and commenced its retrogradation? The author of the article before us, as we have seen, expresses, though with a *perhaps*, his belief of the affirmative. Throughout the whole article, with the exception of the last paragraph or two, of which the complexion is somewhat more encouraging, he draws most cheerless conclusions from the course which human affairs are taking. If the writer do not, as he humanely assures us in the end, ultimately despair of the destinies

From Timothy Walker, "Defense of Mechanical Philosophy," *The North American Review*, XXXIII (July 1832), 122-36.

of our ill-starred race, he does, nevertheless, perceive baleful influences hanging over us. Noxious ingredients are working in the caldron. He has detected the "midnight hag" that threw them in, and her name is Mechanism. A more malevolent spirit, in his estimation, does not come from the hateful abodes. The fated inhabitants of this planet are now under her pernicious sway, and she is most industriously plotting against their weal. To countervail her malignant efforts, the author invokes a spirit of a character most unlike the first. Her real name, as we shall see, is Mysticism, though this is not pronounced in the incantations.

Now we cannot help thinking, that this brilliant writer has conjured up phantoms for the sake of laying them again. At all events, we can see nothing but phantoms in what he opposes. In plain words, we deny the evil tendencies of Mechanism, and we doubt the good influences of his Mysticism. We cannot perceive that Mechanism, as such, has yet been the occasion of any injury to man. Some liberties, it is true, have been taken with Nature by this same presumptuous intermeddler. Where she denied us rivers, Mechanism has supplied them. Where she left our planet uncomfortably rough, Mechanism has applied the roller. Where her mountains have been found in the way, Mechanism has boldly levelled or cut through them. Even the ocean, by which she thought to have parted her quarrelsome children, Mechanism has encouraged them to step across. As if her earth were not good enough for wheels, Mechanism travels it upon iron pathways. Her ores, which she locked up in her secret vaults, Mechanism has dared to rifle and distribute. Still further encroachments are threatened. The terms uphill and downhill are to become obsolete. The horse is to be unharnessed, because he is too slow; and the ox is to be unyoked, because he is too weak. Machines are to perform all the drudgery of man, while he is to look on in self-complacent ease.

But where is the harm and danger of this? Why is every lover of the human race called on to plant himself in the path, and oppose these giant strides of Mechanism? Does this writer fear, that Nature will be dethroned, and Art set up in her place? Not exactly this. But he fears, if we rightly apprehend his meaning, that mind will become subjected to the laws of matter; that physical science will be built up on the ruins of our spiritual nature; that in our rage for machinery, we shall ourselves become machines. This we take to be the import of the following unusually plain passages; "Not the external and physical alone is now managed by machinery, but the internal and spiritual also."—"Philosophy, Science, Art, Literature, all depend upon Machinery."—"Men are grown mechanical in head and in heart, as well as in hand."—"Their whole efforts, attachments, opinions, turn on Mechanism, and are of a mechanical character." These are pretty broad and sweeping assertions, and we might quote many equally positive, and of the same style and meaning. In fact, the whole article is a series of repetitions of this leading idea, under various shapes; and this idea we propose to examine and controvert.

And, on the face of the matter, is it likely that mechanical ingenuity is suicidal in its efforts? Is it probable that the achievements of mind are fettering and enthralling mind? Must the proud creator of Mechanism stoop to its laws? By covering our earth with unnumbered comforts, accommodations, and delights, are we, in the words of this writer, descending from our "true dignity of soul and character?" Setting existing facts aside, and reasoning in the abstract, what is the fair conclusion? To our view, directly the contrary. We maintain, that the more work we can compel inert matter to do for us, the better will it be for our minds, because the more time shall we have to attend to them. So long as our souls are doomed to inhabit bodies, these bodies, however gross and unworthy they may be deemed, must be taken care of. Men have animal wants, which must and will be gratified at all events; and their demands upon time are imperious and peremptory. A certain portion of labor, then, must be performed, expressly for the support of our bodies. But at the same time, as we have a higher and nobler nature, which must also be cared for, the necessary labor spent upon our bodies should be as much abridged as possible, in order to give us leisure for the concerns of this better nature. The smaller the number of human beings, and the less the time it requires, to supply the physical wants of the whole, the larger will be the number, and the more the time left free for nobler things. Accordingly, in the absolute perfection of machinery, were that attainable, we might realize the absolute perfection of mind. In other words, if machines could be so improved and multiplied, that all our corporeal necessities could be entirely gratified, without the intervention of human labor, there would be nothing to hinder all mankind from becoming philosophers, poets, and votaries of art. The whole time and thought of the whole human race could be given to inward culture, to spiritual advancement. But let us not be understood as

intimating a belief, that such a state of things will ever exist. This we do not believe, nor is it necessary to our argument. It is enough, if there be an approach thereto. And this we do believe is constantly making. Every sober view of the past confirms us in this belief.

In the first ages of the world, when Mechanism was not yet known, and human hands were the only instruments, the mind scarcely exhibited even the feeblest manifestations of its power. And the reason is obvious. As physical wants could only be supplied by the slow and tedious processes of handwork, every one's attention was thereby completely absorbed. By degrees, however, the first rudiments of Mechanism made their appearance, and effected some simple abbreviations. A portion of leisure was the necessary result. One could now supply the wants of two, or each could supply his own in half the time previously required. And now it was, that mind began to develope its energies, and assert its empire over all other things. Leisure gave rise to thought, reflection, investigation; and these, in turn, produced new inventions and facilities. Mechanism grew by exercise. Machines became more numerous and more complete. The result was a still greater abridgment of labor. One could now do the work of ten, or each could do his own, in one tenth of the time before required. It is needless to follow the deduction farther. Every one knows that now, in many of the departments of labor, one can perform, by the help of machinery, the work of hundreds; or, supposing no division, each could perform his own in a hundredth part of the time before required. The consequence is, that there has never been a period, when so large a number of minds, in proportion to the whole, were left free to pursue the cultivation of the intellect. This is altogether the result of Mechanism, forcing inert matter to toil for man. And had it been reached gradually, commencing at the Creation, and continuing until now, the blessing would have been without alloy. But unhappily the progress has not been gradual. Of late, Mechanism has advanced *per saltum*, and the world has felt a temporary inconvenience from large numbers being thrown suddenly out of employment, while unprepared to embark in any thing else. But this evil must be from its nature temporary, while the advantage resulting from a release of so large a proportion of mankind from the thraldom of physical labor, will be as lasting as the mind. And hence it is, that we look with unmixed delight at the triumphant march of Mechanism. So far from enslaving, it has emancipated the mind, in the most glorious sense. From a ministering servant to matter, mind has become the powerful lord of matter. Having put myriads of wheels in motion by laws of its own discovering, it rests, like the Omnipotent Mind, of which it is the image, from its work of creation, and pronounces it good.

When we attempt to convey an idea of the infinite attributes of the Supreme Being, we point to the stupendous machinery of the universe. From the ineffable harmony and regularity, which pervade the whole vast system, we deduce the infinite power and intelligence of the Creating Mind. Now we can perceive no reason, why a similar course should not be pursued, if we would form correct conceptions of the dignity and glory of man. Look at the changes he has effected on the earth; so great, that could the first men revisit their mortal abodes, they could scarcely recognize the planet they once inhabited. Fitted up as it now is, with all the splendid furniture of civilization, it no more resembles the bleak, naked, incommodious earth, upon which our race commenced their improvements, than the magnificent palace resembles the low, mud-walled cottage. From the effect, turn your attention to the cause. Examine the endless varieties of machinery which man has created. Mark how all the complicated movements cooperate, in beautiful concert, to produce the desired result. Before we conclude that man's dignity is depreciated in the contrivance and use of this machinery, let us remember, that a precisely analogous course of reasoning must conduct us to the conclusion, that the act of Creation subtracted from the glory of the Creator; that the Infinite Mind, as it brooded from eternity over chaos, was more transcendently glorious, than when it returned from its six days' work, to contemplate a majestic world. We accordingly believe there is nothing irreverent in the assertion, that the finite mind in no respect approximates so nearly to a resemblance of the Infinite Mind, as in the subjugation of matter, through the aid of Mechanism, to fixed and beneficial laws,—to laws ordained by God, but discovered and applied by man.

If the views now presented be correct, it follows that the mechanical enterprise, with which our age is so alive, far from being unfavorable to our spiritual growth, is the one thing needful to furnish the freedom and leisure necessary for intellectual exercises,—to establish mankind in the *otium cum dignitate*, in a higher sense than even Cicero conceived it. But we may be referred, by way of refutation, to some of the renowned nations of antiquity, for which

Mechanism effected little or nothing, but which, nevertheless, "in true dignity of soul and character," would be pronounced by the writer, whose views we are examining, superior to any of the present day. . . . Greece may be selected as the most prominent illustration. To Greece, then, let us look. But let it be borne in mind, that we are speaking of society in the mass, and that our doctrine is, that men must be released from the bondage of perpetual bodily toil, before they can make great spiritual attainments. And now the question is, how came Greece to achieve her high intellectual supremacy, when all her work was performed by hand? The answer, so far as it respects this discussion, is ready. The Greeks themselves did not toil. Every reader of their history knows, that labor, physical labor, was stigmatized as a disgrace. Their wants were supplied by levying tribute upon all other nations, and keeping slaves to perform their drudgery at home. Hence their leisure. Force did for them, what machinery does for us. But what was the condition of the surrounding world? It is explained in a word. All other men had to labor for them; and as these derived no helps from Mechanism, manual labor consumed their whole lives. And hence their spiritual acquisitions have left no trace in history.

Now if we are willing to recur to that barbarous principle, that one nation may purchase itself leisure, as the Greeks did, by aggressions upon the rest, and if all other nations can be persuaded to submit to the experiment, we may no doubt behold a people, spurning all mechanical improvements, and yet attaining to a surprising "dignity of soul and character." But so long as it continues to be settled by compact among the nations, that each shall produce the means of subsistence within itself, or else an equivalent to exchange with others and so long as the balance of power continues to be so adjusted, as to prevent any one from living upon the rest through the force of superior numbers; we see not how we can avoid the conclusion, that that nation will make the greatest intellectual progress, in which the greatest number of labor-saving machines has been devised. It may not produce a Newton, Milton, or Shakespeare, but it will have a mass of thought, reflection, study, and contemplation perpetually at work all over its surface, and producing all the fruits of mental activity.

But this writer has not confined his warfare to the world as a whole. He has divided mankind into classes, and attacked them in detail. We shall try to follow him through his campaign. One remark, however, upon the name which he has given to the age. "It is not an Heroical, Devotional, Philosophical, or Moral Age, but, above all others, the Mechanical Age. It is the Age of Machinery, in every outward and *inward* sense of that word." It may puzzle our readers as much as it does ourselves, to understand what is meant by the "inward sense of machinery." We are still more perplexed to understand how the following charge, which seems intended as unusually severe, can be construed by thinking men into any thing else than substantial eulogy. "With its whole, undivided might, it [this age] forwards, teaches, and practises, *the great art of adapting means to ends.* Nothing is now done directly, or by hand; all is by rule, and calculated contrivance. For the simplest operation, some helps and accompaniments, some cunning, abbreviating process is in readiness." Now take away the lurking sneer with which this is said, and we see not how it would be possible to crowd more praise into a smaller compass. It is no small part of wisdom, to possess "the capacity of adapting means to ends." What would the writer have us do? Pursue ends without regard to means?

But to the specific charges. And first, the world is full of literary, scientific, and religious associations. It is one of the mechanical features of the age, that large numbers of men are in the habit of combining together to effect those objects, which no individual could accomplish alone. Now we have been accustomed to consider this prevailing tendency, as one of the greatest modern improvements. In no propensity do we discover *a more prudent adaptation of means to ends.* We employ the mechanic lever to lift weights, which our unassisted strength could not lift. Why not employ the *social lever* in the same way? We are aware that some great and good men have expressed apprehensions, that the individual is in danger of being lost in the mass. But, for aught we can perceive, the individual is as free as ever, and his influence is even greater. Let him unite with those whose opinions agree with his, and he adds another unit to the sum. Let him stand out alone, and he must be transcendently gifted, if he do not lose his unit of influence. And as to his freedom, there is no reason why he should part with that, when he joins himself to a society. He may act with it so long as he approves its course. When he disapproves it he may attempt a change; and if he cannot prevail, he may separate, and, at worst, he will stand in the position in which he was placed before he joined the society.

The writer next indulges in pleasantry at the expense of Physical Science and its votaries. "No Newton, by silent meditation, now discovers the system of the world from the falling of an apple; but some quite other than Newton stands in his Museum, his Scientific Institution, and, behind whole batteries of retorts, digesters, and galvanic piles, imperatively 'interrogates nature'; who, however, shows no haste to answer." If this mean any thing, it is to cast ridicule upon the universal practice of demonstrating and illustrating scientific truths by actual experiments. And in what school has the writer been brought up, if he really need to be reminded, that nature *does* answer, and hastily too, when thus interrogated? Again and again did she make haste to answer to Franklin, Priestley, Black, Lavoisier, Davy, and a host of other *imperative interrogators.* Where was this writer, when she was questioned as to the cause of lightning, the composition of water, the nature of heat, the mode of guarding against the fire-damp of the mine, and a hundred other equally momentous secrets?

The Mathematics are next subjected to our author's criticism. "Its calculus, differential and integral, is little else than a more cunningly constructed arithmetical mill, where the factors being put in, are, as it were, ground into the true product under cover, and without other effort on our part, than steady turning of the hand. We have more mathematics, certainly, than ever; but less *mathesis.* Archimedes and Plato could not have read the *Mécanique Céleste;* but neither would the whole French Institute see aught in that saying, "God geometrizes!" but a sentimental rodomontade." Now we are much in the same predicament with regard to this passage, as the French Institute with regard to that saying. We can see naught in it but "rodomontade." We learn from it, that Newton, Leibnitz, and Laplace, were nothing more than mill-wrights, and that their work was very easy. Indeed, the author had just before asserted, that to excel in the higher departments of mathematics, required no great natural gifts. Did we entertain our author's opinion of the facility with which a man, by setting himself patiently to work, could produce a treatise like the *Principia* and the *Mécanique Céleste*, we would certainly give up writing for the reviews; and we almost wonder that our author adheres to it, instead of placing his name by the side of those of Newton and Laplace. As to the remark about *mathesis*, it is true that Plato had the honor of *saying* "God geometrizes!" but to *prove* it, was reserved for the mechanicians above mentioned.

The next thrust is made at Metaphysics. And here we are informed that nobody has gone to work right. The whole world are now, and always have been, totally in the wrong. Even Locke, the great master, was at fault in the outset. But to avoid mis-statement, let the reviewer speak for himself. "The whole doctrine of Locke is mechanical, in its aim and origin, in its method and results. It is a *mere* discussion concerning the origin of our consciousness, or ideas, or whatever else they may be called; a genetic history of what we see *in* the mind. But the *grand secrets* of Necessity and Free-will, of the mind's vital or non-vital dependence on matter, of our *mysterious relations* to Time and Space, to God, to the Universe, are not in the faintest degree touched on." So because Locke confined his inquiries to what can be known, instead of med-

dling with "grand secrets," and "mysterious relations," he is a mere mechanic. Commend us to such mechanics. Give us Locke's Mechanism, and we will envy no man's Mysticism. Give us to know the "origin of our ideas," to comprehend the phenomena "which we see in the mind," and we will leave the question of the mind's essence to transcendental speculators. So of Necessity and Free-will; mechanical as the age is, we have heard of no machinery which can be brought to bear upon their explanation. And as to "the mind's vital or non-vital dependence upon matter," we are compelled to plead ignorance of what it means. We are bound, however, to suppose it has a deep meaning, since Locke did not get at the bottom of it. And should the writer give some of his leisure moments to the investigation, we hope the world may have the benefit of his researches. He may next find it profitable to undertake with Entities, Quiddities, Essences, and Sensible Forms, those stubborn secrets which did so puzzle some of the schoolmen. After brushing away these mists, there will still remain a rich field for discovery, in "our mysterious relations to Time and Space." And these relations being fully ascertained, the way will be cleared for a discussion of the celebrated question,—Whether spirits can pass from one point of space to another, without passing through the intervening space.

From Metaphysics, the reviewer passes to Politics. "But the trail of the serpent is over them all." Mechanism has twisted his coils fast even about the slippery politician. "No where," complains the writer, "is the deep, almost exclusive faith we have in Mechanism more visible, than in the politics of the time." If this had been written within the last month or two, we should request to be informed, by what rare combination of mechanical powers the recent political changes have been effected in Europe. Truly, there is something in these vast movements, which rather looks as if mind were the mover. Mr. Canning predicted that the next war in Europe would be a war of opinions. That war is not yet commenced. But, to use the language of our author, the *revolutionary machine* is working with a tremendous *momentum,* such as the world never before witnessed. But that we may not mistake the writer on this subject, we quote his words. "It is no longer the moral, religious, spiritual condition of the people that is our concern, but their physical, practical, economical condition, as regulated by public laws. Thus is the *body politic,* more than ever, worshipped and tended; but the *soul politic,* less than ever." We are almost tempted to believe that this was intended particularly for the United States, where "public laws" have left the "religious and spiritual concerns" of men, exclusively to themselves and their God. But then the writer must, on his own principles, allow us due credit for managing to get along without that expensive and complicated piece of machinery, a *Church Establishment.* Time was, it must be confessed, when the "soul politic" was more cared for by government, than it is any where at present. But this sort of care has always been found to require a great deal of machinery, and among the rest, the rack, the fagot, and the axe. The writer, therefore, in his anxiety for the *soul politic,* seems to be placed in a dilemma. He has such an antipathy to machinery in general,—and to that above mentioned, we will do him the justice to suppose, in particular,—that he would

probably reject the only means, by which governments have hitherto been able to "tend" the souls of their subjects.

Having proceeded thus far in his assault upon notions, which must be allowed to possess a very general currency, the writer proposes a new illustration, or, perhaps we should say, theory of our nature, which he supports with great vivacity and learning; and which, that we may do him no injustice, we state in his own words. "To speak a little pedantically, there is a science of Dynamics in man's fortunes and nature, as well as of Mechanics." This would hardly carry perfect conviction to the mind, without the following lucid explanation. "There is a science which treats of, and *practically* (?) addresses the primary, unmodified forces and energies of man, the *mysterious* springs of Love, and Fear, and Wonder, of Enthusiasm, Poetry, Religion, all of which have a truly *vital and infinite character,* as well as a science which practically addresses the finite, modified developements of these, when they take the shape of immediate 'motives,' as hope of reward or fear of punishment." Having thus stated his theory, our author illustrates it by several examples, of which we shall notice one or two. Among others, the French Revolution,—not the recent glorious one,—is drawn in. "The French Revolution had something higher in it than cheap bread and a *habeas corpus* act. Here too, was an Idea; a Dynamic, not a Mechanic force. It was a struggle, though a blind, and at last an insane one, for the infinite, divine nature of Right, of Freedom, of Country." We do not exactly understand what is meant by "a struggle for the infinite, divine nature of Country." If by saying, that "cheap bread and a *habeas corpus* act" were not the motives of the Revolution, the author means that neither the wants of the populace, oppressed by misgovernment, nor the political theories of the Philosophers occasioned this explosion, we can only say that he denies it to have been produced by the action of those causes, to one or both of which it is universally ascribed.

Another example, scarcely less unfortunate, is the Christian Religion. We desire always to approach this subject with the most profound reverence. And when we are told by the reviewer, that "the Christian Religion, under every theory of it, in the believing or the *unbelieving* mind, is the crowning glory, or rather the life and soul of our whole modern culture,"—we most cordially concur in what we can understand of the panegyric. Of religion in the believing mind, too much cannot be said. How religion in the *unbelieving* mind can be a crowning glory, we are at loss to conceive. But our chief concern is with the assertion, that the Christian Religion has been promulgated "Dynamically, and not Mechanically." This is in direct conflict with our historical information. It seems to us, that there has been, unfortunately, altogether too much machinery employed in the propagation of Christianity. In the beginning, we know that it was not so. Then the simple but powerful "preaching of the word" was sufficient. But afterwards, external helps were employed in such a degree, as to suggest to the sceptical historian, Gibbon, the idea of accounting for the establishment of Christianity, exclusively by human means.

We can notice but a few more complaints of this dissatisfied writer, and those briefly. He is very much scandalized, that "we should have our little theories on all human and divine things,"

and particularly that "even Poetry is no longer without a scientific exposition." But wherefore should it be? Does the poet merely rave? Is his mind lawless in its wanderings? Or does it, according to Dr. Channing, obey higher laws than it transgresses? If so, we can perceive no harm or absurdity in a "scientific exposition." Such an one has been given by the eloquent author just mentioned, in his remarks on the poetry of Milton; and a passage of more transcendent beauty is not to be found in our mother tongue.

Another cause of complaint with our author is, that "our first question with regard to any object is not, *What is it?* but *How is it?*" This is equivalent to saying, that it is the fashion of the present age not to analyze; and a suggestion wider of the fact could not easily be made. Every one knows that Chemistry, which more than any other science is the off-spring and growth of this age, is one perpetual reiteration of the question, *What is it?* The author would find it difficult to name a substance to which Chemistry has not put this question, and received a satisfactory answer. But he would have us go still further, and waste our investigating energies upon fruitless inquiries into the essence of matter and mind. We know that there has been a strong propensity among men to press their discoveries to this verge; and that even Newton was so far beguiled by his "wish to know," as to speculate upon the nature of the cause of gravitation, after he had ascertained its laws. But we had supposed, that mankind were now generally agreed as to the inutility of thus invading the Deity's inscrutable mysteries. If the clear teachings of Lord Bacon on this subject were not sufficient, one would think that the practical *reductio ad ab-*

surdum exhibited in the incompatible, yet equally plausible hypotheses of Berkeley and Hobbes, would be sufficient. One resolves every thing into matter, the other resolves every thing into mind; while the only satisfactory proposition, which both conclusively demonstrate is, that the resolution of such questions is beyond the capability of the human mind. Reason affords no clue to guide those who plunge into the labyrinths of mystic speculation.

On the whole, we have no wish to disguise the feeling of strong dissatisfaction, excited in us, by the article under consideration. We consider its tendency injurious, and its reasoning unsound. That it has some eloquent passages must be admitted, but when we hear distinguished philosophers spoken of as "logic-mills,"—the religion of the age as "a working for wages,"—our Bible societies as "supported by fomenting of vanities, by puffing, intrigue, and chicane," —and all descriptions of men "from the cartwright up to the code-maker," as mere "mechanists"; when we further hear "the grand secrets of necessity and free-will,"—"our mysterious relations to time and space,"—and "the deep, infinite harmonies of nature and man's soul,"— brought repeatedly forward under the most varied forms of statement, as the legitimate objects of philosophical inquiry, and the most illustrious of the living and the dead, men whom we never think of but as benefactors of our race, made the objects of satire and ridicule, because they have preferred the *terra firma* of mechanical philosophy to the unstable quagmire of mystic conjecture;—we find it difficult not to regard the Essay rather as an effort of paradoxical ingenuity,—the sporting of an adventurous imagination with settled opinions,—than as a serious inquiry after truth.

Indeed the writer himself seems to think, towards the end, that he has gone too far; and deems it prudent, in contradiction, as it seems to us, to the assertion first quoted, as well as to the whole tenor of the article, to insert the following *saving clause:*—"It seems a well ascertained fact, that in all times, reckoning even from those of the Heraclides and Pelasgi, *the happiness and greatness of mankind at large, have been continually progressive.*" This is one of the few assertions in the article, in which we altogether agree with the author. We do entertain an unfaltering belief in the permanent and continued improvement of the human race, and we consider no small portion of it, whether in relation to the body or the mind, as the result of mechanical invention. It is true, that the progress has not always been regular and constant. In happy times it has been so rapid, as to fill the benevolent with inexpressible joy. But anon, clouds have gathered over the delightful prospect,—evil influences, but not mechanical, have operated,—evil times have succeeded,—and human nature has undergone a disastrous eclipse. But it has been only an eclipse, not an extinguishment of light. And frequent as these alternations have been, mankind are found to have been constant gainers. The flood has always been greater than the ebb. Each great billow of time has left men further onward than its predecessor. This could be proved, if necessary, by a thousand references. Darkness has indeed given a name to some ages, but light on the whole has immensely preponderated; and it is this conviction which nerves the heart and invigorates the arm of philanthropy. They who feel this divine impulse, know that the labors of kindred spirits in past ages have not been in vain. They see Atlantis, Utopia, and the

Isles of the Blest, nearer than those who first described them. These imaginary abodes of pure and happy beings, which have been conceived by the most ardent lovers of their kind, we delight to contemplate; for we regard them as types and shadows of a higher and better condition of human nature, towards which we are surely though slowly tending.

But let us not be misunderstood. The condition we speak of, is not one of perfection. This we neither believe in, nor hope for. Supposing it possible in the nature of things, it would be any thing but desirable. For with nothing left to achieve nor gain, existence would become empty and vapid. But if, with this explanation, our views should pass for visionary, we cannot help it. We cannot go back to the origin of mankind and trace them down to the present time, without believing it to be a part of the providence of God, that his creatures should be perpetually advancing. The first men must have been profoundly ignorant, except so far as the Supreme Being communicated with them directly. But with them commenced a series of inventions and discoveries, which have been going on, up to the present moment. Every day has beheld some addition to the general stock of information. When the exi-

gency of the times has required a new truth to be revealed, it has been revealed. Men gifted beyond the ordinary lot, have been raised up for the purpose; witness Cadmus, Socrates, and the other sages of Greece, Cicero and the other sages of Rome, Columbus, Galileo, Bacon, Newton, and the other giant spirits of modern times. We cannot regard it as an abuse of language to call such men inspired, that is, pre-eminently endowed beyond all their contemporaries, and moved by the invisible agency of God, to enlighten the world on subjects, which had never till they spoke, occupied the minds of men. In other words, we believe that the appearance of such men, at the exact times when all things were ready for the disclosures they were to make, was not the result of accident, but the work of an overruling Providence. And if such has been the beneficent operation of Providence upon the minds of men in all past times, —if whenever a revelation was needed, He has communicated it, and in the exact measure in which it was needed,— how can we, without irreverence, adopt any other conclusion, than that He, who changeth not, will still continue, through all future time, to make known through gifted men, as fast as the world is prepared to receive them, new truths from His exhaustless store?

PART III AGRICULTURE

Until the twentieth century most Americans earned their living by farming. Even though the nation's cities always played a role out of proportion to their size, the vast bulk of the population (94 per cent in 1800) lived on farms or in very small villages, and Americans thought of their society as agrarian.

Improvements in the techniques of farming came in two separate areas during the nineteenth century. First, science was increasingly called upon to help solve agricultural problems. There was a growing certainty, inherited from the eighteenth-century development of modern chemistry, that the problem of soil fertility could be illuminated by careful analysis of soil and an identification of its constituent parts. This movement—which became almost a cult—reached its dramatic climax in the work of Justus von Liebig (1803-73). As the life sciences developed, they too were called upon to improve the practice of agriculture.

Second, both the type and the number of implements available to the farmer were improved. Once again, the advances of the nineteenth century were an extension of the interests that characterized the Agricultural Revolution in England in the previous century. One area of improvement was in the development of implements for such difficult and labor-intensive agricultural chores as the harvesting of grain and hay. The most famous of these new implements was the McCormick reaper, but it should be noted that this large and expensive machine was not typical. The ordinary farmer could not afford one. Although the reaper proved indispensable for certain crops in certain parts of the country, most farm work remained a matter of hard hand-labor. Not until the appearance of the rubber-tired gasoline tractor in the twentieth century did the farmer have available efficient and flexible power commensurate with his needs.

A less dramatic development, but to most farmers more important, was the application of the American System of manufacture to the production of im-

79

plements for the farm. By mid-century many tools with interchangeable parts were being made (of wood) in large numbers, all by power machinery. One result of this was that it cost remarkably little to equip a typical family farm—only $968 in 1862 according to one estimate. In a country where the official ideology (and to some extent the social reality) demanded easy access to farming, cheap implements were as important as cheap land.

1. Tools of the Trade, 1851

JAMES F. W. JOHNSTON, *Notes on North America*

One of the main reasons that America remained a nation of small, family farmers for so long was the abundance and cheapness of farm tools. Inventors spent an enormous amount of time and ingenuity in creating and simplifying farm implements. Although the application of machinery to farming marked one of the most important advances in the early nineteenth century, and although the large and complicated pieces of machinery captured the public attention, to the small farmers the improvement of hand tools was more relevant. One of the best places to see the wide range of tools available was at the innumerable agricultural fairs, which had already become a familiar part of rural life in the nation. The following brief account was left by a Scots chemist who visited the United States at mid-century.

This morning I visited the show-yard, along with my friend Professor Norton of Yale College, who had thus far accompanied me in my tour through his native country. The show was held in a large inclosed area, quite as spacious as those usually devoted to this purpose by the Royal Agricultural Society of England. The two main divisions of implements and stock occupied the chief place, as with us; farm and dairy produce, however, and fruits, receive much attention from the New York State Society, and had an appropriate place assigned to them under the tents and sheds which were scattered over the grounds.

The general character of the implements was economy in construction and in price, and the exhibition was large and interesting. I know of no more instructive lesson, in regard to the practical condition of the husbandry of a country, than that which a man gets in

From James F. W. Johnston, *Notes on North America: Agricultural, Economical, and Social* (Edinburgh, 1851), I, 160-61.

surveying a collection of implements—actually in use, or coming into use—such as these exhibitions supply. Our English chaff-cutters and food-crushers, and drill and thrashing and tile machines, and cultivators and subsoil-ploughs and clod-crushers, tell more of what is going on in the country than months of travelling would make known to the most active agricultural inquirer. It is not so much the construction and cost and usefulness of a machine, as the number and variety of each seen on the ground, which shows what implements are in most request, and in what direction the practice of the farmer is progressing.

Ploughs, hay-rakes, forks, scythes, and cooking-stoves, were very abundant, and many of them well and beautifully made. American ploughs are now exported in considerable numbers. At a subsequent period, a dealer in Boston informed me he had this season sold a hundred of one of the varieties made in Massachusetts to a single individual for sale in London. The potato grips and forks, of various kinds, cut out of sheet-steel, were very elastic, light, strong, and cheap. They seemed to leave noth-ing in these articles to be desired. The cradle-scythes were also excellent: an active man was said to be able to cut four to six acres of wheat a-day with them. That, of course, would depend something upon the quantity of straw upon the ground.

Among the more novel instruments to me were the corn-shellers and crushers. The former were very pretty implements, and the larger kinds were said to be capable of shelling two hundred bushels of Indian corn an hour.

Of reaping-machines there were several varieties on the ground, and several are actually in use in the Western States. Hussey's, which I saw on the ground, was said to cut twenty-five acres of wheat a-day. My friend, Mr Stevens, who went round the yard with me, assured me he had seen one of them cut sixteen acres. M'Cormick's machine, I suppose, must be a good one, from the information here given me that as many as fifteen hundred of them have been made at Chicago, in Illinois, this last year, and sold for cutting wheat on the prairies of the North-Western States.

2. The Manufacture of Implements, 1854

JOSEPH WHITWORTH AND GEORGE WALLIS, *The Industry of the United States*

When the British commission assigned to observe the New York exhibits at the Crystal Palace turned its attention to American agricultural implements, its members were struck by the fact that the recently developed American System of mass production was applied to their manufacture. Many of the

From Joseph Whitworth and George Wallis, *The Industry of the United States in Machinery, Manufactures, and Useful and Ornamental Arts* (London, 1854), pp. 19-21.

principles and machines (such as Blanchard's copying lathe) that were first developed for use in the mass production of small arms were now being applied to the making of plows and other farm tools. The method of production kept prices down and allowed the prospective farmer to stretch his small capital to buy a wide variety of implements, from rakes to wagons.

Labour-saving machines are most successfully employed in the manufacture of agricultural implements. In a plough manufactory at Baltimore, eight machines are employed on the various parts of the woodwork. With these machines seven men are able to make the wooden parts of thirty ploughs per day.

The handle-pieces are shaped by a circular cutter, having four blades, similar to those of smoothing-planes, fixed on a horizontal axis, with about 2 inches radius, and making nearly 4,000 revolutions per minute. The work to be shaped is fastened to a pattern, which is pressed against a loose roller on the axis of the cutter as the workman passes it along, and it is thus cut of exactly the same shape as the pattern.

All the ploughs of a given size are made to the same model, and their parts, undergoing similar operations, are made all alike. Some of the sharp edges of the wood are taken off or chamfered by a cutter revolving between two cones; these guide and support the work as it is pressed down edgewise on the cutters, and passed along by the workman.

The other machines in use consist of a circular and vertical saw, and machines for jointing, tenoning, drilling, and for making round stave rods, and giving them conical ends, the whole being of a simple and inexpensive character.

The curved handle-pieces of the ploughs, which require to be steamed and bent, are obtained already shaped from the forests where they are cut, and are advantageously supplied to the large manufacturers. The prices of the ploughs vary from $2½ to $7 (10s. 6d. to 30s.).

In a manufactory at Buffalo, mowing-machines are made in large numbers; one of these machines drawn by two horses, can mow on an average six acres of grass per day.

The machine is similar in its construction to the common reaping-machine, but it has only one wheel, furnished with projections to prevent it from slipping. This wheel gives motion to the cutters, and supports one side, the other rests on a runner like that of a sledge. It has a pole, to which two horses are attached in the ordinary way, and the driver sits on a seat fixed behind the cutters.

In an establishment at Worcester, 250 hands are employed principally in making ploughs, hay-cutters, and churns.

Templates and labour-saving tools are used in the manufacture of these implements, which are sold in very large numbers.

The churns consist of a double case, the inner one being of zinc, which receives the milk or cream, and in which the arms revolve, the outer one being of wood. It is found by experience that butter is formed most rapidly when the milk or cream is churned at a certain temperature; and in order to obtain this temperature, which is indicated by a thermometer inserted in the churn, warm or cold water is introduced between the inner zinc and outer wooden casing, as may be required.

Many of the carriages, especially those technically called "waggons," are made of an exceedingly light construction, and are intended generally to carry two and sometimes four persons.

Their wheels are frequently made with only two felloes, which are bent round by the operation of steaming, and are strengthened at the joining with iron clamps. The wheel of a carriage constructed to carry four persons had felloes only 1½ inch square. They are generally made of white oak, and the spokes are obtained ready shaped from shops where their manufacture forms a special trade.

It would seem as if the elasticity of these carriages peculiarly fitted them for the very bad roads on which they in general have to run, and it is evidently a principle with the Americans to use their light carriages and save their horses.

Every man in America who is able to keep his waggon is free to do so, unfettered and unquestioned, consequently their use is so general that it may be said to be almost universal. Their manufacture is of one great importance, and supports a vast number of wheelwrights and artizans of that class, who from the nature of their employment attain great skill and aptitude, enabling them to turn their hands to almost any variety of work, and rendering them a most useful and important class.

3. Soil Analysis in Maryland, 1851

JAMES F. W. JOHNSTON, *Notes on North America*

Besides the growing mechanization of farm work, foreign observers noted an increasing reliance upon the science of chemistry by mid-century. Modern chemistry had been developing from the last decades of the eighteenth century, and its application to agricultural problems was inevitable in an age that considered agriculture to be the queen of occupations. Indeed, modern chemistry and the physiocratic philosophy were both largely products of the French Enlightenment. In America such gentleman farmers as Thomas Jefferson had long encouraged both science and the idea of agricultural supremacy. It is not surprising, then, that agriculture was one of the first bene-

From James F. W. Johnston, *Notes on North America: Agricultural, Economical, and Social* (Edinburgh, 1851), II, 318-20.

ficiaries of government support for science. James Johnston, one of the leading agricultural chemists in his native Scotland, was particularly interested in the extent to which science was being harnessed to improve farming in the United States.

At Baltimore I was met by Dr Higgins, Agricultural Chemist to the State of Maryland, with whom I spent a very pleasant afternoon. The city is beautifully placed at the head of a wide bay, partly on a flat margin of the water, but now chiefly on the slope and summit of the elevated banks from which the eye commands the flats, and is carried over the creeks and lowlands beneath, towards the broader waters of Chesapeake Bay. It is well built, prosperous, and increasing in size. Employment is plentiful, and skilled labour commands a wage of about a dollar and a half a-day. The mechanics usually live in self-contained houses owned by themselves, of which there are whole streets in the city. These houses are fifteen feet in front and three stories high, and are built of brick, on leasehold sites held for ninety-nine years, renewable for ever. In a slave State, where the aristocratic principle is recognised, the dread of long leases and reserved rents does not exist, which so strangely agitates the communities of New England and New York.

The southern pro-slavery sentiment is still strong in Maryland, though the number of slaves has rapidly declined during the last twenty years. In 1830 the slave population of this State numbered 102,000, but in 1840 it had decreased to 90,000, while the number of free coloured people exceeded 62,000. The census of the present year (1850) will probably show a still more rapid diminution.

The city of Baltimore contains a population of about 120,000; and it is an exhilarating symptom, in connection with the slavery question, that not less than sixteen large free schools have been built in different parts of the city, and are maintained at the public expense. The progress of general education, the increase of a willingly labouring free population, and, above all, the growing unprofitableness of slave labour in cultivating worn-out land, must gradually loosen the hold which slavery has hitherto maintained upon the public mind of this State.

There is no State agricultural society in Maryland aided or supported by the public funds. An attempt was making at the time of my visit to form a general society for the three small States of New Jersey, Delaware, and Maryland, which, if liberally supported, would possess a strength and power not to be looked for or to be attained by the exertions of the friends of agriculture in either of these States separately.

Still the Legislature of Maryland has not been unmoved by the recent contributions of science to the progress of agriculture, and has been among the first to recognise the especial usefulness of chemistry by creating the office of "State Agricultural Chemist," and nominating Dr Higgins to the appointment, with the salary of 1500 dollars a-year. Part of the duties of this officer is to visit the different counties of the State, to give private advice and public lectures to the farmers, to collect soils, marls, and other substances, which it may be desirable to analyse, and to *an-*

alyse them on the spot. The last of these duties is the only one to which any serious objection can be made. A peripatetic laboratory is inconsistent with correct analytical research. Besides yielding very imperfect results, it must also involve a great loss of the chemist's time to the State, and an unnecessary expenditure of money to himself, in securing rooms to work in in every different locality. This arrangement indicates a very juvenile knowledge of the nature and requirements of chemical analyses, and will, no doubt, be altered as soon as the members of the Legislature become a little more enlightened as to the measures which are best to be adopted, with the view of effectually bringing about the important objects they have by this appointment so laudably desired to accomplish.

4. Growth of Agricultural Chemistry

H. W. WILEY, "The Relation of Chemistry to the Progress of Agriculture"

The efforts described by Johnston formed but one link in a chain of concern which extended from the gentlemen farmers of the eighteenth century through to the establishment of large agricultural research facilities by the United States Department of Agriculture. The evolution of chemical knowledge made it possible to solve agricultural problems. It also encouraged the American people to create institutions that would bring such knowledge to bear on farm problems on a significant scale. H. W. Wiley, the USDA chemist who was soon to make a public reputation through his crusade for pure food and drug legislation during the Progressive era, was interested in both developments.

Chemistry as a science has undergone such a wonderful transformation during the century as to make any just comparison of its relation to any particular industry at the present time with that it held a hundred years ago somewhat difficult. We regard with a feeling akin to compassion the ideas entertained one hundred years ago in reference to chemistry, especially in its relations to agriculture; but the pride we may feel in our present knowledge of this science should not be allowed to carry us too far, since at the end of the next century the writer who shall undertake a review of this subject may look

From H. W. Wiley, "The Relation of Chemistry to the Progress of Agriculture," *Yearbook of the United States Department of Agriculture. 1899* (Washington, D.C., 1900), pp. 201-58.

with equal compassion on the views we now entertain.

The efforts which were made by Lavoisier and his school to place the science of chemistry upon a sure foundation some twenty-five years before the beginning of the century, although making great progress, had not yet entirely dominated the world of chemical theory. The crude notions of the earlier chemists concerning phlogiston, phlegms, essential oils, exudations, evaporation, and other processes still held sway, and agricultural chemistry was probably the last of the different branches of chemical science to be liberated from the thraldom of these erroneous theories. In spite of this fact, however, the observations which scientific men had made of the chemical aspects which agricultural science possessed are not without value nor are they wholly false. . . .

It is now possible to give a general view of the knowledge of the relations which chemistry held to practical agriculture at the beginning of the century. In regard to soils, some general notions of a true character were held as to their composition. The real plant foods in the soil, however, were not appreciated. While in a general way it was recognized that phosphoric acid, potash, and lime entered into the composition of the plant, it is evident from a study of the literature of the time that silica was regarded as more beneficial to the plant than any of the other mineral matters mentioned. The manner in which the food was furnished to the plant was imperfectly known, save that it was generally conceded that the mineral matters must first enter into solution before they could be distributed throughout the plant.

In regard to the physical nature of the soil, it was a matter of common observation that it had much to do with the efficacy of plant growth. The open and porous soils were more prized than those of a hard and impenetrable nature, and the general distinctions between sandy, loamy, and clayey soils were well understood.

The notion was extremely prevalent that the soils serve more as a resting place and support for the root system of the plants, while the materials for plant growth in some way resemble exudations, or emanations, which come partly from the soil itself and partly from the atmosphere. The actual chemical composition of soil was but little understood, and this arose from the fact that the means of chemical analysis were so meager and its processes so unsatisfactory as to preclude the possibility of securing exact data. Nevertheless, a reasonably accurate knowledge was had of the chief constituents of the soil, if not of the functions which they played in plant growth. That the soil was a vehicle for the administration of the nourishing elements of food, was not fully appreciated at the beginning of the century. The nitrogen, or azote, as it was called in that day, was supposed to reach the plant exclusively in the form of ammonia, and no accurate knowledge of the relation of the soil to the production of azotized foods was extant.

Perhaps, however, the most striking error in connection with the notions relating to the constitution of the soil itself in respect of plant growth is found in the fact that the true functions of phosphoric acid and potash in the nutrition of plants were imperfectly, if at all, understood by even the most advanced agricultural chemists of that day.

It is true that the chemical composition of manures which were then in use was not well known, nor were the processes by which manures became available as plant food at all understood, but the practical knowledge of the use of stable manures, of marls, of gypsum, and of lime was generally diffused and acted upon. Of artificial manures, other than those mentioned, little was known save that the aborigines of the New England States had taught the early settlers the great value of using fish as a fertilizer.

Some idea also was entertained of the value of the refuse of the slaughter-houses for fertilizing purposes, and it was known that blood, bone, and horn were useful in promoting the growth of crops, but how and why were not understood.

The value of clover and other leguminous crops in increasing soil fertility was recognized, but the causes which established this value were not at all known. The process of fermentation was recognized in the manufacture and preparation of manures, but the nature of this fermentation was wholly unknown to the investigators and chemical agriculturists of that time. Empiricism in the use of manures through thousands of years had led to most valuable practical results, but little was due at that time to the discoveries and researches of chemistry. When we look at the knowledge which was possessed of the composition of plants, we do not wonder that the relations of the soil and fertilizers to plant growth were so little understood. The methods of investigation in vogue were totally inadequate to reveal the true constitution of plants, and it is a matter of wonder to us at the present time that with such crude apparatus and such imperfect methods

so much accurate knowledge could have been obtained. The processes of organic analysis had only just been introduced, and only the general constitution of the carbohydrates, as represented by the gums, mucilages, starches, and sugars of that day, was definitely established, but the percentage of nitrogen contained in the albumin and gluten recognized as existing in plants is scarcely more accurately known at the present day than it was then.

The more important organic acids also existing in plants had been discovered, separated, and identified, and in general it must be confessed that, in so far as the progress of chemistry relating to the composition of plants is concerned, the agricultural chemists of the beginning of the century are to be congratulated on the attainments which they had made. The weak point of their researches and investigations was that they had made no systematic effort to correlate the composition of plants and of the soil to the principles of plant growth. With their imperfect ideas of the nature of plant nutrition, it did not occur to them that a great system of scientific agriculture could be based upon investigations of this kind. They, however, had done enough to pave the way for the great impetus which the investigations of Liebig, Gilbert, Boussingault, and others gave to systematic agricultural chemistry some thirty or forty years later.

The publication of Liebig's work entitled "Chemistry in its applications to agriculture and physiology," in 1840, marked a complete change in the theories of chemistry in respect of agriculture existing at the beginning of the century as portrayed in preceding pages, and inaugurated the new science of agriculture, resting upon his investigations as a foundation. If Wurtz could say, "Chemistry is a French science, founded by Lavoisier, of immortal memory," with all the greater propriety may we say of the agriculture of to-day, "Agriculture is a chemical science, founded by Liebig, of immortal memory." "Perfect agriculture," Liebig says in the preface to the first edition of his book, "is the true foundation of all trade and industry; but a rational system of agriculture can not be formed without the application of scientific principles, for such a system must be based on an exact acquaintance with the means of nutrition of vegetables and with the influence of soils and actions of manure upon them; this knowledge we must seek from chemistry, which teaches the mode of investigating the composition and of studying the character of the different substances from which plants derive their nourishment."

Within a year after Liebig's book was published it was translated into English, and soon thereafter was found in the languages of all the leading nations of the world. Liebig, however, must not be given the sole praise for the establishment of the true theory of scientific agriculture. Very much earlier in the century De Saussure, a celebrated French chemist and botanist, published his "Chemical researches on vegetation," and a decade before Liebig published his first work Boussingault, the most celebrated French agricultural chemist of the early part of the century, had produced a great many works on the relations of chemistry to agriculture. To both of these authors Liebig is largely indebted, and to each of them he gives full credit. The part which Davy took in preparing the way for

these later investigations has already been pointed out.

Previous to the time of Liebig, as already indicated, it was commonly understood that organic substances, such as sugars and oils, were the chief foods of plants, either in the fresh state or in the partially decayed condition known as humus. In fact, the attitude of chemistry toward agriculture in the first four decades of the century was so strongly marked on this point that the whole system of plant nutrition, as understood at that time, might with propriety be designated the humus theory. Although other writers before the time of Liebig had intimated that the air and water, and not the earth, were the source of the carbon, oxygen, and hydrogen in plants, it must be admitted that it was through the researches of Liebig that the great principles of plant nutrition, founded on the elaboration of the elements of carbohydrates from the air and water, were fully developed. As in most other instances, however, the tendency of mankind to reach extremes was shown on this point. Liebig in his fight against the humus theory naturally went to the other extreme of denying that the humus took any part at all in plant nutrition. He based his chief objection to the humus theory on the ground that humus was practically insoluble, and that therefore it could not enter into the circulation of the plants. This argument we know now is not a valid one, but it served as the basis of an attack upon an erroneous theory which had established itself firmly in the minds of advanced agriculturists. . . .

It is evident, therefore, that even at this time, almost the middle of the century, the view was still stoutly maintained by eminent men that the organic matters of which plants are composed were derived chiefly from the soil, and not from the atmosphere and water. Hence it was, that with wonderful pertinacity the agricultural chemists clung to the theory that the organic matters of plants were directly derived from the decaying organic matters of the soil, and that therefore humus was the chief element in the nourishment of plants.

Perhaps there is no other method in which the researches of chemistry have been made practical for agricultural purposes in a more general way to the agriculture of the United States than through the work of the Department of Agriculture. So long as the work of the Department was conducted in the Patent Office, chemical investigations of agricultural subjects continued to be the chief scientific inquiry.

The first appropriation in this country for purely scientific services in agriculture was made at the first session of the Thirtieth Congress, when $1,000 was given "for the institution of a system of analyses of different grains produced in this country and of flour manufactured here and exported abroad."

The important problems which it was sought to solve in these investigations were the effect of soil and climate upon the different varieties of grains and the effect of a sea voyage and store upon the flour and meal manufactured from grains produced here and sent abroad. . . .

In 1862 the Department of Agriculture was organized on an independent basis. In the organic act establishing the Department it is stated that the Commissioner of Agriculture shall "employ other persons for such time as their services may be needed, includ-

ing chemists, botanists, entomologists, and other persons skilled in the natural sciences pertaining to agriculture."

It is thus seen that chemistry was recognized, by its assignment in the order of mention, as of the first importance in the scientific work of promoting agriculture throughout the country. In accordance with the authority vested in him by the organic act, Isaac Newton, who was the first Commissioner of Agriculture, established the Division of Chemistry by the appointment of Dr. C. M. Wetherill, a distinguished chemist, as the first chief of Division. . . .

The foregoing sketch of the relations of chemical research to the progress of agriculture during the past hundred years present an outline view of the status of this industry and its debt to science at the close of the nineteenth century. The true composition of the soil and its relations to plant growth are now known. The methods of utilizing plant food and of conserving it for the coming years have been fully established. The principles of plant growth and the chemical changes attending it are understood. The laws of animal nutrition have been experimentally elucidated, and by their application great economy in the use of nutrients is effected. The methods whereby organic nitrogen is prepared for plant food have been revealed, and some of the ways in which atmospheric nitrogen enters into organic combination are marked out. The application of the principles of chemical technology to the elaboration of raw agricultural products has added a new value to the fruits of the farm, opened up new avenues of prosperity, and developed new staple crops.

The closing of the century sees in this country an endowment for agricultural research which excites the admiration of the whole civilized world, and a study of the personnel of the scientific corps shows that fully half the amount expended for strictly scientific investigations has been for chemical studies. We find chemistry intimately associated with nearly every line of agricultural progress and pointing the way to still greater advancement.

When we contrast the condition of agricultural chemical knowledge which now obtains with the nebulous, empirical, and illogical theories which characterized it one hundred years ago, the distance we have traversed seems indeed long; but we should not forget that we are still only on the threshold of knowledge. The achievements of the next century ought to surpass those which the past one looks upon with pride.

To him who writes the story of the progress of agriculture as influenced by chemical research during the twentieth century may come a feeling of pity for the ignorance which now surrounds us; but he will at least accord to our workers the merit of being emancipated from the slavery of opinion and the worship of authority. He will certainly say they were patient, industrious, and truth loving. To the leaders of progress for the next century we commit our unfinished work, confident of their integrity and hopeful of the good which they will bring to mankind.

PART IV   SPREAD OF AMERICAN TECHNOLOGY

From the time the first colonists brought their hand tools to America, this country has depended upon technological innovations originating abroad. The United States before 1900 was probably a "debtor nation" in technology. Even so, beginning in the late eighteenth century there was a significant and growing flow of new technology outward from New England and the Middle Atlantic states. Thus even while British machines and processes were being introduced into the workshops of the North, machines and mechanics from this same area were moving southward, into the states below the Mason-Dixon line, beyond, into the Caribbean, and, even further, into the developing areas of Europe.

In part, this flow was attributable to the fact that there tends to be a movement of technology from areas of greater sophistication to more backward areas. In part also, the technology that had developed in parts of the United States was well suited to particular problems in other parts of the developing world. And finally, new technology tends to follow the established routes of trade; the area that controls commerce often controls technology as well.

These several patterns produced some dramatic examples of exploitation. The building of railroads across Czarist Russia, for example, was entrusted to American engineers, because the vast distances involved, the ruggedness of the terrain, and the need to rely on wood for construction all paralleled the American experience rather than the British. Equally surprising was the appearance of American inventions (and some early mass-produced items, such as clocks) in the British market—the mechanical equivalent of sending coals to Newcastle.

Less dramatic but perhaps more important was the fact that the northern part of the United States extended a kind of technological imperialism over the southern regions of the nation. Not only were new cotton mills built and equipped from the North, but the steam engines and other machines used on Southern plantations were regularly serviced by Northern mechanics. Following the routes of trade down the Mississippi or around the coast from New York to New Orleans, Northern men and machines dominated the mechanical needs of the South.

In many ways the Caribbean islands and Latin America were considered to be simple extensions of the American South. The same tropical setting, the same debilitating climate, the same dependence upon the labor of slave and serf (who were thought to be devoid of mechanical ability), the same dependence upon extractive industry based upon staple agriculture—all these, along with the political attitude characterized by the Monroe Doctrine (1823), combined to make Central and South America an important field for the exercise of Yankee mechanical ability. By the time the infection of imperialism became epidemic in the late nineteenth century, American engineers and mechanics were well used to applying their talents to the exploitation of underdeveloped areas—both at home and abroad.

1. American Inventions in Britain

J. C. DYER, "Notes on the origin of Several Mechanical Inventions"

Although the flow of technology was preponderantly from east to west across the Atlantic, by the end of the eighteenth century a flow the other way had begun. Increasingly, during the early part of the nineteenth century, American innovations were being used in England. One main figure in this movement was Joseph Cheeseborough Dyer, who was born in Rhode Island in 1780 and died in Manchester, England, in 1871.

Dyer showed an early interest in mechanics but chose instead a career in commerce. In 1811 he moved to England to carry on his business, but an increasing amount of his interest was taken up in acting as an agent for American inventors. A model Victorian gentleman with wide and influential connections, Dyer was responsible for the introduction and improvement of many American machines, not the least of which was one for making nails. Late in his life he recalled how he had handled this device.

From J. C. Dyer, "Notes on the origin of Several Mechanical Inventions, and their subsequent application to different purposes.—Part III," *Memoirs of the Literary and Philosophical Society of Manchester*, 3rd ser., III (1868), 253-59.

ON NAIL-MAKING BY MACHINERY

Until the early part of the present century, the use of *wood* in the construction of dwelling-houses and other buildings was very general in America. This caused a great consumption of nails, which were mostly imported from England, for the high price of labour among iron-workers prevented domestic nail-making, unless a more summary method could be devised for making them than by the hammer and anvil, which was then the general practice. In this state of the trade many attempts had been made to substitute machinery for the hand-working, to supply the home market for nails.

The kind of nails without heads, called "brads," had long been made by cutting angular slips from the ends of hoop-iron plates, so that the new process to be discovered was that of forming the nail-heads by uniting the process of cutting the slips with one for pressing, in forming the heads of nails, and to effect these two operations by continuous movements from a driving-shaft. A machine was constructed for this purpose and patented in America by Mr. J. Odiorne about the year 1806. Shortly after, a patent was also obtained by Mr. Jacob Perkins for his nail-making machine, which differed widely in its construction from the former, and effected the like purpose by completing the nails in one course of rotative action. At the time of obtaining those two patents, it was held doubtful as to which of the parties had first succeeded in putting his machine into practical operation; and since the forms and principles of action were quite distinct, each of the machines was held to be so far a new invention as to render both patents good in law.

A third patent for a nail-making machine was obtained by a Mr. Reed; but as this machine consisted of a mere combination of those of Odiorne and Perkins, it could at most be considered as containing some improvements on the former inventions. I understood it was so decided shortly after by the tribunals in some legal contests between the respective patentees. In the year 1810 a company in Boston, having arranged with the patentees above mentioned, sent out to me in London models and specifications of each of the said nail-machines, with directions for patenting them in England, as "a communication from abroad," and for the joint account of the company and myself.

It will suffice here to explain the main features of the mechanism in each of the above-named inventions, as the details of them may be seen at the Patent Office. The processes are as follows:—

(1) In feeding the machine, plates of the proper width and thickness to form the nails are pushed endways over the fixed cutter, against a stop-gauge under the traversing cutter, and they are advanced at such an angle with the line of the cutters as to give to the severed pieces the proper taper to form the point and head ends of the nails, and the plates are turned over after each cut, to reverse the angle at the end for the next nail. The plate-iron is first rolled into sheets, some thirty inches wide, and then sheared transversely into slips to form the nails. By this means the fibres of the iron are lengthwise with the nails, which renders them flexible.

(2) To cut off the slips to form the nails (the width of the plate being the length of the nails), fixed and moving

cutters are used, the one placed on a solid bed, the other passing up and down their edges in contact, in the common way of shearing iron.

(3) One of the "gripping" or holding dies is placed just under the fixed cutter, the face of it and the cutter lying in the same plane, and the counter die moves forward to bring the grooves in both together, so as to hold the nails firmly, allowing a portion of the large ends to stand out beyond the dies, to form the heads of the nails.

(4) The slips when severed are pressed down by the cutter, and a sliding piece advances (under the face of the cutter) to hold the nail against the face and prevent its falling, until it reaches the groove in the gripping dies.

(5) The heading die then advances (the cutter having risen out of the way) and presses the projecting end of the nail into such kind of heads as are sunk in the end of the heading-die, say into the "rose," "clasp," or "clout" heads of the trade.

It often happens that success or failure, with power-driven machines, turns upon slight points in their construction; and this appeared to apply to the patent nail-machines when they were first brought into use in this country. The making of cut nails was not a new manufacture at that time: the method in practice was to cut and head the nails by two separate processes, the passing from one to the other, being done by hand; and this labour was saved by uniting the cutting and heading in one course of operations by the patent machines.

The practical advantages obtained by these machines were found to be nearly inversely as the size of the nails made by them; hence the motive for using them chiefly to make the smaller sort

of nails required in the market; but here an unlooked for obstacle arose—the new machine never having been used for, or adapted to, the making of any nails of less than about one inch in length, so that they could not be employed for making tacks, or very small nails, although this branch of the trade offered the greater chance of saving by self-acting machinery. It thus became an object of importance to make such changes in the patent machines as would fit them for making the tacks and small nails as well as the larger ones.

To ascertain whether this could be effected, I began by tracing the successive movements to find where the defective action took place, and *its cause.* After the nails were cut, they were carried down to the heading-dies below the cutter so that the head ends would stand out from the gripping dies when the cutter rose out of the way of the heading die; but before the gripping dies closed upon the nail, a small presser advanced to hold the nail near the point, and prevent its falling out of the line of the dies; but in the case of tacks or small nails, the greater weight of the other end caused it to fall and spoil the work. It therefore became necessary to have the nail held at the head end, in lieu of the point, when thus brought between the gripping dies, and for removing the holder out of the way to admit the advance of the heading die. To effect this purpose I made the bed-cutter in two pieces to act together in one line for cutting, and the portion cutting the head end, after serving to support the nail as above, to slide back out of the way of the heading, and by this simple contrivance, of dividing the bed-cutter into two parts, one fixed, the other moveable, the machine was quite as well adapted for making tacks and minute nails as it was before for making large ones; and this simple change rendered the patent nail-making a complete success; and by far the larger profits accruing from their use came from the machines to which this slight change was applied.

The course of movements of the several machines and their rate of working were exhibited by means of wooden models, constructed and adapted to make the nails and tacks from *lead plates*, merely by turning a winch. These working models were shown and explained to many of the large manufacturers from the districts where the nail-making was mostly carried on.

The average rate of working was about 100 per minute for nails, and 120 per minute for tacks. In after practice the tack-machines were found to average about 80,000 tacks per day of 10 working hours, whilst the best hand workers could only produce from 1200 to 1400 per day. Each machine being tended by one youth (similar to those employed in hand making), it followed that one hand with the machine turned out as many tacks per day as would require over 60 working on the old plan with the hammer and anvil; wherefore this labour-saving machine, of 60 for 1, was sure to supersede the hand makers in all kinds of tacks, except the few sorts required for special purposes; and the average cost of the nails was also so far reduced as to ensure a very extensive demand for them; but the Dudley and other nail-makers could not be induced to change their system of working by adopting the patent machines.

Shortly after, I succeeded in forming a company in London for establishing a patent nail manufactory on a large scale, to which company I transferred the patents, and undertook to superintend the building and starting of the machines for a period of six months; after which the concern was left wholly in charge of the company, the principal party in which was then an eminent London banker, who supplied the capital, and, as head of the concern, selected the parties to be charged with the management of the business. Besides a small sum received in money, I was to receive in compensation for the patent rights a certain share of the profits to arise from their exercise; but, from the lack of mechanical knowledge and business talents that appeared in the management, as also from some differences about the capital in the concern, I was induced to consent to an outright sale to the Company of my contingent share of its profits at a price which did not exceed what my share ought to have produced *per annum*, if the affairs had been conducted with judgment and prudence. I refrain from naming any of the parties, and have merely stated the above facts in justice to myself and to my friends in America before mentioned.

The principal movements in the nail-machine were given by the crank, lever, and wedge actions in common use, and therefore require no special notice; but in that invented by Mr. Perkins the heading dies were worked by what he called a "Toggle-joint," this being the finger-joint. It was suggested to him by observing the process of laying down floor-boards by carpenters:—that of nailing down two boards at some distance apart and placing several loose boards between them; then, bringing the edges of the latter together, they are pressed down between the fixed boards with *a force* that pinches them into the smallest practicable space without crushing the wood. This joint acts upon the principle of the wedge, with two circular faces meeting at the tangent to the circle, and thus acting like a pair of rollers, to pinch or press any body brought between them with a force limited only by the rigidity of the meeting faces. Now this force was found very efficient in pressing the ends of large nails into the several forms of heads required, and is here referred to because it has been since adopted and found very efficient in riveting-machines for making steam-boilers, bridge-gird-ers, and in some others of recent invention.

The new system of nail-making, originating as above stated, has been so widely extended as to give profitable employment to many thousands of workmen, and to supply an important article of very extensive use, both for home consumption and for exportation; wherefore it seemed proper briefly to record the names of the parties from whose joint labours have sprung this important and successful branch of manufacturing industry and trade.

2. America at the Crystal Palace, 1851

BENJAMIN P. JOHNSON, *Great Exhibition of the Industry of All Nations*

By the mid-nineteenth century, Great Britain, already acknowledged as the birthplace of the Industrial Revolution, had firmly established herself as what Victorians liked to call the Workshop of the World. In 1851, at the suggestion of Prince Albert, England invited all the civilized nations of the world to bring examples of their manufactures to London and show them in a Great Exhibition of the Works of Industry of All Nations. A huge hall, popularly known as the Crystal Palace, was constructed for the exhibits. Before it closed some six million people came to view that mechanical progress which characterized the age.

The exhibition revealed to many Englishmen for the first time the extent and quality of American technological progress. Such exhibits as that of small arms made from interchangeable parts, and especially that of the McCormick reaper, made a lasting impression on the British. These exhibits foreshadowed the eventual eclipse of British leadership in the mechanic arts. The following report communicates the sense of pride the Americans took in their role as technological innovators.

From Benjamin P. Johnson, *Great Exhibition of the Industry of All Nations, 1851. Report of Benj. P. Johnson, Agent of the State of New-York, Appointed to Attend the Exhibition of the Industry of All Nations, Held in London, 1851* (Albany, 1852), pp. 13-16, 93-95, 161-62.

It should be borne in mind that the exhibitors from this country were placed in a very different position from any other foreign country. The exhibition from the United States was made by the exhibitors themselves, *without aid or assistance,* in their preparation, from the government, and although many have complained of this want of apparent interest on the part of the government in the objects of the exhibition, it is not by any means certain but that the influence of our exhibition has been far better upon the world, has more powerfully demonstrated the peculiar advantages of our free institutions, in the development of the energies of the people, than could have been done if the government had made a large appropriation for the purpose of preparing articles specially for the exhibition. Our exhibition was made by our citizens themselves, and showed their enterprize, their energy, their skill and ingenuity; and when this was known, it was a matter of surprise to foreigners that we exhibited as much as we did. The character of our articles were such as to show to the world that we worked for the great masses, not for the luxurious and privileged few.

In articles of utility and comfort, and for the advantage of the middling classes, who are the great producers of the world, as distinguished from the nobility and gentry, there was a very marked difference between the exhibition of our citizens and all the other countries. An English writer, in speaking of the difference between their contributions and those of continental nations, says: "In those productions that imply what would here be considered, and truly so, a waste of labor, the utility of the article bearing no proportion whatever to the time spent upon it, and

which only shows the degradation of the countries in which they are produced, as indicating at once the almost senseless luxuriousness of the rich, who must be the purchasers, and the starvation wages which the citizens must be brought to before such articles could be produced at all; in these productions we are unquestionably surpassed."

These remarks apply with much more justice to the exhibition from this country, as compared with the continental and eastern exhibitors, and with a very considerable portion of the English exhibition also. There was nothing from this country to compete with those splendid articles, designed only to minister to human pride, which composed so large a portion of the exhibition; as an American I rejoiced that this was so; and it will be, in my opinion, a sad day for our country when articles of this character shall attain a *preëminence* here, over the useful and necessary, as they do in the Old World. The condition of the laboring classes who perform the work is far different from that of our own population, and I trust the day may never arrive when we shall substitute for the intelligent, free and virtuous population of our country, the ignorant, vicious and degraded operatives of the countries across the Atlantic.

Our exhibition was designed to show, as it did, that in this country "genius, industry and energy find no barriers to their career." The number of inventions exhibited which were calculated to reduce the cost of production in agriculture, manufactures and the mechanic arts, was in the highest degree creditable to us, and elicited from distinguished sources in Great Britain the admission that to "the department of American 'notions'" they owed "the most important contributions to their industrial system," and after the exhibition was closed, and its advantages to the English nation were being summed up, the following admission, in regard to our contribution, was made in their leading journal: "Great Britain has received more useful ideas, and more ingenious inventions from the United States, through the exhibition, than from all other sources."

What higher tribute could be paid to the character of our articles, as claimed by those who knew and appreciated their value, than this—especially from the admission, that "more useful ideas" were received through us than from all other sources. Thus showing what every unprejudiced mind must, we think, admit—the great advantages which our free and liberal institutions afford for the development of the powers of the human mind.

In the early part of the Exhibition, the U.S. Department was the subject of much invidious remark, and our contributions were considered as far behind the times. Located in the buildings as we were, adjacent to France, Russia and Austria, there was indeed a striking difference in the appearance of the contributions from the different countries. While that from the United States was mainly of a character of utility in the Implement and Machinery department, and of the productions of the soil, the others consisted of the most costly articles, wrought with exquisite taste, silks, statuary, diamonds, jewelry, &c., which attracted the eye and called forth the warmest encomiums. During the first three weeks, while the admissions comprised only the wealthy classes, the United States Department was hastily passed over—a glance given, an inquiry made at the implements, a remark occasionally,

"These may do for a new country, but would not answer in England—unless *our* mechanics have the altering of them, &c.," was the principal notice which was given them. In answer to these remarks upon our implements— the reply was frequently given that no "*English mechanic*" would have the privilege of practising upon our implements, until they were tried, and we had the opportunity of showing what our implements could perform. It was not a very pleasant position, to be met with remarks similar to these, day after day for several weeks. As the jurors, however, began to make their examinations, and as exhibitors and others interested in the articles on exhibition were called upon to explain to intelligent and practical men, what were the properties claimed for our articles, more interest was manifested in our department. . . .

TRIAL OF THE REAPERS AT TIP-TREE HALL.—Succeeding the trial of the plows came that of the Reapers, on the 24th of July. There were three machines on exhibition. McCormick's Virginia Reaper, Hussey's American Reaper, and an English Reaper, made after Hussey's, but which, I believe, had not been tried. The place selected for trial was at Tip-tree Hall, Kelvedon, Essex, the farm of Mr. J. J. Mechi, about forty-five miles from town. The day selected was the annual gathering of gentlemen at the farm of Mr. Mechi to inspect his crops and method of farming, which is exciting much interest in England. The day proved a very unfavorable one, as it rained during the whole day. The wheat upon which the trial was to be made was quite green and remarkably heavy, and everything as unfavorable as could well be. There were from 150 to 200 gentlemen present, many of whom had come upwards of 300 miles to witness the trial.

The Sub-jury assigned to conduct the trial was composed of Colonel Challoner, one of the English Jurors, Baron Merten d'Ostins, of Belgium, and B. P. Johnson, United States, and W. Fisher Hobbs, Esq., though not a member of the Jury, was present by invitation, at the trial. The first machine tried was Hussey's, which did not succeed, as it clogged very soon, and passed over the grain without cutting it. After this had been tried two or three times and failed, it was proposed by one of the Jurors that no further trial be made by the Reapers—but it was insisted that the other American Reaper should be tried. The gentlemen present expected it, and I was not willing they should leave the ground without satisfying those present that the American Reapers would perform the work which it had been affirmed they could do. Mr. McCormick's Reaper was then brought up, managed by D. C. McKenzie, of Livingston county, in this State, who is entitled to no little credit for the successful result of the trial. This was a moment, as may well be imagined, of no ordinary interest. One reaper had not operated as was expected—another, and the only remaining American reaper to be tried, was now to be tested. The gentlemen present were anxious that something should succeed that would cheapen the gathering of their crops—but from expressions made around me, I was satisfied they had no confidence in the reaper. They said, after the first trial, "It is as we expected—they will not work until *perfected* by an English mechanic." The laboring men, too, when the first one was started, seemed perfectly astonished, fearing their vocation was gone—but when it failed to work, they brightened up and would doubtless have given vent to their feelings, if another one had not been found ready for the trial, and might succeed. It can well be imagined that the Americans, of whom only three were present, beside myself, were in quite as great a state of excitement as the others. The machine was started. After it had passed its length, the *clean path* made by the reaper—the grain falling from its side, showed that the work was done, and the reaper was successful. After proceeding as far as was deemed necessary, the team was stopped, and Mr. Mechi jumped upon the platform and said, "Gentlemen, here is a triumph for the American Reaping Machine. It has, under all its disadvantages, done its work completely. Now let us, as Englishmen, show them that we appreciate this contribution for cheapening our agriculture, and let us give the Americans three hearty English cheers." They were given, and with a fourth added, satisfying all that they were heartily given. Another trial was then had, and the reaper timed—cutting, in 70 seconds, 74 yards in length, entirely clean, and to the satisfaction of the Jurors and the gentlemen present. The Jurors recommended the award of a Medal to Mr. McCormick.

The result of this trial gave a new turn to affairs, and on the return of the Reapers to the Palace, crowds were continually examining them, and the American department from this time to the closing of the exhibition, was no longer the "Prairie ground," but was thronged with inquiring visitors. The London Times, whose Agricultural reporter was present, gave a very full account of this successful trial; and in an article published soon after the trial, it was said, "That every practical success of the season belonged to the Americans, their consignments showed poorly at first, *but came out well upon trial."* And again, "it will be remembered that the American department was the poorest and least interesting of all foreign countries. Of late, it has justly assumed a position of the first importance, as having brought to the aid of our *distressed agriculturists,* a machine, which if it realizes the anticipations of competent judges, will *amply remunerate* England for all her outlay connected with the Great exhibition. The reaping machine from the United States is the *most valuable contribution* from abroad, to the stock of our previous knowledge, that we have yet discovered."

Previous to the trial of the reaper, the same observations as to the value of the reaper if successful, were made to me by several distinguished agriculturists of Great Britain. An attempt has been made since the close of the Exhibition, to show that the reaping machine is an English invention, and that those from this country are mere imitations of theirs. It requires no great sagacity however to perceive, that so far as grain reapers were a *practical reality,* they were unknown in Great Britain, until the successful trial of those from this country. For surely the London Times, ever posted up on every thing that pertains to the advance of England, would not have hazarded the assertion, "that the American Reaper will amply remunerate England for all her outlay connected with the exhibition"; if, England had anything like a *living, working reaper,* known among her distressed agriculturists. The truth is, that until the American reapers were exhibited with their improvements, reaping by machinery was not even spoken of among the agriculturists of

Great Britain, so far as I had an opportunity of ascertaining. The unbelief in the success of the reapers must satisfy every one, that there was no expectation in England of a reaper to do their work unless ours succeeded. If England had a practical working reaper in use, one would have supposed that it would have been on exhibition at the Palace, and that Garret, one of the most celebrated implement makers in England, would have exhibited an English grain reaper, instead of one copied from Hussey's American reaper, and which he is now manufacturing and vending as the American Reaper. . . .

I am fully sensible that, as a country, we have much to learn in every direction, and this has been, to my mind, most clearly shown in the Exhibition; and I shall be greatly mistaken in my countrymen if they do not largely profit by the lessons which this great Exhibition has taught them. Not an intelligent American who visited the Exhibition, and examined its contributions with care and attention, but must have been led to the conclusion, that in it there was much every way calculated, if rightly improved, to benefit his country—to enlarge not only our views as to the capabilities of other countries, but to satisfy us of our deficiencies and to encourage us to direct our energies to still higher attainments in every branch of domestic industry; that we may, as a nation, not only be independent, in a great degree at least, of other countries, so far as the leading articles necessary for our own comfort are concerned, but also be enabled to supply others with a great variety of articles which heretofore we have never done.

It appears to me from all that has been developed by the Exhibition, so far as the character of our country is concerned and its resources have been shown, the result of this meeting together of the nations of the world in friendly rivalry, will not prove unfavorable; and if we but improve, as we may and as I trust we shall, from the lessons here given, we shall be prepared when another convocation shall be held, after a few years shall have elapsed and time has been given to develope the fruits of this, to show to the world that we have not been inattentive to these lessons. We should, however bear in mind that the same influences which operate upon us will more or less affect others, and that no ordinary attainments will enable us fully to compete with those who are now far advanced in many departments and who may be expected to redouble their efforts to retain a position which they have long maintained.

The Exhibition most clearly showed, that science and art have done much for the advance which has been made in every branch of manufacture, and I think it may with safety be affirmed that whenever science or art was put in requisition, there progress was shown superior to others. This lesson I trust will not be lost upon this country, but that it will be so improved as to lead to renewed efforts, to a more complete and thorough education in every branch of arts and manufactures, that we may not only keep pace with the world's progress, but make such advances as will secure to us a pre-eminence.

3. Cotton Mills for the South, 1850

DeBow's Southern and Western Review

The export of Yankee ingenuity and mechanical know-how was not limited to Europe or the British Isles. Within the borders of the United States itself, the South represented a vast area of technological underdevelopment. For a wide variety of reasons, social, political, economic, and ideological, the South failed to develop a strong mechanical tradition in the years before the Civil War. Indeed, the fact that it remained tributary to Northern technology was itself one of the major causes of that bloody war. By 1838 the sugar plantations of Louisiana had more steam engines at work than did any other state in the Union except Pennsylvania—yet both the engines themselves and the men who operated and repaired them more often than not came from the North.

From "Charles T. James, of Rhode Island," *DeBow's Southern and Western Review,* IX (December 1850), 671-75.

In agriculture, transportation, and as time went on, in manufacturing, this technological imperialism of the North became a political issue. Its perpetuation was sought by those whom it favored and was condemned by the increasingly restive Southern nationalists. One remarkable Northern technologist who had a wide experience in the Southern market was Charles T. James, a consulting and manufacturing engineer from New England. The following sketch of his activities appeared in a militantly pro-Southern journal.

Charles Tillinghast James is now about forty-five years of age. He was born in the town of West Greenwich, in the state of Rhode Island. His father was a respectable farmer. Rather inclined to mechanics than to literary studies, he approached the years of manhood with but the rudiments of an English education; and is, emphatically, a self-educated and self-made man. Many persons consider him merely as a sound theoretical man, or at best, a practical manufacturer. This is a mistake. At the age of nineteen, he turned his attention to mechanics, with the determination to qualify himself for the prosecution of his undertaking by the study of books. But soon becoming satisfied that he could obtain but little practical aid from them, he laid them aside, and determined to prepare himself by practice. He accordingly commenced as a practical working mechanic; and, step by step, proceeded through all the departments of the machine shop connected with the manufacture of cotton. By this method, Mr. James qualified himself not only to operate, but to build, with his own hands, any and every machine used in the cotton mill. Thus, and by the aid of the mathematical and mechanical sciences, for which he has an unusual aptness, and to which he has paid unremitting attention, he has been able to place himself at the head of his profession. Such was the position to

which he had attained as early as the year 1836, or thereabouts, that he was presented with the honorary diploma of Master of Arts, from the Faculty of Brown University, in his native state.

Mr. James' style of work is peculiar to himself. With him it is original, and grows out of his practical knowledge of the business. He acknowledges no leader, and copies no model; and his mills are different in their general arrangement, and in many of their details, from any others in the United States. A scientific adaptation of every machine to every other machine, causing the whole to work in unison, without excess or deficiency in any one, produces complete harmony, and a perfect effect. This is the true secret why his mills do more and better work than others, at smaller cost. That they do better work is evident from the fact, that cloths made in them bear the highest value in the market, and have, in every case in which they have been exhibited at public fairs, in New-York, Philadelphia, and Boston, the latter city being the very focus of New England manufactures, borne off the palm; and a large number of medals has been awarded them, against all competition. That these cloths are made at smaller cost, published extracts from the books of the mills determine.

Mr. James, when his present contracts shall have been completed, will have put in operation a number of spindles considerably exceeding 300,-000, being more than one-eighth of the entire number in the United States. In such extensive practical operations, with a mind ever on the alert to remedy all deficiency, and to bring forward and adopt all improvements, as opportunity may occur,—the knowledge thus obtained must confer on him great advantages in the practice of his profession. On the other hand, he has been careful to keep himself, as far as practicable, thoroughly advised of the progress of the manufacturing business in Europe, and of the improvements made there; and to adopt such as were found to be of much practical utility. The course he has pursued has wrought, and is working, a great revolution in the manufacturing business, as respects motive power. A few persons in this country had, before he made the attempt, so far disregarded public opinion, as to undertake the manufacture of cotton by means of steam power. Most of these attempts proved abortive; and the supposition seemed to have been converted to a certainty, that cotton, to be manufactured at a profit in this country, must be taken to the waterfall. In the face of this almost universal conclusion, accompanied with the sneers and ridicule of some, and predictions of certain failure by others, Mr. James confidently became the advocate of steam power, and adopted it with complete success. Since that period he has erected and put in operation a considerable number of mills, which are driven by steam power; and which, by their doings, have fully substantiated his statements, that, for the reason that steam power may be had wherever wanted, as well as from its superiority in the manufacture of cotton, it is more

beneficial to the manufacturer than water power, because it can be brought into connection with many local advantages which are unavailable to water power. The manufacture of cotton by steam is no longer an experiment in favorable locations. The business, by its means, is being extended to many sections in which it could not otherwise have been established, greatly to the benefit of such communities. All others in the United States combined, have not done as much as Mr. James, to bring about this result.

The engines used by Mr. James, as well as his mills, are originated by himself. Notwithstanding the great amount of business done by him—having generally in hand three, four, or five mills, in various parts of the country—every engine and boiler, all the shafting and machinery, together with the buildings, foundations, and every thing else connected with the mills, are designed and drawn in his office, either by himself, or under his immediate direction. Of all these, duplicates are furnished to the workmen in the several departments, and the originals kept on file. To his acquaintance with machinery as a practical mechanic, his knowledge of the mathematical and mechanical sciences, the business of designing and planning, and carrying out his multifarious operations,—his long experience as a manufacturer,—with the ability, and the abundant means at hand, to compare results with regard to the working of the numerous mills constructed by him, the superiority of these mills is to be attributed. With such a mind as we have attempted to describe, he has devoted about twenty-six years of his life to close and unremitted application to business; and it is by no means strange that, under such circumstances, he should have reached a pre-eminent standing.

His mills are, as a general thing, equalled by no others in America. Among them we notice particularly, because it is his largest, the Naumkeag Steam Cotton Mill, at Salem, Mass. This mill has now about 33,000 spindles. It is a noble establishment, and is considered, even by foreign engineers who have viewed it, as one of the greatest specimens of mechanical engineering of the age, if not the greatest. Certainly there is nothing in the United States to compare with it, and to persons curious in such matters, a visit to it is worthy of a journey of a day or two.

Another very important fact should be here stated. In all the mills constructed by Mr. James, there is no one which has been left to his general management that has not, as far as management and the mill were concerned, proved successful. It is this fact, after all, which has conferred on him his reputation as a mill builder, and caused him to become known throughout the Union. It is this that has thrown into his hands a larger amount of business in the line of his profession than was ever done by any other man in this country.

The subject of our sketch has raised up to himself many opponents in New England, by a work published by him some time since, on the "Culture and Manufacture of Cotton at the South." That work, which in a great degree identified its author with Southern interests, was well calculated to produce the effect already partially realized, to open the eyes of the Southern people to the true state of the case, and to induce them to engage in the manufacture of their own staple, in competition with the manufacturers of the North; an enterprise which will, at no very distant period, add millions to Southern capital, and effect, in the cotton growing states, a great and salutary change. Some persons at the North were alarmed at the *expose* made in the work alluded to; and a reply was attempted, to impeach its veracity. But the rejoinder of Mr. James completely prostrated his reviewer, and silenced all cavil, besides substantiating the statements in his former work by numerous additional proofs, which no one yet has had the hardihood to question. He passed through the controversy unscathed; and, in his writings, has conferred a gift on the people of the South, which, if duly appreciated, and rightly applied, will prove to them of incalculable value.

Mr. James is a resident of the city of Providence, in his native state, in prosperous circumstances; having accumulated a handsome fortune by means of his mechanical ability and close application to business. He expressed the wish, long since, to relinquish the business of constructing cotton mills, and relieve himself from the great amount of labor, physical and mental, which the business imposes on him. But numerous and pressing applications, and the desire to benefit a class of people among the laboring population who stand in need of aid, under circumstances beyond their control, still keep him in the field.

NOTE.—This pamphlet of Mr. James's we have published in parts in our Review, during the past year, or at least the greater portion of it, and believe that it has effected much good. Mr. James, ten years ago, first opened our eyes to the importance of steam power in manufactories, in an article in the Charleston Mercury, and he has since taken a prominent part in promoting the manufactures of that city, being, as we learn, a stockholder to a large amount in the new mill now in construction there. He has also an interest in the great cotton movements at Cannelton, Indiana, under our friend Hamilton Smith.

For the reader's instruction we copy the following passages from Mr. James's reply to the attacks of Mr. Lawrence:

MR. LAWRENCE'S DISINTERESTEDNESS

Perhaps Mr. Lawrence wished to persuade the cotton planter *to promote the planter's interest,* no doubt—not to hazard his capital in the manufacturing business, with its small and diminishing profits, while the profits of cotton planting were large, and scarcely lessened at all in fifteen years; or, perhaps, as we subsequently have a few pretty plain hints, to embark his capital at the North, to aid in the upbuilding of northern manufacturing cities, in progress or in embryo, or to arrest the fall of certain mills, by purchasing their stocks, already 40 per cent. below par. Such may have been the case. Let others judge. It may be otherwise; but his frequent croakings about the hazards, the disasters, the failures, and, at best, the small profits of the manufacturing business, seem mightily like a sort of squinting toward the object of restraining the southern people from entering into competition with those of the North; or, that failing, to persuade them to embark their funds on board the new northern ship LAWRENCE, or some other craft, belonging in whole or in part to the same firm. Thus, with honeyed words, and abundant fraternal sympathy, he exhorts *"our friends"* at the South, in effect, either not to enter the manufacturing field at all, or, if they should, to invest their funds in northern mills. The substance is, they must pay freight and expenses on their own cotton to Lowell, and on their cloth back again; and leave at the North all the wealth created by labor, with the use of that capital, to build up northern towns and cities, equalling, once in two years at least, the amount of capital invested, with the exception of 8 9-10 per cent. per annum on its amount, in the way of dividends! How kind! how considerate!

STRUGGLES OF FACTORIES, NORTH AND SOUTH

On looking back to the commencement of the cotton manufacturing business in New-England, and tracing its progress up to the present period, we shall find that our manufacturers have had difficulties to contend with, which the people of the South will not have to overcome. The business, at that period, was in its infancy, even in England. The machinery introduced here was very imperfect in form, finish, and operation. From that time to this, there has been kept up a continual race of improvement, which has rendered the expenditure of vast sums of money necessary to those who have kept up with the times; while those who have refused to do so, have either broken themselves down by a spurious economy, or, at best, plodded on with little profit. The southern people will enter the field with all these improvements ready made to their hands; and, what is also of vast importance to them, the new and improved machinery can, at this day, be had at smaller cost than could have been that of former days, even but a few years since. Take, also, into account, the advantage of more than 20 per cent. on an average, which the manufacturers of the South will have over those of the North, in the cost of cotton at Lowell, and no good reason can be assigned why the former should not find the business more profitable than the latter. The difference in cost of cotton alone will pay more than 6 per cent. per annum on the capital employed, even if that difference were but one cent per pound. If the southern people cannot, under such circumstances, manufacture their cotton at a very handsome profit, certainly no other people can live by the business. We will now pay some attention to Mr. Lawrence's remarks on the comparative cost of steam and waterpower.

CAUSE OF SOUTHERN FACTORIES

For years, the northern press has been loud and frequent in recommendations to the South, to enter the field of enterprise, and manufacture her own staple; and, by way of encouragement, the success of New-England in the same branch of business, with the enhanced cost of the raw material, has been held out as an example. No fault, to my knowledge, has ever been found with that course. During the time, however, the manufacturers have uttered no note of encouragement, keeping a continual studied silence, when their business was prosperous, and only opening their lips to give utterance to doleful complaints, if occasionally a reverse occurred. Though myself a New-England man, I am also an *American,* and claim brotherhood with the American people, as a whole. It gives me pleasure to witness the prosperity of New-England; but, as an American citizen, it gives me equal pleasure to witness the prosperity of the whole country. Hence, in what-

ever has been written by me on the subject of manufactures at the South, my object has been to promote the interest of that section of our common country, without the most remote wish to injure that of any other. Business has never been sought by me there, nor ever will be. The pamphlet was written by the special request of southern men, and the abridgment was made also by request. The southern people wished for information on the subject of cotton manufactures, in order to know whether it was, or was not, prudent for them to engage in the business. They applied to me to impart that information. The call was, after a time, responded to by me, and, as in duty bound, I gave them facts in an honest and truthful manner—facts that I have fully substantiated—and to establish which, on the basis of future operations, also, I hold myself pledged and bound to do. I have not only the *ability,* but the *means* to do it. Fully aware of the reluctance of northern manufacturers to have the details and results of their operations exposed, and wishing neither to excite their animosity, to alarm their cupidity, nor to injure their interests, I carefully abstained from all interference with their concerns, and merely stated the general results of the business in New-England, and what could be done, and what had been done, with a steam-mill of my own construction. And what has been the result? I have been attacked from all quarters, and in all forms—and why? Evidently because my statements were calculated to give encouragement to manufactures at the South, and to bring them into competition with those of the North. What other motives could have animated those who have assailed me? I pretended not, though I could have done

BOSTON MACHINISTS IN CUBA, 1855

it, to penetrate the veil hung over the doings of northern manufacturers. My effort was to show the southern people what *they might do*—not by reference to the doings of a number of pretended "first class mills," but to others of my own building. Mr. Lawrence, and others, apparently alarmed at this, and fearing the result, entered the arena, and, by insinuations, inuendos, and broad statements, have endeavored to fix the falsehood upon me; not because I had misrepresented northern mills, or their products or profits, but because, as they would have it to be understood, I had made exaggerated statements relative to mills erected by me. And how have they succeeded? There is scarcely a statement made by them that has not been proved fallacious—not a statement of mine that has not been substantiated.

Mr. Lawrence has driven me, in self-defence, to bring out facts, relative to which, if let alone, I should have been silent. If they have a heavy and injurious bearing on the northern manufacturing interest, those connected with it may thank their champion. I flatter myself that no one can tell me much that I do not know about the cotton manufacture in New-England, or the cost, condition, product, and profit and loss of a great number of New-England cotton mills, and among them, most of the twenty-six "first-class mills." Thus far, they have just been touched on by me, and there it is my wish to leave them; yet much remains behind, that some would rather should be permitted to rest undisturbed. So shall it rest, unless farther provocation shall call it out.

4. Boston Machinists in Cuba, 1855

Scientific American

Latin America, and especially the islands of the Caribbean, had an agricultural economy specializing in staple crops, owned by wealthy white families but tended by black men—much like the economy of the southern United States. Efforts to extend political control over the Caribbean islands in the wake of the Monroe Doctrine were not successful until late in the century, but Yankee technological domination of the area, as of the South, began almost as soon as the agricultural process had been mechanized. This country's "special interest" in the area was based as much on technological as upon ideological or political ties. In 1855 the following news item was picked up and reprinted by the *Scientific American.*

From *Scientific American*, XI (October 13, 1855), 38.

MACHINISTS IN CUBA

During the sugar cane season in Cuba, say from November to April, there are usually employed on the various plantations about twelve hundred machinists as engineers and repairers. Few of these machinists are Cubans, and few of them remain the whole year on the island. A large number are Scotchmen, a few English, while the United States furnish a large share. These machinists repair to the island during the month of October, and secure situations usually at most excellent wages, and then remain until May, when they leave the island and spend the warmest weather in a more healthy climate. Not a few have families who remain in the United States. For years the demand for machinists in our own country has been so great, and the prices paid for labor so good, that the higher rates paid in Cuba have not been sufficient to entice very many to so warm and unhealthy a climate. There are some twenty or thirty residing in South Boston, however, who have every year for several years visited Cuba, and spent the working season.

5. The New Imperialism, 1898

Scientific American

In 1898, the United States became an overseas imperial power. After nearly three centuries of expansion to the north, south, and west, the American empire jumped to the islands of the Caribbean and Pacific. In terms of technology, little had changed. The major problems were still those of resource exploitation and its ancillary, improved transportation. Whether they were opening new mines, extending railroad networks, building urban sewage systems, or constructing naval coaling stations, American engineers and entrepreneurs, who previously had to work under foreign sponsorship, were now able to take a free hand in the technological transformation of these "backward" societies. An honest and straightforward perspective was provided by an editorial in the *Scientific American*.

From *Scientific American*, LXXIX (September 24, 1898), 194.

OUR NEW POSSESSIONS AS A FIELD FOR ENGINEERS

We have been asked to state our opinion as to the possibilities of our newly acquired possessions as a field of employment for engineers, both civil and mechanical. There is in our midst a large and rapidly increasing body of young men, graduates from technical schools and colleges, with more or less practical experience in the shop or in the field, who think they see in Cuba, Porto Rico, the Hawaiian Islands, and the Philippines an immediate field of employment of a more remunerative kind, and with opportunities for more rapid promotion, than are possible at home. The expectation is based upon the conviction that our possession or control of these islands will be followed by an immediate and extensive development of their natural resources, in the course of which the services of the civil and mechanical engineer will be in active demand.

The enterprise and ambition which are likely to send many professional men to these new fields are highly commendable; but we fear that those who hasten there at once are doomed to much disappointment. While the next decade is certain to see a wonderful change in much of our newly acquired territory, the development will occur in the latter rather than in the former half of it. We must remember that the Spanish possessions, at least, have been under the control of one of the most conservative races in the world, and that the people of the islands are wedded to old ideas, to customs and habits that crystallized far back in medieval times. Before a period of building up there will have to be a period of pulling down and clearing away, and the process, at least in the earlier stages, will necessarily be slow.

In the reforming and development of the islands the two extremes of modern civilization will meet, for two types of character and temperament more opposite than the Spanish and American it would be difficult to find. The one is conservative, romantic, and wedded to tradition, the other is elastic, practical, and supremely utilitarian; and while it is true that the inhabitants of these islands are not of pure Spanish blood, centuries of Spanish rule and customs have stamped their impress deeply upon the native islanders. For these reasons it is unreasonable to expect that the invasion of these possessions by the railroad, the electric light, the telephone, and the trolley will be as rapid as it was in our Western States, where there was an American population to welcome and assist these prime movers of an up-to-date civilization.

At the same time it must be borne in mind that the operations of the engineer, especially in the civil branches of the profession, presuppose the employment of capital on a vast scale; and capital is always shy of investment in countries where the government is in a disturbed condition. Before any large sums are invested in the construction of railways and highways, in the improvement or provision of water supply, and the general sanitation and reconstruction of cities, the government of the islands must be placed on a satisfactory basis and prove itself to be in a thoroughly stable condition.

When this has been accomplished and the people have adjusted themselves to the new conditions and begun to realize the increased value of property and sanctity of personal rights which have come to them by virtue of the change of government, we may look for an era of material development such as the world has rarely witnessed. The location and construction of a railroad system in Cuba alone will call for the services of a very considerable force of engineers, and the rebuilding of sugar mills, the installing of electric light and power plants, the development of mines and other material resources of the island will present many excellent openings for young men in electrical and mechanical engineering.

For the present, however, we would advise those who are contemplating a trip to one or other of our possessions to stay at home and watch the course of events, meanwhile keeping in touch, as far as possible, with such companies as may be formed for the exploitation of the West Indian and South Pacific possessions.

PART V   THE RISE OF NEW INDUSTRIES

The promise that led Civil War leaders to look to science as a source of innovation animated some industrial leaders as well in the years after the war. Like the Revolutionary War, the Civil War tended to depress the indices of economic growth and divert for a time the nation's attention from industrial innovation and an awareness of British developments. After the war, however, the American economy continued its expansion—the new Bessemer steel industry and the engineering feat of constructing a transcontinental railroad nicely stimulated each other and carried the nation to new heights of development. At the same time a number of entirely new industries, based upon a knowledge of recent scientific discoveries, sprang up to create new fields for investment and profit.

One industry that was transformed during the last third of the century was iron. In 1855 and 1856, in England, Henry Bessemer (1813-98) patented his new method for producing iron. Calling the product "steel," manufacturers for the first time since the beginning of the Industrial Revolution were prepared to provide sufficient quantities of first-class iron to meet the growing demands for buildings, railroads, machines, and other types of construction. The iron industry has never been a leader in the application of scientific research, but the new Bessemer steelmaking process (and the open-hearth method introduced soon after) put a premium on trained engineers and analytical chemists.

Another ancient craft transformed during these years was that of the chemist. The colonists from the earliest times had manufactured simple chemical products—potash, salt, gunpowder, and so forth. During the nineteenth century, however, the study of chemistry in the universities, particularly in Germany, and the conscious efforts to apply the latest chemical knowledge to industrial processes, also in Germany, led to a complete reformation of the industry. Scores of America's best science students went to

Germany each year to study in the world's finest laboratories, and when they returned to this country they were prepared to apply their new knowledge.

One important industry was totally new and almost totally dependent upon science. In the 1870's and 1880's a group of men, the best known of whom was Thomas Edison (1847-1931), created an industry by discovering how best to produce, transport, and utilize a new product—electricity. Indeed, the parallel development of the science and the industry led inevitably to the disappearance of the talented but untrained "inventor" and the innovation of a new institution, the industrial research laboratory.

1. The Steel Age, 1876

ROBERT W. HUNT, "A History of the Bessemer Manufacture in America"

None of the new industries that sprang up in America in the post-Civil War period was more basic to the increased scale of industrialism than was the steel industry. Iron had been an important product in this country since the seventeenth century, but the industry had tended to lag behind its British rival in technological innovation. Then, on the eve of the American Civil War, Henry Bessemer developed his process of making cheap "steel" and one of the major bottlenecks of the Industrial Revolution was broken. The transfer of this new and vital technical process to American practice is a classic story of perseverance and adaptation. The author of this sketch was, at its writing, general superintendent of the Albany and Rensselaer Iron and Steel Co., at Troy, New York, and was himself a participant in many of the events he described.

In 1863 the Kelly Pneumatic Process Company was formed and an arrangement entered into with William Kelly, who had taken out letters-patent of the United States, Nos. 16,444; 17,628, reissued as 505; 18,910, dated January 10th, 1857; June 23d, 1857; November 3d, 1857; and December 22d, 1857, respectively. This association was composed of the Cambria Iron Company,

From Robert W. Hunt, "A History of the Bessemer Manufacture in America," *Transactions of the American Institute of Mining and Metallurgical Engineers,* V (1876-77), 201-16.

E. B. Ward, Park Brothers & Co., Lyon, Shorb & Co., Z. S. Durfee, and, later, Chouteau, Harrison & Valle joined the combination. Not satisfied with possessing the control of the Kelly patent, they sent Mr. Z. S. Durfee to England, to secure for this country Mushet's patent on recarburization, No. 17,389, dated May 26th, 1857, the same having been taken out in England on September 22d, 1856. In this Mr. Durfee was successful.

Previous to the application of William Kelly for a patent, Henry Bessemer, of England, had taken out patents dated February 12th, 1856, and August 25th, 1856, in this country. Kelly claimed priority in the discovery of the principles of the process, and the Patent-office allowed his claim by granting him his patents.

In the autumn of 1862 Mr. Alexander L. Holley, while in England, was impressed with the importance of Mr. Bessemer's invention, and so fully foresaw its future, that, upon his return to the United States, he induced Messrs. John A. Griswold and John F. Winslow, of Troy, New York, to join him in endeavoring to possess Bessemer's American patents. Mr. Holley returned to England in the summer of 1863, but not until the spring of 1864 did he succeed in purchasing for Messrs. Winslow, Griswold & Holley the desired rights.

Thus, at about the same time, there were two separate and distinct organizations seeking to control the future of the then undeveloped industry. While Mr. Durfee was abroad his company determined to erect experimental works at Wyandotte, Michigan (where one of its members, Captain E. B. Ward, owned extensive iron works), with the view of testing the adaptability of American irons to the new process. Mr. William F. Durfee undertook the erection of the plant, and located it in the casting-house of the Eureka Blast-furnace, intending to take the metal direct from the furnace. He put in a 2½-ton vessel with a long narrow casting-pit, and arranged a system of rotary steam-engines to hoist and pour the melted iron into the converter and to rotate the latter. As Mr. Durfee was instructed to avoid as far as possible Bessemer's mechanical patents, he was very much hampered in designing his plans. But it was in these works, in the fall of 1864, under the direction of Mr. William F. Durfee, that the first Pneumatic or Bessemer steel was made in America.

Mr. Z. S. Durfee brought with him, on his return from England, Mr. Lewellen M. Hart, who had acquired some experience in the business at the works of Messrs. Petin, Gaudet & Co., in France. Upon the arrival of Mr. Hart at Wyandotte, he decided to build a reverberatory furnace for the purpose of melting the charges of iron, so as to be able to use a mixture of English and American irons, and it was from metal melted in this furnace that all the steel made by him at Wyandotte was produced. The works remained under this gentleman's charge until the beginning of 1865, when he severed his connection and went to Troy, New York, entering the service of Messrs. Winslow, Griswold & Holley. He subsequently went to the Pennsylvania Steel Works, at Harrisburg, Pa., and afterwards left their employ to engage in other business in Philadelphia, where he died.

In March, 1865, Mr. Ignatius Hahn assumed charge of the Wyandotte works. This gentleman had lately arrived from Prussia, where he had been connected with the works of Krupp, at

Essen. He conducted the works until July 4th, 1865, when he resigned his position. As Mr. Hahn's retirement left the company without any practical steelmaker, and the works had thus far been conducted on an experimental basis, the proprietors determined upon making the most hazardous experiment of all, and put them in charge of the writer, who had gone there a few weeks before, in the interest of the Cambria Iron Company. In accordance with this arrangement the writer made his first "blow," and, by some strange fatality, happened to "turn down" at just the right time.

In the fall of 1865 the reverberatory furnace was torn down, and thereafter, during the continuance of the works, the iron was taken directly from the blast-furnace, excepting that which was sent to the works to be tried experimentally, and which was melted with anthracite coal in a McKensie cupola, this cupola having been put up by the writer during the summer of 1865. In October, 1865, the first heat of Bessemer steel made from Missouri Iron Mountain pig was blown by the writer, it having been melted in this cupola; the resulting steel was extremely satisfactory.

During Mr. Hahn's administration Mr. Z. S. Durfee made several attempts to convert iron melted in the small cupola of a foundry attached to the works, and located on the opposite side of the furnace casting-house. But owing to the cupola being so distant and so small, thus requiring the iron to remain so long in the accumulating ladle, and then to be run so far in an open runner into another ladle, and to be hoisted and poured into the converter, the iron containing also a low percentage of silicon, each trial was a failure. But I believe this was the first attempt to utilize the cupola as a melting furnace for the Bessemer process. At all events, it certainly was the first time it was tried in America, and of its ultimate success Mr. Durfee was fully convinced. Mr. Holley must have been impressed at about the same time with the same idea, for the records of the Troy works show that on July 20th, 1865, the cupola was there used for the first time, and with complete success.

The writer remained in charge of these works until May 14th, 1866, when he turned them over to Mr. A. S. Aubrey and returned to the Cambria works, that company then intending to at once erect Bessemer works. During the year 1865 Captain Ward bought the works from the Kelly Process Company, and they were thereafter conducted entirely in his interest, and, after many alterations, finally abandoned in 1869.

Upon Mr. A. L. Holley's return from England, in the spring of 1864, he at once commenced the erection of a 2½-ton experimental plant at Troy, New York, for the firm of Winslow, Griswold & Holley, and started it February 16th, 1865. While at the Wyandotte works steel was made at an earlier date, the Troy establishment was the first to bring the process near to a commercial success. Not having been personally connected with these works during those early days, I cannot so fully realize the doubts and difficulties through which they passed, but I do know from the Wyandotte, to say nothing of any later experience, that it has required faith made perfect, to carry one through the sea which seemed to be bounded by no shores. As I have often expressed it, if we, knowing there was a way through all our troubles, felt so hopeless, what must have been Bessemer's pluck, to enable him to persevere through his difficulties, when the desired end was known only through faith!

But, before entering into chronological details of subsequent works, I must here state that, after building the first experimental plant at Troy, Mr. Holley seems to have at once broken loose from the restraints of his foreign experience, and to have been impressed with the capabilities of the new process. The result is that mainly through his inventions and modifications of the plant we, in America, are to-day enabled to stand at the head of the world in respect of amount of product.

But to return to the detailed history. As before stated, there were, in 1865, the two rival organizations claiming control of the process in this country—the Kelly Process Company, through their Kelly and Mushet's patents, and Messrs. Winslow, Griswold & Holley, through their Bessemer and Holley American patents. Both parties felt strong in their respective positions, and in possessing the necessary means to maintain them. But, after spending large sums of money in counsel fees, they wisely concluded that their fight would at best be a "Kilkenny cat" affair, and so, early in 1866, they combined their respective interests, the Bessemer, or Winslow, Griswold & Holley, party taking 70 per cent., and the Kelly Process Company 30 per cent. of all royalties collected. To this wise compromise may we attribute the subsequent establishment of many works. Under this organization Messrs. John F. Winslow and John A. Griswold, of Troy, New York, and Daniel J. Morrell, of Johnstown, Pennsylvania, were elected trustees, and they appointed Mr. Z. S. Durfee their general agent.

But great difficulty was even yet experienced in inducing capitalists and manufacturers to attempt the introduction of the new manufacture. While the metal produced was wonderful in its qualities, still the necessary first outlay was so large, and the details of the process were so uncertain, and the time-honored prejudice against anything new, held such powerful sway, that our people hesitated, doubted, and waited. Wonderful tales came to us of what was being done abroad, and some venturesome railway managers even dared to import and place in their tracks trial lots of foreign Bessemer rails.

Messrs. Winslow, Griswold & Holley had, from the very first erection of their works, wisely pursued the plan of extending every facility to blast-furnace owners, in all parts of the country, to have their irons tried for steel; and under this system many brands were tried, and most were found wanting. These failures to obtain good results, of course, built up still greater barriers against the spread of the process. In the light of our present chemical knowledge of the manufacture, it is amusing to think of firms sending a few tons of iron to Wyandotte, Troy, or even England, to be tried in actual practice, when a few hours of laboratory work would have settled the entire question. But still it was this very blind using of unknown irons that first opened the eyes of steelmakers to the possibility of making good product from metals pronounced unfit by the then authorities.

The records of the Troy Steel Works show that on March 1st, September 26th, November 22d, and November 30th, 1864, trials of Wassaic, Copake, Fort Edward, Hudson, and Crown Point irons were made, in Henry Bessemer & Co.'s 1½-ton vessel, in Sheffield, with the following results: Wassaic, "slopped over badly, but hammered very well; very hard and not very ductile. Small ingot reheated when hot from mould, and crumbled under the hammer." Copake, "slopped some, hammered tolerably well; harder and less ductile than Wassaic." Fort Edward and Hudson, "worthless, and crumbled under the hammer." Crown Point, first trial, "a little sloppy, very ductile, pretty soft, no cracks;" second trial, "blew well with moderate blast; very good." The earlier of these were, undoubtedly, the first trials made of American irons.

In accordance, I presume, with these results, I find that the first conversion made at Troy was from Crown Point charcoal iron, the first at Wyandotte having been from Lake Superior charcoal, direct from the blast-furnace. The success of the Troy works, whenever good metal was used, encouraged the proprietors to commence the erection of new works on a more extended scale, and early in 1867 Mr. Holley completed the new or 5-ton plant, Mr. John C. Thompson then being superintendent of manufacture. Mr Holley at this date assumed personal charge of the Pennsylvania Steel Works, having previously furnished plans for the machinery, and Mr. Thompson soon after took charge of the Cleveland Rolling Mill Co.'s works. Mr. Z. S. Durfee then entered upon the management of the Troy works. He built the forge, and made some alterations both in plant and details of manufacture. Among other things, he adopted for the small or experimental plant the practice of melting the recarburizing metal in crucibles, and obtained most excellent results. At this time the capacity of the works was stated to be forty tons of ingots per day,

but the records of the works fail to show any such actual results.

On October 19th, 1868, the roof of the 5-ton plant caught fire and was almost completely consumed, destroying much of the machinery. Soon after Mr. Durfee resigned his connection with the works, and Mr. Holley once more became the manager, the property having been possessed by the firm of Messrs. John A. Griswold & Co., Mr. John F. Winslow selling to them his interest. Upon rebuilding, Mr. Holley availed himself of his Harrisburg experience, and remodelled the works in a great degree, particularly as to the melting or cupola house and the blowing engines. The first blow was made in the rebuilt works, on January 12th, 1870. The small plant had been running most of the time while the large works were being rebuilt.

The ingots produced at these works, up to January, 1871, had either been hammered in the forge or bloomed from 9-inch ingots, at the Rensselaer Rail Mill and the Spuyten Duyvil Rail Mill, and then rolled into rails at these respective establishments. In January, 1871, Mr. Holley had a 30-inch three-high blooming train ready to run, having located it in the forge; he used the hammer already there, to cut and chip the blooms as they came from the rolls. The mill was provided, front and back, with lifting-tables, containing loose rollers, and raised by hydraulic power. The rolls were turned to receive 12-inch ingots, which were cast heavy enough to make two-rail blooms. These ingots, after being placed on the rollers of the front table, were pushed into the rolls, both front and back, by hand, it requiring the power of eight men to operate the mill. The train was built with the top and bottom rolls stationary; the middle roll was moved up and down by four screws running through the bolsters carrying the necks of this roll, these screws being rotated by a friction-clutch, which was driven by a belt off the main shaft of the mill engine, and reversed by a hand-lever at the end of the rolls. This mill proved to be a great advance upon the old practice, and ran until the fall of 1872, when George Fritz's patent driven table rollers and pusher were added. By the use of these tables the force was reduced to four men, or, rather, three men and a boy.

The works continued steadily running after being rebuilt, Mr. Holley relinquishing the management in 1871, but still retaining a connection as consulting engineer, which position he still holds. He was succeeded by Mr. Barney Mee, who died February 11th, 1872. His place was filled, for a short time, by Mr. John C. Thompson, who returned to the scenes of his first experiences, but, his health failing, the works were without a head until October 1st, 1873, when the writer assumed control. Mr. J. Wool Griswold has been in direct charge since May 1st, 1875. On March 1st, 1875, the firm style was changed to "The Albany and Rensselaer Iron and Steel Company."

I must be permitted to mention, as an amusing incident, and as showing how little we can foretell what time will bring forth, that in 1865, while connected with the Wyandotte works, I called, in passing through Troy, at the steel works, and presented a letter of introduction to Mr. Holley, who, in the gracious manner of which he is so capable, most blandly, but equally firmly, declined letting me inside the works, and, with the best grace possible under the circumstances, I bowed myself out of his presence. Ten years later I am in charge of the works, proud to consider Mr. A. L. Holley my most intimate friend, and very careful to frequently remind him of our first interview. These works are now producing about 1300 tons of ingots per week, which is sufficient to keep the rail mill running double turn. Their largest month gave a yield of 5498 gross tons.

The Pennsylvania Steel Works were the third Bessemer works started in the United States. The company was organized under the presidency of S. M. Felton, Esq., and under the auspices of such prominent railroad men and engineers as the late J. Edgar Thomson, Nathaniel Thayer, M. W. Baldwin & Co., William Sellers & Co., Bement & Dougherty, R. P. Parrott, H. R. Worthton, Merrick & Sons, Morris, Tasker & Co, and others. Upon the first organization of the company Mr. William Butcher, of Sheffield, England, was elected as the engineer, and ground was broken, but, later, other arrangements were made, and the works were built upon plans furnished by Mr. A. L. Holley, and on January 1st, 1867, that gentleman severed his connection with the Troy works and, removing to Harrisburg, assumed entire charge of the construction, being assisted by Mr. H. S. Nourse. In June, 1867, the Bessemer works were first started, and have been ever since in constant operation. The rail mill of the company not then being completed, most of the ingots were rolled into rails at the Cambria Iron Works, Johnstown, Pennsylvania, this arrangement lasting until May, 1868. I find it stated, in an official publication of July 27th, 1868, that the "annual capacity of the present Bessemer plant (two 5-ton converters) is about 10,000 tons, and of the rail mill 30,000 tons. Additional converters will be erected from time to time." The time for such additions has not yet arrived, but the product has been increased fully five hundred per cent., the heaviest day's product up to date having been 281; week, 1291; and month, 5455 gross tons.

The writer had charge of the rolling, at Cambria, of the Pennsylvania Steel Company's steel, and well remembers with what proud satisfaction Mr. Holley visited Johnstown and proclaimed to us all that at last his dream was realized; that the Pennsylvania works were making four conversions on each turn, or eight per day, producing forty tons of ingots. I presume that "official document" was inspired just about this time. In May, 1868, the rail mill was completed, and since then the company have taken care of their product at their own works. At first they pursued the same plan (rolling 8¼-inch ingots with a reheat) under which their steel had been rolled at Cambria, but subsequently introduced hammering; two hammers have up to the present time drawn the ingots into rail blooms, but the company are now erecting a blooming mill constructed by Mr. James Moore at Bush Hill Iron Works, Philadelphia.

Upon Mr. Holley's relinquishing the management of these works, in 1868, he was succeeded by the joint management of Mr. Nourse and Mr. John B. Pearse. This arrangement was in turn succeeded by another, by which, in 1870, Mr. Pearse took charge of the company's business as general manager, Mr. Nourse remaining as superintendent. Mr. L. S. Bent is now in charge of the works.

The first ingots made at Harrisburg and sent to Johnstown to be put into rails, were drawn into blooms under a 5-ton hammer. A limited number were also hammered at the works of Seyfert, McManus & Co., Reading, and the blooms sent to Cambria. While watching the behavior of the steel under the hammer, Mr. George Fritz, chief engineer of the Cambria works, became convinced that it was not the proper manner of treating the material, and he and Mr. Holley had many consultations on the subject. Mr. Fritz at once turned up a set of blooming rolls which he placed in a 21-inch rail train, and Mr. Holley caused 8¼ inch ingots to be cast and sent him. These were drawn to 6½ inches square, then recharged and wash-heated, and then rolled into rails. So well did this work, that Mr. Holley adopted the system in the Pennsylvania Steel Company's rail mill, which he was then building. After many discussions and consultations he decided, on his return to Troy, to build the heavier blooming mill to which I have before referred.

The Freedom Iron and Steel Works, near Lewistown, Mifflin County, Pa., were the fourth Bessemer Works started in this country. They were organized under the presidency of Mr. John A. Wright, and absorbed the interests of the Logan Iron Company, which company had been successfully working for many years. Mr. Wright visited England, and made purchases of the most complete machinery there known, and with the exception of the blowing engine, which Messrs. I. P. Morris & Towne, of Philadelphia, built, the works may be said to have been of English construction and arrangement. The company intended to manufacture principally boiler plates and tires, but the plate mill, which was driven by a Ramsbottom reversing engine, was soon changed to a rail mill. The works were under the direction of Mr. R. H. Lee, and ran for about one year, when, owing principally to the unsuitableness of the company's irons for Bessemer steel, the works were stopped, and much of the machinery subsequently sold. Their first blow was made May 1st, 1868.

The Cleveland Rolling Mill Company's Bessemer Works, situated at Newburgh, six miles from Cleveland, were the fifth works erected. These were built after the same general plans as the Pennsylvania Works, but Mr. H. Gmelin, the engineer in charge of construction, made many modifications. This gentleman returned to Austria before the blowing in of the works, which task was assumed by Mr. John C. Thompson, he making the first blow on or about October 15th, 1868. Mr. Thompson soon resigned the charge, owing to failing health, and the works have since then been conducted by Mr. Chisholm. In a short time, a second pair of 5-ton vessels were erected, and all four remained in operation until 1875, when the later pair were removed to make way for Siemens-Martin furnaces, which are now running.

This company deserves credit for being the first parties in this country to make a commercial success of the application of Bessemer steel to wire, screws, and several other specialties.

The Cambria Iron Company, of Johnstown, Pa., were the sixth parties to build Bessemer Works, their first blow being made by the writer on July 10th, 1871. As stated, the Cambria Iron Company did not erect Bessemer works until after five other concerns had started theirs, but nevertheless they were the very first corporation to give encouragement to attempts to perfect the new process. When Mr. Kelly

turned his attention to endeavors to shorten the process of refining iron by blasts of air, he was part proprietor and manager of a blast-furnace at Eddysville, Kentucky. As in the case of many another seeker after the unknown, he spent all of his own money, and seriously embarrassed himself. It was about this time that Bessemer obtained his American patents. After filing his claims as the original discoverer, Mr. Kelly succeeded in interesting the Cambria Iron Company, and under its patronage he transferred his experiments to its works at Johnstown, in 1859, and there met with the usual number of encouraging failures.

The first Bessemer converter ever erected in America, was built at Cambria, by Mr. Kelly, and still remains there, a cherished relic. It was calculated to convert about half a ton of metal, and received its blast from the foundry blowing engine. But I never heard even a tradition of a perfect conversion made in this vessel. Still the Cambria Company, and more particularly its general manager, the Hon. Daniel J. Morrell, were impressed with the possibility of success, and when the Kelly Process Association was organized, the Cambria Company was among the most earnest members. But the conservatism of other members of the company prevailed, and they did not complete their Bessemer works until 1871.

Their chief engineer, George Fritz, had been personally familiar with all of Mr. Kelly's experiments, and had closely watched the progress of the process as developed by Bessemer and others, and during the time the steel made at the Pennsylvania Steel Works was rolled at Cambria, he had abundant opportunities of studying the manufacture in its various mechanical details, and fully realized the advantages of the innovations introduced in the arrangement and details of Bessemer plant, by Mr. Holley. These two gentlemen had been thrown, during this time, into the closest personal intercourse, and while Mr. Fritz was only too happy to assist Mr. Holley with his advice and large experience in perfecting the plans of the rail mill for the Pennsylvania works, he was equally willing to avail himself of the latter's experience and advice in arranging his plans for the Cambria Bessemer plant.

But George Fritz could not blindly copy, and while cheerfully acknowledging everything taken from Mr. Holley, he introduced many new ideas in his arrangement of plant. He built vertical, disconnected blowing engines, and arranged his converting building under one roof, without any dividing wall between the melting and casting houses. And when he came to the blooming mill, he introduced the entirely new features of driven rollers in the tables, and a hydraulic pusher for turning over and moving the ingots on the tables. These two features constitute the Fritz Blooming Mill patent, now used by most of the Bessemer works of this country. The merits of rolling as compared with hammering had been fully discussed between Mr. Fritz and Mr. Holley, and they had, at various times, gone over the numerous details of a blooming mill, and Mr. Holley, as already stated, had built one at the Troy works. Mr. Fritz had availed himself of the benefit of the extensive knowledge and sound judgment of his brother, Mr. John Fritz, of Bethlehem, Pa., and the result of all was the Johnnstown Blooming Mill, which marked a new era in the Bessemer manufacture. While living to see many difficulties overcome, and

great progress made, George Fritz died too soon, his country losing one of her noblest and ablest sons. He died August 5th, 1873.

The writer remained in charge of the works until September, 1873, when he went to Troy, and was succeeded by Mr. John E. Fry, who is still in charge. The greatest yield at these works has been as follows: March 21st, 1876, 297 gross tons in 24 hours; week ending May 20th, 1876, 1475 gross tons; month ending March, 1876, 6051 gross tons.

The seventh works to go into operation, the Union Iron Company's, are owned by the same parties who control the Cleveland works, and are located at Bridgeport, or South Chicago, Ill. Their first blow was made on July 26th, 1871, and the works have been in almost constant operation ever since. They contain two 5-ton vessels, and the general arrangement is similar to the Newburg plant.

The North Chicago Rolling Mill Company, of Chicago, Ill., built and started the eighth Bessemer works. Captain E. B. Ward, of Detroit, was one of the heaviest owners in this company, and he, as before stated, had owned the Wyandotte works, and was fully convinced of the merits of the process, and while abandoning the last-named establishment, took steps to have a larger and more complete plant erected in Chicago in connection with the extensive iron works of the company. Mr. A. L. Holley was engaged to furnish the plans, and the works were erected under the direction of Mr. O. W. Potter, then the general superintendent of the company. Mr. Holley, profiting by the experience acquired in building the several other works with which he had been connected, and by the already advanced state of the art, introduced many improvements in the arrangement of this plant, and when completed it was undoubtedly the most perfect in existence. The first blow was made on April 10th, 1872, under the direction of Mr. Robert Forsyth, who had received his Bessemer education at the Troy works. This gentleman has ever since remained in charge of the converting works, and has been most eminently successful in his management. His works are to-day making the largest output of any in the world. The plant contains two 5-ton vessels. I might here say that while all the present American plants are said to consist of two 5-ton converters, the general practice is to convert nearer six tons in them. The ingots are bloomed in a three high 30-inch mill with the Fritz tables.

The records of the North Chicago Company show their largest product for 24 hours to have been 330¼ gross tons; for one week 1583 gross tons; and for one month 6457 gross tons.

The Joliet Iron and Steel Company, having rolling mills at Joliet, Ill., and blast-furnaces at Chicago, determined to erect the ninth Bessemer plant in connection with their Joliet works. They purchased of the Freedom Steel Company their blowing engine, converters, hydraulic cranes, etc. Mr. Holley was engaged to furnish the plans, and the works were built under his general direction, Mr. A. L. Rothman and Mr. P. Barnes being the engineers in direct charge. The converting plant consists of two 5-ton vessels, and the blooming train is similar to that of North Chicago. The general arrangement of the two converting works is also very similar. The first blow was made on March 13th, 1873, under the direction of Mr. Dunning, who still remains in charge of the works. Their records show the

greatest product in 24 hours to have been 350 gross tons; in one week 1528 gross tons; and in one month 5367 gross tons.

The tenth Bessemer plant was built by Mr. John Fritz for the Bethlehem Iron Company, of Bethlehem, Pa., of which he was, and is, general superintendent and chief engineer, Mr. Holley being connected with him as consulting engineer. Mr. Fritz had studied the various American plants, and also visited England and the Continent, and after mature deliberation concluded to take a new departure. He arranged his melting-house, engine-room, converting-room, blooming and rail mills, all in one grand building, under one roof, and without any partition walls. He placed his cupolas on the ground and hoisted the melted iron on a hydraulic lift, and then poured it into the converters. The spiegel is melted in a Siemens furnace, also on the ground floor, and the melted spiegel is also hoisted and poured into the vessels.

The blooming train has the middle roll stationary, the same as the Cambria mill, the top and bottom rolls screwing up and down. Instead of depending upon friction to drive the rollers of the tables, Mr. Fritz put in a pair of small reversing engines. This feature has since been adopted in a method which dispenses with belts, by means of a direct connection of the engines with the table, as arranged by Mr. Holley, in several of the other works. The works made their first blow on October 4th, 1873, under the charge of Mr. Owen Leibert, who is still the superintendent. The highest product has been 264 gross tons in 24 hours; 1340 gross tons in a week, and 5282 gross tons in one month.

The Edgar Thomson Steel Company,

limited, of Pittsburgh, Pa., were the eleventh parties to enter the business, locating their works at McKinneys, now called Bessemer Station, on the Pennsylvania Railroad, about nine miles from Pittsburgh; Mr. Holley furnishing the plans and Mr. P. Barnes being the resident engineer, he having severed his connection with the Joliet Works. In the fall of 1873, Mr. William R. Jones, who had been George Fritz's assistant at Cambria, became connected with the Edgar Thomson Company, and upon the starting of the works in August, 1875, assumed charge of them. He is now the general superintendent of the company. The largest product for 24 hours has been 265 gross tons; largest for a month's work, 5403 gross tons.

In arranging these works, Mr. Holley made many improvements over any of his previous efforts, and assisted as he was, the works stand to-day as a fit monument of the progress of the Bessemer process in this country.

The twelfth and last works to start were those of the Lackawanna Iron and Coal Company of Scranton, Pa., being added to its already large iron plant. The converting works were built by Mr. A. L. Rothman, Mr. Holley acting as consulting engineer. The former gentleman started the works on October 23d, 1875, and remained in charge until May, 1876, when he was succeeded by Mr. George F. Wilhour, who obtained his Bessemer experience at Johnstown, Pa. The blooming mill was built from Mr. Holley's plans, under the supervision of Mr. W. W. Scranton, the general superintendent of the company, and has all the late improvements.

The Vulcan Iron Company, of St. Louis, Mo., has their converting works and blooming mill nearly ready to start,

they being an addition to its already large iron mill and extensive blast-furnaces. Mr. Holley has furnished the plans and Mr. D. E. Garrison, the general manager of the company, has had immediate charge of the erection, Mr. John Hogan being his assistant. When these works start there will be in operation eleven 5-ton plants with 22 vessels, capable of turning out, in the aggregate, 550,000 gross tons of ingots per year.

Having enumerated the various Bessemer works according to the order in which they started, and in so doing having referred to the wonderful increase in product, it seems a fitting conclusion to briefly review the causes of such wonderful strides in capacity. As stated, after building the original experimental plant at Troy, Mr. A. L. Holley seems to have appreciated that the manufacture was capable of a development far beyond that which had been attained in those countries in which it was already considered a success.

Even if his mind did not fully realize this conclusion, his mechanical intuition was alive to the possibilities of improvement, and the result of his thought gave us the present accepted type of American Bessemer plant. He did away with the English deep pit and raised the vessels so as to get working space under them on the ground floor; he substituted top-supported hydraulic cranes for the more expensive counterweighted English ones, and put three ingot cranes around the pit instead of two, and thereby obtained greater area of power. He changed the location of the vessels as related to the pit and melting-house. He modified the ladle crane, and worked all the cranes and the vessels from a single point; he substituted cupolas for reverberatory furnaces, and last, but by no means least, introduced the intermediate or accumulating ladle which is placed on scales, and thus insures accuracy of operation by rendering possible the weighing of each charge of melted iron, before pouring it into the convertor. These points cover the radical features of his innovations. After building such a plant, he began to meet the difficulties of details in manufacture, among the most serious of which was the short duration of the vessel bottoms, and the time required to cool off the vessels to a point at which it was possible for workmen to enter and make new bottoms. After many experiments, the result was the Holley Vessel Bottom, which, either in its form as patented, or in a modification of it as now used in all American works, has rendered possible, as much as any other one thing, the present immense production.

Then he tried many forms of cupolas at Troy, adopting in the original plant a changeable bottom or section below the tuyeres, and developing this idea still further in the first 5-ton works; then later, at Harrisburg, assisting Mr. J. B. Pearse the furnace was improved to a point which rendered these many bottoms unnecessary, chiefly by deepening the bottom and enlarging the tuyere area. Upon his rebuilding the Troy works after their destruction by fire, Mr. Holley put in the perfected cupolas. At this time the practice was to run a cupola for a turn's melting, which had reached eight heats or forty tons of steel, and then dropping its bottom. This was already an increase of one hundred per cent. over his boast about the same amount in twenty-four hours.

The Cambria works were now running, and Mr. Holley had become offi-cially connected with them as consulting Bessemer engineer. Many discussions and consultations took place between Mr. George Fritz, Mr. Holley, and the writer, as to the possibility of increasing the product of the works. Among other things, tapping cinder from the cupolas was thought of, and decided upon. These works had already placed their turn's work at nine instead of eight heats. The Pennsylvania works under Mr. J. B. Pearse's management, followed with an increased production. The Cambria works applied the cinder tap, and the production went up to the unanticipated amount of thirty heats, or one hundred and fifty tons in twenty-four hours. Grand as we thought this, it is only about one-half of the present yield of each of several works. During all this time many details were modified, and as the new ways proved successful they were adopted in the regular practice. I think one thing which had a strong bearing on the increased production was the labor organization of the Cambria works. In compliance with the policy decided upon, I started the converting works without a single man who had ever seen even the outside of Bessemer works, and, with a very few exceptions, they were not even skilled rolling-mill men, but on the contrary were selected from intelligent laborers. The result was that we had willing pupils with no prejudices, and without any reminiscences of what they had done in the old country or at any other works. Of course when one works went ahead, the others had to follow. Mr. George Fritz was the embodiment of push, and with such men to call on as William R. Jones, J. E. Fry, Charles Kennedy, Alexander Hamilton, and D. N. Jones, his efforts were ably seconded, and Cambria for a long time maintained the lead.

Mr. Z. S. Durfee tried at Wyandotte to fill an ingot mould from the bottom, the steel being poured into the top of an adjoining mould. Upon taking charge of the works, I still further carried out this idea, and later Mr. John E. Fry and myself took out a patent on the process. At about the same time Mr. Holley, at Troy, was elaborating the same idea, and later, at Harrisburg, carried it much further and patented it. After the starting of the Cambria works, the process of bottom casting was fully gone into, and Mr. William R. Jones's improvements, since patented by him, rendered it a complete success. I know that some makers do not fully acknowledge its merits, but it certainly has a right to rank among the prominent features of the American Bessemer practice.

While I am not able to mention all of the very many good things accomplished by the gentlemen at each and all the various works, I am, at the same time, well aware they have all done their share toward achieving the great end; and, fortunately, their mutual relations have been so pleasant, that each one's experiences have been freely imparted to the others. This has done wonders to advance the science. But without one element, all skill and all mechanical talent would have been wasted, and with it nearly all things have been possible. That element has been, and is, "American push."

2. The Potentialities of Chemical Research, 1894

Scientific American

By the last decade of the nineteenth century, the role of the lone, practical inventor was doubtful. Already the intrusion of science and engineering into the process of innovation was defining new avenues for improvement of industrial processes which were closed to all except those with considerable academic training. The heroic age of invention was coming to a close, but the era of large-scale industrial research was not yet begun. In this interim period, the true path for inventors was not at all clear. One suggestion for future progress was offered by the *Scientific American*.

From "The Potentialities of Chemical Research," *Scientific American*, LXX (January 20, 1894), 34.

The men of brains—the leaders in the progress of our race—have of late become so wrapped up in one comparatively narrow branch of science, the mechanics and dynamics of electricity, that there has unquestionably been a growing neglect of the greatest and most universal, the most practical and fertile, the most far-reaching and civilizing of all the sciences. A science, moreover, which is scarcely older than that of electricity, that is, one which emerged but little earlier from the swaddling clothes of empiricism. Nevertheless, the young giant, chemistry—of which we speak—has a future before it which involves that of the race of man more intimately and more completely than all the other sciences combined.

Those who pursue electricity, by the inductive method—that of practical experiment and generalization therefrom—have lately entered the complaint that electricity has become nine-tenths mathematics. In a certain sense, this may be all right, but it is not the way in which electricity itself was founded. The men of the laboratory laid its foundation; and it may be asserted that it is still in the experimental laboratory that all the new fundamental facts are and will be born. Mathematics is not a discoverer, though a highly valuable expounder. To many real experimental discoverers, the higher branches of mathematics constitute a trackless maze. Indeed, the peculiar brain powers needed by the expert mathematician resemble those of the musical composer, and the methods of each require the same constant and assiduous cultivation, memorization, practice, mental absorption and abstraction, which together make up that rare combination called "genius."

There is no doubt that in America experimental chemical research has but a slight foothold. The causes are on the surface, and easily understood, but are outside our present scope. It is proposed here to show cause for the conviction, in reasoning minds, that the prospects of our race—some already in sight—depend mainly on the cultivation of experimental, analytical and synthetical chemistry.

First, to present a generalization or induction from the whole field of chemical research. Much of such research has been, is and will yet be, pervaded with what may be called the *random* element. All experimental attempts to penetrate the unknown necessarily partake of this element. It is only when facts have so multiplied as to render *generalization* possible that *systematic* research begins. The great amount of more or less random research yet prevailing proves that chemistry is as yet but an infant, destined to a gigantic growth—a growth in fact illimitable.

We now know with certainty 72 elements of matter. Each one of these is —according to the results of research— the basis of an incalculable number of compounds, no two of which are exactly alike in any one of their relations to other bodies. The changes to be rung on nine bells, or even on nine thousand, are but a drop of water to the ocean, compared with the possible variety of chemical bodies, each possessing certain salient potencies, which are to be found only by experiment, and can rarely be predicted. The number of chemical species or forms of matter, each distinct from all others, is therefore *practically* infinite. The generalization based on this is as follows: A form of matter must be capable of existence, and must, therefore, be within the power of chemical research to discover and prepare, which will possess *any assignable or conceivable potency,* or influence over any given species of matter, dead or living.

If we have here been successful in shaping a form of words so as to make this general induction clear, the results that proceed therefrom will quickly present themselves to any rational mind.

Here, and now, we can only comment on one deduction therefrom. This relates to a new subject which, though of a vital importance to mankind beyond the power of words to convey, is yet in a condition of incipiency—scarcely half born. We might call it chemical pathology—the chemistry of diseases. It relates to the chemical *nature, origin* and *cure* of diseases. We are, by dint of numerous random investigations, made mainly in this, our century, beginning to see quite plainly a new induction, which will doubtless form the cornerstone of this new branch of experimental chemical research. The "germ theory" of diseases has gone through long controversies. It has been but quite recently recognized, however, that the germs themselves and their living progeny do not constitute the diseases, and are not even the *immediate* agents, generally speaking, of such diseases. It is now becoming a matter of belief that in some (and of strong suspicion that in almost, if not quite all) of this class of diseases, it is the distribution throughout the circulation of the animal, of specific poisons, similar to snake poisons, products of the conversion or rather *perversion* of vital tissues by the progeny of the disease germs, that constitutes these diseases. The ancients said: "Fas est ab hoste doceri." (It is right to be taught by your enemy.) This applies here. Now that we know that the enemies born from the disease germs kill us by poisoning our blood—if we cannot deal with these enemies directly, we may destroy, or neutralize, or paralyze their weapons. The next step is for the chemist to discover, analyze, and experiment upon these specific poisons—these *tox-albumens,* or *ptomaines,* or whatever they may prove to be—and discover how to destroy them, or combat them with antidotes.

According to the generalization propounded above, such antidotes—and, moreover, we may add, chemical compounds capable of poisoning or dislodging the disease fungoids themselves —must be susceptible of existence, and will sooner or later be discovered. No nobler aim than this could animate a chemist. The prospect is plain that all these hitherto invisible and inscrutable foes of our race will yet be disarmed and defeated by the weapons of the chemical laboratory. Life will then be prolonged, and our vital energies enhanced.

3. A Record of Achievement in Chemistry, 1912

HERMAN FRASCH, "Address of Acceptance"

Like the iron industry, the chemical industry had a long history in America, dating back to the earliest colonial days. And like the iron industry, the chemical industry underwent a spectacular growth in the last third of the nineteenth century. But this growth, unlike that in the iron industry, was based not so much on any one process as on a combination of increased demand and, more importantly, on the application of exact scientific knowledge to the processes involved. One of the first chemists to make a career of innovation in industrial chemistry was Herman Frasch, who was born in Germany (the center of industrial and academic chemistry) and came to the United States in 1868. In 1912 Frasch was awarded the Perkin Medal of the Society of Chemical Industry. In his acceptance speech, he reviewed his career in the chemical and petroleum industries.

Very little is known of the impurities contained in petroleum. They influence the price, however, to a remarkable degree. The best illustration of this is the case of Ohio oil. This contains about 0.75 per cent. of sulphur, and before my desulphurizing process was known sold at 14 cents per barrel, while Pennsylvania oil, with a sulphur content of only 0.03 per cent., sold at $2.25 at the same time. Sulphur affects the value of petroleum in a greater degree than phosphorus does that of iron ore.

One of the oils which contains an objectionable amount of sulphur is that found near Petrolia, Ontario. It is the only crude that has been found in the Dominion of Canada. When this oil was first discovered in 1868, it was refined in the usual way—treated with sulphuric acid and soda, and then put on the market. The result was disastrous. The odor emanating from the oil was very offensive and penetrating, so much so that the cargoes of ships carrying flour and bacon, anchored near a vessel loaded with Canadian oil, were spoiled, as the flour and bacon absorbed this odor. Law-suits based upon these facts were decided against the shippers of Canadian oil, and all export ceased. In order to protect the home industry, the Canadian Government imposed a duty of 9 cents per gallon on Pennsylvania oil, but in spite of this almost prohibitive duty, half the oil consumed in Canada was imported from Pennsylvania.

The offensive odor of this oil, moreover, was not its only objection. It had also the property of depositing soot upon the lamp chimney, so that a large

From Herman Frasch, "Address of Acceptance," *Journal of Industrial and Engineering Chemistry,* IV (February 1912), 134-40. Copyright 1912 by the American Chemical Society. Reprinted by permission of the copyright owner.

percentage of the light emitted by the flame was lost.

The Canadian Government, as well as the Canadian producers and refiners, made every effort to discover a method by which the objectionable properties of this crude oil could be eliminated, but practically nothing has been accomplished in twenty years, except perhaps in the matter of covering up the odor, when in 1885 I bought a refinery in Canada and made a thorough investigation of the character of this crude and decided to discover a remedy, if possible.

This dreadful odor, which the Canadians called "skunk," arose from a peculiar hydrocarbon-sulphur compound, and the clouding of the lamp chimney was due to its sulphur content. The sulphur in the oil burned into sulphuric acid, which condensed against the lamp chimney, and any unconsumed carbon of organic particles in the air would adhere thereto and form this objectionable soot. To remove the sulphur from the oil completely meant the elimination of the smoke as well as odor, and when this was effected the oil furnished an illuminant equal in quality to the best Pennsylvania.

To free petroleum of elementary sulphur or hydrogen sulphide presents comparatively little difficulty, but the sulphur compound which is the cause of this offensive odor is very stable and cannot be broken up into hydrogen sulphide or any other sulphur compound which can be eliminated. It was because of the presence of this peculiar compound that Canadian oil for so many years resisted all the efforts made to refine it.

This sulphur compound has the peculiarity of dissolving a number of metallic oxides. When the oil is saturated with all the oxide it can carry in solution, the disagreeable odor disappears. It reappears, however, if an attempt is made to free the solution of its metal. I found that this solution of metal in petroleum has an intense affinity for sulphur, and also that when a portion of the sulphur has been precipitated with the metal as a sulphide, additional quantities of metal oxide can go into solution. If more oxide than that necessary to precipitate all the sulphur is added to the petroleum while it is being distilled, a complete desulphurization of the petroleum is effected.

When this petroleum solution is made with water-white petroleum distillate, which has been freed of elementary sulphur and hydrogen sulphide, the solutions assume colors characteristic of each metal. The lead solution is a canary-yellow; mercury, orange; copper, blood-red; silver, brown.

I selected copper as the metal most suitable—first because it dissolves in the petroleum, and in the second place because of the readiness with which the sulphide of copper can be reconverted into oxide.

When the laboratory work had been completed, I applied for letters patent and erected a 1,200 barrel still, carrying on the process on a large scale. The shell of the still was 22 feet in diameter and 16 feet high, and was supplied with a stirring device which kept the copper in suspension while distillation was carried on. After 80 per cent. of the contents of the apparatus was distilled, the remainder, when cool, was pumped through a filter press. The solid portion was ignited and roasted, while the liquid residuum was mixed with a new charge of revivified oxide of copper to be used for the desulphurizing of a further quantity of sulphur-containing distillate. I used a shelf furnace, operated by hand, to roast the resulting sulphide of copper. In this manner I produced a burning oil containing 0.02 per cent. sulphur, which is the percentage contained in Pennsylvania oil of similar specific gravity, while Canadian oil, refined by the ordinary method, has a sulphur content of 0.6 per cent.

It was about this time that oil almost identical with the Canadian was discovered in Ohio, and while the question of refining Canadian oil was interesting, the problem became intensely important when 30,000 barrels per day were being produced in Ohio. The new field proved to be very extensive, and the Standard Oil Company bought property near Lima, Ohio, upon which they erected a large refinery. They disregarded the enormous difference in the sulphur content of Pennsylvania and Ohio oils, decided to refine the latter in the usual way and put it on the market. When the refined product had been distributed among their customers, it all came back as unfit for use. Every effort was made to solve the difficult problem, but in 1887, after two years of experimentation and with all the skill which the Standard Oil Company could call to their assistance, it was decided that no illuminating oil could be made from Ohio crude and that it was fit only for fuel. A pipe line for this purpose was built to Chicago, and long-term contracts made at 14 cents per barrel.

My patents had now been granted and I was selling refined Canadian oil with a guarantee that it would burn equal to the best Pennsylvania. After an investigation which convinced them that I had solved this problem, the Standard Oil Company bought my patents and my refinery, and as soon as possible Lima, Cleveland, Whiting, Philadelphia and Bayonne were refining oil by the new method.

The Ohio field was found to extend into Indiana and the production increased to 90,000 barrels per day. The price of this crude went up to nearly $1.00 per barrel, fluctuating between 60 cents and $1.00 for a great many years. The advantage resulting from the ability to use these oils for illuminants did not stop with the large profits of the Standard Oil Company, but the farmers and oil producers of Ohio and Indiana benefitted by the enormous advance in the value of Ohio crude, which amounted to many millions of dollars per year.

In desulphurizing petroleum, the oxide of copper is mixed with the petroleum distillate in a still supplied with an upright shaft and arms radiating therefrom, to keep the oxide in agitation during the process of distillation, flexible chains attached to the arms being used to prevent the copper from adhering to the bottom of the still. One hundred thousand pounds of oxide of copper are used for the first charge of 2,000 barrels of distillate. After 80 per cent. has been distilled off, a new charge of distillate is added with an additional charge of 30,000 pounds of copper, which is followed by two further runs, so that about 200,000 pounds of copper material are in the still when the fourth run is made. The residuum is pumped through a filter press, and the solid product of the filter press has the oil adhering thereto burned off. The dry mixture of oxide and sulphide of copper is then put into a roasting furnace, where it is desulphurized to 1 per cent. or less.

A variation of my method treats the vapor coming from a still charged with crude petroleum, and consists in passing the vapor through two brushes made of No. 10 steel wire, the brushes being 5½ feet in diameter and 16 feet long. They are inserted into a shell which is almost the same diameter as the brush, and the requisite amounts of copper and heavy oil are pumped into two shells, each containing one brush. The vapor passes in series, first around the shell to prevent condensation; then through the shells on to the condenser. The brushes are made to revolve at about six revolutions per minute. These wires immersing continually in this oxide of copper magma, the shells containing the brushes are surrounded by the vapor coming from the still, and as the temperatures of the vapors increase, anything condensed thereon during the prior period is re-evaporated by the hotter vapor following.

Both these processes are now in operation at different works.

When the question of supplying the copper necessary for the works at Lima was under discussion, it was found that 160 furnaces, such as I used in Canada, would be required to do the work. In order to avoid the handling and transportation involved in such a gigantic furnace plant, I was obliged to construct a mechanical roasting furnace of a capacity in conformity with the magnitude of the business.

To eliminate the difficulties of the warping of the shaft and the arms which had caused the failure of the McDougal furnace, I constructed a stirring device, the shaft and arms of which were cooled artificially to withstand the high temperature of the roasting furnace. I first forced air as a cooling medium through the stirring device, but found that the oxidation of the sulphide of copper and the carbon from the residuum of the petroleum produced a temperature even higher than that of the ordinary pyrites furnace. It therefore became necessary to substitute hot water for air as a cooling medium, which proved very satisfactory. This made possible an increase in the size of the furnace to 16 feet inside diameter, and to-day these shafts and arms are connected with steam drums and are used like a water tube boiler, so that the surplus heat extracted from the stirring device of the roasting furnace is converted into steam and utilized in the plant. The capacity of a furnace is fifty tons per day, and four to six are used in one refinery. After the copper has been revivified, it is ground and mixed with residual oil from the filter press. In this manner the copper charge is pumped into the still which may be half a mile away. During the twenty years that this process has been in operation many millions of barrels of oil have been desulphurized.

In 1902 the California field became important, and it was discovered that another oil which smoked chimneys had to be refined. This oil, however, was practically free from sulphur, the smoke being due to a large percentage of the aromatic series of hydrocarbons and to the fact that the percentage of hydrogen to carbon was too small to maintain the flame temperature necessary to consume all the carbon. I ascertained further that sulphuric anhydride converts the aromatic series into sulpho products, insoluble in petroleum, and that by treating the distillates from the crude oil with sulphuric anhydride, the members of the aromatic series in the petroleum can readily be extracted.

The existence of a petroleum containing nearly 50 per cent. of the coal-tar products is intensely interesting, especially in view of the theories advanced upon the origin of petroleum. The percentage of these hydrocarbons in the crude varies from the percentage contained in coal tar, benzol existing in a smaller proportion than toluol, while xylol represents 7 per cent. of the volume of the crude. Naphthalene, entirely free from all traces of carbolic odor, is quite prominent, while anthracene and carbolic acid are entirely absent.

I employed numerous methods for separating the products of California crude by physical means. Distillation, with large back-flow condensers attached, showed very encouraging results, as did also the method of washing the distillates with alcohol, carried on in series, the aromatic series being more soluble in alcohol than the paraffine series. However, the sulphuric anhydride treatment, which I first used in determining the amount of the two series contained in the petroleum, has proved to be very simple and effective on a large scale, and is now used by the Standard Oil Company at their plant in Port Richmond, California. The process of making the sulphuric anhydride employed there is the one purchased from the Verein Chemischer Fabriken of Mannheim. The capacity of the plant has been increased a number of times, until to-day it is by far the largest in the United States, if not in the world.

In 1865, while boring for petroleum in Louisiana, a sulphur deposit was discovered beneath a layer of quicksand about 500 feet thick. As a result of this discovery, quarrels and controversies arose as to whether the lease covering the petroleum rights also included the sulphur. It was some time before the matter was decided, and by the time a decision had been reached, both parties had lost a great deal of money, and

those who got the sulphur deposit lost still more in trying to exploit it. The deposit seemed to bring misfortune to every one connected with it, and I have heard many stories and met many people who told me of having lost money in the various schemes that marked the progress of the sulphur mine. Progress there seemed to mean failure. An Austrian company, a French company, and numerous American companies—everybody failed and not a ton of sulphur was produced.

When I heard of this extraordinary situation, in 1891, I obtained a core from the sulphur deposit and many pamphlets from the various companies who had tried to operate it, each one telling the prospective purchaser that his fortune was made if he but owned a few shares of the stock of that particular company. I became interested, and having had a great deal of experience in drilling and mining petroleum and salt, I thought the problem might be solved if all the facts concerning the deposit were known. Unfortunately, all the drilling records had been colored by the people who expected to float companies—everything unfavorable was concealed, and only that given which would be likely to induce investment, so that what I had considered a correct report proved later to be entirely wrong.

Being misinformed as to the character of the deposit, I reached the conclusion that the sulphur was distributed in the rock as in Sicily, and when I heard of the limestone roof covering the deposit, I felt that sulphur could be found anywhere within reasonable proximity to the sulphur mine.

To meet the extraordinary conditions existing in this deposit, I decided that the only way to mine this sulphur was to melt it in the ground and pump it to the surface in the form of a liquid. After careful study and consideration, I became convinced that this could be done. In view of the information obtained from the various companies, I believed that there was sulphur over miles of territory, and started to drill on land I had purchased within a mile and a half of Sulphur Mine. I went down over 2,000 feet without finding anything, then I located a second, a third, and a fourth well, but found no sulphur in any instance. This took much time and money, and I finally reached the conclusion that all the sulphur was located on the land owned by the New York company operating it at the time. They had a very ingenious scheme for sinking a shaft with a shield, but after the expenditure of a great deal of money, the shield was lost, and the danger due to the presence of water containing hydrogen sulphide was demonstrated by the death of a number of men. It was decided to abandon this method, especially after a drilling record had been made by a drilling company who reported direct to the owners, when it was discovered that there was no roof over the sulphur, and that sulphur water was permeating the deposit in inexhaustible quantities.

I realized at the outset that a method entirely different from that employed in the mines of Sicily was necessary for success here, as the class of labor required to operate this mine would demand at least $5.00 per day, while the Sicilian miners were being paid 60 cents.

I succeeded in getting possession of the property and at once set to work to drill a well of sufficient diameter to determine finally the character of the existing material. When this had been done, I was obliged to modify completely the process and apparatus I had expected to employ.

At that time the drilling of a well in an alluvial deposit containing quicksand, etc., was a very tedious task, and it took from six to nine months to get through the alluvial material to the rock —work which we do now in three days.

I drilled a well through the alluvial deposit to the rock with a 10″ pipe, then continued through the sulphur deposit, which was about 200 feet thick, with a 9″ drill, and immersed a 6″ pipe from the surface to the bottom in this well. The 6″ pipe had a strainer only 6″ long, at the very bottom, and a seat to receive the 3″ pipe through which we expected to lift the sulphur to the surface. The 6″ pipe, directly above the seat for the 3″ pipe, was also perforated for a distance of three feet.

After the well had been drilled and before the pipes were inserted, it was filled up with sand in order to insure a tight receptacle at the bottom for the liquid sulphur. After the sand had been washed out, the pipes were inserted and equipped, and the well was ready for the melting fluid.

This melting fluid consisted of water superheated to 335° Fahrenheit. The porosity of the rock in which the melting had to be done seemed to furnish an almost insurmountable obstacle to success, as I feared that the wild waters in the rock would break into the melting zone I expected to create and reduce the temperature of the fluid with which I expected to melt below the temperature necessary to fuse the sulphur. I had supplied a large number of boilers to furnish the heat necessary to maintain in the well a temperature higher than that required for the fusion of the sulphur.

The water was superheated in columns in which 100 pounds per square inch pressure was maintained, and the apparatus which I had constructed to accomplish this proved very efficient. We used twenty 150 h. p. boilers for a well, which represents experimentation on a ponderous scale.

When everything was ready to make the first trial, which would demonstrate either success or failure, we raised steam in the boilers, and sent the super-heated water into the ground without a hitch. If for one instant the high temperature required should drop below the melting point of sulphur, it would mean failure, consequently intense interest centered in this first attempt.

After permitting the melting fluid to go into the ground for twenty-four hours, I decided that sufficient material must have been melted to produce some sulphur. The pumping engine was started on the sulphur line, and the increasing strain against the engine showed that work was being done. More and more slowly went the engine, more steam was supplied, until the man at the throttle sang out at the top of his voice, "She's pumping." A liquid appeared on the polished rod, and when I wiped it off I found my finger covered with sulphur. Within five minutes the receptacles under pressure were opened and a beautiful stream of the golden fluid shot into the barrels we had ready to receive the product. After pumping for about fifteen minutes, the forty barrels we had supplied were seen to be inadequate. Quickly we threw up embankments and lined them with boards to receive the sulphur that was gushing forth; and since that day no further attempt has been made to provide a vessel or a mold into which to put the sulphur.

When the sun went down we stopped the pump to hold the liquid sulphur below until we could prepare to receive more in the morning. The material on the ground had to be removed, and willing hands helped to make a clean slate for the next day. When everything had been finished, the sulphur all piled up in one heap, and the men had departed, I enjoyed all by myself this demonstration of success. I mounted the sulphur pile and seated myself on the very top. It pleased me to hear the slight noise caused by the contraction of the warm sulphur, which was like a greeting from below—proof that my object had been accomplished. Many days and many years intervened before financial success was assured, but the first step towards the ultimate goal had been achieved. We had melted the mineral in the ground and brought it to the surface as a liquid. We had demonstrated that it could be done.

This was especially gratifying as the criticisms I had received from technical papers and people who had heard of what I was attempting to do had been very adverse. Every one who expressed an opinion seemed to be convinced that this thing could not be done, one prominent man offering to eat every ounce of sulphur I ever pumped. A fair illustration of public opinion is the remark of the mail boy who drove me to the railroad the morning after our first pumping. He said: "Well, you pumped sulphur sure, but nobody believed it but the old carpenter, and they say he's half crazy."

This severe criticism, while not agreeable, did not carry very much weight with me. I felt that I had given the subject more thought than my critics, and I went about my work as best I could, thoroughly convinced that he who laughs last, laughs best.

At first we pumped with an ordinary deep-well oil pump, changed to meet the corrosive action of the sulphur. We experienced great difficulty with the valves in the pump, the high specific gravity of the sulphur, the great depth from which it had to be raised, and the corrosive action of the mineral itself making the maintenance of valves very difficult. Zinc and aluminum are practically the only two metals unaffected by liquid sulphur, but both these, being soft and easily disintegrated, would not withstand the shock at the change of stroke of the pump. I decided that if the specific gravity of the sulphur could be raised by the admixture of some other body much lighter, a point might be reached where the hydrostatic pressure of the water in the ground would raise the sulphur. Air seemed the most suitable, and we introduced compressed air into the column of liquid sulphur standing in the well, using a volume of two parts of air and one of sulphur. We have raised our sulphur discharge lines 70 feet above the ground, so that we can fill bins to a height of 65 feet without machinery or pump of any kind in the sulphur proper.

The first well lasted long enough to demonstrate the possibility of success, and to indicate in what directions improvements must be made. At that time, my sulphur enterprise was merely a hobby, the bulk of my time devoted to my Standard Oil work.

Many difficulties arose which we had not foreseen. We lost some wells because of the parting of the pipes. As the mineral was melted from the bottom, the earth above would follow as the sulphur rock settled. The grip of the sand and earth against the pipe was so great that instead of sliding, it would pull the pipe in two and the well would be lost. A 12″ pipe outside of the 10″, with stuffing box and telescope joints, obviated this difficulty. All wells, however, are eventually broken and crushed, when the abstraction of sulphur becomes so great that the cavity made cannot withstand the weight of the ground above it.

We succeeded in increasing the life of a well greatly by lining the hole drilled through the rock with a 9″ perforated pipe.

About that time we found that some wells gave out and ceased to pump when there had been no breaking of the pipes. I reached the conclusion that the cold sulphur water permeating the rock had broken into the melting zone, and brought the temperature of the melting water below the melting point of sulphur. I thought this might be remedied by pumping large amounts of a material like sawdust into the mine with the melting fluid, and that if the quantities of sawdust were large enough, the channels through which the wild waters in the rock entered the melting zone could be sealed.

One well, after pumping about 7,000 tons, at the rate of approximately 350 tons per day, ceased to produce. The pipes were all in good order, and we started to pump sawdust into the ground with the melting water. After pumping in about six carloads per day for five days, the well "sealed" with sawdust and promptly produced 39,000 tons more before the caving of the rock broke the pipes.

We perfected this method of artificially "sealing" the rock surrounding a melting zone, so that the amount now obtained from a well has been greatly increased. Whenever a well breaks, we shoot off with dynamite the 10″ pipe in the quicksand above the rock, and permit the sand to follow into the cavity from which the sulphur has been abstracted, filling up the space of the extracted sulphur rock with sand. The surface, consisting of about 200 feet of clay, follows the quicksand, gently but surely, and in order to maintain the pressure which is necessary to prevent the melting water from breaking into steam, the volume of the sulphur abstracted from below must be replaced by earth from above. To do this a dredge with a capacity of 4,000 cubic yards per day became necessary. Numerous reservoirs have been dug on the outskirts of the mine to supply the material required to do this. This filling has been going on constantly, and the ground has sunk to such an extent that where our house once stood is now 80 feet below the original surface.

These improvements were made slowly, as all experiments had to be made on a ponderous scale and the smallest change required a great deal of time. During the long intervals which necessarily elapsed between my visits to the mine, I could give this new enterprise no attention. It took months to drill a new well when an old one was lost. At one time the work lay idle for a whole year before I could take it up again, and it was not until 1903 that we could see financial success ahead. In that year we produced 35,000 tons, and in 1904 enough to supply the entire consumption of the United States. It was in that year that we sent the first cargo of American sulphur to France.

In order to demonstrate what the mine could do with six wells, we pumped that number simultaneously for two months, producing 122,000 tons of sulphur, which is more than the consumption of the whole world for that period of time.

Prior to the development of the Louisiana sulphur mine, the sulphur production of the United States was less than one-half of one per cent. of its consumption, practically the entire amount required being supplied by Sicily and Japan. The former really had a monopoly of the sulphur business for a great many years.

4. Edison as Inspiration, 1915

RICHARD C. MACLAURIN, "Mr. Edison's Service for Science"

The inventor who made the major transition from the practical inventions of the nineteenth century to the industrial research laboratory of the twentieth was the most famous of all American inventors, Thomas Alva Edison. Working with less academic training than Frasch but with better institutional sup-

From Richard C. Maclaurin, "Mr. Edison's Service for Science," *Science*, XLI (June 4, 1915), 813-15. Reprinted by permission of *Science* and the American Association for the Advancement of Science.

port, and working more methodically, Edison bridged the gap between the theoretical science and practical cut-and-try technology. Significantly, his best work was in that very field of electricity which the *Scientific American* warned was soon to be closed to all those who did not have a grasp of higher mathematics. Edison, characteristically, merely hired some mathematicians and concentrated his own efforts on conceptualizing the whole system, both technical and commercial, which he was attempting to develop. The breadth and detail of Edison's work defies summary, but his total impact on American technology was clear to his contemporaries.

All the world is indebted to Mr. Edison, but the portion of it that is under special obligation is the educational world, particularly the schools of technology. It is not merely that he has helped them by criticism and constructive suggestion; it is not merely that by financial assistance he has enabled them to carry on scientific investigations in fields that he has cultivated with such remarkable success; but it is mainly because he has himself been for a generation an educational institution of the first rank. As much as any other school he has had a profound influence throughout the country in arousing in the minds of young men some sense of the limitless possibilities of science when devoted to the service of man and some appreciation of the conditions under which great problems of industrial improvement must be attacked if lasting victories are to be won. It has been a great thing for America to have such a central figure in this age of applied science—a man with such a hold on the popular imagination as to force men to watch what he is doing, for in studying Edison there can not fail to be revealed something of the underlying forces that mould the world of modern industry.

I have said that Mr. Edison is an institute of technology or a school of applied science. Such an institution, if it be worth anything, stands preeminently for three things: for belief in science and in its powers of service, for understanding and appreciation of the method of science, and in the third place, for faith in the gospel of work.

Edison more than any one else in this country has taught men to see something of what science can do. It would, of course, be impossible on such an occasion as this to enumerate the accomplishments of a life so rich in great achievements. With such an embarrassment of riches, it is scarcely practicable even to single out a few of his great accomplishments. Many of you are familiar with what he did in the early days by way of improving the duplex and quadruplex systems of telegraphy, you know of his invention of the contact transmitter and his development of the loud-speaking telephone, of his marvelous invention of the phonograph (Edison being the first to make a record that would *reproduce* sound), you think of his wonderful work in 1878 and later years in developing the incandescent lamp, and you realize that he practically made the *whole* incandescent system, not only inventing the lamp, but turning his attention to all its adjuncts, improving the dynamos for such work and providing the necessary means for the distribution of power over large areas. You recognize that he laid the foundations for the design of central power stations and that his Pearl Street Station was a landmark in the history of science. His work in this field is truly phenomenal, the three-wire distribution, the system of feeders entering the network of mains at different points, the underground conductor system, the bus system in stations, the innumerable accessories of switches, fuses, meters, etc., that he provided are each achievements that would make the fame of any individual. You appreciate the remarkable character of his later work in developing the apparatus of moving pictures and you agree that what he has done still more recently in perfecting the alkaline storage cell is a splendid example of energy and persistence in attacking a difficult problem. Thinking of all these things, you can not fail to be impressed with two things—the enormous range of his activities and the wonderful simplicity of many of his devices. After all, simplicity of device is always the sign of the master, whether in science or in art. In studying Edison you have something of the same impression as in studying Newton—you are surprised how easy are the steps. Some one asked Lord Kelvin why no one before Edison had invented so *simple* a thing as the feeder system. "The only reason I can think of," he said, "is that no one else was Edison." As to the range of his activities, he has been associated in some way with so many of the great modern developments that people sometimes speak as if he had invented *everything*, even electricity itself, or if they do not go to this length, they find it necessary to explain why he did not invent this or that. The fact that his name is not intimately associated with one of the great modern achievements—the development of the aeroplane—has called forth numerous ingenious explanations. One of these is that it is due to discouragement resulting from his experience as a boy with an experiment that has often been described. It is said that he induced another boy to swallow large quantities of Seidlitz powders and encouraged him to believe that sufficient gases would be generated to enable him to fly. Whether this be history or fable I know not, but, seeing that he has done so much, we need not spend much time in wondering why he has not done more. Nor need we attempt the impossible in the effort to measure the debt that mankind owes to him. Such statements as have been made to the effect that his inventions have given rise to industries that employ nearly a million of men and thousands of millions of capital really give no adequate sense of the value of his achievements, although they may be of some use as a very rough indication of the scale of his activities.

Not only has he shown his faith in science by great achievements, but he has proved himself a great force in education by giving so brilliant an exhibition of the *method* of science, the method of experimentation. When we get to the root of the matter we see that nearly all great advances are made by improvements in method. There is no evidence that men are abler in the twentieth century than they were in the Middle Ages, but they have learned a new method. "It was in Boston," said Edison, "that I bought Faraday's works, and appreciated that he was the master experimenter." It is interesting to think what Edison's appreciation of this fact has meant for the world. His popularity and the place that he holds in the public esteem have forced newspaper men to write so much about him that they have often had to rely upon imagination. It is not surprising, therefore, that there are many current myths regarding Mr. Edison. The popular desire for dramatic contrast suggests that to reach the heights of prosperity and public esteem that he has occupied for long, he must have risen from the depths of poverty and neglect. This is a pure myth, harmless, perhaps, and possibly useful as a spur to ambitious youth. A less innocuous myth is the one that sets him up as a "practical man" in the narrow sense. It is true that he has described himself as "pure practise" in distinction from Mr. Steinmetz whom he has called "pure theory," but this, of course, was a joke. Newspaper men have expanded it so as to make it appear that Edison knows nothing about science, cares nothing for the achievements of the great experimenters and thinkers who have preceded him, and merely tries everything that he can think of until he happens upon what he is seeking. Few things more absurd could be suggested. He is no slave to theory; he is ready, as every scientific man is ready, to try anything that seems reasonable, but practically always he has what seems to him a good reason for everything that he tries. In the rare

cases where he has tried blindly, it has been because there was absolutely no light.

Just one more observation and I am done. His other great contribution to the progress of education has been his constant insistence on the gospel of work. Genius was long ago described as "an infinite capacity for taking pains." We all feel this to be inadequate, and Edison has put the underlying thought more accurately and more picturesquely by his aphorism that "genius is one per cent. inspiration and ninety-nine per cent. perspiration." Contrary to the general notion, very few of his inventions have been the result of sudden inspiration. Practically all have been evolved by slow and gradual processes. His day is said to be a twenty-four-hour day, and he is always working when there is anything to do. Weeks and months and sometimes years of tedious experimenting, dauntless patience and unflagging industry, have marked his onward march to victory from the beginning until now. His is a splendid example of scientific pertinacity rarely if ever surpassed in the history of human achievement. He has won and held the admiration of the world; and his influence must remain as a permanent source of inspiration both within the schools and without.

PART VI WINNING THE WEST

However it has been defined geographically, the American West in both economic and emotional terms has always been a vast treasure house of untapped resources. The West was where one could find pelts, gold, farmland, or timber, and when Americans ran out of frontier they merely took more—from the Indians, from Mexico, and, when the Pacific was reached, by purchase from Russia and conquest from Spain.

So central in importance was technology to the exploitation of the West that its resources were defined in technological terms. Without the requisite technology, gold could not be dug, distances could not be covered, streams could not be harnessed for power or irrigation. And indeed, without science it was not even clear what potential resources existed. The conquest of the West, therefore, usually went through at least three stages—the survey of resources and their potential for development, attempts to exploit them through traditional methods, and, when these proved inadequate, the creation of new technologies to meet the new needs.

At first, efficiency seemed the least relevant of considerations. The very scale of wealth dwarfed any concern for systematic exploitation, and the small scale of traditional, individual, or family production worked to the same effect. Soon, however, the naturally watered land was taken up and all the gold nuggets were plucked from the stream beds. Then came the need for large-scale, expert technology, backed by large-scale capital. Mines were dug deep into the ground and smelters, using complex chemical processes, were built. Plans for irrigation projects with large dams and a network of canals had to be laid out. Giant traction engines had to replace the mules that struggled to harvest the bonanza farms in the grain belts. The nature of the resources demanded a new and larger technology; this in turn required large amounts of capital; and this finally had the effect of systematizing and socializing the freewheeling individualism of early exploitation.

1. An Unusual Engineering Survey, 1855

GEORGE HORATIO DERBY, "Official Report of Professor John Phoenix, A.M."

In the opening of the Far West the most pressing technical problem was that of adequate transportation. Although key rivers such as the Missouri were navigable for long distances, the relative scarcity of such waterways made overland transport the only possibility in most cases. The railroad was immediately seen as the solution to the problem of overcoming the vast distances and rugged topography of the West. Before the Civil War no one transcontinental railroad scheme was supported by the federal government, but a number of surveys, carried out under the auspices of the War Department, were conducted in the hope that technical considerations would somehow rule out all but one of the competing routes.

George Horatio Derby (1823-61) graduated from West Point in 1846 and, as a trained engineer, was assigned to the Pacific railroad surveys. His reports were unexceptional, save one, which he wrote under the pen name of John Phoenix. As Phoenix, Derby became one of the first of that breed of Western humorists which reached its zenith with Mark Twain. The opening chapter of *Phoenixiana; or, Sketches and Burlesques,* which first appeared in 1855, was entitled "Official Report of Professor John Phoenix, A. M. Of a Military Survey and Reconnoissance of the route from San Francisco to the Mission of Dolores, made with a view to ascertain the practicability of connecting those points by a Railroad." Since the Mission Dolores was only two and a half miles from downtown San Francisco, the report was a perfect vehicle for a typically Western parody of a typically Western technological survey.

Mission of Dolores, Feb. 15, 1855. It having been definitely determined that the great railroad, connecting the City of San Francisco with the head of navigation on Mission creek, should be constructed without unnecessary delay, a large appropriation ($120,000) was granted, for the purpose of causing thorough military examination to be made of the proposed routes. The routes which had principally attracted the attention of the public, were "the Northern," following the line of Brannan street, "the Central," through Folsom street, and "the extreme Southern," passing over the "Old Plank Road" to the Mission. Each of these proposed routes has many enthusiastic advocates; but "the Central" was, undoubtedly, the favorite of the public, it being more extensively used by emigrants from San Francisco to the Mission and, therefore, more widely and favorably known than the others.

It was to the examination of this route, that the Committee, feeling a

This sketch was reprinted in *Engineering News* (December 31, 1887), 469-71.

confidence (eminently justified by the result of my labors) in my experience, judgment and skill as a Military Engineer, appointed me on the first instant. Having notified that Honorable Body of my acceptance of the important trust confided to me, in a letter, wherein I also took occasion to congratulate them on the good judgment they had evinced, I drew from the Treasurer the amount ($40,000) appropriated for my peculiar route, and having invested it securely in loans at 3 per cent. a month (made to avoid accidents in my own name), I proceeded to organize my party for the expedition.

In a few days my arrangements were completed, and my scientific corps organized as follows:

JOHN PHŒNIX, A. M., Principal Engineer and Chief Astronomer.

Lieut. MINUS ROOT, Apocryphal Engineers. First Assistant Astronomer.

Lieut. NONPLUS A. ZERO, Hypercritical Engineers, Second Assistant Astronomer.

Dr. ABRAHAM DUNSHUNNER, Geologist.

Dr. TARGEE HEAVYSTERNE, Naturalist.

Herr VON DER WEEGATES, Botanist.

Dr. FOGY L. BIGGUNS, Ethnologist.

Dr. TUSHMAKER, Dentist.

ENRY HALFRED JINKINS, R. A.,
ADOLPHE KRAUT, Draftsmen.

HI FUN, Interpreter.

JAMES PHŒNIX (my elder brother), Treasurer.

JOSEPH PHŒNIX ditto, Quarter-Master.

WILLIAM PHŒNIX (younger brother), Commissary.

PETER PHŒNIX ditto, Clerk.

PAUL PHŒNIX (my cousin), Sutler.

REUBEN PHŒNIX *ditto*, Wagon-Master.

RICHARD PHŒNIX (second cousin), Assistant Wagon-Master.

These gentlemen, with 184 laborers employed as teamsters, chainmen, rodmen, etc., made up the party. For instruments we had 1 large transit (8-in. achromatic lens), 1 mural circle, 1 altitude and azimuth instrument (these instruments were permanently set up in a mule cart, which was backed into the plane of the true meridian, when required for use), 13 large theodolites, 13 small theodolites, 8 transit compasses, 17 sextants, 34 artificial horizons, 1 Siderial clock, and 184 solar compasses. Each employé was furnished with a gold chronometer watch, and, by a singular mistake, a diamond pin and gold chain; for directions having been given, that they should be furnished with *"chains and pins,"* meaning of course such articles as are used in surveying—Lieut. ROOT, whose "zeal somewhat overran his discretion," incontinently procured for each man the above-named articles of jewelry, by mistake. They were purchased at Tucker's (where, it is needless to remark, "you can buy a diamond pin or ring"), and afterwards proved extremely useful in our intercourse with the natives of the Mission of Dolores, and, indeed, along the route.

Every man was suitably armed with four of Colt's revolvers, a Minie rifle, a copy of Col. BENTON's speech on the Pacific Railroad, and a mountain howitzer. These last named heavy articles required each man to be furnished with a wheelbarrow for their transportation, which was accordingly done; and these vehicles proved of great service on the survey, in transporting not only the arms but the baggage of the party, as well as as the plunder derived from the natives. A squadron of dragoons, num-

bering 150 men, under Capt. McSPAD-
DEN, had been detailed as an escort.
They accordingly left about a week before us, and we heard of them occasionally on the march.

On consulting with my assistants, I
had determined to select, as a base for
our operations, a line joining the summit of Telegraph hill with the extremity
of the wharf at Oakland, and two large
iron thirty-two pounders were accordingly procured, and at great expense
imbedded in the earth, one at each extremity of the line, to mark the initial
points. On placing compasses over these
points to determine the bearing of the
base, we were extremely perplexed by
the unaccountable local attraction that
prevailed; and were compelled, in consequence, to select a new position. This
we finally concluded to adopt between
Fort Point and Saucelito; but, on attempting to measure the base, we were
deterred by the unexpected depth of
the water intervening, which, to our
surprise, was considerably over the
chain bearer's heads. Disliking to abandon our new line, which had been
selected with much care and at great
expense, I determined to employ in its
measurment a reflecting instrument,
used very successfully by the United
States Coast Survey. I therefore directed my assistants to procure me a
"Heliotrope," but after being annoyed
by having brought to me successively a
sweet smelling shrub of that name, and
a box of "Lubin's Extract" to select
from, it was finally ascertained that no
such instrument could be procured in
California. In this extremity I bethought
myself of using as a substitute the flash
of gun powder. To satisfy myself of
its practicability by an experiment, I
placed Dr. DUNSHUNNER at a distance
of forty paces from my theodolite, with

a flint-lock musket carefully primed and
directed him to flash in the pan when I
should wave my hand. Having covered
the doctor with the theodolite, and by
a movement of the tangent screw
placed the intersection of the cross lines
directly over the muzzle of the musket,
I accordingly waved, when I was astounded by a tremendous report, a violent blow in the eye, and the instan-
taneous disappearance of the instrument.

Observing Dr. DUNSHUNNER lying on
his back in one direction, and my hat,
which had been violently torn from my
head, at about the same distance in another, I concluded that the musket had
been accidently loaded. Such proved to
be the case; the marks of three buckshot
were found in my hat, and a shower of
screws, broken lenses and pieces of
brass, which shortly fell around us, told
where the ball had struck, and bore
fearful testimony to the accuracy of Dr.
DUNSHUNNER's practice. Believing these
experiments more curious than useful,
I abandoned the use of the "Heliotrope," or its subtitutes, and determined
to reverse the usual process, and arrive
at the length of the base line by subsequent triangulation. I may as well
state here, that this course was adopted
and resulted to our entire satisfaction;
the distance from Fort Point to Saucelito by the solution of a mean of
1,867,434,926,465 triangles, being determined to be exactly *three hundred
and twenty-four feet*. This result differed very much from our preconceived
ideas and from the popular opinion; the
distance being generally supposed to be
some 10 miles; but I will stake my professional reputation on the accuracy of
our work, and there can, of course, be
no disputing the elucidations of science,
or facts demonstrated by mathematical

process, however incredible they may appear *per se*.

We had adopted an entire new system of triangulation, which I am proud to claim (though I hope with becoming modesty) as my own invention. It simply consists in placing one leg of a tripod on the initial point, and opening out the other legs as far as possible; the distance between the legs is then measured by a two-foot rule and noted down; and the tripod moved, so as to form a second triangle, connected with the first, and so on, until the country to be triangulated has been entirely gone over. By using a large number of tripods, it is easily seen with what rapidity the work may be carried on, and this was, in fact, the object of my requisition for so large a number of solar compasses, the tripod being in my opinion the only useful portion of that absurd instrument. Having given Lieut. Root charge of the triangulation, and detached Mr. Jinkins with a small party on hydrographical duty (to sound a man's well, on the upper part of Dupont street, and report thereon), on February 5, I left the Plaza, with the *savans* and the remainder of my party, to commence the examination and survey of Kearney street.

Besides the mules drawing the cart which carried the transit instrument, I had procured two fine pack mules, each of which carried two barrels of ale for the draftsmen. Following the tasteful example of that gallant gentleman—who conducted the Dead Sea Expedition, and wishing likewise to pay a compliment to the administration under which I was employed, I named the mules "Fanny Pierce," and "Fanny Bigler." Our *cortege* passing along Kearney street attracted much attention from the natives, and indeed, our appearance was sufficiently imposing to excite interest even in less untutored minds than those of these barbarians.

First came the cart bearing our instruments; then a cart containing Lieut. Zero with a level, with which he constantly noted the changes of grade that might occur; then 150 men, four abreast, armed to the teeth, each wheeling before him his personal property, and a mountain howitzer; then the *savans*, each with note-book and pencil, constantly jotting down some object of interest (Dr. Tushmaker was so zealous to do something, that he pulled a tooth from an iron rake standing near a stable-door, and was cursed therefore by the illiberal proprietor), and finally, the Chief Professor, walking arm in arm with Dr. Dunshunner, and gazing from side to side, with an air of ineffable blandness and dignity, brought up the rear.

I had made arrangements to measure the length of Kearney street by two methods; first, by chaining its sidewalks, and secondly, by a little instrument of my invention called the "Go-it-ometer." This last consists of a straight rod of brass, firmly strapped to a man's leg, and connected with a system of clock-work placed on his back, with which it performs, when he walks, the office of a *ballistic pendulum*. About one foot below the ornamental buttons on the man's back appears a dial-plate connected with the clock-work, on which is promptly registered, by an index, each step taken. Of course, the length of the step being known, the distance passed over in a day may be obtained by a very simple process.

We arrived at the end of Kearney street, and encamped for the night about sundown, near a large brick building, inhabited by a class of people

called "The Orphans," who, I am cred-
ibly informed, have no fathers or moth-
ers! After seeing the camp properly arranged, the wheelbarrows parked and a
guard detailed, I sent for the chainmen
and "Go-it-ometer" bearer, to ascertain
the distance traveled during the day.

Judge of my surprise to find that the
chainmen, having received no instructions, had simply drawn the chain after
them through the streets, and had no
idea of the distance whatever. Turning from them in displeasure, I took
from the "Go-it-ometer" the number of
paces marked, and on working the distance, found it to be 4½ miles. Upon
close questioning the bearer, WILLIAM
BOULDER (called by his associates,
"Slippery Bill"), I ascertained that he
had been in a saloon in the vicinity, and
after drinking five glasses of a beverage,
known among the natives as "Lager
Bier," he had danced a little for their
amusement. Feeling very much dissatisfied with the day's survey, I stepped
out of the camp, and stopping an omnibus, asked the driver how far he
thought it to the Plaza? He replied,
"Half-a-mile," which I accordingly
noted down, and returned very much
pleased at so easily obtaining so much
valuable information. It would appear,
therefore, that "Slippery Bill," under
the influence of five glasses (probably
2½ quarts) of "Lager Bier," had actually danced four miles in a few moments.

Kearney street . . . is a pass, about
50 ft in width. The soil is loose and
sandy, about 1-in. in depth, below
which Dr. DUNSHUNNER discovered a
stratum of white pine, 3-ins, in thickness, and beneath this again, sand.

It is densely populated, and smells
of horses. Its surface is intersected with
many pools of *sulphuretted protoxide
of hydrogen*, and we found several specimens of a vegetable substance, loosely
distributed, which is classed by Mr.
WEEGATES as the *stalkus cabbagiensis*.

It being late in the evening when our
arrangements for encamping were completed, we saw but little of the natives
until the next morning, when they
gathered about our camps to the number of eighteen.

We were surprised to find them of
diminutive stature, the tallest not exceeding 3 ft. in height. They were
excessively mischievous, and disposed
to steal such trifling things as they
could carry away. Their countenances
are of the color of dirt, and their hair
white and glossy as the silk of maize.
The one that we took to be their chief,
was an exceedingly diminutive person-
age, but with a bald head which gave
him a very venerable appearance. He
was dressed in a dingy robe of jaconet,
and was borne in the arms of one of
his followers. On making them a speech,
proposing a treaty, and assuring them
of the protection of their great Father,
PIERCE, the chief was affected to tears,
and on being comforted by his followers, repeatedly exclaimed, "da, da, da,
da," which, we were informed by the
interpreter, meant "father," and was
intended as a respectful allusion to the
President. We presented him afterwards
with some beads, hawk-bells and other
presents, which he immediately thrust
into his mouth, saying "Goo," and
crowing like a cock; which was rendered by the interpreter into an expression of high satisfaction. Having made
presents to all his followers, they at
length left us very pleased, and we
shortly after took up our line of march.
From the notes of Dr. BIGGUNS, I tran-
scribe the following description of one
of this deeply interesting people.

Kearney Street native; name—Bill;—height, 2 ft. 9 ins.;—hair, white;—complexion, dirt color;—eyes, blue;—no front teeth; opal at extremity of nose;—dress, a basquine of bluish bombazine, with two gussets, ornamented down the front with *crochet* work of molasses candy, three buttons on one side and eight button holes on the other—leggings of tow-cloth, fringed at the bottoms and permitting free ventilation behind—one shoe and one boot;—occupation, erecting small pyramids of dirt and water; when asked what they were, replied "pies," (word in Spanish meaning *feet;* supposed they might be the feet or foundation of some barbarian structure)—religious belief, obscure;—when asked who made him, replied "PAR," (supposed to be the name of one of their principal Deities).

We broke up our encampment and moved north by compass across Market street, on the morning of the 6th, and about noon had completed the survey as far as the corner of Second street.

While crossing Market street, being anxious to know the exact time, I concluded to determine it by observation. Having removed the Sidereal clock from the cart, and put it in the street, we placed the cart in the plane of the meridian, and I removed the eye and object-glass of the transit, for the purpose of wiping them. While busily engaged in this manner, an individual, whom I have reason to believe is connected with a fire company, approached, and seeing the large brazen tube of the transit pointed to the sky, mistook it for a huge speaking trumpet. Misled by this delusion, he mounted the cart, and in an awful tone of voice shouted through the transit, *"Wash her, Thirteen!"* but having miscalculated the strength of his lungs, he was seized with a violent fit of coughing, and before he could be removed had completely coughed the vertical hairs out of the instrument. I was in despair at this sudden destruction of the utility of

our most valuable instrument, but fortunately recollecting a gridiron, that we had among our kitchen apparatus, I directed Dr. HEAVYSTERNE to hold it up in the plane of the true meridian, and with an opera glass watched and noted by the clock the passage of the sun's center across the five bars. Having made these observations, I requested the principal computer to work them out, as I wished to ascertain the time immediately; but he replying that it would take some three months to do it, I concluded not to wait, but sent a man into the grocery, corner of Market and Second, to inquire the time, who soon returned with the desired information. It may be thought singular, that with so many gold watches in our party, we should ever be found at a loss to ascertain the time; but the fact was that I had directed every one of our employes to set his watch by Greenwich mean time, which, though excellent to give one the longitude, is for ordinary purposes the meanest time that can be found. A distressing casualty that befell Dr. BIGGUNS on this occasion may be found worthy of record. An omnibus, passing during the time of observation, was driven carelessly near our Sidereal clock, with which it almost came into contact. Dr. BIGGUNS, with a slight smile, remarked that "the clock *was nearly run down,"* and immediately fainted away. The pursuits of science cannot be delayed by accidents of this nature, so two of the workmen removed our unfortunate friend, at once, to the Orphan Asylum, where, having rung the bell, they left him on the steps and departed, and we never saw him afterwards.

From the corner of Market to the corner of Second and Folsom streets, the route presents no object of interest worthy of mention. We were forced to the conclusion, however, that little throwing of stones prevails near the latter point, as the inhabitants mostly live in glass houses. On the 8th we had brought the survey nearly up to South-wick's Pass on Folsom street, and we commenced going through the Pass on the morning of the 9th. This pass con-sists of a rectangular ravine, about 10 ft. in length, the sides lined with pine boards, with a white oak (*quercus al-bus*) bar, that at certain occasions forms across, entirely obstructing the whole route. We found no difficulty in getting through the Pass on foot, nor with the wheelbarrows; but the mule carts and the "two Fannies" were more trouble-some, and we were finally unable to get them through without a consid-erable pecuniary disbursement, amount-ing in all to one dollar and fifty cents ($1.50). We understand that the city of San Francisco is desirous of effect-ing a safe and free passage through this celebrated cañon, but a large ap-propriation ($220,000) is required for the purpose.

The following passages relating to this portion of the route, transcribed from the Geological Notes of Dr. DUN-SHUNNER, though not directly connected with the objects of the survey, are ex-tremely curious in a scientific point of view, and may be of interest to the general reader.

The country in the vicinity of the route, after leaving Southwick's Pass, is very productive, and I observed with astonishment, that red-headed children appear to grow spontaneously. A build-ing was pointed out to me, near our line of march, as the *locale* of a most as-tounding agricultural and architectural phenomenon, which illustrates the ex-

treme fertility of the soil in a remark-able degree. A small pine wardrobe, which had been left standing by the side of the house (a frame cottage with a piazza), at the commencement of the rainy season, took root, and in a few weeks grew to the prodigious height of 30 ft., and still preserving its propor-tions and characteristic appearance, ex-tended in each direccion, until it cov-ered a space of ground some 40 by 20 ft. in measurement.

This singular phenomenon was taken advantage of by the proprietors; doors and windows were cut in the wardrobe, a chimney erected, and it now answers every purpose of an addition to the original cottage, being two stories in height! This, doubtless, appears almost incredible, but, fortunately the house and attached wardrobe may be seen any day, from the road, at a trifling ex-pense of omnibus hire, by the sceptical. Some distance beyond, rises a noble structure, built entirely of cut-wood, called "The Valley House, by Mrs. Hub-bard." Not imagining that a venial species of profanity was conveyed by this legend, I concluded that Mrs. Hub-bard was simply the proprietor. This brought to my mind the beautiful lines of a primitive poet, Spenser,* if I mis-take not:

"Old Mother Hubbard went to the cup-
        board
    To get her poor dog a bone;
But when she got there, the cupboard was
        bare,
    And so the poor dog got none."

Feeling curious to ascertain if this were, by any possibility, the ancient residence of the heroine of these lines, perchance an ancestress of the present proprietor, I ventured to call and in-

* The Doctor is in error; the lines quoted are from Chaucer. J. P.

quire; and my antiquarian zeal was rewarded by being told that such was the case; and that, if I returned at a later hour during the evening, I could be allowed a sight of the closet, and a view of the skeleton of the original dog. Delighted with my success, I returned accordingly, and finding the door closed, ventured to knock; when a sudden shower of rain fell, lasting but about five seconds, but drenching me to the skin. Undeterred by this *contretemps*, I elevated my umbrella and knocked again, loudly, when a violent concussion upon the umbrella, accompanied by a thrill down the handle, which caused me to seat myself precipitately in a bucket by the side of the door, convinced me that electrical phenomena of an unusual character were prevalent, and decided me to return with all speed to our encampment. Here I was astounded by discovering inverted on the summit of my umbrella, a curious and deeply interesting vase, of singularly antique shape, and composed, apparently, of white porcelain. Whether this vase fell from the moon, a comet, or a passing meteor, I have not yet decided; drawings of it are being prepared, and the whole subject will receive my thorough investigation at an early day.°

I subsequently attempted to pursue my investigations at the "Valley House," but the curt manner of the proprietor led me to suspect that the subject was distasteful, and I was reluctantly compelled to abandon it.

Near the "Valley House," I observed an advertisement of "The Mountain View," by P. Buckley, but the building in which it is exhibited being closed I

° This curious antique, to which I have given the name of the "Dunshunner Vase," has singularly the appearance of a *wash basin!* When the drawings are completed, it is to be presented to the California Academy of Natural Sciences. J. P.

had no opportunity to judge of the merits of the painting, or the skill of Mr. Buckley as an artist. A short distance further, I discovered a small house occupied by a gentleman, who appeared engaged in some description of traffic with the emigrants; and on watching his motions intently, my surprise was great to find that his employment consisted in selling them small pieces of pasteboard *at fifty cents apiece!* Curious to know the nature of these valuable bits of paper, I watched carefully the proprietor's motions through a window for some hours; but being at length observed by him, I was requested to leave—and I left. This curious subject is, therefore, I regret to say, enwrapped in mystery, and I reluctantly leave it for the elucidation of some future *savant.* The beautiful idea, originated by Col. Benton, that buffaloes and other wild animals are the pioneer engineers, and that subsequent explorations can discover no better roads than those selected by them, would appear to apply admirably to the Central Route. Many pigs, singly and in droves, met and passed me continually; and as the pig is unquestionably a more sagacious animal than the buffalo, their preference for this route is a most significant fact. I was, moreover, informed by the emigrants, that this route was "the one followed by Col. Fremont when he lost his men." This statement must be received *cum grano salis,* as, on my inquiry—"What men?" my informant replied, "A box of chessmen," which answer, from its levity, threw an air of doubt over the whole piece of information, in my mind. There can be no question, however, that Lieut. Beale has frequently traveled this route, and that it was a favorite with him; indeed, I am informed that he took the first om-

nibus over it that ever left San Francisco for the Mission of Dolores.

The climate in these latitudes is mild;
snow appears to be unknown, and we
saw but little ice; what there was being
sold at twenty-five cents per pound.

The geological formation of the country is not volcanic. I saw but one small
specimen of trap during the march,
which I observed at the "Valley House,"
with a mouse in it. From the vast ac-
cumulations of sand in these regions, I
am led to adopt the opinions of ethnol-
ogists of the "California Academy of
Natural Sciences," and conclude that
the original name of this territory was
Sand Francisco, from which the final
"d" in the prefix has been lost by time,
like the art of painting on glass.

Considering the innumerable villages
of pigs to be found located on the line
of march, and the consequent effect
produced on the atmosphere, I would
respectfully suggest to the Chief Engineer the propriety of changing the
name of the route by a slight alteration
in the orthography, giving it the appropriate and euphonious title of the
"Scentral R. R. Route."

Respectfully submitted,
ABRAHAM DUNSHUNNER, LL.D.
P.G.C.R.R.R.S.

From Southwick's Pass, the survey
was continued with unabated ardor until the evening of the 10th instant, when
we had arrived opposite Mrs. FREE-
MAN's "American Eagle," where we encamped. From this point a botanical
party under Prof. WEEGATES was sent
over the hills to the south and west for
exploration. They returned on the 11th,
bringing a box of sardines, a tin can of
preserved whortle-berries, and a bottle
of whiskey, as specimens of the products
of the country over which they had

passed. They reported discovering on
the old plank road, an inn or hostel kept
by a native American Irishman, whose
sign exhibited the Harp of Ireland en-
circling the shield of the United States,
with the mottoes

"ERIN GO UNUM,
E PLURIBUS BRAGH."

On the 14th the party arrived in good
health and excellent spirits at the
"Nightingale," Mission of Dolores.

History informs us, that

"The Nightingale club at the village was held,
At the sign of the Cabbage and Shears."

It is interesting to the antiquarian to
look over the excellent cabbage garden,
still extant immediately opposite the
Nightingale, and much more so to converse with Mr. SHEARS, the respected
and urbane proprietor.

The survey and *reconnoisance* being
finished on our arrival at the Mission, it
may be expected that I should here give
a full and impartial statement as to the
merits or demerits of the route, in connection with the proposed railroad.

Some three months must elapse, however, before this can be done, as the triangulation has yet to be perfectly computed, the sub-reports examined and
compiled, the observations worked out,
and the maps and drawings executed.
Besides, I have received a letter from
certain parties interested in the Southern and Northern routes, informing me
that if I suspend my opinion on the
"Great Central" for the present, it will
be greatly to my interest,—and as my
interest is certainly my principal consideration, I shall undoubtedly comply
with their request, unless, indeed,
greater inducement is offered to the
contrary.

Meanwhile I can assure the public,

that a great deal may certainly be said in favor of the Central Route. A full report, accompanied by maps, charts, sub reports, diagrams, calculations, tables and statistics, may shortly be expected.

Profiles of Prof. HEAVYSTERNE, Dr. DUNSHUNNER and myself, executed in black court plaster by Mr. JINKINS, R. A., one of the artists of the expedition in his unrivalled style of elegance, may be seen for a short time at Messrs, LE COUNT & STRONG's—scale, 1½ in. to 1 ft.

In conclusion I beg leave to return my thanks to the professors, assistants, and artists of the expedition, for the energy, fidelity and zeal, with which they have ever co-operated with me, and seconded my efforts; and to assure them that I shall be happy at any time to sit for my portrait for them, or to accept the handsome service of plate, which I am told they have prepared for me, but feel too much delicacy to speak to me about.

I remain, with the highest respect and esteem for myself and everybody else,

JOHN PHOENIX, A. M.,
Chief Eng. and Astronomer,
S.F.A.M.D.C.R.

The annexed sketch of our route, prepared by Mr. JINKINS and KRAUT, is respectfully submitted to the public. It is not, of course, compiled with that accuracy which will characterize our final maps, but for the ordinary purposes of travel, will be found sufficiently correct.

J. P., A. M. C. E. & C. A.

ILLUS.

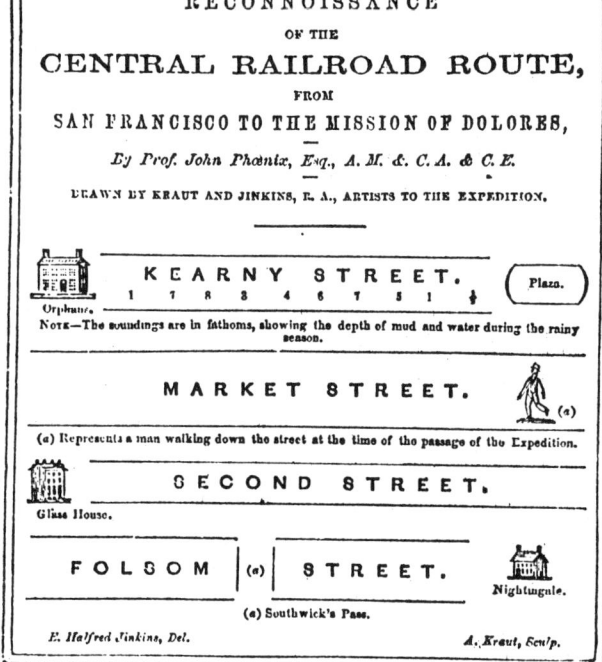

RECONNOISSANCE
OF THE
CENTRAL RAILROAD ROUTE,
FROM
SAN FRANCISCO TO THE MISSION OF DOLORES,
By Prof. John Phœnix, Esq., A. M. &. C. A. & C. E.
DRAWN BY KRAUT AND JINKINS, R. A., ARTISTS TO THE EXPEDITION.

KEARNY STREET.
1   7   8   3   4   6   7   5   1   4   Plaza.
Orphans.
NOTE—The soundings are in fathoms, showing the depth of mud and water during the rainy season.

MARKET STREET.
(a)
(a) Represents a man walking down the street at the time of the passage of the Expedition.

SECOND STREET.
Glass House.

FOLSOM (a) STREET.
Nightingale.
(a) Southwick's Pass.

F. Halfred Jinkins, Del.   A. Kraut, Sculp.

2. A Self-Made Mining Engineer, 1917

T. A. RICKARD, *Interviews with Mining Engineers*

All the Western surveys, even those that had a very specific purpose, such as finding an appropriate route for a railroad, tended to emphasize investigation of the geological formations of the territory explored. The great mineral wealth of the West was already exposed in the Mother Lode country of California, and in the years after the Civil War it was assumed that more bonanzas would appear as the geology of the region became better known. Mining was one of the major industries of the West, and one which was particularly responsive to technological change. The American Institute of Mining Engineers was formed in 1871, an event which symbolized the passing of the isolated prospector and the coming of corporate mining with large-scale investment in scientific and technological knowledge and equipment.

Denis M. Riordan was one of the early Western mining engineers. As time went on a college education, often supplemented with graduate work in the mining schools of Germany, became more necessary for success in the field. But in the early years, it was still possible for a self-educated expert to succeed in the mines, just as decades before, self-educated civil engineers had started the transportation network of the nation.

Mr. Riordan, your name is Irish?

It is. My father was Irish, and his forbears as far back as our records go. My mother was English. I am an American, having been born in New York state. Your question reminds me of the time my youngest grandchild came to her mother, crying, when she was about three years old, and amid sobs managed to say: "Aint, ain't m-my grandfawther of Irish deecent?" Her mother responded soothingly that I was. Alicia's rejoinder was: "W-w-well, that's what I said, but Muriel says he is just plain Irish."

In what town were you born?

In Troy, New York, on June 26, 1848.

What was your father's occupation?

My father was a carpenter, of the kind the old country produced when they served seven years as apprentices before they were even allowed to become journeymen. He could do almost everything with tools in wood, except carving.

What was your early education?

I did not get much early education,

From "Denis M. Riordan: An Interview," *Interviews with Mining Engineers*, ed. T. A. Rickard (San Francisco, 1922), pp. 457-68, 479-81. The section entitled "The School of Experience" appeared first as an editorial in the *Mining and Scientific Press*, October 6, 1917.

but what I did get was in common schools, intermittently. I left school for good at the age of ten, and have never seen the inside of a school-house since, except as a visitor. I have worked to help out family finances and to make my own living, continuously from the age of ten, in Chicago at first.

You speak of Chicago. Your parents evidently moved from New York while you were a child.

They did. My father decided to move to Chicago before any railroad had been completed, and therefore went around the lakes, by boat. Our family landed at Chicago in October, 1852. We lived there until I went into the Army.

You first left home then to enter the Army?

Yes, in 1864. But I started to enlist in 1861; I enlisted five times, but was taken out of the Army each time by my father, until the fifth enlistment. On the fifth I succeeded in getting into the field, in my 16th year.

Did you see much of the Civil War?

Not a great deal. I served with the Army of the Cumberland in the second separate division, mostly on detached scouting service in Missouri and Kentucky, and after being discharged I re-enlisted, which made the sixth enlistment, serving in Tennessee and Georgia, and was finally discharged at Memphis in 1865, after Lee surrendered.

Were you in any battle?

The only engagement of importance in which I participated was the battle of Nashville.

Were you wounded?

I was knocked down by a bullet, which struck the brass plate of my cartridge-box belt, but was not injured.

After the War, what did you do?

I went into various occupations as opportunity offered, the first job being that of a freight brake-man on the Rock Island railroad.

You were getting near the occupation of engineering?

Well, you might look at it that way; I found that there was a decided reluctance to hire a man who had been in the Army. I never knew why, but assumed from the nature of the inquiry, as well as the manner of it, that most employers had the idea that a man who had been a soldier would not work at any regular occupation unless he had to. Therefore, I refrained from mentioning the fact that I had been in the Army until after I got a job and had shown my willingness, at least. I was particularly anxious to have this job of brakeman, although the work was hard, the hours long and irregular, and necessitating exposure to all weathers, because my "bunkie" in the Army had moved to Davenport, Iowa, which was the end of my run, and I thus gained frequent opportunities for a pleasant visit with him.

How long did you serve as brake-man?

Probably four or five months. My father objected to the occupation, both on account of there being no likelihood of advancement, and on account of the danger.

What did you do then?

Upon leaving the railroad I succeeded in getting employment with Palmer & Leiter, which firm subsequently became Field, Palmer & Leiter, and then Marshall Field & Co. I worked as shipping-clerk with them through these changes, until the fall of '68, when I made up my mind to go West, being then 20 years old. At this my father again demurred, and offered to stake me to a store in Chicago if I would remain and cared to follow merchandising as an occupation. But my experience in the Army and my natural bent for out-of-doors made me determined to strike out for the West. I liked to tackle Nature, rather than human nature; and the building of a railroad, the subduing of a forest, or the opening up of a mine, were even then dreams in my mind. So I went West in January 1869, my first stop being at Bear River in Wyoming, whence I worked on the Union Pacific as a carpenter—being handy with tools, as the result of my father's training—until I reached Echo City in Utah. There six of us decided to leave the railroad and go to Salt Lake City, inasmuch as the approaching completion of the transcontinental railroad was in sight. We went to Salt Lake, and after spending a couple of weeks there, all being carpenters and having our tools with us, we flipped up half a dollar to decide whether we would go east or west from there. I did the flipping, and West won. So we bought a six-horse team and a wagon and started for White Pine, a booming mining camp in eastern Nevada. We passed around the southern end of the Great Salt Lake and through Tooele across the Steptoe valley, which was then a quagmire, in which we spent three bitter days, thence through Egan canyon, until we made our way into Hamilton, White Pine district, Nevada. That was in 1869.

And there your mining began?

Only in a temporary way. I started to work as a carpenter at $9 per day.

Miners were being paid from $5 to $6. Everything was high; to illustrate: flour was worth $36 per hundred, lumber $300 per thousand feet, and all other things in proportion. It was a typical raw frontier mining-camp in mid-winter. Most of the miners lived in tents or dug-outs, and a reckless good-natured lot they were.

What were the principal mines in the locality?

Up to the time I left there, there was nothing developed that could be called a "mine." There were innumerable holes all over Treasure Flat, anywhere from 10 to 50 ft. apart, but each claiming "1500 ft. on this lead, lode, or vein," and it was not at all unusual for a shot put into one hole to throw rocks that fell fairly into the next "mine." The ore was principally silver, and some of it ran as high as $20,000 per ton.

It was not long before you went into mining yourself?

I did some prospecting on Treasure hill, but nothing that could be called "mining." I worked principally at carpentry. I left White Pine early in May 1869 to go to Virginia City, where I arrived with $1.60. I walked from Hamilton to Elko, something like 180 miles, and also from Reno, with my blankets on my back, to Virginia City, a distance of 21 miles, and on my arrival at Virginia City I took a glass of beer. This cost me 10 cents, and was all I had that day. I then divided the remainder of my fortune into a three-day grub-stake, eating one meal each day while looking for work. I hunted faithfully for a job all the way from Virginia City down Six-Mile canyon to the Devil's Gate and in all the quartz-mills down Seven-Mile canyon, but at that particular time there had been a fire in the Yellow Jacket group and the town was filled with idle men, many of whom were disgusted White-Piners; others had come from the railroad-camps, the transcontinental railroad having been recently completed.

So you had a poor show?

A mighty poor show; but when my last half-dollar was under my belt, I decided, after consultation with Phil Smith, the foreman of the Kentuck mine, to go to the Washoe valley, which I did, afoot, and got a job in Dall's mill at Franktown. I worked in that mill at different jobs, from battery-feeder to amalgamator, but did not learn assaying at that time. In the fall of 1869 I went back to Virginia City, to work underground in the Chollar Potosi, of which I. L. Requa, father of M. L. Requa, was then superintendent. I worked in that mine until I was again persuaded to change my occupation, going into a store-office, and later, through the friendship of Capt. T. M. Hart, who was time-keeper at the Chollar Potosi, I was brought into a conference with H. M. Yerington, and within two hours I was placed in charge of the business of the Carson lumber-yard, in which duty W. O. Mills, a nephew of D. O. Mills, was my predecessor.

This was at Carson City?

Yes. My duties covered not only the Carson lumber-yard, but grew into the handling of the mills, large and small, that were cutting lumber at Lake Tahoe. When I first went to Carson, the Virginia & Truckee railroad had recently been completed from Carson to Virginia City. The rails and locomotives were hauled by horses from Reno to Carson. I can recall an argument be-

tween H. M. Yerington and William Sharon (who was then the agent of the Bank of California at Virginia City), when Yerington was importuning Sharon to support his recommendation that the road buy another engine. They had two engines, but Mr. Yerington insisted that they should have a reserve engine, and should have their trains so arranged as to start one from each end of the road practically simultaneously. Mr. Sharon demurred strongly, but Mr. Yerington's recommendations finally prevailed with Mr. Mills. At the time of this argument the railroad was being run without even a telegraph-line, but before I left the road it was running 40 trains per day and was easily paying 100% per annum.

You are now referring to the Comstock boom, I presume.

Yes, to one of them. From 1870 to 1872 there was a boom on the Comstock. Those who were there at the time will recall that Crown Point stock went from about $2.50 to about $2000 per share; and the shares of other companies, notably the Con. Virginia, Kentuck, and Belcher, made almost equally phenomenal gains.

Did you speculate yourself?

I had no money for speculating. But only a few days ago I met Mr. A. M. Ardery, who was my chum, is now vice-president of the Virginia & Truckee and Carson & Colorado railroads, and is still my friend; he reminded me of the time we decided that we would put $20 apiece from one month's salary into Crown Point stock. This would have bought us 16 shares at the price then prevailing. We flipped up a $20 piece to decide the matter, the flipping decided against us, and we did not buy.

How long did you remain at Carson?

A couple of years. Then I went back to Virginia City and worked in the Hale & Norcross and other mines as a miner.

What wages did you get?

Four dollars a day.

What did board and lodging cost?

Board cost $8 per week, and lodging anywhere from $10 to $20 per month. Many of us "batched" and did our own cooking. I was one of three, all old soldiers and members of the same G. A. R. post, that batched in a cabin on the divide between Virginia City and Gold Hill. I had not been long in the mine, however, before Mr. Yerington met me one day and asked if I wasn't tired of such dangerous and heavy work, and if I didn't want to come back to my old position at Carson. This resulted in my doing so, and subsequently I was appointed station-agent at Mill Station in the Washoe valley, where I had a large flume under my direction, in addition to my routine work as agent. From there Mr. Yerington brought me back to his office, and although I had no title I acted as private secretary for him until he asked me one day how I would like to go to Bodie.

When was that?

That was in '78. I don't know whether Mr. Yerington knew I had previously had quartz-mill experience, but I was put in charge of the Syndicate mill at Bodie. There was no job in the mill that I couldn't do with my own hands, but I recognized my deficiencies in that I had no knowledge of assaying or metallurgy. I decided to correct this, and made an arrangement with a Freiberg graduate, who had an assay-office in Bodie, to teach me how to assay for gold, silver, and copper. In pursuance of my ambition to learn, I performed my routine duties until half-past nine or ten in the evening, then went up to Bodie, about a mile and a quarter, and worked until eleven or twelve, as the case might be, then back to the mill, and to bed, and was usually on deck again at half-past five. In addition to my duties as mill-superintendent, I served as assistant-superintendent of the Tioga and the Bulwer, and looked after all the underground work of the Syndicate, and did all the office-work for the three companies. My superiors were S. B. Ferguson and Warren Rose. My old foreman, John F. Parr, who lives in Berkeley now, and has since been in Alaska, Siberia, South Africa, and other mining regions, and is now mining in Tuolumne county in this State, was one of the most resourceful men I ever knew. We were 120 miles from a railroad. We had odds and ends of six different plants collected from among the idle mills of the then deserted camp of Aurora, in Nevada, and put together in an old mill-building. Mishaps of all kinds were continually occurring, but no excuse would be accepted for allowing the mill to shut down, and we practically had to run it on "rawhide and wire," and did. Shoes and dies were obtained from Pittsburgh at a cost of about 15 cents per pound. Wood cost $12 per cord. Other supplies in proportion. We had an old 40-ft. two-flue boiler, and an old marine engine, 18 by 40, slide-valve; yet with all these handicaps we managed to keep our milling cost down pretty low—to within $6 per ton, and sometimes as low as $5.

What was your total cost per ton?

We ran mostly on custom ores.

Then you made a profit?

Oh, yes. We received $12 per ton for doing the work. During this time we had one rather unusual run on ore from the Bodie mine, and from this run we produced about a million dollars in six weeks. We seldom could run more than two of the 5-stamp batteries at a time, and frequently only one, because the ore was so rich that it kept the tanks, pans, and settlers full of amalgam. I have frequently known the amalgam to cling to the pan, shoes, and mullers so as to slow down the engine until it would stop on the centre. Any millman who lives near enough to his mill to have it become a part of himself will realize that if a stamp goes wrong, or a belt breaks during the night, it will bring him out of a good sleep into the middle of the floor standing, almost before he has time to recognize what the sound is. Therefore any old-fashioned millman will recognize the fact that an unusual sound caused by one of the stamps going wrong would cause me to hurry on my clothes and go out to the mill to find that sometimes the stamp was not striking ore, neither was it striking iron, but that the bottom of the mortar had become filled up to and above the level of the dies until the material overflowed onto the dies themselves, and that the stamp was falling on malleable gold, deadening the sound. Under such circumstances I have removed the screen and filled a Wells Fargo express-box full of gold from one mortar. Pretty good ore!

This ore came from the Bodie Consolidated?

Yes. We got 900 pounds of gold amalgam one day.

How much of this was gold?

About one-third was metallic gold. During the run on this Bodie ore, I now remember sending a message to Mr. Yerington, who was treasurer of the company, announcing the recovery for that day. He made the remark, "Riordan is probably excited. He speaks of 900 pounds of gold amalgam, but, of course, he means ounces. But that's good enough." I did not mean ounces; I meant pounds.

What was the yield of the ore per ton?

It averaged about $1000 per ton; but some of it ran as high at $50,000 per ton.

Was it a pocket?

It proved to be a pocket; and it was opened up quite accidentally, against orders. The Bodie company had sunk a shaft to the depth of 250 ft. on the south end-line of the Standard mine, with a horse-whim. At that depth they started a cross-cut and intersected some 17 veins. The principal vein, which was the Standard main vein, was very low-grade at that point; but one of the night-foremen, finding some pieces of quartz showing free with gold-bearing quartz, the ore running thousands of dollars gold in a vein about 18 inches wide, afterward called the Burgess vein, decided, without orders, to start a drift south on that vein. In 27 or 28 ft. this drift widened out to about 9 ft. and was filled per ton.

What was the later history of the Bodie mine?

That I cannot tell without making fresh inquiries, because I left Bodie in the fall of 1880 and went to Arizona. I only know that before this phenomenal run the stock was selling at about 50 cents per share and that it increased in value on the market to $50 per share, and before the "pocket" was exhausted it began to pay dividends at the rate of $5 per share per month. I went down to Arizona as the result of a proffer of a position as superintendent of a mine in what is now, I think, Cochise county.

Where was the mine?

It was in the southern end of the Santa Rita mountains. Prior to my leaving Bodie, a number of samples of the ore were sent to me here for assay, together with maps. The samples went within $1 or $2 of the amounts shown on the assay-certificates that accompanied them, and some of them ran over $150 per ton. When I went down there to look the property over, I found that all of the maps and descriptions were accurate. But I also discovered that the ore never came from that mine. That fact had not been stated. So I refused to accept the superintendency of the property.

How old were you then?

About 32.

What did you do next?

The next thing I did was to spend several months with Fred F. Hunt, who is now an analytical chemist in New York City, and who was then covering the South-West in a search for possible copper opportunities for the Orford Nickel-Copper Company, with Thomas A. McElmell, an ex-naval officer, who was a member of the American Institute of Mining Engineers. We three were cabin partners and to a certain extent prospecting partners, especially McElmell and myself, although we had no formal agreement. I decided to take up a property adjoining the Copper Queen

at Bisbee, and two business men from Iowa and myself formed a partnership and put some $40,000 into this property in the search for copper ore.

You had saved money from your salary?

I had saved money from my salary and I had made several lucky turns in mining stocks, at both Virginia City and Bodie.

So you were a capitalist?

In a small way. I was always willing and ready to take chances, and have been flush and broke perhaps twenty times, and expect to be broke again a few times before I pass in my checks. This copper-mining venture at Bisbee not proving profitable, I tackled another prospect in the Silver Bell district, northwest of Tucson, a venture in which one of my previous partners and Senator Norwood, of Georgia, now deceased, were principals. The enterprise languished and finally expired for want of capital.

What has since then happened to the prospects that you tackled both at Bisbee and Silver Bell?

The prospect at Bisbee I do not believe ever developed into a mine, but the prospect in the Silver Bell district was afterward developed by E. B. Gage and Frank Stanton, associated with Frank M. Murphy, into the Imperial Copper Co., which, I understand, has been acquired by the Guggenheims. From Silver Bell I went to Prescott, and there became associated with the then Governor of Arizona, F. A. Tritle, whom I had known previously at Virginia City. Governor Tritle, F. F. Thomas, and myself at one time had the United Verde property under option, but we had to lay down our hands for the want of $14,000. This was before it had been examined by W. A. Clark. While associated with Tritle I made examinations of properties in the South-West and down into northern Sonora, as far as Altar. Subsequently, and perhaps growing out of our intimacy, I was asked by the Governor to take the agency for the Navajo Indians in northeastern Arizona, because rumors had reached the trading-posts of discoveries of valuable minerals—gold and silver, lead and copper—on the reservation. The Governor wanted somebody in whom he reposed confidence to go up there and take charge of the Indians, as agent for the Government; and while in that capacity to ascertain whether the rumors were true.

Before we proceed further, I shall ask whether you had been trying to supplement your practical experience with the reading of technical books?

When I was a "cub" miner, in Virginia City, a working miner who knew five or six different kinds of rock was regarded as being something of a geologist. For instance, if he knew granite, limestone, quartz, porphyry, slate, and sandstone, he was regarded as being a fellow who was observant and a good judge of rock. I was always desirous to know the reason of things. In working on the lower levels of the Comstock in bad air I had occasion to notice that the heat of the water coming from the face of the drift was sufficient to cook eggs. I wanted to know what made that water hot. On inquiry among men who had a technical education, I learned that it was caused by the chemical reactions in the rocks themselves when exposed to oxidation.

What books did you have?

Usually none, because of my wander-

ing life. I did manage to get hold of Dana's "Mineralogy," and occasionally I would have my attention called to some book on geology by such men as Fred Hunt, who knew; and I made it a habit to make a humble exposure of my ignorance, so that I never failed to elicit information from anyone who was near me. Another thing that helped me was that, for a number of years, the members of the U. S. Geological Survey, many of whom I knew personally, including Major Powell, Arthur Davis, Prof. Thompson, and Prof. Hiller, camped in that part of the South-West where I happened to be, and I got the benefit of their criticisms and their observations, in many cases extending back 25 years, while sitting around camp-fires, and the information they imparted would be etched on my memory. In 1882 I became a member of the American Institute of Mining Engineers, and learned more through my acquaintance with such men as Dr. R. W. Raymond, Anton Eilers, George W. Maynard, E. G. Spilsbury, John Stanton, and Charles Macdonald. Some of the younger men with whom I made friends were Arthur S. Dwight, Karl Eilers, Dr. Spencer, and Dr. Hess of the Geological Survey, and such engineers as John B. Keating, Herbert R. Hanley, and others with whom I was in close association both in discussions over practical operations, as well as technical methods.

Then Mr. Riordan, you got your technical equipment from nature and from men, rather than from books?

Exactly so. Or, to put it in another way, I got it from hard knocks and absorption. My books were few.

You have given me the impression that you read a great deal now.

Yes, I do now, but then I had neither the time nor the facilities. Some sixteen years ago I was asked by the General Electric Company to analyze for them 700 or 800 mining reports. I have never quite known how they came to hear of me. But I took up the task, and out of the 700 or 800 badly mixed manuscripts I picked seven mines that I thought were worthy of investigation and recommended that they get some high-class engineer to make the investigations; but, instead of doing this, they gave me authority to choose the engineers and have the investigations made. For a number of years I had a free hand in the making of examinations in various parts of the continent, and naturally in company with these engineers, analyzing the facts they ascertained and giving me the reasons why, I was bound to get some of the knowledge they had acquired by study as well as by observation, but which I could not have got in any other way. Then when I found I lacked information in any particular I would not hesitate to ask where I could get the original authority or the original source of information on this or that point. If I heard an ore spoken of as "bornite," when I did not know what that mineral was, I made it my business to go and hunt it up. And thereafter that was fixed in my memory. Habitually for 15 years I read reports and articles on mining subjects from two to three hours each day, besides the work I did during office-hours. . . .

THE SCHOOL OF EXPERIENCE

In this issue we publish another of those biographical records from which so much of human interest can be learned. Our subject, Mr. Denis Mathew Riordan, is a veteran whose kindliness of heart and wide sympathy with all that concerns the profession have kept him young amid the vicissitudes of a checkered career. That career did not start in the conventional way; he did not graduate from a school of mines or a university; he did not have an indulgent uncle to give him a job as soon as he wanted one; on the contrary, he had a struggle to reach even the lowest rung of the ladder that leads to promotion and success. A carpenter and the son of a carpenter, he began life with but little prospect of achieving his present place as an honored member of a highly technical profession. Perhaps he was fortunate in the time of his debut, for the Civil War was followed by a remarkable era of mineral exploration and industrial development. He followed Greeley's advice and came West, to grow up with the country that offered many chances to the intelligent and energetic; but first he did his duty as a good citizen by serving as a soldier. In these days when "slackers" are not far to seek, it should be more inspiring than amusing for our young men to read of the boy that tried five times to enlist before he succeeded in getting into uniform. Those who know Mr. Riordan need not be told that the soldier-boy of 50 years ago is a keen patriot today and as eager to serve the national cause now as he was then. We met Mr. Riordan in Europe when he went thither on the "Tennessee" to distribute the funds for American refugees, and we recall that he avowed himself "neutral," but he used the word in an ironical way that left no doubt about his feelings on the subject—feelings strengthened by later events. He served a varied apprenticeship; soldier, brakeman, shipping clerk, carpenter, millman, miner, all of these occupations he tried before, at the age of 22, he obtained a position of responsibility as superintendent of a lumber-yard. But the call of the mine was insistent; he returned to Virginia City; and when 30 years old he won his first real promotion, becoming superintendent of a stamp-mill at Bodie. He tells the interviewer how he taught himself in his spare time, overcoming not easily, but slowly and laboriously, the lack of a special training. We were not at Bodie in 1878, but from another we learn that Mr. Riordan was "a live wire" in those exciting days; he was ambitious and speculative; he was fond of hunting, proving himself a good scout but a poor shot; our informant remarks that "he had to shoot oftener and tramp farther than most of us, but he always got birds." Apparently he was persistent in small as well as in big things. He was keenly interested in politics and local affairs, as he is now in national and world affairs; his mental horizon has been enlarged, but his mind is as full of movement as heretofore: never provincial, he asserts the best right of civilized man: to make all knowledge his patrimony. When working underground on day's pay he began to acquire scraps of mineralogy and geology. As a young man he had the good sense and the good fortune to make friends among the leaders of the profession, and to learn from them by daily association more than books could tell. The reading of reports and technical writings was supplemented by an intelligent inquisitiveness. He was never afraid to acknowledge ignorance and always quick to ask questions. Here is a hint to our young men. Nothing is more foolish than the false assumption of knowledge, the intellectual "bluffing" that checks the acquirement of accurate information. To

realize ignorance and to be eager to correct it are the marks of the real student. Later, in his first experience with the General Electric people, Mr. Riordan was true to form; he refused to undertake work for which he considered himself unqualified; he was glad to avail himself of the assistance of specialists. His saying is true that a mature man, if intelligent, and honest, knows his capabilities and his limitations, and is wise if he recognizes them. He knew his own and that made him a safe adviser. Our readers will note with keen interest the names of the mines he selected as likely to become profitable enterprises. Any man might be proud of such a record. It was the result of native sense, keen observation, and wide information. Again there is a lesson for our young friends: the proper study of mankind is man; to know men is better than to devour books; the understanding of one's fellows is capital of an indestructible kind. The interview also suggests that men differ greatly in their capacity to be helped by their surroundings; some sink to the bottom, others swim to the top. "Men live their future now. They determine by today's behavior and aspiration the strength or weakness that will tomorrow honor or shame them." Such is the moral of this story; but no maxims can give to a man the genius of friendship. This our friend possesses, and it is the very crown of life. He has the social gifts of quick understanding and willing co-operation; more particularly the happy knack of making congenial persons known to each other, for work as well as for pleasure. His friends know him to be a charming letter-writer and a winning teller of stories either by mail or across the table. The equanimity shown by him in times of trouble is largely the product of an essential sanity and of a philosophic temperament disciplined by a keen sense of humor—a salt that is the savor for making palatable even the unpleasant happenings of checkered days. And one thing more this mining engineer possesses, and shares with his fellows freely: an innate kindliness that has found fruition in acts of service to the less fortunate whose trails he has crossed. Many that read this will jump to affirm what we have just said, for in his trail across the waste places of the earth where mines are found there grow for him many flowers of grateful remembrance.

3. Making the Desert Bloom, 1899

ELWOOD MEAD, "Rise and Future of Irrigation in the United States"

After its great wealth, the single most important fact about the West is its aridity. Most Americans thought of the West in terms of settlement rather than hit-and-run exploitation. Indeed, the American ideal of the yeoman farmer demanded that the territory be settled by small farmers. With little or no rain in most parts of the country, however, the dream of self-sufficient family farms was hardly reasonable. Yet by the turn of the century a handful of government scientists and engineers had come to the conclusion that the very latest engineering and science could be harnessed to the ideal of a pre-industrial, agrarian past.

This approach received its most concrete embodiment in the establishment of a Reclamation Service in 1902 to bring irrigation to the West. Writing shortly before this action, Elwood Mead, director of the Office of Irrigation Investigations and later commissioner of reclamation, traced the practice and future of hydraulic engineering in the West. At the same time his description clearly shows the complex interaction of social, economic, and technical imperatives which were to plague reclamation engineers in the decades to come.

BEGINNINGS OF MODERN IRRIGATION

For the beginnings of Anglo-Saxon irrigation in this country we must go to the Salt Lake Valley of Utah, where, in July, 1849, the Mormon pioneers turned the clear waters of City Creek upon the sunbaked and alkaline soil in order that they might plant the very last of their

From Elwood Mead, "Rise and Future of Irrigation in the United States," *Yearbook of the United States Department of Agriculture. 1899* (Washington, D.C., 1900), pp. 592-97, 607-12.

stock of potatoes in the hope of bringing forth a crop to save the little company from starvation.

Utah is interesting not merely because it is the cradle of our modern irrigation industry, but even more so as showing how important are organizations and public control in the diversion and use of rivers. Throughout the pioneer period of their history the settlers of Utah were under the direction of exceptionally able and resourceful leaders, who were aided by the fact that their followers were knit together by a dominating religious impulse. These leaders had the wisdom to adapt their methods and shape their institutions to conform to the peculiar conditions and environment of a land strange and new to men of English speech. They found that irrigation was necessary to their existence in the home that they had chosen, and that the irrigation canal must therefore be the basis of their industrial organization, which was largely cooperative; hence, the size of their farms, which are less than 30 acres upon the average, the nature of their social relations, which are close and neighborly.

That the great material results which quickly followed could have been realized without the cohesion which came from an association dominated by religious discipline and controlled by the superior intelligence of the head of the Mormon Church, is doubtful; but that the character of institutions in the valleys of Utah, both industrial and social, was chiefly due to the environments in which they were placed is beyond dispute. Cooperation became the dominant principle simply because the settlers were in a land without capital, and it was beyond the power of the individual to turn the mountain current

from its course and spread it upon his lands. Only the labor of many individuals, working under organization and discipline, could make the canals or distribute the waters. A small farm unit was chosen, not because men were less greedy for land than in all other new countries, but because it was quickly seen that the extent of the water supply was the measure of production, and their ability to provide this was small. Diversified farming, which is one of the leading causes of the remarkably even prosperity of Mormon agriculture, was resorted to because the Territory was so far removed from other settlements that it was compelled to become absolutely self-sustaining. The small farm unit made near neighbors, and this advantage was still more enhanced by assembling the farmers' homes in convenient village centers. One reason for adopting this plan, in the first place, was doubtless for protection against the Indians, but it has become a permanent feature, which is still adhered to in making new settlements because most satisfactory to the social instinct.

COOPERATIVE COLONIES IN COLORADO AND CALIFORNIA

The discovery of gold in California created the Overland Trail, which wound its tortuous course across the hitherto trackless wastes of the arid domain. Its stations were usually along the banks of the streams. In the neighborhood of these, settlers had established themselves, and by means of simple furrows turned the waters of the streams upon the bottom land. This was the extent of irrigation throughout the vast region it traversed, outside of Utah, before the Union Colony at Greeley, Colo., became the second historic instance of the beginnings of the present system, and one which furnished a different standpoint for a study of the subject.

As Utah is the result of a religious emigration, so Greeley is the creation of the town meeting. Its founding marked the beginning of a new and different industrial development in Colorado. Before this it was the wealth of the mines or the migratory and adventurous experiences of the range live-stock business which had attracted settlement. Greeley, on the contrary, represented an effort of homemaking people, both to enjoy landed independence and social and intellectual privileges equal to those of the towns and cities they had left. Among its first buildings was Colony Hall, and among its first organizations the Lyceum, in which all the affairs of the community were debated with a fervor and fearlessness quite worthy of Horace Greeley's following. Cooperation was adopted in the construction and management of public utilities, of which the irrigation canal was the first and most important. The wisdom and justice of making common property of the town site, the beauty and value of which could only be created by the enterprise and public spirit of all, was recognized and put into practice with satisfactory results. The only deliberate extravagance was the erection at an early day of a school building worthy of the oldest and richest New England community. The highest methods both of irrigation and cultivation were sought out through numberless experiments, until Greeley and its potatoes grew famous together. The home and civic institutions of the colony became the pride of the State, and the hard-won success of the community inspired numerous similar undertakings and furnished an impulse which resulted in the reclamation and settlement of northern Colorado. Boulder, Longmont, Loveland, and Fort Collins were the outgrowth of success at Greeley, and each adopted many of the ideas and tendencies of the parent colony.

Twenty years subsequent to the beginning of Utah, and contemporaneously with the settlement of Colorado, similar influences began to make themselves felt in California, especially in its southern part. Anaheim is called the mother colony. This was cooperative in its inception, and its principal irrigation system has ever remained such. Riverside followed a few years later and represented a higher ideal; but the spirit of speculation in which California civilization was born soon fastened itself upon irrigation, as it had done in the case of mining, and ran a mad race through southern California. Irrigation in this State became corporate and speculative. Where Utah and Colorado had depended only upon their hands and teams for the building or irrigation works, California issued stocks and bonds, and so mortgaged its future. Men began to dream of a new race of millionaires, created by making merchandise of the melting snows, by selling "rights" to the "renting" of water, and collecting annual toll from a new class of society, to be known as "water tenants."

CORPORATE CANAL BUILDING

The investment of corporate capital in canals to distribute and control water used in irrigation began in California, but spread like a contagion throughout the West. For a quarter of a century it has been the leading factor in promoting agricultural growth of the western two-fifths of the United States. It has been the agency through which many millions of dollars have been raised and expended, hundreds of miles of canals constructed, and hundreds of thousands of acres of land reclaimed. It has built the largest overfall dam ever placed in a large river. It has been the chief agency in replacing temporary wooden structures by massive headworks of steel and masonry, and has, by the employment of the highest engineering talent available and the introduction of better methods of construction, promoted the economy and success with which water is now distributed and used. The question which is now to be considered is how the vast fabric created through its agency is to be directed and controlled in order that it may not crumble of its own weight.

The construction of irrigation works by corporate capital came as a natural if not inevitable evolution. There came a time in the districts first settled when the opportunities to divert water cheaply had largely been utilized, and when the expenditure required was beyond the means of either the individual or the cooperation of many individuals. The preliminary outlay was too great. In older European countries experience has shown that no agency can be so wisely intrusted with these larger expenditures as the State. Large irrigation canals have been considered as being, in their nature, as much public improvements as are works to supply water to cities and towns. Being for the service of the public, those in older European countries have largely passed under public ownership.

In this country corporations have, so far as construction is concerned, taken the place of governmental agencies in other lands. Practically all of the larger and costlier works built within the last two decades have been of this character. The High Line Canal, which waters the land surrounding Denver, Colo., with its tunnel through the mountains and its aqueduct carried along the rocky cliffs below; the canals of the Wyoming Development Company, with its tunnel alone costing more than all the Greeley Colony canals combined, and its reservoir for storing the entire year's discharge of the Laramie River; the Sunnyside Canal of Washington, which when built traversed 60 miles of sagebrush solitude, are illustrations in three States of the nature of corporate contributions to irrigation development. Even in Utah, cooperation was not sufficient to reclaim all of Salt Lake Valley. For forty years the tableland north of the lake, one of the largest and best tracts of irrigable land in the valley, remained unoccupied, while the sons of the pioneers were compelled to seek homes in the surrounding States. To reclaim this land, a canal had to be carried for 3 miles along the precipitous sides of Bear River Canyon. The flow of the river had to be controlled by an extensive dam and the Malad River twice bridged by long and high aqueducts, and the million-dollar outlay required was more than home seekers could provide.

The creation of water-right complications came with the building of corporate canals. Previous to this it had been the rule for those who built ditches to own the land they watered, and there was little difference as to whether the right to water went with the ditch or with the land, because the ownership of both was united in the same person. But when companies were organized to distribute water for others to irrigate with and to derive a revenue from water rentals, there arose the question as to who was the owner of the right to the water diverted—the company transporting the water or the farmer who used it. The laws of nearly all the Western States make the ditch owner the appropriator. This has created a divided ownership of land and water, and many canal companies have framed water-right contracts on the theory of absolute ownership. These have proven a source of constant irritation to farmers. Some of these contracts require the farmer to pay, at the outset, a royalty or bonus for the "right" to receive water, the charge for this right varying from $5 to $500 per acre, depending on the scarcity of the water supply or the value of land and its products. There is a very prevalent feeling among farmers that as they are the actual "beneficial users" of the stream, they should be considered the appropriators, or at least that the owner of the land should share with the owner of the ditch in the right to water.

OBJECTIONS TO CORPORATE CANALS

Having dealt with the benefits derived from corporate investments in irrigation works, it is now proper to point out their defects. The most serious one is that nearly all large canals have been losing investments. The record of these losses is so stupendous that it is reluctantly referred to. A single enterprise in one of the Territories represents to its projectors a loss of over $2,000,000. The Bear River Canal, in Utah, which cost over a million dollars, was recently sold under a judgment for about one-tenth of this sum. A single canal in California represents a loss to its build-

ers of over $800,000. These are isolated cases. Similar instances might be multiplied indefinitely. They are not due to bad management, to dishonesty, or faulty engineering. Some of the worst failures in a financial sense have been handled by the brightest and most experienced men in the West, but they were not able to make their enterprises pay, that is, they have not paid their builders. Nearly all have been a success so far as the section interested was concerned, but the benefits have gone to the public and not to the investors. The reasons for this should be more generally understood. The following are the most important:

(1) The necessarily long delay in securing settlers for the land to be irrigated and in obtaining paying customers for the water to be furnished.

(2) The large outlay and several years of unprofitable labor required, as a rule, to put wild land in condition for cultivation. Settlers of limited means can not meet this outlay and in addition pay water rentals. Nearly all of the settlers on arid public land are men of limited means; hence, canal companies have at the outset to furnish water at small cost, or furnish to a small number of consumers.

(3) The unsuitability of the public-land laws to irrigation development.

(4) The acquirement of the lands to be reclaimed, in many instances, before canals are completed by nonresident or speculative holders, who would do nothing for their improvement.

(5) Expenses of litigation. Experience has shown that in the estimates of cost of a large canal provision should be made for a large and long-continued outlay for litigation. It begins with the

adjudication of the stream and is protracted through the controversies over water rights. . . .

METHODS AND MEASURES NEEDED TO DEVELOP THE ARID REGION

It is well to consider now by what methods and by what measures of legislation the splendid resources of the arid region may be opened to development.

The first step is to determine the proper control and just distribution of the water supply. The problem varies with different portions of the arid region. In the South, streams are generally torrential in character, furnishing the bulk of their waters in heavy floods, which must be stored in the many natural sites available in the mountains at a distance from the places where the water is to be applied to the soil. In the North, on the other hand, the problem is not that of storage, but of the diversion of great rivers like the Yellowstone, the Snake, the Columbia, and the Missouri. Here works adequate to the reclamation of the areas of arid land which remain can only be built at great cost, rivaling those along the Ganges and the Nile.

Before such development proceeds further it is desirable that some common agreement should be reached concerning the true character of water rights. The idea of private ownership in water apart from the land can not prevail without creating institutions essentially feudal in character. A water lord is even more undesirable than a landlord as the dominant element in society. It is indisputable, as has already been said, that the man who owns the water practically owns the land. A proposition which contemplates the turning over of all the land to a private monopoly, thus making a tenantry of those who may have their homes upon it in the future, could not hope to command popular support. But the idea of a private ownership of water, amounting to a virtual monopoly of this vital element, has been permitted to grow up in the West. To a certain extent it has obtained recognition in legislation and protection in judicial decrees and decisions. In other countries the doctrine has largely disappeared, and in our country it should give place to a more enlightened conception, and to the only principle that can safely be adopted as the foundation of the agricultural industry in the West.

The right to water which should be recognized in an arid land is the right of use, and even this must be restricted to beneficial and economical use in order that the water supply may serve the needs of the largest possible number. Ownership of water should be vested, not in companies or individuals, but in the land itself. When this principle is adopted, the control of the water is divided precisely like the land, among a multitude of proprietors. Reservoirs and canals are then like the streets of the town, serving a public purpose and permitting ready access to private property on every hand. Water monopoly is impossible under this method, and no other abuse is encouraged by it. Years of painful experience have abundantly proven that peaceful and orderly development can not be realized except as water and land are forever united in one ownership and canals treated merely as public or semipublic utilities rather than as a means of fastening a monopoly upon the community. In Wyoming and Nebraska the true principle has already been adopted by the State boards of control and put into practice with the best results. If it can be maintained and speedily extended to the other States, as it surely must be in time, it would mark an economic reform of the highest significance in the life of the West.

APPROPRIATION AND DISTRIBUTION OF THE WATER SUPPLY

Next in importance to the correct solution of the question of water ownership are the great problems of appropriation and of distribution. As soon as possible all ditches used in irrigation should be carefully measured by some public authority and the results of this measurement be given the widest publicity, in order that irrigators may know approximately how much is taken and how much remains to be taken by new canals. The need of this information is so obvious that it will perhaps be difficult for readers unfamiliar with the subject to credit the assertion that in all but four of the Western States the matter has been wholly neglected. This fact is largely responsible for the disheartening litigation which prevails so widely.

It is of almost equal importance to have a scientific determination of the practical duty of water, showing the amount required for different soils and crops. Still further, there must be some form of public control in the distribution of water. Trouble always results when this is left to rival users to determine how much they need, especially in years of partial drought, when the supply may be insufficient for all, and it is consequently necessary to recognize appropriations in the order of their priority.

PUBLIC SUPERVISION AND CONTROL OF IRRIGATION

The entire discussion leads up to one inevitable conclusion: This is that irrigation, over and above all other industries, is a matter demanding public supervision and control. Every drop of water entering the head gate, and every drop escaping at the end of the canal, is a matter of public concern. The public must determine, through constitutions and statutes, the nature of water ownership. The public must establish means for the measurement of streams and for ascertaining how much water may be taken for each acre of land under the principle of beneficial use. The public must see that justice is done in the distribution of water among those who have properly established their rightful claims to it. We have thoroughly tried the method of leaving all this to private initiative and management, and, along with magnificent material progress, we have reaped a large crop of deplorable financial results.

While much must be left to the action of States and communities, there is still a wide field for national effort. Only the nation can legislate as to the public lands and reform the abuses which have been referred to in connection with the present system of land laws. There is a strong popular demand in the West for legislation providing public aid in the construction of works of too great magnitude and cost for private enterprise and a growing belief that one of two things should be done: Either the arid States should be placed in a position to extend this aid, or the General Government should extend the work it is now doing in the reclamation of certain Indian reservations to the reclamation of the unoccupied public lands. One policy much discussed and widely favored is legislation which will permit of the leasing of the public grazing lands for a term of years at a small annual rental, the proceeds to be given to the several arid States and applied by them to irrigation development. If this is carried out, the settlers owning the contiguous irrigated land should be favored; the object being to unite with the lands reclaimed a certain portion of the public pasture.

The National Government alone can make the best and broadest study of the various economic questions related to the development of agriculture on arid lands. This includes not only the measurement of streams and survey of reservoir sites, but also a consideration of practical methods of applying water to the soil and of social and industrial institutions adapted to the environment of the arid region. The nation alone can deal with the conflicting rights in interstate and international streams and with the construction of great reservoirs at their head waters, with a view to benefiting the several States lying along their course. The National Government is already active along all these lines, and the field for the expansion of its efforts is wide and inviting.

INFLUENCE OF IRRIGATION UPON PEOPLE AND COUNTRY

While a description of existing conditions in the far West necessarily includes references to many evils and disappointments, there is a brighter side to the picture, and the future is luminous with new hopes for humanity. A vast population will make its homes in valleys now vacant and voiceless, yet potentially the best part of our national heritage. They will create institutions which will realize higher ideals of society than the world has yet seen. Irrigation is much more than an affair of ditches and acres. It not only makes civilization possible where men could not live without it, but it shapes that civilization after its own peculiar design. Its underlying influence is that which makes for democracy and individual independence.

IRRIGATION PRODUCTIVE OF SMALL PROPRIETORS

Where land can only be cultivated by means of the artificial application of water, and where that water is not under speculative control, it is owned in small holdings. This is so because irrigation intensifies the product of the land and so demands much labor. It is a kind of labor which can not profitably be left to hired hands. The result is a multitude of small proprietors working for themselves. This fact is strikingly illustrated in southern California. Here the farms are small and almost exclusively occupied by their owners. But the great wheat ranches in other parts of the State, notably in the Sacramento Valley, depend chiefly upon hired laborers, who make no homes of their own. The Sacramento Valley has less population now than it had twenty-five years ago. Of the increase of the rural population of the State between 1880 and 1890, 77 per cent went to the irrigated counties, and largely consisted of families who bought small farms and proceeded to do their own work. The influence of a great mass of small proprietors tilling their own land can not fail to have a very marked effect upon the character of the institutions.

DIVERSIFIED FARMING A FEATURE OF IRRIGATION

Irrigation lends itself naturally to diversified farming and tends to make population self-sufficient within itself. Although in certain localities, especially those where the climate is favorable to raisins and oranges, the contrary has sometimes been true, the tendency of irrigation as a whole has been to discourage the production of single crops and make families independent by producing the variety of things they consume. This tendency is steadily gaining ground. The diversified farming which irrigation both permits and encourages will be an important element in contributing to the independence of the people who shall inhabit the arid region of the future.

IRRIGATION AS A TRAINING IN SELF-GOVERNMENT

Another interesting feature of irrigation is the training it gives in self-government. A farmer under irrigation can not remain ignorant and indifferent of public questions. He has to consider his interest in the river which feeds his canal and the nature of his relation to other users along its course. It is a training school in self-government and gives the first impetus to civilization in rainless regions. The capacity of the American farmer has already been demonstrated. He is the author of the best of our irrigation laws. Colorado was the first State to enact a law providing for the public control of streams and some sort of systematic procedure for the establishment of rights, but the credit of that is not due to her statesmen, but to the discussions of the Greeley Lyceum and the public spirit and independence of the irrigators under the Colony Canal. Opposed by the conservatism of the legal profession and the prejudices of those not practically familiar with the subject, they had a long and doubtful struggle to secure the adoption of a statute which for a time made the State the lawgiver of the arid region.

In Utah the practices of water users are a hundred years in advance of the State laws. This is due to the fact that irrigators recognize insensibly the community nature of their interest in the streams. The old feudal idea of private ownership in water has never made an irrigated district prosperous, and it never will.

IRRIGATION AND COOPERATION

Another feature is the tendency toward cooperation. Under the Wyoming law accepting the Carey grant this cooperation is made obligatory. Every settler under a canal becomes a shareholder therein. Not only does the right to water attach to the land, but a share in the canal sufficient to carry the water also goes with it. In fact, the need of watering many farms from a common source and of organizing a community under rules and discipline for the distribution of the supply make a nursery of cooperation. Its most conspicuous manifestation is in the widespread and successful fruit exchanges of California. There are many instances of smaller and more local organizations of a co-operative industrial character, and they are multiplying rapidly. They seem likely to deal with yet larger affairs in the future as communities gain in age, numbers, and wealth.

EFFECT OF IRRIGATION ON SOCIAL LIFE

Heretofore one of the evils of the irrigated home has been its isolation. The valleys of many streams are narrow. The broad areas which lie between these valleys are the home of cattle and sheep, but not of men. The Anglo-Saxon thirst for land, and the opportunity which the desert-land act gave to gratify it, resulted at first in a wide separation between homes, and in a loss to the pioneer of the advantages of schools, churches, and social life. Under the larger and later canals the tendency has been in the other direction. The European custom of making homes in village centers has been adopted in parts of Utah, Wyoming, Idaho, and California, and steadily gains in public favor. Where farmers live in villages, their families enjoy ready access to schools, churches, libraries, and entertainments. The agricultural society of the future in the Western valleys will realize a happy combination of town and country life—the independence which springs from the proprietorship of the soil and the satisfaction of the social instinct which comes only with community association. Such conditions are favorable to the growth of the best forms of civilization and the noblest institutions. This is the hope which lies fallow in the arid valleys of the West. Its realization is well worth the struggle which is impending for the reform of our land and water laws, and which will impose high demands upon our statesmanship and call for the exercise of the best order of patriotism.

THE COMMERCIAL IMPORTANCE OF IRRIGATION

The commercial importance of the development of irrigation resources is being realized in the West at the present time as never before. Especially in California there is a new awakening, and an effort on the part of the best elements of citizenship to remove the obstacles which have formerly hampered both public and private enterprise. The East, as a whole, is beginning to realize the great part which the West is to have in the events of the twentieth century. World-wide forces are working to hasten the day of its complete development and of the utilization of all its rich resources. The Orient is awake and offering its markets to the trade of the Pacific coast. With the development of this trade there will come an impulse for the completion of the material conquest of arid America by the enlistment of public as well as private means in the storage and diversion of its streams for the irrigation of its hundred million acres of irrigable soil; the harnessing of its water powers to mill and factory wheels; the crowding of its pastures with new millions of live stock; the opening up of its mines and quarries; the conversion of its forests into human habitations; the coming of a vast population, and the growth of institutions worthy of the time and the place.

4. Harvesting with Steam, 1898

FRANK CORRY, "California Harvesting Machinery"

Where agriculture did flourish in the West, its scale dwarfed anything yet seen in the East. On the bonanza wheat farms of the plains states and the Central Valley of California, vast acres of grain challenged the ingenuity of machine builders and focused on one of the major problems of American agriculture in the nineteenth century—the shortage of cheap power in adequate quantities. By the end of the century, the steam traction engines—for those who could afford them—had presented one solution to this problem. The pulling of combine reapers through the fields by these great leviathans was the furthest extent of mechanization to appear on the farm before the advent of rural electrification and the gasoline tractor. By 1910, some 3,600,000 horsepower were being provided by steam for farm work. One center of this power lay in the river delta country around Stockton, California.

The accompanying illustrations show a right and left side view of the Laufenberg traction engine and combined harvester as used in the great wheat fields of California and the Pacific coast States.

The harvester cuts a swath 28 feet wide and thrashes, cleans, and sacks the grain as it moves along. It would seem that a machine cutting a strip of grain 28 feet wide would be handling straw fast enough to satisfy almost anyone, but the Laufenberg machine has been built to cut a nice little swath of 52 feet and sack the grain, completely cleaned and ready for market. While the combined harvester is not a new feature in the handling of crops on the coast, only recently, and not until the traction engine became a success in the field, did they ever attempt a cut wider

than 18 feet; 16 feet being the standard machine, requiring from 30 to 40 head of stock to handle them.

In the machine shown herewith an auxiliary engine is located on the front end of the harvester to operate the thrashing and separating machinery and is furnished steam from the boiler of the traction engine. The engine and boiler of this monster outfit are also a departure from the stereotyped plan usually met with in traction engine construction, there being two upright stationary engines, one on each side, and bolted to the main frame, instead of being attached to the boiler, as usual in engines of this character. The cylinders are 9 by 10 inches, and combined they are capable of developing 60 horse power, and either may be run independently of the other. The same pat-

From Frank Corry, "California Harvesting Machinery," *Scientific American,* LXXIX (October 8, 1898), 235.

A GREAT TRACTION ENGINE AND HARVESTER USED IN THE WHEAT FIELDS OF CALIFORNIA.

terns are used in the auxiliary engine on the harvester, and with this plan the steam power harvester has been made a complete success. While the horse power machines are still in the majority, yet for extensive harvester work, where large acreage is to be dealt with, the steam rig will undoubtedly become the favorite, the separator capacity thereby being increased. The cylinder of the machine shown in the cut is 40 inches and the separator or shoe is 56 inches wide. It would seem that the small boiler used to supply the three 9 by 10-inch engines would be hardly equal to the task, but, from its peculiar construction and adequate steaming qualities, it more than supplies the demand. It is a 40-inch shell boiler, but Mr. Laufenberg claims it to be—which undoubtedly is correct—a compartment boiler, the shell extending back into or over the fire box, and the flues are so constructed that as a steamer it is a marvel.

The extension wheels are put on to carry the heavy machine over soft or sandy ground, this particular engine having been built especially for use on tule or reclaimed swamp land. When the writer visited the ranch to obtain data regarding this monster of California farming, they were cutting, thrashing, cleaning, and putting in sacks at the rate of three sacks per minute of barley, each sack weighing one hundred and fifteen pounds, requiring two expert sack sewers to take the grain away from the spout, sew the sacks, and dump them on the ground. Seven men constitute the whole crew, including engineer and fireman. The machine is the property of Brant Brothers, of Union Island, near Stockton, California.

PART VII THE BUILDING OF INSTITUTIONS

One early result of the American experience was the dissolution of the institutional forms that traditionally had regulated technical training and practice. The craft guilds of Europe were never transplanted to this side of the Atlantic, and the apprentice system that the guilds supervised and enforced soon died out for want of proper nourishment. Furthermore, the new scientific societies which were then forming, although they had American members, could not play the same role in the New World as they did in the Old. Even gentlemen found themselves without sufficient leisure to pursue philosophical pleasures; the hazards of transatlantic travel made communications difficult; the demand for skilled labor forced men to accept responsibilities out of proportion to their formal training.

By the end of the eighteenth century, however, the technical needs of the new nation and the increasing opportunities for specialization and communication led to a slow and painful rebuilding of institutions for the training and regulation of technical practice. Some formal training in engineering was available at the military academy at West Point beginning in 1802. The atmosphere of uplift and reform current during the Jacksonian era led to efforts to improve the education of mechanics and workingmen generally. With the founding of the land grant colleges, technical education became widely available on an increasingly sophisticated level.

At the same time, practitioners banded together for professional purposes: they set standards of practice and education, exerted discipline, organized for mutual support, and so forth. As engineering became increasingly professional and specialized, a whole host of societies sprang up, beginning with the foundation of the American Society of Civil Engineers in 1852. Some of these societies were defined by specialty, some by geography.

The professional engineer was something new in society. He was neither a scientist nor a businessman. He thought of himself as a professional expert,

173

but his employer considered him a hired hand. Engineers were in many ways in an anomalous position, but by the end of the century they were well on their way toward defining and expanding the role of their profession in American society.

1. The Mechanics' Institute, 1841

CHARLES CIST, *Cincinnati in 1841*

In the early nineteenth century, one of the most popular educational institutions—used by both engineers and mechanics—was an English import, the mechanics' institute. Such institutes were formed in many American cities during the Jacksonian era, and while no two were exactly the same, the Ohio Mechanics' Institute of Cincinnati was probably typical.

By 1828 Cincinnati, a center of both commerce and the mechanic arts, was already called the Queen City of the West. The Mechanics' Institute was only one of an ambitious number and variety of cultural institutions undertaken in the name of civic improvement. Like the other institutions, it was designed to serve the needs of the middle class of the city. Its curriculum went beyond that of the common school, but it was less classically oriented than the typical college.

The importance of popular education to a people whose institutions are founded on the principle of universal suffrage, has long been duly appreciated by our citizens, generally. Our free-school system, and the pride we all take in directing the attention of those who visit us to our commodious and handsome school-houses, are proofs of the correctness of our principles on this subject. There are, however, those among us, who think that something more is neces-sary to be done in the cause of general education, than to establish common schools. They consider it necessary to the prosperity of our country and its progress in improvement, that the sciences, which have heretofore been taught only in our higher seminaries of learning, should be made accessible to all who possess taste and talent to cultivate them to advantage. They are of opinion that those who are engaged in the mechanic arts and manufactures,

From Charles Cist, *Cincinnati in 1841: Its Early Annals and Future Prospects* (Cincinnati, 1841), pp. 128-32.

would make better progress by being acquainted with the scientific principles on which those arts are founded, by which means a constant advance towards perfection may be made. They consider also, that as the poor and the rich are alike eligible to office in the government of the country, they ought to have like opportunities of fitting themselves for usefulness, by cultivating any branch of knowledge which their taste and talents might indicate.

From such considerations, a number of our citizens were induced, some years since, to attempt the establishment of an institution which should afford the means of instruction in any, and all, the sciences taught in our country, to all the young men of our city who desire improvement, and thirst for knowledge. They adopted the name of the Mechanics' Institute, because institutions under that name were already established, and had acquired favor with the public, in many parts of our country and of Great Britain. But their hope and intention was to form an establishment, differing in some respects from, and superior to, any of the institutions bearing the same name. The plan was, not only to establish a library and reading room, with regular series of scientific lectures on two or three evenings of each week, but also, to provide for the formation of classes for the cultivation of the different sciences; to be conducted on the principle of mutual instruction, with such aid as might be necessary from professional teachers, some of whom were among the founders of the institute, and its most zealous friends. It was intended that a foundation should be laid, so broad, that all associations for the cultivation of the arts or sciences might be embraced in it, and all the efforts for the advancement of learning,

or improvement in the arts, be there concentrated, and thus the waste of that effort of enterprise be prevented which had already established various literary and scientific societies in our city, to continue two or three years in existence, and then dwindle and die and be forgotten.

A charter was obtained in 1828, and the operations of the institution commenced on a very humble and limited scale, in the north wing of the Cincinnati College, Dr. John D. Craig, who had long been an eminent teacher of natural philosophy in Philadelphia, Baltimore and our city, being the first president of the institute. Instructions were given in botany, chemistry, mechanics, geometry and arithmetic, by Drs. Locke, Cleveland and Craig, and Messrs. Kinmont and Talbott, and popular lectures by Messrs. Noble, Foote, Peters, Drake, and others. Dr. Craig, however, being soon after appointed superintendent of the patent office, removed to Washington. His valuable philosophical apparatus was left here, and after some time was purchased by the late J. D. Garrard for the sum of $2000, and presented to the institute. Contributions of books were also made for the library, which was soon opened for the benefit of the members. Several of the most distinguished of our public teachers volunteered their aid, in the instruction of the classes, which were formed for cultivating various sciences; and in which the pupils displayed great zeal for improvement. The want of a suitable building was felt as soon as the operations began, and an opportunity offering of purchasing the old Baptist church on Walnut street, on favorable terms, four of the directors ventured to make the purchase, and become accountable for the payments, which were extended to periods of several years. As this was a favorable purchase, it was expected that the public would afford such aid to the institution, as would enable it to meet the payments. This expectation, however, was not well founded; for although the institute was for several years in a prosperous condition, as far as it related to the benefits it was conferring, yet its funds from contributions of membership were not equal to its ordinary expenses; and instead of acquiring the means of paying for the building, it was increasing its debts; and the commercial embarrassments of the city occurring, it was found impracticable to meet the payments, and, that the building must be sold. Previous to this period, Dr. Craig had returned from Washington, and was engaged in delivering regular courses of lectures in natural philosophy, and superintending the operations of the institute generally. For the purpose of continuing to the public the benefits of the institution, a building was rented, fitted up, and occupied for two or three years; but not affording suitable accommodations, a gradual declension of interest in the institute, on the part of the public, was experienced, until the directors began to despair of being able to continue its existence, and appointed a committee to report on the subject. This committee, however, reported that it was too valuable an institution to be suffered to fall without making some further efforts for its support; which report was adopted, and fresh exertions commenced in its behalf. Soon after this period a suggestion was made in one of the newspapers, of giving a public ball for its benefit, which was immediately carried into effect. On this occasion so much spirit was displayed by the citizens generally,

in contributing in various ways to increase the receipts, that the sum of three thousand dollars was raised, which was ordered to be kept entire, and appropriated towards the purchase or erection of a building. An opportunity offered, soon after, of purchasing the building erected by Mrs. Trollope, and called the bazaar, for the sum of ten thousand dollars, which was considered a very advantageous purchase, and was therefore effected. This building affords more commodious accommodations than the institute had ever enjoyed previously, and has been so fitted up as to adapt it to its new occupation.

In 1838 the institute held its annual fair, for the exhibition of *western manufactures* and the encouragement of western artists. The exhibition was opened also in 1839 and '40, improving each year in its character, in public regard, and in profits to the institution; affording an opportunity to our artisans and manufacturers of displaying their taste and skill in their various vocations; and by gathering from year to year new visitors to the fair, diffusing more widely a knowledge of the character, and an interest in the operations of the institute.

Among the manufactures exhibited at the fairs, particularly worthy of notice as evincing a high degree of perfection in the workmanship, were saddlery, harness and trunks, boots and shoes, scale-beams, philosophical apparatus, mathematical instruments, silver ware, clocks, chairs, cabinet furniture, piano fortes and other musical instruments; locks, cutlery, edge-tools, castings in brass and iron, machinery, cotton-gins, carding and spinning machines, blacksmithing, carriages, sheet-iron stoves, grates, &c.; cut-glass, porcelain, carpeting, agricultural implements, hats and caps, oil-cloths, &c. The fairs commence on the third Monday in June annually.

Soon after the last fair, Dr. Craig resigned his situation as lecturer, and returned to Philadelphia; and a short time since Dr. John Locke, professor of chemistry in the Medical College of Ohio, was appointed his successor. Dr. Locke was one of the founders of the institute, and had devoted much time and labor to aid its progress. He had established its chemical class, and inspiring in the members an uncommon degree of interest in the subject, has had the satisfaction of witnessing its rapid progress in the science. He is now delivering a regular course of lectures on natural philosophy, on two evenings of each week; and on Saturday evenings popular lectures, on various subjects, are delivered by different gentlemen of learning and talents, which have been highly instructive.

The library has lately received some valuable additions from the contributions of Messrs. J. H. Perkins, D. B. Lawler, J. W. Blachly, P. S. Symmes and others, and is still increasing.

The terms of membership of the institute are the payment of three dollars per annum, or thirty dollars for life, which entitles the members to the use of the library and all the other privileges. Apprentices and minors, sons of members, are entitled to the same privileges, upon payment of fifty cents per annum.

The hall of the institute is situated on Third street, east of Broadway; it is thirty-seven feet front by one hundred feet in depth. The basement contains apartments for the janitor and curator, with two class-rooms; the first floor contains the lecture-room, apparatus-room, library, directors'-room, and a room devoted to the use of the Western Academy of Natural Sciences; the second floor contains the reading room and a large saloon, which was formerly a ball room. There is a rotunda over the portico in the rear, which was originally intended for the exhibition of paintings, but which is now occupied by the drawing class. At the annual fairs, the first and second floors are devoted exclusively to the purposes of the exhibition, as well as a vacant lot adjoining. The business of the institute is managed by a board of fifteen directors, which is divided into standing committees on finance, library, lectures, classes, building, &c.

2. The Apprentice System

EDWARD APPLETON, "Some Reminiscenses of Early Railway
Engineering in New England"

In addition to the self-help encouraged by the various mechanics' institutes, the old apprentice system was still used for the training of engineers during the first half of the nineteenth century. This practice seems to have flourished especially in New England. In a period before civil engineering was taught in the colleges, for example, young men learned from the masters of the craft. Many of the other professions, such as law and medicine, also relied upon the apprentice system to provide a large percentage of their practitioners. Formal instruction was often minimal, but it usually satisfied the American urge for practical experience. The following recollections were those of a seventy-six-year-old civil engineer who had been a member of the first Board of Railroad Commissioners for Massachusetts.

The first charters for steam railroads in New England were granted in 1830 and 1831, for roads leading from Boston to Lowell, to Worcester, and to Providence. These were opened for use in 1835, and soon proved themselves of such great advantage over former means of transportation, that other communities became eager to avail themselves of the new method.

There were not a great many civil engineers in the country at that time. There were no scientific schools attached to the colleges then to give instruction in the studies appropriate to such a profession, and the few who practiced it had educated themselves. West Point, to be sure, gave some instruction in engineering, but it was with reference to military objects rather than to any calls for the purposes of ordinary civil life.

Still, the graduates of West Point were often called upon to attend to works of construction that were entirely devoid of any warlike purpose.

Some fifteen years before this time the Erie canal was opened for use, and was speedily followed by others in various parts of the country, among them the Middlesex canal in Massachusetts, from Boston to Lowell, which had begun to do a fair amount of business when the railroad was opened between the same points, and soon absorbed all the business of its predecessor. Other canals were also built in New England, but most of them have fallen into the same state of "innocuous desuetude" as the Middlesex.

Besides building these canals, our civil engineers of that day had work to do in building dams and factories to make use of the water power of our

From Edward Appleton, "Some Reminiscences of Early Railway Engineering in New England," *Engineering News*, XXVIII (November 24, 1892), 497-98.

streams and rivers. But there was no call then for water-works for our cities and towns, nor for comprehensive and well designed sewerage. So if the civil engineers of the day were not numerous, the calls for their services were not extensive, demand and supply balancing each other as in other matters.

But the advent of railroads brought quite a change. The seniors in the profession had more calls than they could personally attend to, and needed many assistants. The new branch of the engineering profession had many attractions for active enterprising young men, especially for new graduates of the colleges. As there were no schools for them to attend, they entered themselves as students in the offices of the heads of the profession, just as students of law entered the offices of the leading lawyers. There they carefully reviewed their college studies of algebra, geometry, trigonometry, and the use of logarithms, read what books on engineering subjects the meager libraries of the day contained, and calculated for themselves tables of excavation and embankment, curve deflections, and such others as they thought would prove useful in practical work. In a few months they found positions on the railroads their principals had in charge, and were sent into the field.

Surveying instruments were not plenty in those days. There were some clumsy theodolites and levels, but scarce any railroad transits, and none of these instruments were equal in finish and accuracy to those of the present day. Moreover, their meager pay did not allow the young men to furnish themselves with the costly instruments, and the corporations thought themselves generous if they provided one set for the whole road. Many a time a party started out to survey a line of railroad, provided only with a common compass to take the bearings of the line occasionally, a level and rod, three or four sighting poles, and the heavy 12 lb. iron chain of those days. Yet with this meager supply of tools they did good work. In running through a wooded district, I sometimes amused myself, when a big tree stood right in the line, by endeavoring to place the sighting pole on the further side of the tree in the true line while the axemen were cutting the tree down. Not infrequently I succeeded, and when the tree was down the pole did not need to be moved. My axemen finally protested that it was of no use to cut a tree down, for I could see right through it. Curves were run in by measuring deflections at each hundred feet. I have known more than one instance of a railroad built upon a line run in this way, which proved sufficiently accurate to lay the track upon and which has been in service ever since. But my sight has grown dim, and I fear I could not now run a straight line by sighting poles even on an open level plain.

In those days, cheapness of construction was the main object sought for, and we looked as carefully for a place to cross a traveled road at grade as we should now for a place to go under or over it. In masonry, we were not expected to plan ordinary abutments with quarried and dressed stone laid in courses. That was reserved for the few prominent and important bridges. The more common ones, such as those for road and farm crossings and small streams, were laid up of ordinary field stone roughly dressed into shape. But we had the work carefully done, and abutments of this sort built 60 years ago are still standing, and are good for 60 years more. For bridges we used

Towne's plank lattice and Howe's truss. Iron bridges did not come into use till a generation later. Some plank lattice bridges, built after my own plan, were in use for over 30 years, carrying engines and trains of double the weight for which the bridges were originally built. Rails of 40 lbs. per yd. were considered strong enough, and were so for the engines and cars of those times. Grades were limited to 40 ft. per mile, as it was doubted if an engine could be built powerful enough to haul a train up a much steeper ascent. Most locomotives of that day were 15 tons weight; one of 20 tons or over was thought extraordinarily large, and of doubtful advantage, being too heavy for the track. New England was well settled, and we did not need to camp out. Our quarters were at the country towns, and sometimes at farmer's houses.

There was a fascination then as now about railroad surveying, fully equal to the hunter's or angler's pursuits, and, for myself, I remember my early railroad surveying as the happiest period of my life. In the 40's, railroad surveys and surveyors were somewhat of a rarity and it was the usual thing for the inhabitants to follow the party all day long, as small boys now follow a circus. The humorous side was not wanting; as when our Chief Engineer, in his red Canada leggins and fur cap, was mistaken for an Indian chief by the awe-stricken grangers; or when the talkative axemen, who did not know a logarithm from a T-square, explained that the distance across a wide stream is obtained by measuring right down-stream and the problem solved, "By logarithms, you darned fool."

3. Higher Education, 1874

ANDREW D. WHITE, "Scientific and Industrial Education in the United States"

During the second half of the nineteenth century, opportunities for higher education in engineering multiplied rapidly in the United States. In the first decade of the century only West Point graduated engineers; during the last decade over fifty schools trained young men for this profession. A good number of these schools were land grant institutions, authorized by Congress through the Morrill Land Grant Act of 1863. Of these land grant schools, none was more successful than Cornell University, at Ithaca, New York. In 1874 the president of Cornell, Andrew D. White, speaking before the New York Agricultural Society, presented a full and vigorous defense of technical education against those who were steeped in the tradition of the classics. As a leader of the movement to reform higher education in this country, White was well qualified to comment on the subject.

From Andrew D. White, "Scientific and Industrial Education in the United States," *Popular Science Monthly,* V (June 1874), 170-91.

A little more than two hundred years ago, in England of the Roundheads and Cavaliers, a voice was raised to propose that young men receive instruction bearing on the various national industries. He who proposed this was a man of great genius—one of the true priests and prophets of his time. He foresaw and foretold many great modern inventions, and among them the steam-engine. His brain helped to think out its principles, his hands helped to shape its groundwork. With pen and tongue he sought to promote the "new education"; but he had fallen on evil times. With Strafford and Laud on one side, and Hampden and Cromwell on the other, there was but poor hearing for the industrial ideas of the Marquis of Worcester. Persecuted, maligned, and a bankrupt, he died, and, to all appearance, his idea died with him. For two centuries afterward Oxford and Cambridge solemnly ground out the old scholastic product in the old scholastic way.

About fifty years ago, a body of the best scholars and thinkers in England made another attempt. Their endeavor was, to found an institution giving an education fitted to the needs of their land and time. They established the University of London. Never had a plan more brilliant advocates. Brougham, Sydney Smith, and Macaulay, spoke and wrote for it; but their success was small. The institution was unsectarian, therefore the Church declared against it as "godless"; it gave instruction in modern learning as well as in ancient learning, therefore the great body of solemn scholars declared it unsound; some of its ideas and methods were new, therefore a multitude of leaders of society declared it unsafe. The institution was kept down, and from that

day to this has never taken the high place to which its plan and work entitled it.

About thirty years since, the strongest man who has ever stood in an American college presidency made an effort in the same direction. Francis Wayland knew what there was of good in the old scholarship and was loyal to it, but he saw that new times make new demands, and he planned out and endeavored to work out a system of education which should meet these demands. All to no purpose. It was the old, old story—another great man, with his great idea, as Carlyle phrases it, "trampled under the hoofs of jackasses," or, as Wayland himself phrased it more mildly, "nibbled to death by ducks."

Various minor attempts were made—some of them, like Eaton's noble effort at Troy, very fruitful; but no general plan, no large institution was created worthy of the great interest involved.

About five years later, Mr. Lawrence, of Massachusetts, a thoughtful manufacturer, made another attempt. He saw the necessity of education bearing on the great industries of the country, and made to Harvard College what in those days was called a princely gift. Thus was founded the "Lawrence Scientific School," at Cambridge, and thus did industrial studies get their first foothold in a great university.

About five years later still, Mr. Sheffield, of Connecticut, also a thoughtful business-man, recognized this great necessity. By a generous donation he founded the "Sheffield Scientific School" at Yale College, and thus these studies got foothold at a second great university.

So much, then, was gained. Some few of the studies bearing on the great modern industries had been taken un-

der the care of great university corporations; but there was one drawback. In
neither of these universities were the
new studies received into full fellowship with the old. The Scientific School
was kept very distinct from the "College proper." Buildings, courses, and
studies, were kept well apart; the student in the sciences was not considered
the equal of the student in "the classics." The student preparing for an industrial profession was not considered
as of the same caste with the student
preparing for a "learned profession." He
lived in a different building, had lectures and recitations in different rooms,
was instructed by different professors,
was graduated at a different time and
place. He was not considered as properly of the graduating class of his year.
Ask any Yale or Harvard man for the
names of his classmates, and it never
occurs to him to mention the graduates
of his year from the scientific departments. Nay, whether it was that young
men taking scientific studies were considered as *ipso facto* lost souls, or as
having no souls to be saved at all, they
were not admitted to the students' seats
at the college chapel—they were practically held as of an inferior order.

The next step was made at the State
University of Michigan. Here, for the
first time in a university, a student in
general or industrial science was admitted to full equality with a student
in classics. So far as their studies were
the same, they sat in the same rooms,
heard the same lectures from the same
professors, were admitted to the same
chapel, received their degrees at the
same time and place, went through the
same ceremonies, and stood as equals
on the roll of graduates.

Still the provision for industrial education was wretchedly meagre. Other

nations had meanwhile shot far ahead
of our own in this respect. Germany,
France, and even England, had been
aroused. They had recognized the fact
that the greatest warfare of the nineteenth century is industrial warfare—
the struggle between great nations for
supremacy in the various industries, and
for the control of the various markets.
France had developed magnificently her
system, putting nearly half a million
dollars into a collection of models for
the School of Arts and Trades alone.
Germany had established a multitude of
"*Real Schulen,*" and of Technical and
Agricultural Colleges. England was already making preparations for her great
institution at South Kensington, on
which she has lavished millions.

But, just as our great rebellion was
drawing on, an attempt was made in
the Congress of the United States.
Years before, that pure and great man,
Dr. Channing, had urged that the proceeds of the sales of public lands be
consecrated to the education of the people. An attempt was now made; but,
though the good sense of Congress carried a bill, it was vetoed by James
Buchanan. But the friends of the measure still pressed on. A chorus of opti-
mists, pessimists, sham economists, hold-
backs, and do-nothings, opposed the
measure; but a true statesman led the
Army of education. Justin S. Morrill, of
Vermont, stood then as now in the
United States Senate. Let his name be
long remembered. Statues shall be
erected to him long after the little great
men who tried to thwart him are forgotten. The bill was passed, and it was
signed by Abraham Lincoln.

I ask you now to look a moment at the
passage of that bill. Centuries hence men
shall look back upon it as one of the noblest things in American annals. Why?

My friends, have you forgotten those days, their discouragements, their forebodings, the morning beginning with "would God it were evening," and the evening ending with "would God it were morning?" It was the darkest hour since Valley Forge; lives, laws, family ties, treasure—all seemed cast into the abyss—and the abyss ever growing wider, and deeper, and blacker—and yet, while the American Congress was providing for the most tremendous home policy, and carrying on the most difficult foreign policy of modern times, they found leisure to plan and carry out a great, comprehensive, and far-reaching system of national education. . . .

But what was this measure?

The question is pertinent, and all the more so now, on account of sundry efforts to misrepresent it. Look at the act of Congress itself. You see at once that it did not provide simply for agricultural colleges, nor simply for colleges of the mechanic arts. No; the intention was broader and deeper than that. It provided that "subjects relating to agriculture and the mechanic arts" should be made "leading branches," "without excluding other classical and scientific branches," and including "military tactics."

What, then, was the purpose? It was to provide fully for an industrial, scientific, and general education suited to our land and time—an education in which scientific and industrial studies should be knit into its very core, while other studies should also be provided for. And, besides this, as it had been seen that the States in rebellion had gained great advantage from the military education of students, it was declared that "instruction in military tactics shall also be included."

The act of 1862 was, then, a noble, comprehensive scheme, looking, as you see, first of all, at the industries of the nation, but at the same time insisting on provision for the broadest scientific and general culture. . . .

But what is this new education? I ask you to look first at its special purpose, and finally at its general scope. And, first among the special departments grouping themselves under such a system, I name the College of Agriculture.

And here let me refer to a misapprehension, which should be corrected at the outset. For a typical example of this, I take up a paper read at the recent Educational Convention at Elmira, by the Rev. Dr. McCosh, President of Princeton College. In that paper, the whole national and State policy regarding scientific and industrial education was condemned. The decision arrived at by two different Congresses of the United States, and by nearly thirty State Legislatures, the plan adopted by nearly thirty Boards of Trustees and Faculties in the various States—many of them after careful study of institutions at home and abroad—were dismissed with contempt. The main argument was, so far as argument can be detected among the multitude of assertions, that Scotland, from which the doctor had not long before emigrated, had got along well enough without any provision for agricultural instruction.

Never was there a more admirable illustration of the thoughts put forth by James Russell Lowell, on "a certain condescension in foreigners." To two institutions the doctor paid his respects by name, one being Rutgers College, in New Jersey; the other Cornell University. The first of these, Rutgers College, it would appear had committed an unpardonable sin. While the doctor's learned predecessors, at Princeton, had been preaching against "science falsely so called," the Rutgers College authorities had received that portion of the college land-grant fund which came to New Jersey, and had established an admirable school for applied science. This it was, doubtless, which led the doctor, in the heart of this State of ours which glories in its descent from the men who founded the Dutch Republic, to stigmatize his sister institution in New Jersey as "managed by a pack of Dutchmen."

His reference to the Cornell University was of another character, and not all my respect for the doctor's ability as a metaphysician will allow me here to suppress the fact that his whole argument was based upon one of the most astounding misrepresentations ever attempted upon an American audience.

This misrepresentation was in regard to the law of Congress of 1862. Throughout the doctor's address the idea is conveyed that the law of 1862 contemplated solely the establishment of exclusively agricultural colleges.

Nothing could be more wide of the fact. Had the doctor ever read that law he would have seen that, while "subjects relating to agriculture and the mechanic arts" were named as "leading branches," it was expressly declared in the act that other scientific and classical branches should not be excluded. Nay, more, he would have seen that so broad was the intention of Congress that the wording of the act is, that "subjects *relating* to agriculture and the mechanic arts" shall be taught, thus giving the authorities permission to extend their teaching into every field of learning which could strengthen these departments or elevate them.

I am aware that, in opposition to the plain intent of the act of 1862, the doctor may fall back upon its title, in which, for the sake of brevity, only the leading objects of the colleges are mentioned; but, had he read even so accessible an exposition of law as Kent's "Commentaries," he would have found that every act is to be construed by its contents and not by its title.

But the doctor was especially hilarious over the small number of graduates from our agricultural colleges.

Let us look at this. The number is at present very small, but I presume that no thoughtful man expected that at so early a period after their establishment the number would be very large, nor, indeed, do I expect that for some years the number will greatly increase. In a new country like ours, those professions which present the most brilliant returns will be sought for first. Hence we find that, when a farmer decides to educate his son, it is not generally with the idea of making him a farmer. And, even when he does bring him up as a farmer, he has great doubts as to the value of any instruction for that purpose outside of the old farm routine.

But while I allow freely that this is the case now, I can state quite as confidently that this condition of things cannot continue for many years. There are those now living among us who will stand among a hundred millions of citizens within the boundaries of our Republic. When that day comes—nay, long before—this present condition of things must change. The present system of routine cultivation—this present system of "skinning" lands and then running away to soils more fruitful, in the intention of robbing and running away from them in turn—cannot last. Men must get a subsistence on less and less land; and they can only get it by bringing

to bear upon it better and better cultivation. How soon we shall come to the
division of property in the Scotch Lo-
thians or the Belgian Pays de Waes,
with their small farms exquisitely tilled,
and supporting well a body of thrifty
men, I cannot say; but the steady ap-
proximation to it is as inevitable as
fate. And at the same time that this goes
on, the professions hitherto known as
"learned" will be more and more thoroughly filled. We see the beginnings of
this now. Already is it becoming less
and less easy for the farmer's boy to be
sure that the little dark office in the
great city block, swarming with lawyers,
is, after all, so much more promising
than the open fields and the work of
the farmer.

And now, what should this industrial
education be? Many men, hastily looking over the subject, have jumped to
the conclusion that it should consist in
simply teaching the plain arts of husbandry and of mechanics; that is, that
the great object should be to train
young men simply or mainly to hoe or
spade or plough in the fields, or to make
chairs or shoes, or hats or boats, in the
shops. There could be no more wretched
perversion of the trust imposed by Congress. The phraseology of the act of
1862 was chosen with great care, and,
when it speaks of "branches *relating*
to agriculture and the mechanic arts,"
it means just what it says. It meant to
provide that all applicable science be
brought to bear on those arts. It meant
to provide for the education of men who
could develop them and improve them.
Merely to add, to the millions now intelligently practising these arts, a few
more intelligent farmers or artisans
each year, would be a wretchedly inadequate return for these endowments.
The places for imparting the simple,

usual practical education for agricultural
and mechanical pursuits are the millions of farms and workshops in the
country. Nowhere else can such practical knowledge be afforded so cheaply or
so effectively.

The national institutions for education should, indeed, have farms and
workshops; but the foremost object of
these should be, not to afford simple
employment to young men, but to give
them, in connection with their studies
in the sciences, what may be called
laboratories, where they can see science
applied in as practical a manner as possible—laboratories, whether field or shop,
where they can see sciences limited by
the necessities of practice. It cannot be
too much insisted upon that the main
object of these institutions should be to
send out men, with minds trained by
observation and experiment, to develop
the various agricultural and other industries, and to improve them, and not
simply to increase, by an almost infini-
tesimal fraction, the number of those
engaged in the usual industries pursued
with a little more intelligence, in the
usual way.

But it is said that scientific and industrial education does not better agriculture. Does it not? Of all assertions
this is the most fearful indictment
against the most extended field of human thought and work. If this be true,
then is agriculture the only industrial
pursuit unworthy of a human being; for
this assertion would not be made
against any other branch of human industry. But it is not true. The whole
history of agriculture shows exactly the
reverse of this. Look at those wonderful
"Tables in Comparative Sociology," by
Herbert Spencer, just issued, and study
there the progress of agriculture and
other industries from their rudest begin-

nings, and you see that skill in observation and reasoning on observation have been steadily improving agriculture, at the same time that they have improved other industries.

But grant that the number of students devoted wholly to agriculture is small, it is not these alone whose education tells upon agriculture. Even a partial course in it has great value. It was the remark of a very distinguished statesman of this Commonwealth—one who occupied this desk as Speaker, yonder chamber as Governor, and who received the suffrages of many of his countrymen for the highest office in their gift—that the main thing in agricultural education is to do something to make agricultural pursuits attractive. His view is that whereas in England every man longs to obtain a competency to enable him to retire from the city, here men seek to escape from the country to the city; and that we should attempt to bring about a change of this sentiment in our educated young men. The author of that remark is Horatio Seymour. It struck me powerfully as sound and just, and, shortly after the establishment of the Cornell University, the trustees adopted a rule by which every student in every department—as a condition for graduation—must hear a course of lectures on general agriculture.

I am glad to state that, although the rule was received with some grumbling at first, that grumbling stopped immediately after the first lecture. Said a student to me at that time, "These lectures make us all wish to get hoes, and go at scratching up the ground at once." The lecturer for this general purpose is John Stanton Gould. . . .

But suppose that no young men came forward to take agricultural studies, the new education would still tell powerfully on agriculture. Think you that we can send out year after year—as we did last year—a hundred graduates from all our various departments, whose powers of observation have been trained and whose real knowledge of subjects bearing on agriculture has been extended by close study in Botany, Animal Physiology, Geology, and Chemistry, without its telling ultimately on the progress of agriculture?

But suppose that not one student was even thus educated, I maintain that the State and nation would receive more than the equivalent of its endowment.

Look at a few figures. The last census gives certain agricultural statistics whose magnitude is almost oppressive. The value of farm productions in the United States, in the year 1870, was considerably over $2,000,000,000.

The value of farm productions in the State of New York, the same year, was over $250,000,000.

Does not common-sense tell us that we can well afford to make a little outlay to promote any sciences which may help such a vast interest? If in the course of years, in all these laboratories and experiments, some one useful idea shall be struck out, it would repay our endowments a thousand-fold.

Says Emerson, "The true poet is an inspired prophet." Did you ever think what an inspiration lies in the poet's declaration that "the greatest benefactor of mankind is he who makes two blades of grass grow where one grew before?" If not, look at the census returns showing the enormous value of the hay-crop of these Northern States.

Knowledge of Nature—coming by research and observation in the laboratory and the field—these are to give us finally our "two blades of grass," and multitudes of other benefactions to our race not less precious.

The Sheffield Scientific School at Yale College has not a single student in agriculture, but Profs. Brewer and Johnson, by their experiments on fertilizers and kindred subjects, have returned the value of their endowment to the nation a hundred-fold already.

Take another item. The dairy products of New York in 1870 were over 100,000,000 pounds of butter, and over 20,000,000 pounds of cheese. Now, there has been quietly at work, in our Laboratory of Agricultural Chemistry at Cornell University, a young professor, Mr. George C. Caldwell. He has made little noise in the world. While Dr. McCosh was striking the stars with his lofty head, and his voice was shaking the Agricultural Colleges, this young man worked quietly on upon the chemistry of the dairy. Said Mr. L. B. Arnold, an authority you all recognize, "Prof. Caldwell's researches on the chemistry of the dairy are worth more to the State than your whole endowment. He has taught us to do such things in dairy matters and to increase dairy products as we never dreamed of doing." And to this, substantially, Mr. Arnold has lately sworn before the Commission of Investigation.

Take a few figures more from the same census. In 1870 the market-garden and orchard products of the State of New York amounted in value to close upon $12,000,000.

Can any one, then, gainsay the wisdom of our employing, as we do, a young naturalist of genius to devote his whole time to investigations regarding insects injurious to vegetation, and to giving lectures based upon these researches?

Take still other figures. The same census shows the value of farm implements in the State of New York to be over $45,000,000. In view of this we have investigations and lectures upon mechanics related to agriculture, and have obtained models and implements at home and abroad to illustrate this subject. Is not the mere pittance this requires well laid out? . . .

The act of 1862 also provides with special care for instruction in "Branches Relating to the Mechanic Arts."

If you doubt the wisdom of this, look again at the last census. There you find the manufactures of the United States valued at $4,000,000,000, and over 2,-000,000 persons engaged in them. Can education be made useful to this vast interest? Other nations think so, and are laying out vast sums in this direction. Some of our sister States are doing admirably in this respect. Illinois and Massachusetts have made excellent provision for mechanical science, and the recent message of Governor Bagby, of Michigan, shows that good work is to be done in that State. In an address delivered before this Society a few years since I described some of those foreign institutions. I trust, then, that you will pardon me for describing that which we have since created in this State.

Thanks to one of our trustees, a noble provision has been added for this purpose to that originally made by the nation.

The Hon. Hiram Sibley, of Rochester, has erected a building, equipped it with lecture-rooms, draughting-rooms, a workshop supplied with the best machinery, and has given an endowment to support a Professor of Mechanical Engineering and a superintendent of the machine-shop. Besides this, Mr. Cornell has erected a shop for woodworking, and has provided water-power for both establishments.

What is the system? Young men come wishing to make themselves first-class mechanical engineers or master-mechanics, or to perfect themselves in any branch of mechanical industry. Under careful instructors, they are carried through the various sciences bearing on their profession. They are taught mathematics in all their relations to mechanics. In one room they go on with the mathematical and mechanical drawing of machinery, in another with free-hand drawing; in the laboratory they are taken through various processes bearing upon their profession. A certain number of hours every day they must give to the workshop, and there, in well-worn apron and rolled-up sleeves, they go on under careful supervision from the use of the simplest machinery and the plainest work to the most complicated. The purpose is to send out every year a body of young men with not merely a very high grade of theoretical instruction, but with most thorough practical instruction—men who cannot merely calculate the size of parts of a machine, but who can draw it after they have calculated it, and make it after they have drawn it. These are the men whom our country sorely needs to complete the organization of its great army of industry. Indeed, I know of no more pressing material need in this country. Our land has more mechanical ingenuity in it than any other; but did you ever think of its wretched misdirection and waste for want of industrial education? If not, stroll through the national Patent-Office. Look at a few facts. In one of our most important cities are engines for supplying that city with water—erected at vast expense. The whole amount was wasted. There is ingenuity

in that vast machine, there is skill in it; but, for want of education regarding certain principles involved, the whole thing is failure and waste.

Take another case. A few years since, with a small party of our fellow-citizens, I visited the West Indies in a national ship. She was a noble vessel, and her engines had cost, it is said, nearly $800,-000. The engines showed ingenuity; but they were so deficient in proper elements of construction that our voyage was prolonged until we were all given up as lost and had the honor of having our obituaries in the leading newspapers! The first voyage of those engines was the last. They were sold for old iron; and the sum lost on them alone was sufficient to endow the finest institution for mechanical engineering in the world! I might multiply examples of this sort, but this is enough to show what need exists for more careful training in this direction, and I pass to a kindred department.

Another great department bearing on a multitude of industries, directly and indirectly, is Civil Engineering. Take one among the fields of its activity. We have in the United States about seventy thousand miles of railway, and every year thousands of miles are added. I do not at all exaggerate when I say that millions on millions of dollars are lost every year by the employment of half-educated engineers. Proofs of this meet you on every side. Lines in wrong positions, bad grades and curves, tunnels cut and bridges build which might be avoided. All of us know the story.

But this is not all. Hardly a community which has not some story to tell of great losses entailed by bad engineering in other directions. I have known the traffic of a great city street interrupted for a year, because no engineer could be found able to make the calculations for a "skew arch" bridge, a thing which any graduate of a well-equipped department of engineering can do. I have known a city subjected to enormous loss by the failure of its water-supply system, because the engineer employed made no calculation for the friction of water in the pipes. I know a whole district sickened by miasma, because a half-taught engineer was intrusted with its drainage. We must prepare men for better work; and, for every dollar thus laid out, we shall create or save thousands.

Take next, then, Sanitary Engineering. Science has, within a few years, made wonderful strides in revealing the origin and propagation of disease. The summaries recently made by President Barnard, Prof. Dalton, and Prof. Chandler, give an admirable view of this conquest. Mr. Baldwin Latham, in his recent book on "Sanitary Engineering," gives careful tables, showing the enormous reduction of consumption, typhus, and typhoid, in several English towns by the application of science to sewerage and water-supply. Dr. Beale, in his work on "Disease-Germs," shows by statistics that a proper application of engineering to sewerage would save 100,000 lives yearly in Great Britain. More and more is this matter becoming important in this country. Hardly one in twenty of our towns has any well-adjusted system of sewerage or water-supply, and in our rural districts vast tracts are made wretched by miasma.

Nor is this probably the worst. Vicious systems of heating and ventilation are probably doing more to break down the physical constitution of our people than all other causes combined. We see it everywhere in sickly women, and puny children, and men but half alive. The study of human physiology and the system of preventing and removing disease-germs should be combined, and young men should have the opportunity to fit themselves for grappling with the problems presented to sanitary engineers.

Few among us dream of the monstrous waste now entailed upon this country by imperfect instruction in Mining Engineering and metallurgy. Take first the losses by fraud. A few years since our people were asked to invest in a Nevada mine of great richness. Half-educated mining geologists had certified to its value. But certain capitalists sent a young man, carefully educated in a scientific school, to examine and report. The young man on arriving found that the mine looked well enough, but on applying more scientific tests he found that an old worthless mine had been taken; that rich sulphurets had been brought and carefully placed in it at a cost of probably $100,000. His report exploded the fraud, and nearly $1,000,-000 was saved—more than five times the sum that this scientific school received from the Government of the United States. This same gentleman also exploded a great diamond-mine fraud of the same sort.

Take another case. Not long since a party of gentlemen determined to invest several hundred thousand dollars in working certain iron-mines in the state. Just before their arrangements were finally made, and much against the will of many of the proposed stockholders, a young graduate of one of the scientific schools which received the national endowment was sent to make an examination. He found that the veins contained titanium, and that the entire investment, should it be made, would be lost. His fee was $250; he prevented a loss of over $400,000.

You see now why Pennsylvania and Missouri and California and Massachusetts are aroused as to this matter also, but you will perhaps say that New York is but little interested here. Look again at the census, and you will see how wretchedly you are mistaken. The value of the mining products in New York in 1870 was more than half that of the entire gold product of California. Here, too, we must follow up the good work, begun by our Chandlers and Raymonds.

Look next at Chemistry applied to Manufactures. More and more the chemical laboratory is becoming a great central point in industrial education. Run over but two or three points out of many. A chemical discovery in coloring-matter has given us a substitute for madder, and restored the great area given to cultivation of that material to the increase of material for human sustenance. An apparently trivial application of another chemical principle has enabled Onondaga to purify its product so that it now competes with the world in the purity of its salt for the dairy. Another application has enabled another part of the State to make quantities of steel formerly undreamed of. And all this is but the beginning of the applications of chemistry to increase the well-being of the State and nation.

We must also make provision for instruction in Architecture. Wealth and public spirit—individual and municipal —are now erecting myriads of costly buildings in all parts of our country. The number of uneducated architects is very great—the number of thoroughly prepared architects is very small. Have you ever considered the waste attendant upon this? Every month you hear of some architectural failure that costs life and treasure. To-day it is a church-floor which gives way, and a multitude of children are taken from the ruins mangled and dead; to-morrow it is a whole city quarter swept away by fire, because some half-taught architects knew no other way of producing architectural effect than by piling up combustible ornaments on inaccessible roofs.

Nor is that all. Our people are laying out millions on millions in buildings which within thirty years—in the advance of taste and knowledge—will be eye-sores and must come down. A building erected by a true architect will grow more beautiful for hundreds of years. A building erected by a sham architect will be an incubus in a quarter of a century. People are beginning to see this, and we are endeavoring to prepare men thoroughly to know the best materials, to calculate their strength in construction, and to combine material and construction according to everlasting laws, and not according to some pretty present fashion; and this is the purpose of our School of Architecture. . . .

And now a few words regarding the general education which goes with these various branches of industrial and scientific education. The student must be not only trained as a specialist, he must also be educated as a man and a citizen. Hence the necessity of blending into the various special courses certain general studies calculated to give breadth and foresight and insight. Among these I name, first, instruction in History and Political Science.

On this subject, the "new education" lays stress, and especially on the history of our own race and country. The subject has been sadly neglected; but more and more it is seen that, to train men to build up the future, we must show them with what successes and failures their predecessors have built up the past.

Thought, too, should be stirred on the more pressing problems in Social Science, and among them the best methods of dealing with pauperism, crime, insanity, sanitary management, and public instruction. Foundations for study on these might, at least, be laid, and right direction given to those whose tastes turn toward participation in public affairs.

No thoughtful man will deny that it is well to give even to students in industrial branches access to the best thoughts of the best thinkers—the study of the great languages and Literature does this—and especially is it done by the study of this wonderful language and literature of our own.

Another most important means of discipline and culture is to be found in the study of the Natural Sciences. On these much of industrial and general progress depends. They discipline the power of observation, and reasoning upon observation. They give, too, a culture to the sense of beauty in form, and fitness in adaptation.

But I am aware that objection is made to the study of Natural Science on the ground of a dangerous materialistic tendency.

But can this objection be well founded? Among the many striking passages in Herbert Spencer's "Treatise on Education" is one of special interest on this point. He asks, what would any author think were a person to come into his presence, praise his works, and dwell upon their beauty and perfection, when the author knew that this flatterer had never read a single page, or even a single line, of them? And what, then, must the Great Author of all things think of one who thus comes into his presence, extols his works in all moods and tenses, the Great Author knowing

that this flatterer has never studied out a line in the great book of Nature—nay, that he has discouraged others from studying it? I come now to certain Guiding Ideas—necessary in carrying out any worthy system of scientific and industrial education.

1. Of these I name Unsectarianism. Our own charter makes "men of all sects and parties, and of no sect or party, equally eligible to all offices and appointments." For this, some good men have thought it their duty to denounce us from pulpit and press as "godless"; but it has proved our salvation. It has enlisted benefactors of every creed. That it has taken strong hold upon the people is shown by the millions given the institutions on this basis, and by the steady support of these despite all calumnies. There is no other possible basis for the development of great institutions for scientific and industrial education. To confine their choice of professors to any one denomination, or circle of denominations, is to dwarf them; to put them under control of any synod, conference, association, council, or convention, is to strangle them.

2. I name Freedom of Choice Between Various Courses of Study. The old way in the more venerable colleges and universities was, to force all students through one single classical course—the same for all. This system the "new education" discards. General courses in literature, science, and arts, are presented, as well as special courses having reference to the great industries; and the student, with the advice of friends and instructors, takes that which best suits the bent of his mind. We believe that the results are already better than those of the old system. Certainly they could not be worse. The famous "Blue-Book of the Parliamentary Com-

mission" on advanced education, in England, shows that under the old system there seventy per cent. of the students in their great schools and universities take no real hold upon classical studies. Few will claim that our system of classical instruction is better than that in England. If any of you think it more promising, look at President Barnard's cogent statistics on this point. We make no opposition to classical instruction. We agree that, for those who take earnest hold of it, it is one of the noblest means of discipline and culture; but it is no less evident that for those who do not take hold of it—who merely "drone" over it—it is one of the worst.

3. I name Equality in Position and Privilege Between Different Courses of Study. I have already shown how courses of study in science, and especially those bearing on industry, have been held, in various places, virtually inferior to courses of study in literature. Against this we stand pledged. We are determined to hold all courses and all students as equal; educating them together, graduating them together, welcoming them back as alumni together. But the "new education" does not merely endeavor to give a greater range of studies, it seeks to improve Methods. Let me mention two of these:

1. I name the Better Use of the Lecture System. Those who knew Louis Agassiz well will never be at a loss to recall conversations, instructive and entertaining; but I think that, among them all, none conveyed a better mixture of philosophy and fun than his delineation of the recitation of text-books by rote, as it has been so long practised in our American colleges. No system was ever better calculated to deaden enthusiasm and stiffen knowledge. More and more we are coming to see that,

wherever possible, we must bring the living mind to bear on the student. Thus may we supplement text-books, and take from them their present woodenness and dreariness.

2. I name the Union of Study of Things with Study About Things. Under the old system it was book in the morning, book in the afternoon, book in the evening—an unceasing round of studying what men have said *about* things. Under the better system of the various institutions for scientific and industrial education, the student passes frequently from study about things to study of the things themselves, in laboratory or workshop, in draughting-room or museum, or in the field. Every science must now have its laboratory practice, and thereby are given to lectures and recitations reality and interest. Thereby is gained ability to bring theory to bear upon practice.

But an objection of another sort is raised. It is said, "Why give instruction in classical branches at all?" I answer, for three reasons: 1. Because the act of Congress declares expressly that they shall not be excluded. 2. Because to those who wish them they are an excellent means of culture. 3. Because we wish to avoid that old mistake of separating industrial and scientific students from classical students. Heretofore students in science and technology have been banished to some little special college in some remote corner of a town or State, while classical students have had all the prestige arising from connection with large and thoroughly equipped institutions. We stand upon the principle of considering one student the equal of another—the student in science and industry the equal of the student in classics. We stand against any separation which shall serve to perpetuate that old subordination of men in the new education to men in the old.

But it is objected that the new system does not provide for mental discipline. Never was a charge more absurd. Discipline comes by studies that take hold of a man, and of which he takes hold. Is it not evident that the new system, which adapts studies to the tastes and aims of men, is more sure to take hold and be taken hold of than the old system, which grinds all alike through the same processes and studies?

But it is said, "Why concentrate your resources in one institution?" I answer, because that is the only way in which you can ever have the work done. To erect, equip and maintain laboratories, work-shops, farms, collections, libraries, observatories—all this demands great sums.

To have such institutions, you must pay the price. While the rule, as already stated, regarding preliminary public instruction, is to distribute resources, the rule in regard to advanced education—scientific, general, or industrial—is to concentrate resources. Look at it. The last report of the Bureau of Education shows in the United States 397 institutions called colleges or universities, and you can count on the fingers of your hands all those worthy of either name.

Wisely, then, have the great States refused to yield to clamors for scattering or frittering away these funds. Wisely have individuals poured out their wealth to supplement them.

To the institution in our own State already over $1,500,000 have been given by individuals, and I trust that this is but a beginning.

Do you say that this endowment may be too large? Compare the endowment for the increase of intellectual wealth with any one of a thousand endowments for the increase of material wealth. Look at the hotels of your great cities. Some of them have cost more than the entire outlay in buildings for advanced instruction throughout whole States.

But it may be said, "Why not devote all your resources to agricultural experiments and instruction?" I answer—1. The law of the United States does not allow it. 2. Because in the interest of agriculture itself we should educate men to develop other industries. What is the great want of our Western States at this moment? Greater agricultural production? No. What they want is, the development of great and varied manufacturing industries, so near them that it shall no longer take two-thirds of a bushel of corn to carry the other third from producer to consumer.

And, finally, it is objected to the "new education" that it is godless. There is nothing new in this charge. It has been made against every great step in the progress of science or education. And yet it has certainly been found that although ideas of religion are changed from age to age, the change has tended constantly to make these religious ideas purer and nobler. The majority of the Fathers of the Church held the new idea of the rotundity of the earth incompatible with salvation. Martin Luther thought Copernicus a blasphemer for his new idea that the earth revolves about the sun, and not the sun about the earth. Dean Cockburn declared the new science of Geology a study invented by the devil, and unlawful for Christians. When John Reuchlin and his compeers urged the substitution of studies in the classics for studies in the mediæval scholastic philosophy, their books were burned, and they themselves narrowly escaped the same fate.

No, my friends; every study which

tends to improve the industry of mankind makes a man nobler and better. Every study which gives man to know more of the history of his race, gives him to see more and more clearly the finger of Providence in history; every study which brings his mind into contact with the thoughts of inspired men as exhibited in our literatures, builds up his manliness and his godliness, and every study which brings him into close contact with Nature in any of its fields not less surely lifts him "through Nature up to Nature's God."

I have thus sketched very meagrely the growth thus far of the "new education." Its roots are firm, for they take fast hold upon the strongest material necessities of our land; its trunk is thrifty, for it is fed by the most vitalizing currents of thought which sweep through our time; nay, the very blasts of opposition to this growth have but strengthened it; the winter of discontent through which it has passed has but toughened it; and in agriculture and every branch of industry; in every science and art which ministers to either; in all the development of human thought which is to make men better and braver, it is to bear a rich fruitage for the State, for the nation, and for mankind.

4. Changing Demand for Engineers, 1892

Engineering News

Even while the demand for engineers grew, and the number of schools offering courses in engineering kept pace, there was continual shifting of demand from one to another branch of the profession. In the schools, new curricula were added and old ones revamped to provide for new technical needs as the economy demanded. In 1892 an attempt was made to gather some statistics which would illuminate both the demand of the economy and the response by the educators.

In the accompanying diagram and table, we show, perhaps, the most striking and important facts which this investigation will develop, viz.: the sudden and amazing increase in mechanical engineering graduates, the relative decline in number of civil engineering graduates, and the great absolute decline in number of mining graduates, which last amounts almost to a complete abandonment of mining engineering as a distinct branch of study.

From "The Engineering Schools of the United States. XVII: The Distribution of Graduates," *Engineering News*, XXVIII (August 11, 1892), 139-40.

The causes for this rapid and radical change (the end of which is not yet apparent) are easy enough to imagine after the event, though few might have ventured to predict in advance that such a change was at hand, and fewer still can have known how great the change had been already.

As for mining engineering, what is there about the ordinary work of the ordinary mining engineer which requires a different training from that of a mechanical engineer? Chiefly a certain amount of metallurgical and prospecting or sampling work. But to become a specialist in this kind of work a man should be a chemist and metallurgist at once, and nothing else. After a mine has once been discovered, and its value approximately determined (the doing of which affords steady and profitable work to few or none), the chief work of the mining engineer is to open and operate the mine advantageously; and the knowledge and experience of a civil or mechanical engineer gives just the right preparation for this kind of work. Such is the result in practice, evidently, for mining engineering itself is a rapidly expanding department of professional work, while the number of graduates from mining schools has been steadily declining since it reached its climax (of 61 graduates only), in 1884.

This has been in substance the experience of all the schools alike, and not of one school only, nor is the decrease caused by the abandonment of mining courses at the several colleges, but simply by a decrease in the number of students taking such courses.

This is shown in detail in the accompanying table giving a substantially complete return of the graduates from all the mining schools of the United States.

The backbone of mining education in this country has always been the Columbia College School of Mines, which is now practically abandoning the special field which its name implies, and turning out large classes in the other branches of engineering instead. In fact, had we taken "the face of the returns" for Columbia, the few "miners" which appear for 1891 and 1892 would not have appeared as such at all. They were returned to us as mechanical engineers with the mining column blank, and perhaps, correctly; but as so complete a change seemed improbable we have included the alleged mechanicals as mining graduates.

As a rule Columbia has turned out each year from half to two-thirds of the total number of mining graduates since it set the fashion of having such a course in 1863-7. It started in with remarkably large classes, which fell off during the panic era of 1873, but sharply recovered up to 1878-85, after which date the turn and permanent decline seems to have begun.

The next most important mining school is the Massachusetts Institute of Technology, which for more than 20 years has managed to graduate a tolerably persistent class of five or six. Lehigh, Washington and the University of California grind out with difficulty a class of two or three yearly. The Michigan Mining School is a promising and vigorous new school, which is likely to graduate a class of 12 in 1893, though special causes, noted last week, are alleged to have caused a decline in the last three years. Whether they really did so, or whether the decline is only another evidence of a general tendency, may be questioned. Five state colleges together, constituting group D of mining schools, turn out an average class of a little over one each! The 15

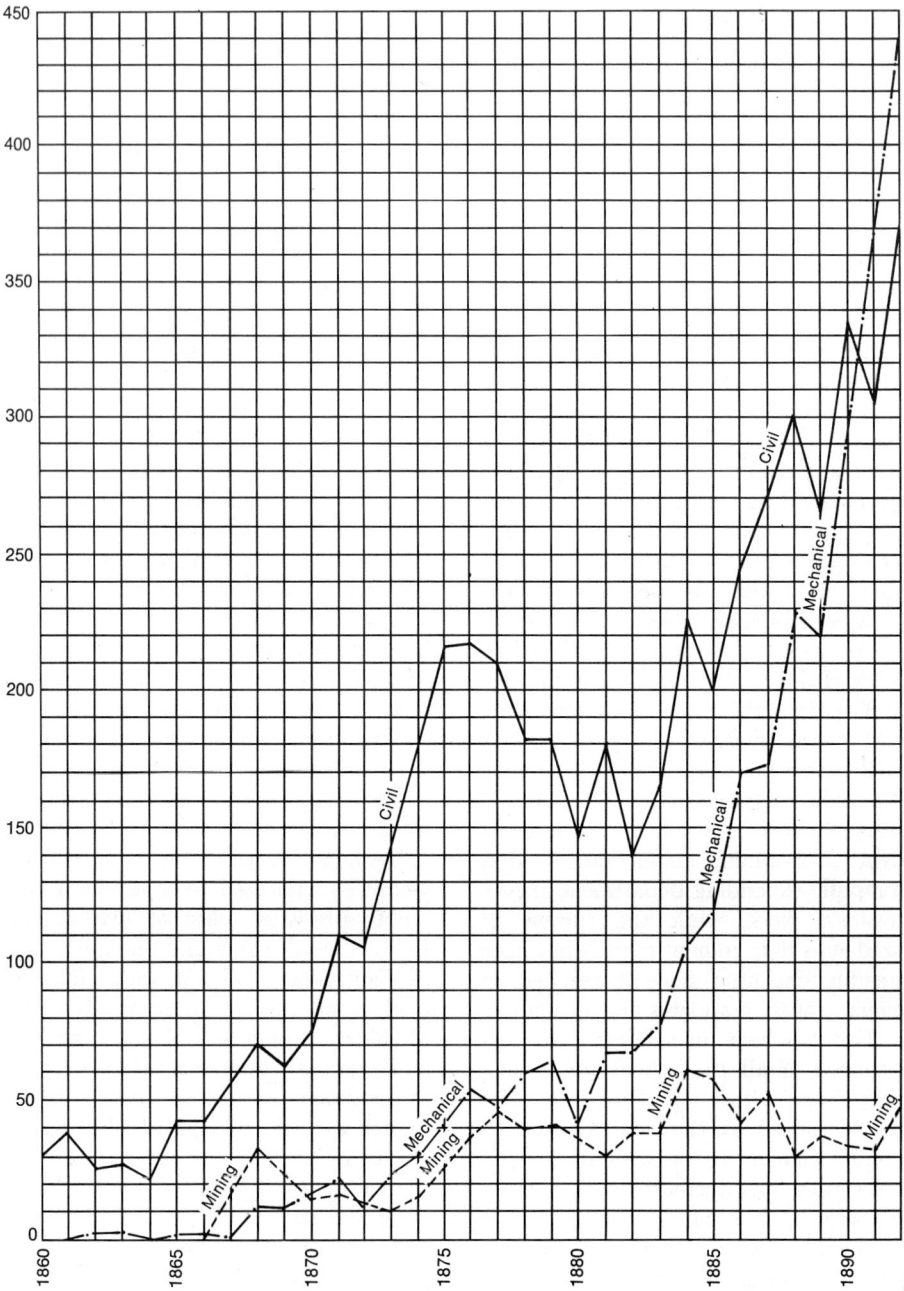

Diagram showing number of graduates from civil, mechanical and mining engineering schools of the United States for each year since 1860.

schools which make up the whole list have averaged from two to three graduates each, only, for 20 years, with no tendency in any one to increase, but rather to fall off!

So much for the mining schools. If there is any real need for them as separate organizations, apparently they are not so organized as to fill that need. It would seem far wiser for most, if not all, of these 15 schools to drop these courses and separate degrees altogether under these circumstances, using the released staff to strengthen their other courses. The training which they give does not seem to be any special help to a man in entering into mining work. Otherwise the number of graduates would increase at least as fast as the mining interest, which grows prodigiously.

As for mechanical engineering, the increase in number of graduates is, indeed, surprising, and yet, it is an increase that might have been foreseen, and can now be foreseen as likely to gain hereafter as heretofore. For years it has been true, and it must continue to be more and more so, that for his highest success the civil engineer must be more or less of a mechanical engineer also. The field which the civil engineer has exclusively to himself is hardly more than he had a thousand years ago, viz., the simpler types of bridges and roads, and aqueducts. All the vast modern expansions of the field of civil engineering, with hardly an exception, are in the mechanical direction. To lay out a railway intelligently a man should know a good deal of mechanical engineering, which is one of the reasons why so many engineers make such bad work of it. Of modern bridge works this is still more true. The construction and operation of cable and electric railways, pumping works, every department of electric work, and much of the new profession of sanitary engineering, depend upon mechanical knowledge very largely for successful practice.

While a country is new and raw, as we have already said in substance, the construction of public works and ways of communication makes the special field of the civil engineer (in the narrow sense), the only one of importance; but there comes a time when the major portion of the bridges, roads, railways and water-works are already built, and the relative amount of such work falls off, while the mechanical problems connected with manufacturing, mining and the operation of public works grow daily more important. That era came long since in England; it is now upon us here.

It is easy to trace in the accompanying diagram just when the change began. It was almost coincident with the organization of the American Society of Mechanical Engineers in 1880. For five preceding years mechanical engineering had been relatively gaining, by holding its own in spite of the depression of the times, while the number of civil engineering graduates was declining rapidly. Since 1880 the number of mechanical graduates has increased by leaps and bounds, until it is now 10½ times greater than it was then, whereas the number of civil engineering graduates has increased only 2½-fold. We shall give next week a table showing for 1891 and 1892 only (for which years only we collected the information), just what proportion of the mechanical graduates take an electrical course. They will soon be a full half of the mechanical graduates, apparently.

The increase in the number of civil engineering graduates cannot be small,

absolutely, however, though the increase in number of mechanical graduates rather dwarfs it. Going back to
another culminating period like that of
1892 (for we take it to be such), in
1873-7, there were over 200 graduates,
against a present normal maximum of
about 350. That is in more than full
proportion to the increase in civil engineering works going on in the respective periods, and is certainly fairly rapid
growth, especially if we remember further that in 1873 there were no mechanical engineering schools of much
importance, and that many men may
have taken the civil engineering course
for lack of one more suited to their
needs. In fact, the only mechanical engineering school of much importance
was then the Worcester Polytechnic Institute. Stevens was just getting ready
to begin, and only seven schools had
any graduates in mechanical engineering. . . . The field for civil engineers is
still expanding, and will long do so. Relatively only is it decreasing. One great
cause for the increase in mechanical
graduates is that, now that there is a
supply of educated mechanical men,
railways and other like works are demanding them to manage their mechanical departments, instead of giving such
positions to the more skilled mechanics.

5. A Professional Society, 1894

EDWIN J. HOUSTON, "A Review of the Progress of the American
Institute of Electrical Engineers"

The increasing specialization evident in American engineering was reflected
not only in school curricula but also in the formation of professional societies.
Typical of these was the American Institute of Electrical Engineers (AIEE).
It was a young group and its members came from various backgrounds, but
all were excited by the sense of adventure and profit present in a new and
rapidly developing field. Edwin J. Houston, in his presidential address to that
body on its tenth anniversary, described the coalition of forces that came
together to found the AIEE, and stated the purposes of the society.

From Edwin J. Houston, "A Review of the Progress of the American Institute of
Electrical Engineers," *Transactions of the American Institute of Electrical Engineers,* XI
(1894), 275-84.

The International Electrical Exhibition, held in 1884, in Philadelphia, under the auspices of the Franklin Institute of the State of Pennsylvania, was called together at an exceedingly favorable moment. Eight years had elapsed since the Centennial Exhibition of 1876, in Philadelphia, had sown broadcast the germs of public interest in electricity, and thus laid the foundation for a belief in the bright promises of the electric future. These germs, carried to all parts of the land, were beginning to bear fruit, and a body of earnest and intelligent workers had sprung up on all sides, so that our comparatively limited knowledge of electrical science was markedly increased, although in an extremely irregular and unsystematic manner.

Between 1876 and 1884, nearly a decade, the work done in the electrical field was necessarily of a pioneer and independent character. The great principles of the science, already discovered and announced, were but vaguely understood, and needed the practical man to carry them into actual commercial use. To a great extent, each investigator trod the path of discovery alone, gropingly penetrating into the regions of the unknown, unaccompanied by his fellow investigator, and often, indeed, unconscious of his existence. Had this early work been properly organized, much of the labor expended in going over ground already trodden might have been saved, but it is by no means clear that this labor was in vain for the weal of the electric future; for, truths thus repeatedly wrested from nature and established again and again by independent investigators, cannot be too highly prized.

In our nineteenth century activity, events move rapidly. In less than a decade from the time of the Centennial Exhibition of 1876, namely, in 1884, the time had come when the advantages of congregation as opposed to segregation were to be demonstrated; when the lonely investigator was to be brought into contact with his brother toiler and taught the advantages of organized work and a free exchange of ideas.

Happily, the International Electrical Exhibition in Philadelphia of 1884, already alluded to, brought together the workers in electricity both in this country, and, to a certain extent, in other parts of the world, not only during the Exhibition itself, but especially during the completion of the buildings and the arrangement of the exhibits. The varied exhibits thus brought together from all sides were a revelation to these hitherto independent workers, and showed them, from what had already been accomplished by electrical science, what might reasonably be expected in the near future. The stimulus, so excited, culminated in the organization of the distinguished body I have now the honor of addressing.

At the same time, the U.S. Government appointed a United States Electrical Commission authorizing it to conduct a National Conference of Electricians in Philadelphia during the progress of the International Electrical Exhibition. Fortunately for the cause of electrical science, the Commission after due deliberation determined to appoint as members of this Conference not only those investigators in the physical laboratory and lecture room, the college and university professors, whose labors have always proved of such great value to the world's weal, but also those equally important investigators, the inventor and actual worker in the commercial electrical field, whose knowledge of principes is based on actual experience; a class that proves the correctness of its ideas by subjecting them to the test of actual trial on a commercial scale.

There was thus convened in 1884, in the city of Philadelphia, a notable gathering of men who had long toiled in the electric field, both in the so-called pure sciences and in the applied sciences, and I feel sure that each class recognized the fact that it learned much from the other.

In this notable assembly of electrical students, our American Institute of Electrical Engineers originated. I may be pardoned if I briefly review the facts attending its inauguration.

The first step was the circulation in April, 1884, by Mr. N. S. Keith, of a paper asking for signatures for the purpose of organizing a National Electrical Society, for affiliation with sister societies; for the possession of a library, the institution of original research; protection from unfavorable legislation; the settlement of disputed electrical questions, and the exchange of volumes of its Transactions with foreign and other electrical scientific societies. A preliminary meeting was called on April 15th, 1884 in the city of New York, at which a series of resolutions were passed, and a Committee of Organization appointed to call a meeting, which was subsequently held on May 13th, 1884, when rules of order were adopted and officers elected. The first regular meeting of the Institute was held in Philadelphia, October 7th and 8th, 1884, in one of the Exhibition Buildings in West Philadelphia.

From this small beginning our Institute has assumed its present proportions. Its growth was, at first, uncertain, but its vitality was undoubted, and its present rate of increase is fully equal to that of our English cousin, viz., the Institution of Electrical Engineers. I append a curve showing the membership of both bodies at different dates, and although the British Institution had the start, and has the advantage of us in membership, yet I look forward in the near future to a membership in our body that will be fully on a par with theirs.

I think it would be difficult properly to estimate the good that has accrued to electric science, not only in this country but also in the world at large, from a properly organized association of specialists in a practical branch of science like that of electricity. If we can properly trace, from the circumstances attending a single electrical exhibition and series of conferences held in Philadelphia in 1884, a great awakening in the field of electricity, what must have been the influence for good, exerted by a body like ours, which I think I am correct in saying includes all the distinguished practical electricians in this country. . . .

A glance at the Transactions of the Institute will show the extended and valuable character of the work of its members. This work embraces notable inventions, extended commercial applications, and valuable researches; as, for example, researches in high frequency discharges; the development of alternating current apparatus for electric welding, and for the transmission of power; improvements in continuous current apparatus; improvements in the practical applications and control of electric motors for traction, mining, manufacturing and other purposes; improvements in telephony and telegraphy; improvements in the application of electricity to various chemical proc-

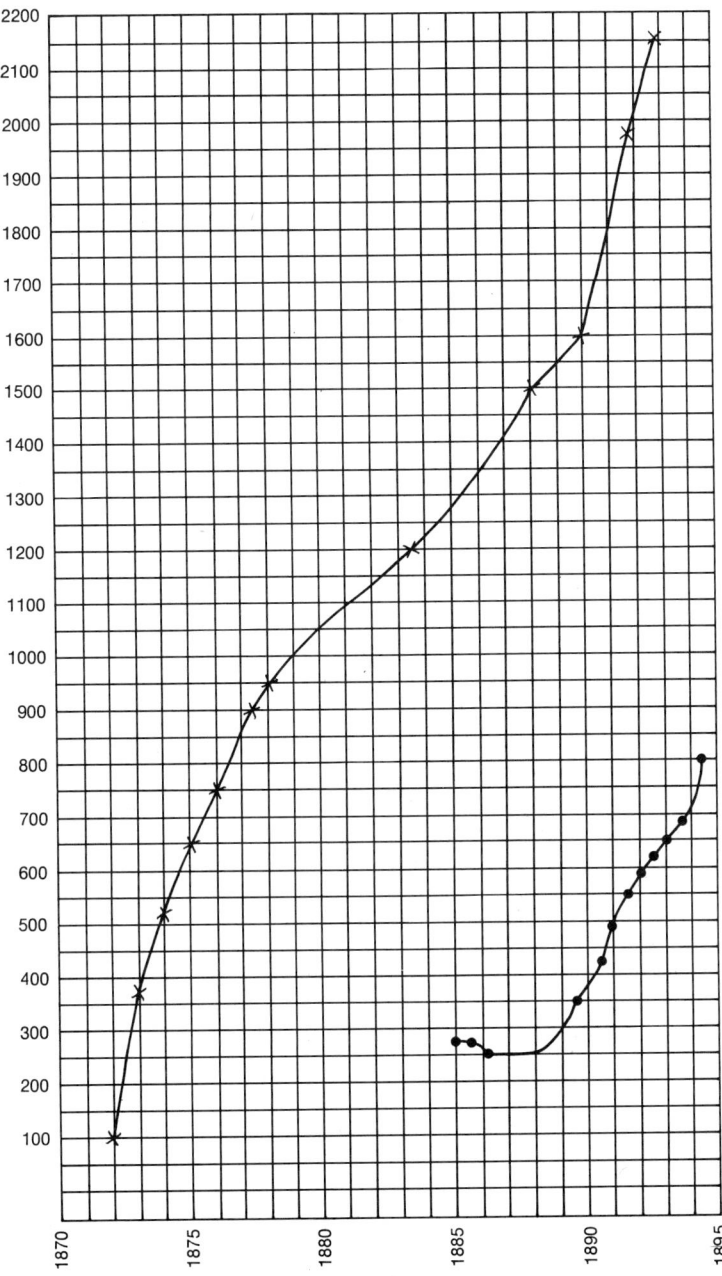

Total membership at different times of the British Institution of
Electrical Engineers, and American Institute of Electrical Engineers.

esses; improvements in designs for electric machinery; improvements in electric lightning apparatus of various descriptions, and developments in electrotherapy. . . .

It would be ungenerous in me, in thus reviewing the causes which have led to the development of electrical science in this country, to fail to mention another potent factor. I refer to the electrical press. I recognize its power and the good it has accomplished in spreading broadcast over the country, not only to the members of the Institute, but to all interested in electrical progress, the knowledge of every great advance made in electric science. In a certain sense, however, the electrical press supplements the influence of the Institute, because the press, unlike the Institute, cannot bring electrical workers together, but can only guide and disseminate the conclusions they have reached.

The growth of the electrical press has kept pace with the growth of electrical science. In 1876 the power of the press was comparatively feeble. The Exhibition of 1884 caused, perhaps, as great an increase in the power and influence of the press, as it did in the development of the science of electricity itself, and, great as has been the marked improvement in electrical science, as demonstrated by the Chicago Exhibition of 1893, I think close observers will agree with me that such progress has been fully equalled by the wonderful improvement in the electrical press of our country.

There is another association of electrical engineers of the same high standing, and governed practically by the same principles as those of the American Institute of Electrical Engineers, and this is our affiliated association, the Institution of Electrical Engineers, with its headquarters in London, England. Like our association its membership contains the leading electrical engineers and experts both in the country in which it is located, and in the surrounding countries.

France has established a somewhat similar body in her Société Internationale des Électriciens, located in Paris. This society has the same general characteristics as the American and English societies, and, like them, publishes regular transactions of its proceedings. In Germany, there is the Elektrotechnischer Verein and the Physikalisch-Technische Reichsanstalt.

Although there are electrical societies in other parts of the world, notably in Italy, and Belgium and Australia, yet in none of these countries is to be found that organized effort and concentration in one central body of the electricians from all parts of the country, as is so markedly seen in the United States, England, France and Germany.

It is, I think, a significant fact, that the countries in which there has been so marked a progress in electrical invention and engineering, are those which possess the advantages of this combined effort on the part of all its electricians. The reason is, I think, evident; under these circumstances, there exists the enthusiasm which comes from properly organized effort; the rapid progress which is encouraged by friendly rivalry and the incentive to increased and continued effort, bred of healthy competition. I think I can safely assert that America, England, France and Germany owe much of their marked advance in electrical science to the existence of their organized bodies of electricians, such as is found in the American Institute of Electrical Engineers, the Institution of Electrical Engineers, the Société Internationale des Électriciens, and the Elektrotechnischer Verein, and I feel sure from the great number of able electricians of Italy, Switzerland, Belgium, Russia, India and other parts of the world, that the progress made in these countries, a progress which is confessedly great, would be still greater if they but tried the advantages of electrical work conducted on the co-operative plan.

It may be advantageous here to review some of the advantages of membership in such learned associations, as, for example, the Institute in which we are the most interested. Among the many advantages are the following: concentration of effort; increased mentality excited by generous rivalry; systematic explorations into the domains of the unknown; a tacit agreement as to what shall be regarded as the standard of good work; the practical establishment of a high court of last resort by whom all disputed technical questions in electrical engineering shall be finally settled; the removal of electric work from the region of guesswork to that of certainty, permitting results to be as surely predicted as in other sciences, and, consequently, an increased stimulus to the successful investment of capital in electrical enterprises; the reduction of misdirected effort by the promulgation of information concerning what has been attempted or achieved in any direction; and last, but not least, the means of establishing a rapid intercommunication of ideas between different parts of the country to others.

As to the privileges of membership in our association, a member in any part of the country, whether in Maine, Florida, Illinois, or elsewhere, can, after submitting a paper to a committee appointed by the Institute for that purpose, have it read simultaneously at the New York and Chicago meetings, and thus not only derive the advantages which come from the broad dissemination of his ideas over the country, but can also have those derived from criticism by those best adapted to judge and discuss them. Instead of being obliged to wait and wonder if his results are valuable or correct, or instead of being forced to endeavor to solve such questions for himself, he is now, by means of the powerful machinery of our association, enabled to hear in a very short time the opinion of those best suited to sit in judgment on his work.

We are naturally and properly proud of the progress shown by our Institute in the first decade of its existence. I ask you now in all seriousness, how has this progress been assured? Clearly by the establishment of a central, organized body, as distinguished from separate, independent, and possibly antagonistic bodies; by the establishment of a central body which derives its authority from a membership extending over the entire country. Is it credible that independent, disconnected, and possibly antagonistic societies, located in as many separate cities as there are groups of members sufficient to form separate societies, can hope to accomplish as much good in so short a time as has been accomplished? Would not the disintegration of our Institute prove to the electrical engineers of this country little short of a calamity? Might not the establishment of separate organizations result in mutual jealousies and intense sectional feeling, and, consequently, in a tendency to the continuance of errors once contracted? Partisanship and intelligent scientific work, in the nature of things, have nothing in common. The true scientific instinct is shown in the desire to know the truth for the truth's sake, and the true electrical engineering instinct is to accomplish the best work in the most economical manner possible. I feel sure you will agree with me that to ensure the greatest sucess, there must of necessity be a central governing body, viz., the Council of the Institute, deriving its authority from a membership extending all over the country, and vested with the power of speaking authoritatively for the Institute between the periods of its recognized official meetings.

In a country like ours, in which distances are so great, a difficulty exists in all our members attending the meetings of a central body, no matter where such meetings might be called. This difficulty is real, and like all geographical difficulties, cannot readily be solved. I think our association has, however, to a great extent, partly solved it by encouraging simultaneous meetings in all parts of the country where the same paper can be read and discussions had thereon, yet at the same time, holding the governing body, the Board of Managers or the Council of the Institute, responsible for the proper direction of its work. That all local meetings must be amenable to the organic law of the Institute, be that law what you may choose to make it, I think needs no discussion. I am glad to say that already, under due authority of the Institute, local meetings have been established in the city of Chicago, and I trust there may

soon be other similar meetings held in all other great centers of population where our membership will warrant it.

Such, I think, are some of the advantages of organization under a central body as opposed to organization under separate, independent bodies. They are, briefly, the advantages of concentration as opposed to those of diffusion; of directed, organized effort as opposed to unorganized, undirected effort. To argue in favor of the latter would be, I think, to deny the advantages of a central government, like our national government at Washington, with its representation from all the various States of the Union, and to revert to the condition of states sovereignity, an un-American and altogether untenable position.

As I look over this assembly of distinguished electricians, I am particularly impressed with this thought; viz., our average member though old in actual experience, is, nevertheless, seldom hoary in years. There must be something in electricity, though what it is I would not venture to say, which attracts the younger and more vigorous members of our race to its study. Perchance it may be that in this mysterious force, there exists some lingering traces of the long sought for "fountain of youth;" but, be it what it may, I find in the fact that such comparatively young men have been able to do so much for the world's weal in a special science, a bright promise of what they may be able to accomplish before their tasks are completed.

6. Some Characteristics of Engineers, 1892

Engineering News

Although nineteenth-century engineers made their presence known through their professional societies, their efforts at educational reform, and their contributions to the nation's economy, we still know very little about who they were in a sociological sense. We do know, for example, that in some fields, such as mechanical engineering, there were sharp divisions between engineers which tended to follow class and educational lines. In 1892 a crude measure was taken of some of the characteristics of American engineers, and, while the conclusions drawn may seem overly tainted with racism and patriotism, the data are still interesting and significant.

This brings us to a tabulation of the birthplaces of members shown in Table XXX., which we were able to supplement also by Table XXXI., showing the nationality of the parents of the members, or, in other words, their real racial nationality, independently of whether they chanced to be born on this side of the water or the other. The latter table is perhaps the most interesting. The two taken together show that of these 668 members reporting (of whom a good many are Canadian engineers) there are:

Born in U. S. of American parentage	524 or	79.3%
" " Canadian, or foreign parentage	62 "	8.8%
Total American born	586 "	88.1%
Born in England, Wales or Scotland	18 or	2.7%
" " Ireland	11 "	1.7%
" " Scandinavia or Germany	29 "	4.3%
" " Canada	13 "	2.0%
Total	657 "	98.8%

This table may be said to represent the racial elements which are, so to speak, native to the blood, i.e., which are either native-born or out of the original racial stocks from which the English-speaking race was formed. The remaining 1.2% also (or only 8 members) are for the most part French or Russian. As such, this table again illustrates for the profession of engineering a truth to which we have often called attention and which is but little appreciated even at home, while foreigners usually ignore it altogether. In spite of the enormous emigration which has been pouring into this country for the last 40 years, the percentage of really foreign elements is as yet insignificant even in the whole population, still more in the higher employments, while the percentage of elements foreign to the blood is vastly smaller yet, and too trifling to consider.

From "Engineering Schools of the United States. XXXI," *Engineering News*, XXVIII (November 10, 1892), 437-38.

Table XXVII. Number of non-graduates and graduates of the several Engineering schools in 668 out of 1,135 corporate members of the Am. Soc. C. E., with the total number of graduates from each college between 1860 and 1884, inclusive, and the percentage of such among those responding. (The numbered colleges, as heretofore, are arranged in order of age, as shown by the year of the first class graduated.)

	No. Admitted as M. Am. Soc. C. E. in							No. C. E. grads. 1860-84 incl.	P. c. now M. Am. Soc. C. E.
	1867-9.	1870-4.	1875-9.	1880-4.	1885-9.	1890-2.	Total.		
Not graduates	10	22	32	48	63	38	213	....	...
Graduates of foreign schools	1	5	7	8	15	9	45	....	...
U. S. Mil. Ac.	...	2	2	5	9	3	21	....	...
U. S. Naval Ac.	...	...	1	...	1	2	4	....	...
1. Rens. Pol. Inst.	14	11	7	15	33	19	99	462	21.5
2. Lawrence S. S.	...	...	1	5	1	2	9	86	10.5
3. Sheffield S. S.	1	5	1	7	13	10	37	223 (323)	16.6
4. Dartmouth	...	4	...	4	6	2	16	133	12.0
5. Union	2	3	2	1	6	3	17	185	9.2
6. Univ. Mich.	...	...	4	6	8	3	21	198 (229)	10.6
7. Brk. Pol. Inst.	...	...	...	...	1	1	2	103	1.9
8. Pa. Mil. Ac.	...	1	...	...	...	...	1	171	0.6
9. Columbia	...	...	2	1	4	3	10	60 (341)	16.7
10. Wash. and Lee	...	...	...	2	3	...	5	42	11.9
11. Mass. Inst. Tech.	...	...	4	10	12	9	35	169 (258)	32.2
12. Lehigh	...	...	1	2	3	4	10	66 (118)	15.1
13. Univ. Va.	...	...	...	5	2	1	8	27	29.7
14. Cornell	...	...	...	6	7	4	17	176	9.7
17. Lafayette	...	...	...	1	1	1	3	79 (110)	3.8
18. Wash. Univ.	...	...	...	2	4	1	7	35 (67)	20.0
19. Univ. Vt.	...	...	...	...	2	...	2	32	6.3
21. Worc. Pol. Inst.	...	...	...	3	5	3	11	88 (232)	12.5
23. Me. Agr. C.	...	...	...	...	2	1	3	77 (104)	3.9

							Total	Number	Per cent
25. Univ. Pa.					3	2	5	84 ...(168)	6.0
26. Stevens					3	1	4	100 (168)	...
27. Univ. Wisc.						1	1	35 (52)	2.9
29. Swarthmore					1		1	32	3.1
32. Univ. Cal.					1		1	62 (105)	1.6
33. Univ. Kans.					1		1	8 ...(16)	50.0
34. Univ. Minn.				1			1	14 (16)	7.2
35. Rutgers				1	1	2	4	67	6.0
38. Univ. Ill.					2	1	3	22 (4)	13.6
39. Univ. Cinc.					1		1	15	6.7
40. Princeton						2	2	35	5.7
45. State Col. Pa.						2	2	1	...
Pol. Coll. Pa.		1	1	4	5		11	Not Known.	Mean: 342 M.
Univ. N. Y.				1	3	2	6	"	
Univ. Ala.						1	1	"	Am. Soc. C. E.
Va. Mil. Ac.	1			1	3		5	"	
Brown Univ.					1	1	2	"	out of 2.72
O. State Univ.					1		1	"	
Mass. Agr. C.					1		1	"	
Haverford					1		1	"	grads.=12.5%
Bowdoin				1			1	"	
Others		1		4	7	1	14	"	
Total	29	55	65	143	239	137	668		
Per cent. not graduates	34.5	40.0	49.3	33.6	26.4	27.6	32.0		
Per cent. grads. foreign schools	5.3	15.2	21.9	8.4	8.5	9.1	9.9		

If the Polytechnic College of Pennsylvania (of which we know nothing) should be added to the Univ. Pa., the percentage then becomes 19.190, which better accords with the standing of that university.

Under this latter head we should include chiefly the Italian and Slavic immigration, a considerable fraction of which makes excellent citizens, while a much larger number come to this country only to get means to end their lives at home on, and leave no descendants behind them. Nevertheless, this undesirable fraction of immigration from all countries should be checked; but there is no need of being alarmed about it, as if its specially bad qualities were likely to make any permanent impress upon our people.

By comparing the total of foreign-born members (79) with the number of graduates from foreign engineering schools given in Table XXVII. (45), it will be seen that the former far more than accounts for the number of engineers educated abroad; in other words there is absolutely no tendency even among students of foreign parentage, to go abroad for their engineering education. [Table XXVII did not originally appear with this article. It was printed as a table in "The Engineering Schools of the United States," *Engineering News*, XXVIII (October 20, 1892), 375. ED.] A good many, both natives and foreign-born (though a small percentage), take a post-graduate course abroad, but other than scholastic motives lead to that, and all post-graduate courses we have uniformly neglected in these records. It is quite certain that from now on no well informed man will ever go to a foreign engineering school with the idea that he can thereby get a better or more thorough education for a practical professional career than at home. It may or may not be a little more professional in the abstract; but in the practical work of training the qualities of mind which make the engineer, there is no reason-

able room for doubt that our American engineering schools lead the world.

A curious proof of this is the insignificant proportion of Germans among the members of the Am. Soc. C. E. It is well known that the country is flooded with university-bred German draftsmen and assistant engineers. They are a trusted and most useful element in every considerable office and corps. There is no prejudice in their way in any part of the country. On the contrary, they do certain lines of work better than any other nationality and are sought for as assistants. They learn the language easily. They get very low pay at home and emigrate in large numbers. But where are they in the ranks of successful engineers who have enjoyed "responsible charge?" Nowhere! Of Swedes, Norwegians, Danes and Germans together there are only 29 members out of the 668 reporting or 4.3%, of which about 17 only, or 2½%, are Germans!

"We say not this to cry them down;" quite the contrary; but the fact deserves chronicle. A partial explanation may be that the German-speaking races have not as great aptitude for (practical) engineering as the English-speaking. History indicates that they have not; but another partial explanation may be defects of their engineering schools, which may tend to crush out executive and originating faculties and make their students mere mathematical machines.

The Irish in comparison have a much more creditable record, though their percentage (1.7) seems low. It is rather larger in porportion to the numbers to draw from than that of any other foreign nationality, even English or Canadian; and considering that there is only one apology for an engineering school in Ireland is far from bad. The English and Scotch make the most surprising

Table XXX.—Birthplaces of Members of the American Society of Civil Engineers (668 out of a total of 1,135).

Dates (inclusive).	No. years.	New England							Middle				No. C.	So. & S.W.	Far. W.	Total U.S.	Eng. or Scot.	Ireland.	Scand. or Ger'y.	Bri. Am.	Other.	Not stated.	Total.
		M.	N. H.	Vt.	Mass.	Conn.	R. I.	Total.	N. Y.	Pa.	N. J.	Total.											
1867-9	3	2			4	1		7	12	2		14		3		24	2				2	1	29
1870-4	5	3	1	2	11	1	2	20	10	7	2	19	4	4		47	1		4	2		1	55
1875-9	5	3	1	1	12	3	1	21	8	9	4	21	8	6		56	2		4	2	1		65
1880-4	5	5	4	3	22	3		37	39	12	5	56	17	13		123	6	1	7	4	1	1	143
1885-9	5	8	6	4	38	12	3	71	44	21	9	74	38	30	2	215	5	6	7	3	3		239
1890-2	3	4	1	2	14	7	3	31	29	19	12	60	17	11	2	121	2	4	7	2	1		137
Totals	26	25	13	12	101	27	9	187	142	70	32	244	84	67	4	586	18	11	29	13	8	3	668

Percentages

	Mass.	N. E.	N. Y.	Pa.	Mid.	No. C.	So. & S. W.	Far. W.	U. S.	Eng.	Ir.	Sc.-G.	B. A.	Other.	Total.
1867-69	14.3	25.0	42.9		50.0		10.7		85.7	7.1				7.2	100.0
1870-74	20.4	37.1	18.6		35.2	7.4	7.4		87.1	1.8		7.4	3.7		100.0
1875-79	18.5	32.3	12.3	13.8	32.3	12.3	9.3		86.2	3.1		6.1	3.1	1.5	100.0
1880-84	15.5	26.0	27.5	8.5	39.4	12.0	9.2		86.6	4.2	0.7	5.0	2.8	0.7	100.0
1885-89	15.9	29.7	18.6	8.8	31.0	15.9	12.6	0.8	90.0	2.1	2.5	2.9	1.3	1.2	100.0
1890-92	10.2	22.6	21.7	13.9	43.8	12.4	8.0	1.5	88.3	1.5	2.9	5.1	1.5	0.7	100.0
Mean	15.2	28.1	21.3	10.5	36.7	12.6	10.1	0.6	88.1	2.7	1.7	4.3	2.0	1.2	....
P. c. of U.S. only	17.2	31.9	24.2	11.9	41.5	15.3	11.4	0.7	100.0						100.0

Table XXXI.—Nationality of the parents of Members of the American Society of Civil Engineers.

Dates (Inclusive).	No. yrs.	America.	England.	Scotland.	Ireland.	Scand. or Germany.	France.	Brit. Am.	Other.	Not stated.	Total.	P. c. Am.
1867-69.	3	22	2½	...	...	½	1½	1	½	1	29	78.7
1870-74.	5	44½	2½	3½	...	3½	...	...	1	...	55	80.9
1875-79.	5	51	1½	1½	½	6	1	1½	1½	½	65	79.1
1880-84.	5	112	10½	3½	3½	9½	...	1	1	2	143	79.5
1885-89.	5	187½	10	4½	9	17½	½	4½	2½	3	239	79.6
1890-92.	3	107	6½	2	3½	14	...	1½	2½	...	137	78.2
Total		524	33½	15	16½	51	3	9½	9	6½	668	79.3
P. c.		79.3	5.1	2.3	2.5	7.7	0.4	1.4	1.3	...	100.0	...

In compiling this table the (comparatively very few) cases in which the parents of a member were of a different nationality were met by classifying the member as half of one nationality and half of another, hence the fractions.

Practically all those shown by this table to be native-born of native parents, nearly 80% of the whole, are Americans by many generations of descent, the reason being that prior to 40 or 50 years ago the emigration to this country was insignificant. A surprisingly large proportion of these members, upward of 150 in all, took the pains to say so.

small showing. Considering how their engineers swarm in the colonies it is surprising that there are not more among the successful men here. They have a perfectly fair field here; after a few years' residence few know them from Americans; but they have "no favor," as probably they do in the colonies.

As between the several states and sections of the United States the showing is somewhat surprising. It is to be remembered that the Am. Soc. C. E. membership represents only the engineers who began practice or study some 10 or more years ago, and is still semi-local in having a somewhat larger proportionate representation from the East than from the West. Still, it is a striking fact that, as shown by the last line of Table XXX., not less than 31.9% of its

members were born in the New England states (more than half of these from Massachusetts alone), while no less than 73.4% were born in the 10 New England or Middle states; the other 32 Southern and Western states having contributed only 26.6% all told. Future events are likely to change greatly these percentages, but they would hardly appear to be due to "local attraction" to any large extent. It is not clear why the Massachusetts or Pennsylvania engineer, not living in New York, has any greater inducement to join the Am. Soc. C. E. than one in the west or south, and the relative percentage for New England, New York and Pennsylvania indicates that not more than a quarter of the percentage for New York at most, or about 5% of the total, is due to the influence of "local attraction."

PART VIII THE ENGINEER AND THE CITY

The cities in America, although they were few in number and contained only a small percentage of the population, set the tone for much of the life of the colonies and states before the nineteenth century. Then, in the years after the War of 1812, cities began to grow both in number and in the percentage of our population which they harbored. In 1800 only 6.1 per cent of Americans lived in cities, by 1900 that percentage had grown to 39.7, and the census of 1920 showed for the first time that over half the population was urban.

The growth of cities put a great strain on their facilities and institutions. Corrupt political machines developed to govern them, and these machines drew much of their profit from the expansion of the technical facilities—gas works, street trolley systems, sewers—required to meet the needs of a rapidly expanding population. The demand for more and better water supplies, buildings, streets, sewers, transportation facilities, and so forth, made it increasingly necessary for cities to employ engineers to help deal with these problems. If city governments betrayed some uncertainty about how they should use and treat engineers, the latter were equally uncertain about their proper relationship with their political masters.

At the turn of the century, when the urban reform movement began, it found ready advocates in the engineering profession. The ideal of disinterested service and technical expertise appealed to reformers and engineers alike. The former, made up of large numbers of the new industrialists, sought to run the cities just as they would run sound business enterprises, and engineers (along with lawyers, social workers, and other rising professional groups) were eager to help. The city was, in fact, a new frontier to be tamed and made productive by the combined talents of the entrepreneur and the engineer.

211

1. A Warning to Engineers, 1892

Engineering News

However much they might have disagreed on other matters, most urban reformers at the turn of the century were loud in their condemnation of municipal rule by political machines. One of the many weaknesses of such a system of government was that it left little room for effective operation by various professional groups, such as engineers. While the voice of scientific truth was often soft, and an ambiguous guide to engineering effort, the commands of urban bosses were plain enough and caused both frustration and humiliation within the engineering profession.

A valued correspondent in Chicago sends us the following letter. We infer that it was not intended for publication, but merely to give information; but we take the liberty of publishing it, after eliminating one or two expressions of a too personal nature, as saying in itself about all that we wish to say:

Sir: Mr. Bernhard Feind, M. Am. Soc. C. E., etc., has been connected with the City Engineering Department of Chicago since 1885, until one month ago. He had by hard work and on his merits, worked himself up from a $100 per month to a $3,000 per year man, and was First Assistant City Engineer. He has had charge of all the large work in hydraulic engineering for several years, and from a personal knowledge of the situation I do not hesitate to pronounce him the most capable engineer of the department, not even excepting the City Engineer himself. But although he has thus worked himself up, on his merits as an engineer, as a politician he was not successful; rather, he refused to resort to political methods to hold his place. A plot was formed to get him out, because he would not give his time to politics instead of to engineering, and it was decided by the Mayor and others that he would have to go. As soon as Mr. Feind heard of this he resigned and has since started an office as a consulting engineer. It seems as if Engineering News should have something to say about occurrences of this kind, thereby raising the standard of engineering and protecting engineers in a measure from such assaults by politicians. The engineers of the country feel that they have a right to expect this of you. This dismissal of Mr. Feind is a clear and a bad case of politics; of throwing out a competent engineer for political reasons only. Moreover, this is not the only case in this city. I know it to be a fact that many, if not all, of the assistants in the City Engineer's Department have been obliged to get the indorsement of the ward club in the ward they live in in order to keep their position, and a number of them, moreover, have been notified that they must "get out and do political work" in their ward to keep their positions. As one particular instance: I am told on most excellent authority that one D. N. Jamieson has been given power to make all appointments and engineer all discharges in the entire engineer's department, i. e., without consulting the City Engineer, the Commissioner of Public Works or any other party except the Mayor. Such things ought to stir up righteous indignation of every engineer and every engineering journal. . . .

From "Politicians and Engineers," *Engineering News*, XXVIII (August 25, 1892), 181-82.

What can be done to remedy such evils as this? We know of nothing which engineers can do except to make facts connected with every such instance as public as possible, and that can be at best but partially effective, for the simple reason that it is impossible for the sufferer himself to expose effectively the nature of the act. The mere fact of his discharge places him under a certain stigma. He is always open to the accusation of being a "sorehead," and of speaking from interested motives to explain away a removal for cause. If some friend takes up the cudgels in his behalf his information comes at second or third hand, and for that reason loses much weight. As for other men in office, they cannot speak without endangering their own heads, and they are therefore rarely willing to speak.

Hence both the sufferer and his friends choose, as a rule, to make the best of a bad matter by saying nothing about it, and either going to work to oust some one else in their turn, or giving up political engineering in disgust and seeking for some other and non-political engagement.

For like reasons it is impossible for a journal like this to do much to stop such procedures; and not wishing to beat the air without effect we rarely say anything about them. The great obstacle to a more positive course is a lack of intimate knowledge of all the facts. Discharges and appointments for political or personal motives only are continually going on, we have every reason to believe. If it were possible to record every such incident exactly as it occurred, and have all the facts believed, we have no doubt that the indignation and disgust of the public would be so stirred as soon to put a stop to them, at least in professional appointments like those on the

engineering staff. But it would not be possible to do this with any amount of trouble, and it would take an immense amount of trouble to even approximate to it. Therefore we can neither do much or say much about these frequent cases of political removals, iniquitous as we know most of them to be.

For example, we fully believe that our correspondent's statements of the main facts in the above case are entirely reliable, but to make sure of it we should have to enter into an extensive investigation of the past and present of every man concerned, and to make other people equally sure of it we should have to spread all these facts with equal detail upon our pages, with the certainty of occupying a great deal of space; with the possibility of falling into some serious error, and with a strong probability that some unimportant alleged error might be made a handle of to obscure the main issue. We have been frequently asked to investigate and expose wrongs of this nature, but have uniformly declined, for this reason alone. The sufferers themselves have like reasons for keeping quiet, and generally do so. The wrong is one without a remedy, which makes it all the meaner when done without cause. In time we may become so civilized that political motives will not control professional appointments at least. We are making some progress in that direction, but we are a long way off from it yet.

Until that happy day arrives our strong advice to every young engineer is to avoid working for cities if he can, as the meanest and most uncertain kind of professional employment, with some honorable exceptions. After that avoid working for states, and after that working for the general government. It is better as a rule to accept a considerably lower salary from a respectable corporation than to work for either of these three. But by comparison with employment under a private individual or firm or a (comparatively) small business corporation, working for any large corporation is itself highly undesirable, if conditions are otherwise equal. And finally, if the engineer has the "stuff" in him to succeed without calling any man master (which is much easier now than ten years ago, and will be easier ten years hence than now) he will be wise to do it even at some considerable pecuniary sacrifice if he does not also sacrifice quality of experience.

2. A Success Story

CHARLES WHITING BAKER, "Looking Back Half a Century"

Despite the discouragement experienced by many engineers who sought service in the nation's cities, the growing scale and complexity of technical problems in the urban setting made it absolutely necessary for cities to hire trained engineers. A few managed to avoid the shoals of political disfavor, and they survived to win the respect of their professional colleagues.

Rudolph Hering, the dean of American sanitary engineers, completed on June 1 his fiftieth year of active work in engineering. It was in June, 1868, that young Hering, just returned to America from four years of study in an engineering school in Dresden, Germany, landed his first engineering job—the humble position of chainman on the survey of Prospect Park, Brooklyn.

Engineers were few in those days, it is true; but engineering positions were few also. In his studies Hering had specialized in bridge and railway engineering, and was eager to put his newly acquired scientific knowledge into practice; but bridge building as a business was hardly born and railway companies in those days used engineers merely in the original surveys and construction. When a railway was once built there was supposed to be no further use for engineers.

Hering had not the slightest premonition of where his future career was to lead. Chance, not intention, determined that—as is very generally the case with engineers as well as other men, regardless of laborious specialization in the schools.

From Charles Whiting Baker, "Looking Back Half a Century: How a Young Engineer, Since Grown Famous, Got His Start in the Engineering of That Day," *Engineering News-Record*, LXXXI (August 8, 1918), 274-76. Reprinted by permission from *Engineering News-Record*, August 8, 1918, copyright, McGraw-Hill, Inc. All rights reserved.

TOLD TO TAKE FIRST JOB
HE COULD GET

Rudolph Hering's father was an eminent scientist and physician of Philadelphia, who immigrated to the United States from Germany in 1826. Among his intimate friends was Julius E. Hilgard, who was later head of the United States Coast Survey. To young Hering, in his quest for work, Hilgard gave letters of introduction to half a dozen well known engineers, among them his personal friend Alfred P. Boller, the bridge engineer. Mr. Boller sent Hering to James P. Kirkwood of Brooklyn, then the most eminent American authority on the filtration of water. Mr. Hering recalls Kirkwood's advice to him to take the first engineering job he could get, no matter how humble or in what field of work, if he wanted to break into engineering. Through Kirkwood's recommendation, Hering became chainman in one of the field parties then working on Prospect Park, in June, 1868.

The first chief engineer on the Prospect Park construction was Joseph P. Davis, who later became city engineer of Boston, and afterward achieved important success as engineer of the Bell Telephone Co. The landscape architects for Prospect Park were Olmsted and Vaux, fresh from their great success in the creation of Central Park. Mr. Davis was a careful, methodical engineer who prided himself on laying out work accurately and computing excavations and embankments to close limits. To change the plans during the progress of work was, to his mind, little short of criminal. Very different were the ways of the landscape architects. Where the merit of work lies in its appearance to the eye, how shall you tell beforehand to a hair's breadth what shall be done?

"Mr. Davis," Vaux would say on one of his frequent visits of inspection, "I don't like the looks of this slope. Won't you fill in two or three feet more here? And this path had better be swung off in this direction instead of where you have built it." Such was the havoc played with the engineer's careful calculations that it worked on Davis's nerves till he resigned in disgust.

Another Nestor of American engineers still in active professional work who was on the Prospect Park survey fifty years ago was John Bogart, who held the position of principal assistant engineer. Mr. Bogart later became widely known to the profession by his services as secretary of the American Society of Civil Engineers for the twelve years from 1878 to 1890. Later he did valuable pioneering in hydro-electric power development in planning the first harnessing of Niagara Falls.

Another important member of the Prospect Park group was C. C. Martin. He was the chief engineer from 1867 to 1870 and later served for many years as chief engineer of the Brooklyn Bridge when that structure was counted among the world's greatest engineering works. Still another was A. M. Wellington, who was leveler in the division adjoining Mr. Hering's, and whose notable work as editor of *Engineering News* from 1887 until his death in 1895 is still fresh in the memory of many engineers.

In 1868, when Prospect Park was in the making, there were only dreams of a bridge connection with New York City. Brooklyn was a residential city for those who did business in New York (which meant the lower end of Manhattan Island) and was famous far and wide as "the City of Churches." Prospect Park was to be just such a recreation spot for these "suburban dwellers" as the newly opened Central Park was to New Yorkers who lived "uptown" (above 14th Street).

The only means of travel for New Yorkers in going to and from business was the Broadway omnibuses (whose chronic congestion in rush hours was the first example of that coming "peak of the load" which was to be such a problem to the engineers of a future generation) and a few newly built horse-car lines. The same class of New York business and professional men who nowadays flock to the New Jersey suburbs to escape the congestion of Manhattan Island went to Brooklyn to find homes in the fifties and sixties. . . .

The work of young Rudolph Hering on Prospect Park lasted only a year. Funds ran low, and in 1870 the work had to be suspended for a time. So the future sanitary engineer, who was still longing to be a bridge engineer, sought another job and found it in his own home city of Philadelphia, where the new Fairmount Park was just then being laid out. Here again his work was surveying, but he was put in charge of a party.

The first task was to make a topographical map of the area. Hering had been instructed abroad in the then little known art of surveying with a plane table, and he suggested its use for the Fairmount Park surveys. He met with no encouragement until he broached his idea to the principal assistant engineer, Hermann Schwartzmann, who had also had experience abroad. To Hering's suggestion that the plane table be used, Schwartzmann replied, "Of course that's the best way to do it; but nobody here knows how to use a plane table." "Well, I know how," said Hering. "Then use it, by all means," said Schwartzmann.

Another young engineer associated with Hering on the Fairmount Park work was Lewis M. Haupt, who a few years later became professor of civil engineering at the University of Pennsylvania. Still another was J. Foster Crowell, who was assistant engineer for the area east of the Schuylkill River while Mr. Hering was engineer for the west side. In later years Mr. Crowell was a well known consulting engineer in New York City and was at one time commissioner of the Street Cleaning Department.

It is a little difficult to realize now that at that day the making of surveys and measurements was considered the chief function of an engineer. An engineer was a man who used a chain, a compass and other instruments set up on three legs, who set down figures in a book and drove stakes marked with red chalk that told where this and that was to go. There was an underlying reason why engineers were not in demand except for the absolutely necessary work of surveying, and were especially not wanted to meddle with anything relating to prices or to the award of contracts. Those were the palmy days of corrupt municipal government in the United States. Most cities were governed by political machines which were run for the enrichment of the "machinists."

Relics of that old-time view of the engineer still survive, as in the State of New York, where the state engineer is required by law to do the scientific and mathematical work in connection with the state's public enterprises, while the award of contracts and the inspection of contract work are reserved to the Superintendent of Public Works, who is by tradition a carefully selected politician.

In January, 1872, about the time the Fairmount Park surveys were completed, the newspapers were full of the discoveries of wonderful spouting springs in the Yellowstone region of the Rocky Mountains. Congress had set aside for a national park a great tract 60 miles square containing these geysers. Hering was becoming a park engineer, so why not seek a job there? Through his father's friend, Hilgard, he was introduced to Hayden, the geologist, who was to head an exploring party to the Yellowstone, and Hering was appointed one of the two astronomers of the expedition, the other being the late Henry Gannett.

PREDICTED FALL OF BRIDGE

After six months of active adventure in the Yellowstone, and another six months in Washington working up the data, Hering returned to his home town of Philadelphia and at length gained his long desired opportunity to practice bridge engineering. Samuel L. Smedley, then city engineer of Philadelphia, placed Hering in charge of the new Girard Avenue bridge over the Schuylkill. Another bridge over the Schuylkill at South St. was at the same time in charge of D. McN. Stauffer, who eight years later became editor of *Engineering News*. This was the ill-fated South St. stone arch structure which fell in ruins before its completion, because there was a stratum of soft clay below the crust of hardpan into which the piles that supported one of the piers were driven.

That failure was one of the notable engineering disasters of the time. The slow, steady settlement of the pier and the consequent distortion of the arch were accurately measured by Hering, and the curves of pressure as well as of settlement were plotted day by day. One Thursday Hering said to his chief, "Mr. Smedley, that arch will fall in a few days." On Saturday he computed that it would fall on Sunday morning about 7 o'clock. At 7 o'clock Sunday morning Hering was at the site of the work, but at 6 a.m., within an hour of the time he had predicted, the huge masonry arch had crashed to the ground.

It should be said here that neither Hering nor Stauffer was responsible for the design of the bridges on whose construction they were the resident engineers.

After three years spent on the Girard Ave. bridge, City Engineer Smedley in 1875 transferred Hering to a field of work in which he was later to become an eminent specialist—the city sewer department. Not that there was much to be learned by a young engineer in the Philadelphia sewer department of that day except the art of how not to do it. Hering was the outdoor assistant, having chiefly to do with the construction of the main sewers and bridges.

In those days in Philadelphia and numerous other cities of eastern Pennsylvania the pedestrian along the streets was continually stepping over a little stream of soapy water flowing in channels across the sidewalk from the house to the street gutters. The smallest sewers built in Philadelphia were 3 ft. in diameter. These were built of a single 4-in. ring of brick laid up, except the arch, without mortar. Indeed, it was explained to young Hering on his entry into the sewer department, by the men of "practical experience" who were in charge, that the sewers must be built without mortar "so that they would drain the ground."

FOUND SEWER BUILT OF BARRELS

Naturally, cave-ins of sewers so built were frequent. One day news came that a street had caved in over a recently built sewer, and Hering was sent down to investigate. Sure enough, there was a long jagged ditch through the center of the street. Taking a pick, Hering started exploring to find the condition of the rest of the sewer, but he could not uncover any bricks. Instead he found barrel staves and hoops. On further inquiry it was discovered that the contractor had obtained a lot of barrels, knocked out the heads, placed them in the ditch, quickly covered them up, collected his money at so much per lineal foot of sewer laid, and departed with all convenient speed.

To a man of Hering's make-up, sewer building in Philadelphia was chiefly instructive as evidence of the need for great reforms—reforms in design as well as in execution. In other cities as well as in Philadelphia the time was ripe for breaking away from the traditions and the prejudices of the old school of sewer builders.

Col. George E. Waring was just then attracting wide public attention by his advocacy of small pipe sewers—a novelty which the leading engineers of that day fought against bitterly, but which the younger and more far-sighted men recognized must receive attention. In one of the discussions between Hering and his chief, Smedley, in 1878, the younger man proposed a trip to Europe to study foreign practice in sewer construction. Smedley approved and put in an application to the city councils for an appropriation to pay Hering's traveling expenses. The item attracted the attention of one of the lynx-eyed "watchdogs of the treasury" in the councils. "Go to Europe to study sewerage!" said he, sarcastically. "I can see through that. He wants a junket to see the Paris Exposition. Not on yer life."

Nevertheless, Hering did go to Europe to study sewer construction. In the spring of 1880, after again unsucessfully trying to obtain aid from the City of Philadelphia, his old friend Hilgard introduced him to Dr. John S. Billings, then surgeon general of the Navy and vice president of the National Board of Health. Dr. Billings promptly welcomed the proposal and Hering went back to Philadelphia to tell his chief that the Federal Government was going to send him to Europe to study sewer design and construction.

So it was that the youth who had specialized in bridge work and railway engineering spent the first dozen years of his professional life on park surveys, bridge building and sewer construction, before he found an opportunity for large development along the line where his future career was to lie.

3. Serving Two Masters, 1915

MORRIS LLEWELLYN COOKE, "Some Factors in Municipal Engineering"

No engineer took his professional and social responsibilities more seriously than did Morris Llewellyn Cooke, for many years an employee of the city of Philadelphia. In an address to the American Society of Mechanical Engineers, he touched upon several of the stumbling blocks in the path of competent and responsible urban engineering. His most telling criticism was of the tendency of engineers to serve the interests of large corporations rather than those of the general public, a charge which led a colleague to comment from the audience, "those who make such an accusation are unworthy of a place in the profession." The following is an abstract of Morris Llewellyn Cooke's speech.

The test by which the role of the engineer is to be determined will be the development in our profession of a genuine spirit of public service. The community is apparently ready to accord the engineer a leading, perhaps a controlling part, if the engineer will consider that in every decision and act there shall be the clearest possible recognition of the public interest. We should remember that democracy can use the engineer without giving him either a leading or a controlling hand in affairs. This use of engineers has been conclusively demonstrated by public utilities companies, especially during the last thirty years. In most of our larger cities during this period there have been operating one or more so-called "big business" men who have built large fortunes and a certain kind of fame in the development of enterprises in which engineering was an important factor and in which it should have been the paramount and controlling factor. In these enterprises engineers have necessarily been used, but not in a leading or controlling capacity.

It would probably require considerable research to get the names of the engineers used by Charles Yerkes in Chicago; by Martin Maloney in Philadelphia; by Anthony N. Brady in New York; and by Patrick Calhoun in San Francisco. As a profession we may as well face this problem and decide whether in the further upbuilding of our cities, we are so to serve democracy as to be warranted in demanding and to be entitled to receive a position comparable to the real importance of our work.

That profession which considers only its own and its clients' interests without a proper regard for those of the general public will be accorded the same position which history has always given those who are led by no higher star than

From "Some Factors in Municipal Engineering," *Mechanical Engineering*, XXXVII (February 1915), 82-84. Reprinted by permission of the American Society of Mechanical Engineers.

self interest, however enlightened that self interest may be. I firmly believe that the engineering profession is rising to meet its broader responsibilities with perhaps an even more quickened pace than that which during recent years has wrought such sweeping changes in the medical profession and that of architecture. There are certain kinds of engineering in which financial and almost all other kinds of preferment depend on an attitude of mind which, while not necessarily anti-social does not provide sufficient opportunity for entertaining a virile public point of view.

As a representative of public, rather than private interest, it is my duty in choosing the advisers of the city, which I have the honor of serving, to satisfy myself not only as to the ability of those we employ, but also as to their disinterested—yes, their public point of view.

No matter how able a man may be, how broad his experience nor how high his standing, his service to those who employ him must at all times be consistent with the public interest if, from my point of view, he is to be available for public employment.

Judged by this standard, there are in certain fields of engineering almost no engineers who are at present available for the service of the public and who at the same time have had sufficient experience for large undertakings. In the past few years we have had unusual opportunities for seeing at close range the professional attitude of those equipped with the technical knowledge required in advisers to cities on utility matters. It has been practically impossible to secure the services of those with reputations already made in the electrical field. Some of our experiences could be considered on the whole rather amusing were it not for the fact that we are left

under the obvious conclusion that for the average city official to get good advice on these matters, is well nigh impossible. What is more objectionable is that this condition is one quite generally recognized as true by city officials.

I must be careful to emphasize the fact that no criticism of any individual is embraced in these remarks and that I am simply pointing out a danger almost necessarily confronting the engineering of an industry dominated by financiers having no knowledge and little appreciation of such professional standards as engineers are supposed to have.

The same tendency is to be noted in other branches of our profession. An eminent authority on concrete, who is in intimate touch with the men who are practising in this line, was recently asked for the name of an engineer who was not in anyway affiliated with the large manufacturers of this material and after considerable study was able to think of only one man. There is nothing necessarily improper in this situation,— it may simply mean that all the competent men in this line receive retainers from manufacturers. Some months ago I wanted to retain an engineer fully posted on the details of a certain subdivision of railroad operation. It was extremely difficult to find a man without recognized affiliations which would preclude his retention. Again I am informed that there are no asphalt experts who do not receive retainers from the manufacturers. It is a condition which should be provocative of thought by engineers.

Public employers up to the present have been almost a negligible factor in furnishing opportunity for employment or for the making of a reputation. It is perfectly natural, and it is in accord with former ideals that engineers should feel their first duty to be to these private employers. But in this time of broader and deeper social consciousness, it seems to me that this standard must change.

The point I wish to make is that engineering has now reached the stage of development where it has become a profession in the highest sense of the word. The engineer being a scientist, his responsibility should be for the development of facts, regardless of whose advantage they may serve. I have in mind that the service of an engineer should be as the service of a judge, as opposed to the service of a lawyer who confessedly seeks out and represents the interests of his client, and often "makes the worse appear the better cause." This is justified by the fact that lawyers are not scientists, and by the assumption that there shall always be opposing counsel.

If this municipal field is to be one in which engineers of ability, sincerity of purpose and high ideals are to find a permanent and satisfactory outlet for their energies, our profession acting as a profession will be one of the main agencies bringing about certain fundamental changes in the attitude of the public. In the minds of too many engineers, participating collectively in matters pertaining to municipal engineering means "getting into politics." Architectural work being a part of the business of The Department of Public Works in Philadelphia, we have had the coöperation of the American Institute of Architects and of its Philadelphia chapter from the beginning. . . . We have had the constant, indefatigable and valuable support of the secretary of The American Society of Mechanical Engineers in our efforts to maintain the highest pro-

fessional standards in the work of the department. But engineering bodies as such have given us no assistance and so far as I know have taken no part in the discussion of federal, state and municipal engineering, except in the matter of conservation which for some reason is considered as innocuous as a prayer meeting.

Many municipal engineers in this country are beginning to adopt the European system of employing non-residents for certain highly specialized positions. Whenever this is practised it excites criticism and abuse. As yet no technical organization, so far as I know, has recognized the opening thus made for technical merit and given moral support to the movement. Again I have tried to get support from organized engineers in the obviously necessary procedure of employing experts outside our regular staff, but without results.

The public must be taught that public service is not different from private service in that forward steps come frequently, even usually, as the result of a large amount of preliminary investigation. Again, the public, of which please remember we are a part, must be educated to place more responsibility on individuals, thus making it possible to do away with the great inefficiencies which inevitably accompany board and committee management. As long as we have boards and committees they will vote,—and they will insist on voting,—on matters that are not questions of personal opinion but questions of facts which ought to be determined by the facts. It is one of our duties as technical men to carry on a propaganda which will show to the public the difference between those problems of policy and public interest, that are properly settled by public opinion and those scientific problems which are improperly settled unless they are settled according to the facts. Mr. Frederick W. Taylor, Past-President of the Society, in recent lectures has very forcibly and lucidly suggested this fundamental difference. For instance, my opinion may be as good as that of any other citizen's as to how fast an automobile should be allowed to operate in different sections of a large city. The opinion of any member of this Society is as good as that of any other citizen as to the penalty which should be inflicted for false registration. On the other hand, the designs for a bridge; or the specifications for a sewer; or the plans for the laying out of a public park; or the organization of the police department; or the fighting of fires; or the elimination of mosquitoes are necessarily the work of experts. Such work will always be indifferently done if done by voting; whether the voting is by the people at large or by a committee or board acting for the people. Notwithstanding all the boards and commissions that are created in the generally approved laws of today, there should be no uncertainty as to what questions they may vote upon. It is therefore one of the duties of the educated to carry this message to the people and in doing so I do not think there will be any more powerful method than to give the great mass of the people a larger and larger knowledge of expert work. . . .

The development of some varieties of municipal engineering is absolutely dependent upon the development of public opinion and must proceed with it. The matter of street cleaning is largely a question of an improved public taste in the matter of street paving. Unless streets are well paved they cannot be well cleaned except at a prohibitive

cost. To jump from one degree of cleanliness in this respect, to another, without a supporting public opinion, may be enough to wreck an administration and to set the tide of civic improvement running in the opposite direction.

The newspaper is the great educator in these matters today. But we are already using in Philadelphia moving pictures, parades and exhibitions. The possibilities of these and other means of publicity are not yet fully understood.

Take, for instance, the movement which has led to the formation of large numbers of business men's associations and improvement associations. This affords one of the very best examples of the present vitality of American public life. Our leading men should accept them as something that has come to stay and coöperate with them in such a way as to direct their activities into profitable channels. It seems to me they afford the most promising agency through which in the first place, the thought of the public on civic questions can be crystallized and secondly through which that thought can be given expression in definite public procedure. I have found these associations ready and anxious to hear from men who had definite knowledge on matters of public interest. It should be the attitude of any engineer who wants to play his part in the community, to affiliate with one of these organizations and to help to make it an influence. You can rest assured that the man who is in public life for his own personal advancement is bending every energy to defile and degrade these institutions and to divert them from the high mission which they have it in their power to carry out, so they need our help.

In such a discussion as this, one cannot ignore the civil service. It is always a pleasure to say that personally I could not hold public office if it were not for the safeguards and reliefs that our Civil Service Act affords. At the same time without repeating what I have said in other public papers on the subject, I want to call attention to one fundamental misconception under which the entire civil service question in this country apparently rests. Civil service appears to be founded on the theory that the best man for the position will apply for it. I think it is the experience of every employer of men—and this is especially true in filling the higher positions—that the best man will not apply. On the contrary you will usually have to go out on the scriptural highways and hedges to find the best man and then having found him, fall on your knees and beg him to accept the positions offering such opportunities for public service and professional independence as are most likely to secure him.

This is the way to get good public servants. It is almost impossible to find men who have many of the qualifications for our work combined with a willingness to enter the public employ. Even if public employment should come to be considered more desirable than it is at the present moment, I think that this difficulty in finding the best man would still be encountered. Therefore, if we are to have the highest class of men in important engineering positions we must develop some merit system by which the appointing officer is given a greater opportunity than he now has of finding the man for the job. In this work it is [not] impossible for our engineering societies to take an important part.

I believe, for instance, that if the secretaries of the four national engineering societies could be authorized by their several councils to associate themselves as a civil service board to act in an advisory capacity to federal, state and municipal civil service commissions, it would be a decided step in the right direction. Suppose the president of the Borough of Manhattan should want to secure a competent engineer to put in charge of the highway department. Through the New York City Civil Service Commission he would state the problem to this suggested advisory board which in turn would appoint say three engineers to act as his counselors in finding the man. The appointing officer would keep these counselors in touch with the search and when he was ready to make a choice, secure their approval before entering into a contract. In this way the merit system would act as a check against favoritism but would allow the appointing officer the widest possible opportunity to search for the best man available.

This procedure is a radical departure from the present idea of civil service, which is based on the assumption that it is impossible to allow the appointing officer to have anything to do with the selection of his men. Even under the most advanced forms of civil service the appointing officer is confined to a full statement of the qualifications he is trying to secure. One never exactly fills a position with just the kind of man in mind when the search started. It is a question of compromise and the appointing officer is the one who is in the best position to know where concessions can be made and which among the several requirements are the most indispensable. There would be no objection to a check on this action of the appointing officer through some kind of a written test. But to choose men for positions paying $5,000 to $25,000 a year on the results of a written examination is absolute folly. So far as I know engineers have never taken a hand in the discus-

sion of methods under which engineers shall be chosen for positions in the public service and it seems to me high time they should do so.

4. The City Managers, 1927

LEONARD D. WHITE, *The City Manager*

One of the newest and most promising avenues through which engineers could attack urban problems was that of city manager. The city manager system, a typical example of Progressive reform, was an attempt to transcend petty politics and machine corruption and bring both technical expertise and executive efficiency to the administration of cities. Since so many urban problems were concerned with engineering works during these years, engineers were frequently hired as managers: in 1917 it was estimated that between 80 and 90 per cent of managers had engineering training.

The origin of the council-manager plan is imbedded in the revolution of the civic and business interests of the American city, aided and abetted by various forward-looking groups, against the waste, extravagance, and sometimes corruption which characterized "politician" government of the last century. With rare exceptions, the pattern of community behavior as it approached the adoption of the council-manager plan has been almost identical. Low standards of municipal accomplishment, waste and misapplication of public funds, lack of vision with regard to the city's future and lack of energy in pursuing even the most limited objectives,

government by political machines for the purpose of maintaining the strength and controlling power of the machine rather than by independent officials for the good of the community, jealousy and ill will between communities even where co-operation was essential, concealment of the real condition of public business rather than frank recognition of the right of the public to know the facts of public affairs—all co-operated in varying degree to produce discontent, distrust, and suspicion of the mayor and council, or the commission, in most of the 375 cities which have adopted the council-manager plan.

The opposition to bad government

usually comes to head in the local chamber of commerce. Business men finally acquire the conviction that the growth of their city is being seriously impaired by the failures of city officials to perform their duties efficiently. Looking about for a remedy, they are captivated by the resemblance of the city-manager plan to their corporate form of business organization. They understand this type of organization readily and believe that what has contributed to the success of their business will make for the success of their city. They sponsor a movement for charter revision, gather around them other organizations, and elect a charter commission to draft a new charter along city-manager lines. The friends of the new charter then carry the campaign for its adoption and almost invariably continue their organization for the purpose of electing the first council, which will select the manager and inaugurate the new régime. They are usually successful in controlling a majority of the council-elect.

With variation in emphasis, this story is repeated from one end of the country to another. Why the "revolution" has been running so swiftly in the last fifteen years is not difficult to understand. The persistent and effective agitation of the former Conference for Good City Government of the National Municipal League has had a profound effect; the constant growth of the physical size of the city and the constantly greater complexity of its problems made "amateur" government more and more an anomaly; the unprecedented increase in municipal expenditures caused an anxious search for every opportunity for economy, leading directly to the manager plan; the decline in the strength of local political machines in the smaller cities,

in part an outgrowth of the manager plan itself, made the transition to government by experts easier. . . .

Occupational Classification of Managers

Prior Occupation of Managers	Number of Cases
Engineering	398
Business	103
Official positions	94
Miscellaneous professions	24
Clerical	22
Law	16
Education	15
Skilled trades	15
Secretarial and promotional	14
Journalism	4
First employment out of college	4
Unknown	154
Totals	863

The conditions of life in America are now such that . . . changes seem almost inevitable. Governmental problems have become intricate and even more insistent. They call for solution with the aid of science, not with the wisdom of a ward politician. The amazing mobility of the American people leaves no community a law unto itself; each and all are responsible for their own good government to the larger whole of which they are a part. What the whole world is witnessing is the emergence of government by experts, by men and women who are trained technicians highly specialized to perform some service by scientific methods. It is indeed a fair question whether we shall not be forced to reinterpret American government as a means for utilizing the services of experts in the performance of ends democratically defined. . . .

SOME LEADING CITY MANAGERS
CHARLES E. ASHBURNER

Mr. Charles E. Ashburner, the first city manager, was born in Bombay, India, in 1870, the son of an English army officer. He was educated in England, France, and Germany, and received an engineering degree from the University of Heidelberg. Shortly afterward he came to the United States and took a minor position on the James River under the army engineers. His experience has been intensely practical; he has been engineer in charge of a Virginia company town, has been connected with the Bureau of Highways of the United States and of Virginia, was engaged for years in engineering work for railroad and electric companies, and had experience as an independent contractor and consultant.

His connection with Staunton as "general manager" came about in a characteristic fashion. A leaky dam gave way one spring, and the local contractors refused to bid under $4,000 for making repairs. Ashburner, then maintenance engineer on the Chesapeake and Ohio Railroad, was appealed to by a friend in the city council. He advised that the repairs could be made for $737 if his recommendations were followed. The council took his directions and completed the job for $736 according to one version and for $712 according to another!

Faced with the deplorable results of chronic misgovernment, and forbidden by the state constitution to adopt the commission form of city government, Hugh C. Braxton, of the then city council, and Stephen Timberlake, a local attorney, devised the idea of a general manager to take full control of city business. The details of the plan and its success need not be recorded here. The council unanimously selected Ashburner to become the general manager of the city at a salary of $2,500. He remained here for three years (1908–11). He retired much irritated by the course of events in his first city-manager venture. Subsequently, after three years in engineering work for the city of Richmond, he returned to the city-managers' profession as manager of Springfield, Ohio (1914–18), at a salary of $6,000; then he became manager of Norfolk, Virginia, at an initial salary of $9,000, rising to $16,000 when in 1923 he was elected manager of Stockton, California, at a salary of $20,000. An initiated ordinance to reduce this salary was defeated by about two to one in November, 1926.

Ashburner is one of the outstanding personalities in the city-managers' profession. His social group, his educational background, and his practical experience, are hardly to be paralleled in the ranks of the managers.

To attempt a catalogue of the amazing mixture of personal characteristics of Ashburner is almost a hopeless task. The effort has been made before, without penetrating far beneath the surface of a dynamic personality. Louis Brownlow was certainly on sure ground when he wrote of Ashburner:

> He is a working whirlwind of a man, who has a clear vision of the future of municipal government and the faith to count that vision among the realities of life. Sometimes, like other whirlwinds, he is tactless of phrase. Sometimes, like other seers, he is impatient with those who cannot see. Always, like other true believers, he wastes no time on those who have no faith.

So also Frederick Palmer,

> Quick of thought, indefatigable, he is a man of strong opinions which he knows

how to express except on partisan politics. No one ever doubts his utter honesty, which he emphasizes by such punctilious- ness that he will never ride in his official automobile unless on official business. At times pugnacious, again very mellow, al- ways driving for essentials, Charles E. Ash- burner, the founder of a new profession, is undoubtedly a personality.

Henry Oyen describes him as

medium sized and twitching with the nerv- ous energy that marks the enthusiast. . . . His strongest characteristics probably are his desire for "doing a job right," his en- thusiasm, his excessive supply of energy, and his inclination to shake hands with everybody, including his avowed enemies.

The original, and in many ways the indelible impression of Ashburner, is that of an inexhaustible human dynamo, forever driving ahead with constant ac- celeration, never content with the achievements of the past, but with full realization burning up the ultimate treasure of reserve power in the relent- less pursuit of the immediate objective. Ashburner's face shows the lines of the restless and unsatisfied effort which has broken him down already four times on the job. He grants that he is burning the candle at both ends; for long periods he keeps up the pace only with the constant attention of his physician; but so long as there is a big job to be done, Ashburner cannot do less than give every ounce of his strength and his will to it.

He is, of course, nervously high- strung. He talks in staccato explosions. He pounds his desk at the least provo- cation. In conversation he shoots straight at the mark. He interrupts a question with his answer as soon as he grasps the point. He makes up his mind with an almost disconcerting abrupt- ness. He has no patience with views contrary to his own, and often con- demns them with unnecessary violence.

He is irritable and sometimes arbitrary.

In spite of these qualities, not infre- quently disturbing to inquiring citizens who pass by his desk, Ashburner pos- sesses a rare winsomeness which unex- pectedly comes smiling through the tempestuous vigor of his characteristic attitudes. Emotions stir him easily. His hearers will not soon forget a memo- rable occasion when, after a peppery tirade directed against a type of city management which he thought hurtful to the profession, he said in softened voice, charged with emotion, "I feel about my *profession* as I feel about my *religion.*"

Surcharged with energy as he is, Ash- burner never creates an impression other than that of complete sincerity. His loyalty to his city, to his profession, and to his own high standards of per- sonal conduct is carried to the last degree. He has often stressed the qual- ity of sincerity in speaking before his co-workers in the managerial profession. In the 1915 convention he said, "It may sound visionary, but it is never- theless true that sincerity is the only influence in public affairs that makes lasting friends, and effectually disarms foes." When the Norfolk city council offered him an increase of salary to meet the offer of Stockton he replied in a flash, "No! If I owe you a nickel, I will stay and work it out. But you can- not increase my salary. I am worth no more to you now than I was a month ago." Parenthetically the reader should know that when Norfolk was caught in the post-war slump and city expenses had to be reduced, Ashburner proposed a cut in salaries of officials and employ- ees ranging from 5 to 10 per cent and a cut of his own salary of 25 per cent.

Ashburner is a man who revels in big things. His whole being is wrapped up in construction. Wherever he has been, his record has given the same picture over and over again. In Staunton it was streets and substructures; in Norfolk, a modern system of streets, a great rail-water terminal, a grain elevator, and a new water system; in Stockton, an elaborate system of flood control, a new city hall, and above all a deep-water canal to tidewater. With the greatest emphasis and decisiveness he declared to me, "By God, I go into a town to build! When I can't build, I get out!"

His very absorption in often spectacular undertakings limits the attention which he gives to other phases of city government. Ashburner is not a manager who follows closely the work of even so important a department as the police, and there is some evidence that his police administration has not been as successful as his development of city plant. He gives a little thought to the detail of management.

Ashburner is essentially a builder and a promoter. Although he repeats the appropriate description of his subordination to the council, and is scrupulously careful never to put the council or himself in an embarrassing public position, it remains true that his personality has dominated the city government of every municipality with which he has been connected. He stands head and shoulders above the members of his city councils in courage, foresight, technical skill, and persistence, and withal has skill in negotiation and diplomacy which rarely fail to bring his council to his way of thinking. He is a leader as well as a manager and a builder.

Ashburner is not reluctant to take the initiative in advocating measures, either before the council or before the people. He openly espoused the bond issue for the deep waterway in Stockton, helped to direct the campaign, and later headed the delegation to Washington to present the case before the army engineers. Competent observers in Stockton said frankly that he handled the case as no other man in Stockton could have done.

While writing up a report on an important matter of public policy in one of his cities, a member of the council requested a conference. Ashburner said there was nothing to confer about at that stage of his report, that it was his report and not a joint report. "But," said the councilman, "I may not be able to agree with it." "All right," replied Ashburner, "in that case one of us will be wrong."

Ashburner has held the center of the stage since he has been in Stockton. The psychology of the situation combined with his own energy to bring this about; there was a general feeling that here was a "big man" brought in to do things for the town, and that if the citizens did not unite behind him they would never be able to get away from the cliques which formerly disputed possession of the town.

In concluding this brief sketch, it is of interest to note Mr. Ashburner's attitudes about his work. He advocates the selection of the manager from outside, but adds,

Any manager going into a community makes a very desperate mistake in not taking the tools at hand and organizing his working force with them. Every community, whether large or small, ought to have men in it who can be trained and who can be made efficient in any position that they are in.

He speaks strongly on the subject of co-operation.

There is one thing every manager should do, let the first word he speaks in coming into a community be "co-operation." . . .

Have a human soul in your city administration and have every one feel that no man has a drag with the administration any more than any other.

But he cannot stand criticism gracefully, and co-operation tends to mean subordination of others to him.

He deplores any public differences with his commission. The manager

should fearlessly state his position in the presence of his governing body, and having done that . . . if the matter is of vital importance and the council decides one way and the manager thinks another, there is but one thing for the manager to do and that is to step down and out.

As long ago as 1915 he stated the heart of the morale problem in his terse phraseology. "To my mind the greatest secret in municipal or in any other organization is to get the heart of the employees in their work." Ashburner has sought this end by attempting to create a sense of fair play, by requiring an honest day's work, by discharging incompetent or dishonest employees; but it does not appear that he has ever developed any more refined methods. He is doubtless more interested in getting a big job well done than in building the morale of his staff.

He is outspoken in his denunciation of the "damn bunk that some managers are going in for." By this he means "frills" and unnecessary expenses, such as municipal research bureaus. He declares that what people want is a man who can do things, not one who can tell about what someone else has done. He doubts whether managers can be trained and is averse to any plan for establishing a training school.

One may suspect that in expressing these views Ashburner is standing counter to the main channel of future development. But he is an aggressive individualist, and his own career gives a perfect illustration of the self-made manager, which can hardly fail to remain for him an adequate justification of the school of experience. Although a professional manager, he rarely attends the annual conventions, and even holds aloof from the meetings of the California City Managers' Association. He is wholly wrapped up in his own situation and pays little attention to his colleagues in other cities. Ashburner's methods and interests are such that he is not content to remain manager after the development phase of the work is done; when Stockton's deep waterway, flood control, and city hall are completed, he will seek new worlds to conquer.

5. The Engineer as Messiah, 1925

ROBERT RIDGWAY, "The Modern City and the Engineer's Relation to It"

Some engineers took a very broad view of their responsibilities and capabilities. Looking at the modern American city, they were ready to accept respon-

From Robert Ridgway, "The Modern City and the Engineer's Relation to It," *Transactions of the American Society of Civil Engineers*, LXXXVIII (1925), 1245-56. Reprinted by permission.

sibility for its existence and to propose measures for its reform. Often conservative by virtue of their class, education, and source of livelihood, engineers at the same time were the custodians of revolutionary power. The uneasy equilibrium between these two forces sometimes led to a somewhat exaggerated opinion of their own potential for public service.

Perhaps the most notable effect of the application of those laws of Nature which have been brought to light by the patient investigations of the scientist during the past century and a half is evidenced in the wonderful growth of cities everywhere, and, as the engineer has contributed so largely to this result, I have chosen to make the theme of my address: "The Modern City and the Engineer's Relation to It," realizing that the thoughts expressed are not original with me, but have long been in the minds of others.

In the simple days when our Federal Constitution was adopted, we were essentially an agricultural people and manufacturing was but an incident. The planter was the man of affairs and when he came to town he was shown the deference befitting his standing in the community. Then, the steam engine began to play its important part in the affairs of the nation and among other applications made transportation over long distances easier. This was followed by the "magnetic telegraph," the result of the good work of Henry and Morse, and, since then, one invention has followed another at an increasing rate up to this time. We do not often stop to think how recent and how new nearly all the inventions which contribute so much to our comfort and well-being really are. It is necessary to go back only to the infancy of those now living to realize this. When I was born, the telegraph was still regarded as a marvel and the locomotive was rather a primitive machine if compared with the great engines of to-day. No trans-Atlantic cable had been successfully laid. The telephone was unthought of and electric lighting and traction were still the dreams of scientists. Water powers were largely going to waste because, although their potential value was understood, the market for the power did not exist and methods of harnessing it for the production of hydro-electric energy were unknown. . . .

The habits and customs of our people as well as their social structure have been profoundly influenced by our wonderful material development. We have been changed from an essentially agricultural people to an industrial nation. When the first Federal Census was taken in 1790, probably more than 90% of the total population of about 4,000,-000 was rural and less than 10% was urban, that is, dwellers in cities of 2,500 or more. Philadelphia, with a population of 42,520, was the largest city and New York was second with 33,131 inhabitants. In 1920, only 46% of the 113,-000,000 inhabitants of Continental United States was rural and 54% was living in cities or towns of 2,500 or more inhabitants. Like the advance in applied science, the change from the rural to the urban condition has been going on at an ever-increasing rate, but some of those who have analyzed the figures believe there are signs of a slowing down of this rate. The automobile, with improved highways, the telephone, and the radio, together with labor-saving farm machinery, with improved living conditions on the farm, have come to make country life more comfortable to such an extent that the migration to the cities is being gradually checked.

These changed conditions are not peculiar to our own country and Canada. Europe and the world over show the same tendency, thus indicating that the fundamental causes are not due alone to the development of a relatively new country, but to the growing substitution of machinery for hand work and the creation of new conditions of living. The change, however, is probably more pronounced in newer countries like our own. . . .

The growth of the cities, however, does not tell the whole story. In the old days, the city was little more than a layout of streets and a collection of houses. Business offices and shops were under the same roof or within walking distance of the homes of both employer and employee. The homes and shops were lighted by candles or lamps. The water supply, in most cases far from wholesome, came from wells or town pumps, and cesspools did in part the work of the modern sewer. Where paving existed at all, it was rough and generally in poor repair. Live stock roamed the streets which were cleaned only occasionally. Living, when viewed from the standpoint of to-day, was primitive. The relations between private and public health were unknown, and the police power of the body politic was confined to the simple preservation of the peace.

The modern city is a most complicated organism. Its streets and buildings are but an expression of the spirit of the city even as a photograph expresses the character of the individual, but the city itself is more than a mere expression. I have often compared the difference between the modern city and the village from which it was developed with the difference between the modern battleship and the wooden frigate of Nelson's day. The latter was driven by the winds of heaven, the sails were set and furled, and the anchor was weighed by hand. The battleship of to-day is a bundle of nerves and in its hull is installed the most intricate machinery of many kinds. The crew knows little of the things that sailors of old had to know, but now includes specialists of many kinds, skilled in the use of steam and electrical machinery and the radio, and experts in scientific gunnery and navigation. Practically all the activities of a large town are represented on the battleship and its personnel includes opticians, dentists, physicians and surgeons, carpenters, painters, barbers, tailors, printers, even the ministry is represented. Its officers have been taught and drilled in almost every science as well as in the principles of local and international law.

The homes and offices of every modern city are equipped with electric lights and telephones and the cooking is done largely by gas, piped from a central plant. Electric cars and vehicles propelled by gasoline-driven motors take the people to and from their homes. Buildings, many stories in height and equipped with elevators, have taken the place of the old low-lying buildings. Detached dwellings are rapidly being replaced with apartment houses, each one sheltering many families. The streets are well paved and lighted and are cleaned more often and much better than they were formerly. Probably there are still as many horses in the streets as there were formerly, yet horse-drawn vehicles have been so largely supplanted by motor trucks of much greater capacity that it seems as if the horse is disappearing.

The unsanitary cesspools have been superseded by sewers which automatically carry away the wastes and the town pump has been supplanted by a wholesome water supply brought from distant sources. The newspapers are supplemented by motion pictures and by the radio, which give the people in their theaters and homes the news of the day. Religious, educational, hospital, and amusement facilities exist in great numbers, as a part of the equipment of the modern city, and are available for the poor as well as the rich to a far greater extent than ever before. The home of the laborer is fitted with comforts and conveniences that the wealthy man of the past could not command because they did not then exist. The general health of the people is better than in the more primitive days of the past. The comforts of yesterday have become the necessities of to-day and what were formerly regarded as luxuries are now demanded as comforts. . . .

Seldom do we pause to think of the enormous power which has been harnessed and is available within the confines of a single large city. It is estimated that the potential power transmitted through the water, gas, and steam mains, and the electric power cables, underlying the streets of New York, is at least three times the amount now being generated by all the hydro-electric plants at Niagara Falls on both sides of the river. The capacity of the central electric generating plants in New York alone is about 3,000,000 h. p. I have been informed that the condensing water pumped for these plants is eight times the quantity of water supplied to the city by its aqueducts.

In a material sense, the modern city is the result of the work which has been done by the pure scientist and the engineer. Without them, the city could not exist. To their skill and toil are due the water supply, the sewers, and the sanitary conveniences, the paved streets, the transportation facilities for local, suburban, and interruban use, the telephones, the electric lights, and all the many other facilities on which a city has come to depend for its very existence. Nor could the city be kept free from epidemics and its health be maintained at so high a standard without the excellent work of the sanitary engineer in co-operation with the chemist, the bacteriologist, and with medical research. So it has come about that typhoid and yellow fever have been largely eliminated and nearly all communicable diseases have been brought under control.

All the utilities which so largely affect our modern urban life require the services of specialists, carefully trained, each in his particular line of work. The day of the "Jack of all trades" has passed, because it is obvious that to-day, with such a tremendous amount of detail in every line of effort, one can no longer be an expert in everything and these experts are engineers by whatever name they may be called. To think of the long and patient study which has been, and is being, given to each one of these problems, to realize that the execution of the work is frequently done under the most discouraging conditions, and that progress is generally made in spite of and not with the help of the multitude, makes us feel the extent of the debt we owe to those who have labored in the laboratory and the designing room, the office, the shop, and the field, to accomplish results we accept so complacently. Few of these men are known to the public because their deeds are not of the sensational character that commands public attention and most of them are too modest to expect any public commendation for their work.

The change to urban life has affected deeply the customs, the habits, and the thoughts of the people. In the simple days during the early life of the Republic, when men lived generally distant from one another, they were largely individualists, believing with Thomas Jefferson that government was a necessary evil and that they should get along with as little of it as possible, depending on their own efforts for success. Modern concentration of vast numbers of people in cities has led to the organization of industrial corporations with hundreds and frequently thousands of employees working under the same roof. Diversities of custom are disappearing. Organizations based on class consciousness are formed with the idea of bettering the material condition of particular classes of workers. More government is demanded. There is a drift toward paternalism and socialism; a tendency to lean on the State or National Government for help out of all difficulties; to lose that Anglo-Saxon spirit of independence which formerly prevailed and which was the foundation on which the structure of our national life was built. The fear exists that these tendencies are going too far; that the worker is being made into a machine and that so much effort is given to developing his material side, that the moral and the spiritual sides are forgotten. While city workers have escaped the hardness of the farm life of the old days, they are paying for the ease of life in a loss of that touch of fundamental things which is so necessary for true happiness and for the full rounding out and proper balance of hu-

manity. We have boasted that the percentage of illiteracy is much lower in our cities than in many of the rural districts, but have forgotten that education consists not only in the ability to read and write, but that its true purpose is the teaching of an understanding of the lessons which Nature teaches, to a reading of "the sermons in the rocks," and "to the dreaming of dreams of human progress and to ultimate happiness and contentment."

The price we have paid for the many advantages which life in the great cities has given us is a large one. The opportunities and advantages of urban life have not yet come to compensate humanity for the restful quiet of the open country, for the simple pleasures it affords, and for the spirit of introspection which it fosters. Their comforts and luxuries are to be enjoyed only at the expense of a certain softening of character. The joy of doing is marred by the prevalent feeling of unrest, and the ever mounting cost of living in cities is a cause of anxiety to those of moderate means. It is becoming increasingly expensive to bring foodstuffs and other supplies into large cities, principally because of the restricted terminal facilities which are, however, in part, the result of a narrow or selfish vision of the particular community.

Large cities have come to stay and will doubtless continue to exist as long as industrial conditions and human nature remain as they are and as long as gregarious man retains the desire to live and work where other men congregate. Recognizing this, the efforts of every good citizen should be directed to making cities what they should be, by each giving of his best thought to improving the quality rather than the number of inhabitants. Many are giving thought to the proposition that it would be better for the well-being of the human race if the tendency it now displays toward urban life could be checked. It is a grave question whether the future rapid growth of cities should be encouraged. It is obvious that our cities cannot continue to grow until they include the entire population. There must come a time when their growth will be checked by the inevitable process of economic laws, if thinking men do not find some way to check it before that time arrives. It does not conduce to the well-being of the people to have cities become too large. It is not economically sound to have them do so. The cost of transporting the people workward and homeward, of bringing food to them, and of providing for them in other ways, adds a great load to an already burdensome tax not only on themselves but on the other people of the nation.

There would be less concern regarding the present and future condition of our cities if the standard of governmental growth had kept pace with that of the material growth of our cities, but it has not. Municipal government in our country still falls far short of being what it should be, but it is to be remarked that municipal government like municipal engineering is a new problem for the world. If cities had not grown so fast there would have been more time to work out this new problem. Rapid growth is not conducive to the development of the best in government. Centuries were required to develop stable systems of self-government for States and Nations with their scattered populations, while these large cities have existed but a few generations and the problems of their government are new. Then, too, the problem is complicated by the fact that in our own country, at least, the population lacks social homogeneity. The immigrant, because of the sudden change from his old standards and conditions and by reason of his inertia toward a new environment, renders the task more difficult of solution. The sociological problems which confront municipal government are staggering in their proportions. We must not lose faith if the many evils of municipal government are not corrected at once. It will require the best efforts of wise and honest men many long years to accomplish this and it is a tribute to those who have thus labored that present conditions are no worse.

I believe we are making progress in the right direction. We find discouragement when, after going upward for a time, we drop back into the trough of the wave, but I believe each trough is higher than the preceding one and the trend is ever upward. Advancement is possible only through persistent, intelligent, and co-ordinated effort on the part of all good citizens. To be both effectual and permanent, reforms in the body politic must come from within and I have faith that they will so come. From an experience in public work of more years than I care to remember, I believe the reason we are so far behind is the apathy of the so-called good citizen. Included in this category are those engineers who show no interest in the affairs of their city except to complain when things go wrong. All such are apparently content to let others run their civic affairs for them and when they do criticize their public servants they are likely, because of a lack of knowledge of the conditions, to condemn the one who has served them well instead of the one who deserves their condemnation. By so doing they work against their own best interests. Because of this apathy, because of lack of knowledge of its own affairs, and because of the habit of jumping at conclusions, the public has the deserved reputation of being a hard taskmaster for those on whom it has conferred the responsibility of directing public business. Many are misled by the mouthings of demagogues and do not take the time to reason out the particular thing which may be under discussion. Frequently, investigations are made of the conduct of public departments, sometimes for partisan reasons and political effect. To those familiar with such matters it is known that such investigations are usually far from being thorough, that they bring out only one side of the case, and that their conclusions, usually based on prejudice, are often fundamentally in error. The inevitable result in such cases is that the faithful and honest official, innocent of wrong-doing, is censured and discouraged. His department is disorganized because nothing is more demoralizing than a sense of injustice done. Every honest man chafes under such conditions and most men are honest. But, worst of all, the body politic suffers in such a case because whatever faith it may have had, has been destroyed. If public opinion was sufficiently alert to demand that all such investigations be rigidly thorough and impartial we would find ourselves a long step in advance. That is the way in which I believe engineers would conduct such investigations. They would bring reason to bear on them and would assemble and analyze the facts before reaching a conclusion.

I have referred to the part the engineer has played in the upbuilding of the modern city and of the debt the public owes him, but if he has done all these wonderful things, he has assumed a responsibility for them and owes a debt in turn. We cannot bring something into being without assuming responsibility for its proper development and for the use that is made of it. After all, works of the engineer's creation are but the means to an end, not the end itself. They contribute to the well-being of humanity and man is more than a physical being. Surely, the engineer has a duty to perform in addition to the development and care of material things, wonderful as they are. I do not like to think that the engineer can see only the steel and masonry structure he designs and builds. I hope he has a vision of what it is built for as the architect of the Middle Ages had of the great cathedral he erected, and that the spiritual, moral, and æsthetic sides of life have a great value to him.

We are justly proud of what the engineer has done and perhaps we have boasted about and given too much thought to his achievements, leaving to others the concern over the grave social and political problems which confront us with those great concentrations of population in our cities. How may he help in the working out of these problems? First of all, as a good citizen, he must do his share in all branches of community work. If he does less he fails in his duty. The engineer is no longer the pioneer of the early days when his work called him to more or less remote sections to build canals or to the frontier of civilization to build railroads. Lacking a permanent abode, there may have been an excuse for neglecting his civic duties in those days, but not in these. There is no frontier with us now and as the engineer has, generally speaking, acquired a settled residence, he should take part in the affairs of the community in which he resides. By this I do not mean that he should enter politics as that expression is commonly understood. There are many ways to help besides that and many are finding the way, serving, as some are now doing, on school boards and other public and quasi-public boards to good effect and aiding in the solving of the multitude of vexing questions which arise. There is much civic work of a special nature that the broad-minded engineer is particularly qualified to assist in doing, such as the framing of building codes, zoning regulations, and of legislation affecting the regulation of public utilities.

It is not enough that he should understand his own problems. He should be able to explain them to laymen in language that is understood by them. Too often, I am afraid, the engineer fails to win approval of the authorities or of the public to a sound and meritorious proposition because he lacks the ability to translate his own sound thoughts into language that others who are not engineers will understand.

Do not let me be understood as claiming that engineers are superhuman beings, that they are made of better clay than others, or that they alone are responsible for all the good that has been accomplished. Like the rest of mankind they are not infallible. Others have been and are doing their duty to the world in their respective lines of endeavor; but it must be remembered that the engineer is trained to deal with fundamental things. He is accustomed to delve for the truth and to reject that which is unsound. Unless there is a foundation of truth in a proposition he will instinctively oppose it. Habit of thought inclines him to reason a thing out from cause to effect. Popular clamor

and newspaper headlines do not sway his judgment. He is trained to look broadly and not parochially on all propositions involving the application of natural laws. Artificial political barriers do not appeal to him as they do to those who consider all things superficially, because he recognizes that the laws of Nature operate in the same way on each side of every State, National, or other political boundary.

For the engineer to bring these qualities to the public service he must in his civic associations be something more than the mere technician. I believe the engineer recognizes more than other citizens, and by force of example, by precept, and by teaching, he must show all men, that the days of waste are passing and the era of conservation has begun. With the waste must go all petty and partisan politics with so-called "logrolling" and in its stead must be substituted constructive statesmanship to go hand in hand with the principles of conservation. If we are to live up to the ideals of our institutions our legislators must be leaders rather than followers. It has often been said that America is law-ridden and that its people have lost respect for its laws. A foreign critic said some time ago that we have more laws than all the other countries of the world combined and that we are the most lawless of all people. Is there not force in this criticism? Why should not engineers join with other good citizens to correct some of the evils of the body politic we all recognize and which are due largely to the apathy of our people? The engineer can be a good citizen without losing his value as a technical man. He yields to none in respect and affection for the institutions of his country. His patriotism was shown by his work in the World War and in many other ways. Through active participation in civic affairs his vision would be broadened and the criticism that has so often been made as to the narrow outlook of the engineer on the affairs of the world would soon fall of its own weight.

As we read day after day the sensational matter that is called news and listen to the harangues of the popular orator and self-constituted regulators of the world we wonder if they represent the standard of the character and of the intelligence of our people. Should we so believe we could easily become discouraged as to the future of our institutions and even of civilization itself. Faith and courage will return if we realize that these are but manifestations of a small and vicious minority who bask in the sunshine of publicity. The great mass of all thinking men do their work quietly and without ostentation wherever right and duty call. In industrial plants, railroads, public works, schools and colleges, churches, hospitals, and on the farms quiet thinking men are doing the real constructive work of humanity and of civilization. With an instinctive reliance on and faith in the integrity of human nature, and believing in the permanency of those institutions of man which make for the advancement of knowledge and good of the world, they make their daily sacrifice to duty. They are representative of that divine force of progress which is irresistible in action because it is based on truth, on reason, and on character. Cannot some way be found to employ this force in the interest of civic betterment? All these workers are of the company of the engineer. With him they must advance to wider fields of greater effort, of greater promise, and of even greater service.

Thanks to the wisdom of our forefathers, the foundations on which our country's institutions rest are broad and deep. Incorporated in the design were high ideals and the superstructure was raised in fidelity and in faith. The task of its maintenance is that of each succeeding generation. As in the case of all structures built by man, repairs, renewals, and additions are necessary, but do not call for destruction of the original fabric. The skeleton of the structure must be maintained intact. The larger duty of the technical man calls him to this task. To the task he brings special qualifications. As a practical idealist his patriotism and civic spirit should be manifested not by a waving of flags and by boasts of superiority to others, but by searching out the defects in our present make-up and then by aiding others to raise the standards of civic affairs in the same deliberate and constructive way in which he designs and builds his physical engineering structures for the use and benefit of mankind.

PART IX THE PROGRESSIVE ERA

The Progressive era, from about 1900 to 1920, was a critical one for American technology. Until this time engineers and mechanics had worked individually to advance their crafts, and in small groups to further their professional standing. By the turn of the century, however, the closing of the West, the flood of immigrants to the nation's cities, the growth of great new industries based on scientific knowledge, the acquisition of an overseas empire, the increasing concentration of wealth (and therefore of power), and the growing social unrest in the country, all pointed to the fact that the nation was entering a new phase of its history. Technology had played a large role in bringing about the changes that troubled the country, and an increasing number of people saw even more technology as the solution to the problems those changes brought.

If urban corruption tended to concentrate around technological problems, then those problems should be turned over to professional technologists who would handle them scientifically, and with professional integrity. If the exhaustion of our natural resources was the result of runaway technology, then improved technology could slow the pace of that exhaustion. If new manufacturing processes tended to alienate and exploit the worker, then scientific management should see to it that every man did his best and was given a just reward for his labor. In short, an appeal was to be made from technology drunk to technology sober.

The new theme was to be rational and systematic. If this led to ever greater concentration of power, then so much the worse for individualism. The arbiters of what was carelessly called "the scientific method" could only be scientists, of course, and if this reliance upon experts undercut the traditional dependence upon democracy, then so much the worse for self-government. Change was to be embraced as it always had been by Americans. But now it was to be planned rather than left to chance; it was to be systematic rather than piecemeal; it was to be based upon natural law rather than prejudice. The watchwords were "efficiency" and "conservation"—terms that came to color every phase of American life during the first two decades of the twentieth century.

1. Scientific Management, 1911

FREDERICK WINSLOW TAYLOR, *The Principles of Scientific Management*

The founder of the movement for Scientific Management and a leading proponent of the concept of efficiency was Frederick Winslow Taylor (1856-1915). Although he came from a wealthy and influential family, Taylor chose to study mechanics in the machine shop as well as in college. Having achieved a degree in engineering as well as practical shop experience, he set about his mission of bringing order out of the chaos he found in American manufactures. Concentrating on the machine shop, which he knew best, he developed both a new alloy for cutting-tools and a new way of handling those tools and the material to be worked. As this system was developed he reported on his progress to his colleagues in the American Society of Mechanical Engineers. Finally, in 1911, he brought his ideas together in a book. It was the classic statement of how and why the workman should become an integral part of the machine process, and it had considerable influence.

President Roosevelt, in his address to the Governors at the White House, prophetically remarked that "The conservation of our national resources is only preliminary to the larger question of national efficiency."

The whole country at once recognized the importance of conserving our material resources and a large movement has been started which will be effective in accomplishing this object. As yet, however, we have but vaguely appreciated the importance of "the larger question of increasing our national efficiency."

We can see our forests vanishing, our water-powers going to waste, our soil being carried by floods into the sea; and the end of our coal and our iron is in sight. But our larger wastes of human effort, which go on every day through such of our acts as are blundering, ill-directed, or inefficient, and which Mr. Roosevelt refers to as a lack of "national

From Frederick Winslow Taylor, *The Principles of Scientific Management* (New York, 1911), pp. 5-7, 15-16, 38-47, 116-19.

efficiency," are less visible, less tangible, and are but vaguely appreciated.

We can see and feel the waste of material things. Awkward, inefficient, or ill-directed movements of men, however, leave nothing visible or tangible behind them. Their appreciation calls for an act of memory, an effort of the imagination. And for this reason, even though our daily loss from this source is greater than from our waste of material things, the one has stirred us deeply, while the other has moved us but little.

As yet there has been no public agitation for "greater national efficiency," no meetings have been called to consider how this is to be brought about. And still there are signs that the need for greater efficiency is widely felt.

The search for better, for more competent men, from the presidents of our great companies down to our household servants, was never more vigorous than it is now. And more than ever before is the demand for competent men in excess of the supply.

What we are all looking for, however, is the ready-made, competent man; the man whom some one else has trained. It is only when we fully realize that our duty, as well as our opportunity, lies in systematically cooperating to train and to make this competent man, instead of in hunting for a man whom some one else has trained, that we shall be on the road to national efficiency.

In the past the prevailing idea has been well expressed in the saying that "Captains of industry are born, not made"; and the theory has been that if one could get the right man, methods could be safely left to him. In the future it will be appreciated that our leaders must be trained right as well

as born right, and that no great man can (with the old system of personal management) hope to compete with a number of ordinary men who have been properly organized so as efficiently to cooperate.

In the past the man has been first; in the future the system must be first. This in no sense, however, implies that great men are not needed. On the contrary, the first object of any good system must be that of developing first-class men; and under systematic management the best man rises to the top more certainly and more rapidly than ever before.

This paper has been written:

First. To point out, through a series of simple illustrations, the great loss which the whole country is suffering through inefficiency in almost all of our daily acts.

Second. To try to convince the reader that the remedy for this inefficiency lies in systematic management, rather than in searching for some unusual or extraordinary man.

Third. To prove that the best management is a true science, resting upon clearly defined laws, rules, and principles, as a foundation. And further to show that the fundamental principles of scientific management are applicable to all kinds of human activities, from our simplest individual acts to the work of our great corporations, which call for the most elaborate cooperation. And, briefly, through a series of illustrations, to convince the reader that whenever these principles are correctly applied, results must follow which are truly astounding. . . .

The elimination of "soldiering" and of the several causes of slow working would so lower the cost of production that both our home and foreign markets would be greatly enlarged, and we could compete on more than even terms with our rivals. It would remove one of the fundamental causes for dull times, for lack of employment, and for poverty, and therefore would have a more permanent and far-reaching effect upon these misfortunes than any of the curative remedies that are now being used to soften their consequences. It would insure higher wages and make shorter working hours and better working and home conditions possible.

Why is it, then, in the face of the self-evident fact that maximum prosperity can exist only as the result of the determined effort of each workman to turn out each day his largest possible day's work, that the great majority of our men are deliberately doing just the opposite, and that even when the men have the best of intentions their work is in most cases far from efficient?

There are three causes for this condition, which may be briefly summarized as:

First. The fallacy, which has from time immemorial been almost universal among workmen, that a material increase in the output of each man or each machine in the trade would result in the end in throwing a large number of men out of work.

Second. The defective systems of management which are in common use, and which make it necessary for each workman to soldier, or work slowly, in order that he may protect his own best interests.

Third. The inefficient rule-of-thumb methods, which are still almost universal in all trades, and in practising which our workmen waste a large part of their effort.

This paper will attempt to show the enormous gains which would result from the substitution by our workmen of scientific for rule-of-thumb methods. . . . Thus all of the planning which under the old system was done by the workman, as a result of his personal experience, must of necessity under the new system be done by the management in accordance with the laws of the science; because even if the workman was well suited to the development and use of scientific data, it would be physically impossible for him to work at his machine and at a desk at the same time. It is also clear that in most cases one type of man is needed to plan ahead and an entirely different type to execute the work.

The man in the planning room, whose specialty under scientific management is planning ahead, invariably finds that the work can be done better and more economically by a subdivision of the labor; each act of each mechanic, for example, should be preceded by various preparatory acts done by other men. And all of this involves, as we have said, "an almost equal division of the responsibility and the work between the management and the workman."

To summarize: Under the management of "initiative and incentive" practically the whole problem is "up to the workman," while under scientific management fully one-half of the problem is "up to the management."

Perhaps the most prominent single element in modern scientific management is the task idea. The work of every workman is fully planned out by the management at least one day in advance, and each man receives in most cases complete written instructions, describing in detail the task which he is to accomplish, as well as the means to be used in doing the work. And the work planned in advance in this way constitutes a task which is to be solved, as explained above, not by the workman alone, but in almost all cases by the joint effort of the workman and the management. This task specifies not only what is to be done but how it is to be done and the exact time allowed for doing it. And whenever the workman succeeds in doing his task right, and within the time limit specified, he receives an addition of from 30 per cent. to 100 per cent. to his ordinary wages. These tasks are carefully planned, so that both good and careful work are called for in their performance, but it should be distinctly understood that in no case is the workman called upon to work at a pace which would be injurious to his health. The task is always so regulated that the man who is well suited to his job will thrive while working at this rate during a long term of years and grow happier and more prosperous, instead of being overworked. Scientific management consists very largely in preparing for and carrying out these tasks.

The writer is fully aware that to perhaps most of the readers of this paper the four elements which differentiate the new management from the old will at first appear to be merely high-sounding phrases; and he would again repeat that he has no idea of convincing the reader of their value merely through announcing their existence. His hope of carrying conviction rests upon demonstrating the tremendous force and effect of these four elements through a series of practical illustrations. It will be shown, first, that they can be applied absolutely to all classes of work, from the most elementary to the most intricate; and second, that when they are applied, the results must of necessity be overwhelmingly greater than those which it is possible to attain under the management of initiative and incentive.

The first illustration is that of handling pig iron, and this work is chosen because it is typical of perhaps the crudest and most elementary form of labor which is performed by man. This work is done by men with no other implements than their hands. The pig-iron handler stoops down, picks up a pig weighing about 92 pounds, walks for a few feet or yards and then drops it on to the ground or upon a pile. This work is so crude and elementary in its nature that the writer firmly believes that it would be possible to train an intelligent gorilla so as to become a more efficient pig-iron handler than any man can be. Yet it will be shown that the science of handling pig iron is so great and amounts to so much that it is impossible for the man who is best suited to this type of work to understand the principles of this science, or even to work in accordance with these principles without the aid of a man better educated than he is. And the further illustrations to be given will make it clear that in almost all of the mechanic arts the science which underlies each workman's act is so great and amounts to so much that the workman who is best suited actually to do the work is incapable (either through lack of education or through insufficient mental capacity) of understanding this science. This is announced as a general principle, the truth of which will become apparent as one illustration after another is given. After showing these four elements in the handling of pig iron, several illustrations will be given of their application to different kinds of work in the field of the mechanic arts, at intervals in a rising scale, beginning with the simplest and ending with the more intricate forms of labor.

One of the first pieces of work undertaken by us, when the writer started to introduce scientific management into the Bethlehem Steel Company, was to handle pig iron on task work. The opening of the Spanish War found some 80,000 tons of pig iron placed in small piles in an open field adjoining the works. Prices for pig iron had been so low that it could not be sold at a profit, and it therefore had been stored. With the opening of the Spanish War the price of pig iron rose, and this large accumulation of iron was sold. This gave us a good opportunity to show the workmen, as well as the owners and managers of the works, on a fairly large scale the advantages of task work over the old-fashioned day work and piece work, in doing a very elementary class of work.

The Bethlehem Steel Company had five blast furnaces, the product of which had been handled by a pig-iron gang for many years. This gang, at this time, consisted of about 75 men. They were good, average pig-iron handlers, were under an excellent foreman who himself had been a pig-iron handler, and the work was done, on the whole, about as fast and as cheaply as it was anywhere else at that time.

A railroad switch was run out into the field, right along the edge of the piles of pig iron. An inclined plank was placed against the side of a car, and each man picked up from his pile a pig of iron weighing about 92 pounds, walked up the inclined plank and dropped it on the end of the car.

We found that this gang were loading on the average about 12½ long tons per man per day. We were surprised to find, after studying the matter, that a first-class pig-iron handler ought to handle between 47 and 48 long tons per day, instead of 12½ tons. This task seemed to us so very large that we were obliged to go over our work several times before we were absolutely sure that we were right. Once we were sure, however, that 47 tons was a proper day's work for a first-class pig-iron handler, the task which faced us as managers under the modern scientific plan was clearly before us. It was our duty to see that the 80,000 tons of pig iron was loaded on to the cars at the rate of 47 tons per man per day, in place of 12½ tons, at which rate the work was then being done. And it was further our duty to see that this work was done without bringing on a strike among the men, without any quarrel with the men, and to see that the men were happier and better contented when loading at the new rate of 47 tons than they were when loading at the old rate of 12½ tons.

Our first step was the scientific selection of the workman. In dealing with workmen under this type of management, it is an inflexible rule to talk to and deal with only one man at a time, since each workman has his own special abilities and limitations, and since we are not dealing with men in masses, but are trying to develop each individual man to his highest state of efficiency and prosperity. Our first step was to find the proper workman to begin with. We therefore carefully watched and studied these 75 men for three or four days, at the end of which time we had picked out four men who appeared to be physically able to handle pig iron at the rate of 47 tons per day. A careful study was then made of each of these men. We looked up their history as far back as practicable and thorough inquiries were made as to the character, habits, and the ambition of each of them. Finally we selected one from among the four as the most likely man to start with. He was a little Pennsylvania Dutchman who had been observed to trot back home for a mile or so after his work in the evening, about as fresh as he was when he came trotting down to work in the morning. We found that upon wages of $1.15 a day he had succeeded in buying a small plot of ground, and that he was engaged in putting up the walls of a little house for himself in the morning before starting to work and at night after leaving. He also had the reputation of being exceedingly "close," that is, of placing a very high value on a dollar. As one man whom we talked to about him said, "A penny looks about the size of a cartwheel to him." This man we will call Schmidt.

The task before us, then, narrowed itself down to getting Schmidt to handle 47 tons of pig iron per day and making him glad to do it. This was done as follows. Schmidt was called out from among the gang of pig-iron handlers and talked to somewhat in this way:

"Schmidt, are you a high-priced man?"

"Vell, I don't know vat you mean."

"Oh yes, you do. What I want to know is whether you are a high-priced man or not."

"Vell, I don't know vat you mean."

"Oh, come now, you answer my questions. What I want to find out is whether you are a high-priced man or one of these cheap fellows here. What I want to find out is whether you want to earn $1.85 a day or whether you are satisfied with $1.15, just the same as all those cheap fellows are getting."

"Did I vant $1.85 a day? Vas dot a high-priced man? Vell, yes, I vas a high-priced man."

"Oh, you're aggravating me. Of course you want $1.85 a day—every one wants it! You know perfectly well that that has very little to do with your being a high-priced man. For goodness' sake answer my questions, and don't waste any more of my time. Now come over here. You see that pile of pig iron?"

"Yes."

"You see that car?"

"Yes."

"Well, if you are a high-priced man, you will load that pig iron on that car to-morrow for $1.85. Now do wake up and answer my question. Tell me whether you are a high-priced man or not."

"Vell—did I got $1.85 for loading dot pig iron on dot car to-morrow?"

"Yes, of course you do, and you get $1.85 for loading a pile like that every day right through the year. That is what a high-priced man does, and you know it just as well as I do."

"Vell, dot's all right. I could load dot pig iron on the car to-morrow for $1.85, and I get it every day, don't I?"

"Certainly you do—certainly you do."

"Vell, den, I vas a high-priced man."

"Now, hold on, hold on. You know just as well as I do that a high-priced man has to do exactly as he's told from morning till night. You have seen this man here before, haven't you?"

"No, I never saw him."

"Well, if you are a high-priced man, you will do exactly as this man tells you to-morrow, from morning till night. When he tells you to pick up a pig and walk, you pick it up and you walk, and when he tells you to sit down and rest, you sit down. You do that right straight through the day. And what's more, no back talk. Now a high-priced man does just what he's told to do, and no back talk. Do you understand that? When this man tells you to walk, you walk; when he tells you to sit down, you sit down, and you don't talk back at him. Now you come on to work here tomorrow morning and I'll know before night whether you are really a high-priced man or not."

This seems to be rather rough talk. And indeed it would be if applied to an educated mechanic, or even an intelligent laborer. With a man of the mentally sluggish type of Schmidt it is appropriate and not unkind, since it is effective in fixing his attention on the high wages which he wants and away from what, if it were called to his attention, he probably would consider impossibly hard work.

What would Schmidt's answer be if he were talked to in a manner which is usual under the management of "initiative and incentive"? say, as follows:

"Now, Schmidt, you are a first-class pig-iron handler and know your business well. You have been handling at the rate of 12½ tons per day. I have given considerable study to handling pig iron, and feel sure that you could do a much larger day's work than you have been doing. Now don't you think that if you really tried you could handle 47 tons of pig iron per day, instead of 12½ tons?"

What do you think Schmidt's answer would be to this?

Schmidt started to work, and all day long, and at regular intervals, was told by the man who stood over him with a watch, "Now pick up a pig and walk. Now sit down and rest. Now walk—now rest," etc. He worked when he was told to work, and rested when he was told to rest, and at half-past five in the

afternoon had his 47½ tons loaded on the car. And he practically never failed to work at this pace and do the task that was set him during the three years that the writer was at Bethlehem. And throughout this time he averaged a little more than $1.85 per day, whereas before he had never received over $1.15 per day, which was the ruling rate of wages at that time in Bethlehem. That is, he received 60 per cent. higher wages than were paid to other men who were not working on task work. One man after another was picked out and trained to handle pig iron at the rate of 47½ tons per day until all of the pig iron was handled at this rate, and the men were receiving 60 per cent. more wages than other workmen around them.

The writer has given above a brief description of three of the four elements which constitute the essence of scientific management: first, the careful selection of the workman, and, second and third, the method of first inducing and then training and helping the workman to work according to the scientific method. Nothing has as yet been said about the science of handling pig iron. . . .

In almost all cases, in fact, the laws or rules which are developed are so simple that the average man would hardly dignify them with the name of a science. In most trades, the science is developed through a comparatively simple analysis and time study of the movements required by the workmen to do some small part of his work, and this study is usually made by a man equipped merely with a stop-watch and a properly ruled notebook. Hundreds of these "time-study men" are now engaged in developing elementary scientific knowledge where before existed only rule of thumb. Even the motion study of Mr. Gilbreth in bricklaying . . . involves a much more elaborate investigation than that which occurs in most cases. The general steps to be taken in developing a simple law of this class are as follows:

First. Find, say, 10 or 15 different men (preferably in as many separate establishments and different parts of the country) who are especially skilful in doing the particular work to be analyzed.

Second. Study the exact series of elementary operations or motions which each of these men uses in doing the work which is being investigated, as well as the implements each man uses.

Third. Study with a stop-watch the time required to make each of these elementary movements and then select the quickest way of doing each element of the work.

Fourth. Eliminate all false movements, slow movements, and useless movements.

Fifth. After doing away with all unnecessary movements, collect into one series the quickest and best movements as well as the best implements.

This one new method, involving that series of motions which can be made quickest and best, is then substituted in place of the ten or fifteen inferior series which were formerly in use. This best method becomes standard, and remains standard, to be taught first to the teachers (or functional foremen) and by them to every workman in the establishment until it is superseded by a quicker and better series of movements. In this simple way one element after another of the science is developed.

In the same way each type of implement used in a trade is studied. Under the philosophy of the management of "initiative and incentive" each workman is called upon to use his own best judgment, so as to do the work in the quickest time, and from this results in all cases a large variety in the shapes and types of implements which are used for any specific purpose. Scientific management requires, first, a careful investigation of each of the many modifications of the same implement, developed under rule of thumb; and second, after a time study has been made of the speed attainable with each of these implements, that the good points of several of them shall be united in a single standard implement, which will enable the workman to work faster and with greater ease than he could before. This one implement, then, is adopted as standard in place of the many different kinds before in use, and it remains standard for all workmen to use until superseded by an implement which has been shown, through motion and time study, to be still better.

With this explanation it will be seen that the development of a science to replace rule of thumb is in most cases by no means a formidable undertaking, and that it can be accomplished by ordinary, every-day men without any elaborate scientific training; but that, on the other hand, the successful use of even the simplest improvement of this kind calls for records, system, and cooperation where in the past existed only individual effort.

There is another type of scientific investigation which has been referred to several times in this paper, and which should receive special attention, namely, the accurate study of the motives which influence men. At first it may appear that this is a matter for individual observation and judgment, and is not a proper subject for exact scientific experiments. It is true that the laws which result from experiments of this class, owing to the fact that the very complex organism—the human being—is being experimented with, are subject to a larger number of exceptions than is the case with laws relating to material things.

And yet laws of this kind, which apply to a large majority of men, unquestionably exist, and when clearly defined are of great value as a guide in dealing with men.

2. An Unlooked-for Effect, 1917

MALCOLM KEIR, "Scientific Management and Socialism"

Like all major innovations, Scientific Management set loose forces that were both unexpected and, in some cases, deemed undesirable by the very people responsible for their release. Where Taylor saw social harmony, others found a kind of proto-fascism, and still others a way-station to socialism. The common denominator was plain enough—Scientific Management would concentrate power; where that power would be lodged was open to some debate. Those who looked into the future and saw broad changes in American society were often naïve in their predictions of coming events. Even so, they were more nearly correct than those who thought that this great cause would have only small, limited, and predictable effects.

Apparently scientific management is as remote from socialism as the east is from the west, yet in reality there are few movements more effectual in promoting government ownership and operation of industry than the one fathered by efficiency engineers. Nothing could be further from the thoughts of the promoters of science in business, indeed, to many of them nothing could be more abhorrent, than the social reconstruction that logically completes their work; equally upon the other hand, socialists little dream of the powerful cooperation that will be given their aims by the men who are now attempting to reform business methods; nevertheless, the end of scientific management is socialism, for the one leads to the other in the evolution of industry. One route by which this end is reached is through the elimination of skill, another is by means of federal supervision of the foreign trade that arises as a result of the overproduction incident to the introduction of efficiency methods,

From Malcolm Keir, "Scientific Management and Socialism," *Scientific Monthly,* V (October 1917), 359-67. Reprinted by permission of *Science* and the American Association for the Advancement of Science.

and the third is the tendency that scientific management has toward installing automatic machinery, a trend that if carried to its logical conclusion—complete automatic production—would require government ownership. It is upon these three features of scientific management, namely, the elimination of skill, overproduction and the replacement of men by mechanisms, that we base our prophecy that scientific management leads to socialism. Since there are almost as many varieties of socialism as there are socialists, it should be understood at the outset that when that term is used we mean the government ownership and operation of the necessary means of production.

Scientific management has been welcomed by manufacturers because it places within their hands a new and powerful tool whereby the strength of skilled labor can be undermined and the power of employers strengthened. Ever since one man worked for another the interests of the two have been opposed in the struggle to determine wages, and a large factor in the favor of the workman has always been the skill he possessed and which the employer was forced to use, and to reward. As long as production was simple, the recompense of any laborer was usually in proportion to the amount of skill involved in his job. The complexity introduced into production by the invention of machinery served to heighten the importance of this ancient rule, for although machines suddenly at one blow usurped a great amount of traditional skill, nevertheless, they did not eliminate entirely the employers' dependence upon skilled labor, with the consequence that under the mechanical *régime* ushered into industry by the industrial revolution, a man's wages

more than ever depended upon the skill involved in his job. Where little or no special deftness was required the machine owner took almost all the proceeds of production, giving the laborer just enough to maintain existence. In the first flush of power in England, manufacturers went even further than this, for they paid workmen less than the exigencies of existence demanded, trusting to charity to make up the difference between wages and life necessities, a situation which was not relieved until the compulsion of national legislation and the demands of labor unions forced manufacturers to relinquish some of the advantages of their position. Highly skilled workmen, on the other hand, were able to demand and receive a share in the proceeds of production, greatly in excess of bare subsistence wages. Skilled workmen have a monopoly and as a result exert monopoly privileges; the extent to which they share in profits is determined by the degree of their monopoly.

Inasmuch as this citadel of labor prevents manufacturers from securing to themselves most of the gains of business, it stands as a constant challenge to them and spurs them onward to make every possible inroad upon their adversaries, by inventing and adopting devices which will eliminate the dependence upon skill; after years of assault of this character, although the band of men within the beleaguered fortress has grown smaller and smaller, the stronghold still maintains its integrity. *It is at this point that Scientific Management comes to the aid of machine owners, for it is virtually a new mechanism that transfers skill from the operatives to the operators, or from another point of view, it is one more step in the subdivision of labor whereby the power of workers is lessened and that of employers strengthened.*

In the past, methods of work or the manner of using a machine has been left largely to the laborers concerned, and manufacturers exercised little supervision over the exact way in which a man turned out any job. The men, unaided, developed "rules of thumb" and secret practises satisfactory to themselves and also to the management, although the office did not know just exactly what went on in the shop. A considerable body of knowledge of this sort rested with the men and constituted a respectable portion of their "skill." Efficiency engineers set themselves the task of bringing this art under the control of the management; the first studies, therefore, were aimed at finding out just what the men knew about their jobs, and classifying, indexing and standardizing the information obtained. Then a first-class workman was studied minutely in every phase of his operations, and the motions, appliances and methods of his work analyzed to the last detail, and, finally, all the parts were synthesized into a new whole which was better than any operation ever performed by any man by himself. Thereafter, this new method of work became the standard of every worker in the plant, for no man was allowed to perform his task any longer just as he pleased, but was required to follow the rules laid down by the management; in other words, the management took over most of the "skill" and the men merely followed instructions. Scientific management, therefore, was a tremendous assault upon the bulwarks of skilled workmen, and after it began to function fully it actually permitted men of much less experience to carry out the duties which formerly required highly trained men;

for instance, day laborers could be put on the more simple operations of machine work, formerly the job of well-paid machinists.

Yet, nevertheless, when first introduced, scientific management increases rather than decreases the laborer's share in the proceeds of production. Efficiency engineers gain by their analytic methods a greatly enhanced out-put with the same machines and the same labor. Of the profits which arise from the augmented product, the management usually takes two thirds and gives the men one third, a fair enough division, since part of the return may be considered as interest arising from the investment in the new "mechanism," and in addition since the men themselves did nothing to create the conditions under which alone the enlarged production was made possible. The one third share of the men so increases the wages of the workers over the customary pay for their particular class of labor that as a rule they are perfectly satisfied with the arrangement. Consequently scientific management is unlike any other innovation that has ever been introduced in industry, for all other improvements have borne harshly upon the workers immediately involved, although in the long run labor in general was benefited; on the contrary, scientific management is advantageous to the workmen who are directly involved in it. Despite high wages, the production under scientific management is so greatly increased that the manufacturers gain a lower labor cost per unit than they formerly enjoyed; high wages in fact are granted to the men as an inducement to work faster, so that this desired output may be attained.

The secret of the success of efficiency engineering lies in the great unevenness of industry. Every step from management on the verge of bankruptcy to the most highly efficient may be found and every stage in industrial evolution from complete hand work done at home—the manufacture of women's neckwear, for example—to factory operation in which every process may be performed by machinery, as the shoe industry illustrates. *Scientific management brings profit to those few who adopt it because the great mass of their competitors is without it.* The price of the product is set by the cost of production found in the great number of plants of *average* efficiency. The scientifically managed plant with a lower cost of production than the average may do one of two things; it may lower its selling price so as to capture the whole market and make its profits by the quantity sold—after the manner of Henry Ford—or it may be satisfied with making a large profit on its smaller volume of sales by leaving the price where it is set by competitors. The second is the more usual method of procedure, because to run a very large business requires organizing ability of the highest and rarest kind, and, furthermore, the second method yields a comfortable profit without involving anywhere near as much work. However, the first method is the safer, for it gives a virtual monopoly when it is easy to acquire, since scientific management is like a machine, if it isn't "patented" and kept for one's own personal advancement, one's competitors will seize it, and hence eventually it will lose all strategic value to the first owner. If a manufacturer chooses to install scientific management and does not attempt to grasp the full monopoly privilege inherent in its possession, but uses it as he would any other piece of new equipment, he

can make it pay handsomely as long as other men in the same line of business do not hire an efficiency engineer, but, just as in the case of any other mechanism, every competitor will be forced to adopt it eventually or go out of business. The profits that arise from the use of scientific management vary inversely with the number of users—to talk mathematically—hence *the increased production due to efficient methods will itself, in the long run, yield no financial returns.*

What then will become of the workman's extra wages? The answer is obvious; that, as the enlarged profits which permit bonus wages to be paid disappear, the additions to wages over and above the market rate will also vanish. The laborer will be worse off than he was in the beginning, because he will have sacrificed to a planning department belonging to the management his "skill," by which he forced high wages; and the pace at which he worked at first in order to gain extra pay will have become required without the greater compensation. Here then is the first place that scientific management will lead to socialism; the men working harder than ever, but witnessing a constant shrinkage in the contents of their weekly envelopes, yielding more and more of their traditional skill to the accurate studies of the "office" and seeing their jobs handed out to less and less trained men hired at lower wages, realizing that the employer is attaining ever greater right to the total income of production, the men will demand that the government regulate industry.

The first form such regulation will take will probably be a national minimum wage law. Once such a law is granted, it will be revised continually in order that the minimum may be raised to ever higher levels. The workers ought to be able to secure this boon in the face of the opposition of manufacturers, because the men will have the vote and can hold a political ax over congress. Massachusetts has long been acclaimed as a leader in industrial legislation whose object is betterment of labor, not because the state is any more enlightened than others, but largely on account of the fact that 50 per cent. of the people in gainful occupations are engaged in manufactures and all but 5 per cent. (4.9 in agriculture) of the remainder are more or less closely associated with the factory enterprises. The workers of the state, therefore, who are voters, have a close interest in labor laws and can force them from the legislature. Not only may the artisans of the future seek to enforce national minimum-wage laws but also they may endeavor to curtail production by lessening the hours of a work day, and make six or four hours the legal work period over the whole country. The profits of the manufacturers, already cut down by competition, will thus shrink further under the enforced higher wages and shorter hours, so, in some future crisis, when aroused labor makes greater onslaughts upon profits, the manufacturers themselves may be glad to sell their plants to the government under which they then may become managers with a salary.

The discontent that must eventually be felt by workmen on account of scientific management may be translated into action such as we have noted, and the logical outcome of the movement of the workers against the efficiency of the managers seems to be government ownership and operation of industry—which state is synonymous with socialism. However, the manufacturers of the future may be shrewd enough to foresee this result and take measures to turn aside labor's dissatisfaction.

The scheme that most probably will appeal to employers as a way out of their difficulties is profit-sharing of some kind, even though the name and aim may be disguised under a different term. If the employees share in the profits of a business, that enterprise is socialized, and the first step toward more comprehensive socialism has been taken.

Likewise *any* device that may be adopted to appeal to laborers must have in it some germ of socialization, for otherwise the workers would disdain it. Hence any attempts manufacturers may make to soften the effects of scientific management only lead them into paths whose final goal is socialism.

The elimination of skill is by no means the only route by which scientific management leads to socialism, for not only do efficiency engineers strive to get rid of operations requiring skill, but they also bend all their energies toward increasing production. This fact gives rise to a set of forces which tend to operate in the direction of socialism.

Before the opening of the Great War, when few industrial plants were operated by efficiency methods the nation faced the necessity of a market abroad, because the mills had reached the point where their production just about filled domestic needs. The home market, therefore, was unable to absorb a surplus, with the consequence that foreign trade became most attractive to American producers. Into this situation we are now introducing scientific management, one of whose tenets is an increased output often double, sometimes triple the average of previous experience. Just as long as the new scheme of organization is limited to a few concerns, industry as a whole is little influenced by the augmented production, but, inasmuch as all concerns must eventually adopt scientific management, the nation is facing a future period when production as a whole will be at least two or three times what it is at present. The multiplication of products will tend to lower prices and thus broaden the domestic market, but it seems hardly probable that the home consumption can absorb the entire surplus, especially since the nation had already commenced to feel the effect of glut, even before the operation of new methods of management influenced out-put. As a result, it does not take a very keen vision to predict that the United States must take an ever increasing interest in foreign trade, a movement that will precipitate an intense commercial struggle between nations for supremacy. In order to meet strenuous international competition, American factories must be so organized that they may be treated as a unit, and all wasteful practices—such as cross freight, unnecessary transportation of raw materials to plants poorly situated or needlessly long hauls for products destined for export—may be eradicated. These ends may be attained at first by government control, but regulation of industry will usually lead to ownership because mere federal methodizing will never prove entirely satisfactory. We have amply proved this in the case of railroads, for, beginning by loose regulation, federal authority over steam-railway transportation has been tightened constantly, until now even railroad presidents themselves declare that they see no relief in sight except such as may come through government ownership. In a similar manner the mere shadow of

government, at first extended over foreign trade, will take on more and more substance until—as is the case with Germany—the state itself shall become the virtual dictator of foreign trade. In order to carry on its affairs satisfactorily, the government agencies in control of foreign traffic must reach backward inland to regulate the sources of production until individual factories come under its powerful sway, and then socialism will be here, although it may be called by some other name.

Starting with scientific management we have arrived at socialism a second time, but our story is not yet done, for there is a third condition that grows out of efficiency methods, and this third one, the increased use of automatic machinery, like the other two, is completed by socialism.

One of the foundations of scientific management is a study of the motions necessary for the carrying on of every process in the making of an article; it aims to simplify the motions continually in order that they may become most nearly mechanical. The next step, namely, adjusting the machine to give the mechanical equivalent of the motion instead of trusting to a man, is an easy one. Scientific management, therefore, greatly hastens the transferal of skill from men to mechanisms, and brings forward more rapidly the day when all machinery will be automatic.

It is not easy to accept this concept, for it seems like flying in the face of truth, yet we can see the tendency toward automatic machinery in every industry around us. Not many decades ago a weaver took care of just one loom, and the passing of the shuttle bearing the weft was a hand operation. One of the first improvements in looms was to kick the shuttle across the warp by a mechanical device and then power was applied to the whole operation of the loom. Later improvements augmented the number of shuttles from one to half a dozen, still later refinements threaded each one of the six shuttles automatically. Furthermore, when any thread breaks, the loom stops automatically and another machine worn on the weaver's thumb reknots the broken strand. Instead of requiring one weaver to each loom modern mills need only one for every twenty machines. It is not an idle dream to suppose that some day no men at all will be necessary for loom operation. Take another illustration from among a great number. To make a screw once required a man and a machine for each operation of heading, tapering, threading, slitting the head and cutting off, or one man had to readjust one machine five times for the five operations. To-day one machine—the turret lathe—performs all five with one adjustment and in addition feeds itself with raw material. As a result, one man can take care of ten screw machines. Is it impossible that some day that one man will not be needed?

Many people will accept the eventual automatic production of all products whose processes require mechanical repeated motions, but to them it seems incredible that machinery can ever displace men entirely, because so many operations as now conducted necessitate judgment, a faculty no machine can acquire. Nevertheless, for every action that demands judgment, there is some mechanical equivalent that will bring about the desired result. For illustrations, we are familiar with the perforated paper roll that plays pianos, the wax record that does the work of stenography, or the mathematical combination of gears that adds, subtracts and

multiplies. There may be a small irreducible minimum of labor essential say for the starting and stopping of machinery, but the great mass of labor will be set free.

This stage of industry will be coming to the front rapidly in the days when scientific management is universally adopted, for efficiency engineers bend their energies constantly toward making motions simpler, easier and more mechanical in nature, and then replacing the man by a cam or a gear which performs the action better than any man could. Scientific management, therefore, greatly promotes the use of automatic machinery. It is clear then that as the tenets of efficiency engineers are accepted by all manufacturers and as, through the engineers' studies, machinery more and more completely ousts men, that the profits of industry will go to the owners of machines even more fully, until, if allowed to go to the logical end, *capitalists will absorb all the proceeds of production because there will be no factory laborers.* To place the control and the emoluments of industry in a few hands, because the few have the money to purchase the needed automatic machines will frighten people for the reason that the few could exercise a terrible power over the many; therefore, the many will insist that the automatically operated industries be owned by the government or in other words by themselves. This means socialism.

The government ownership and operation of industry—or in other words, socialism, therefore, grows out of scientific management by three different branches. Inasmuch as scientific management tends to eliminate skill, it may come about that labor will try to retain its hold on high wages through government interference with industry; furthermore, since scientific management goes in the direction of over-production, the United States must become an exporter and, in order to compete, the government must control and perhaps endeavor to make operations as simple as possible, and when it attains the desired simplicity, change the operator from a man to a mechanism. If this tendency ever becomes a universal fact —that is, all industry conducted by means of automatic machinery, the government will be forced to own and operate industry because to place such power in private hands would be too dangerous. Because scientific management as a movement is yet young, it is worth while to make this examination into its tenets and to point out its tendencies, for our attitude toward it can then be based upon reasonable ground. If you favor socialism you ought to uphold scientific management, but if socialism is a nightmare to you, then you should condemn this new industrial revolution. It makes little difference whether or not you are pleased with scientific management because it is in industry to stay, for the same reason that machinery has been maintained; it is the most efficient method of production. Since it is economic it must become universal, and when it is everywhere employed some degree of socialism must prevail.

3. Democracy and the Expert, 1930

FELIX FRANKFURTER, "Democracy and the Expert"

An essential problem for Scientific Management was that it shifted decision-making from the workmen to the managers. Through this process, the workmen lost a large measure of the control over their own lives. This was occurring on the level of American politics as well. The incursion of the "scientific method," the growing demand for the "facts" about every problem, was leading to a steady erosion of the traditional competence of the democratic electorate to decide public issues for itself.

Felix Frankfurter, soon to be appointed to the Supreme Court by President Franklin D. Roosevelt, was a keen student of the changes in American government. Comparing the operations of the British Civil Service, he was able to gauge how far short Americans were from adequately confronting the complexities of modern government. The problem was, as he saw it, to preserve the spirit and vitality of participatory democracy while still leaving room for the experts' disinterested solution of problems.

From Felix Frankfurter, "Democracy and the Expert," *Atlantic Monthly*, CXLVI (November 1930), 649-60. Reprinted by permission of American Security and Trust Company.

Epitaphs for democracy are the fashion of the day. Both Left and Right acclaim the failure of democracy. Those who chafe at governmental intervention are as distrustful of popular institutions as are the romantics who expect from government heaven upon earth. Dictatorships are dramatic and *coups d'état* feed the imagination, while democratic régimes have about them the humdrum qualities of John Bull, who, first in the modern world, devised talk as the chief instrument of government. Sensational and violent rule in Russia and Italy throws out of perspective more plodding popular institutions. But it is simply not true that the area of democratic government has contracted. Barring Italy, no country has abandoned democratic institutions, whereas democratic government has extensively replaced oligarchy, and the democratic idea is steadily corroding ancient autocratic traditions. The replacement of Romanoffs by Bolsheviks was certainly not a democratic loss. Nor did the short-lived Spanish dictatorship supplant a virile democracy. For the democrat, only Fascist Italy is a retrogression. But, on the other hand, a stable German Republic has displaced the Germany of the Kaiser. In succession to the feudalism of the Hapsburgs, Hungary and Jugoslavia have reigns at least not more autocratic than they were in pre-war days, while Czechoslovakia has the heartening rule of President Masaryk, and Austria is a stout though poverty-stricken little republic. The ferment of democracy is active in modern Turkey, and is leavening the ancient fabrics of India and China with hope and danger. Nor should the most summary account of recent democratic trends omit the steady invigoration of the mentality as well as the processes of democracy in Latin-American countries, particularly Mexico.

The ultimate justification for democracy still remains the lack, in the long run, of a decent and workable substitute. . . .

. . . The tasks and conditions that confront democracy leave no true friend without concern. Over-simplification is a great deceiver of reason, and nineteenth-century democracy suffered from the illusions of simplicity.

This early democratic faith was sustained by a gracious and civilized conception of society. But the difficulties in the way of its attainment were grossly undervalued. The tenacity of old habits, the fragility of human material, the conflicting forces within the individual no less than the clash of interests within society—all these and more were much too lightly weighed. The appeal of a generous society subordinated the question of means by which it was to be attained. Vast hopes were founded on simple devices. Popular rule was expected to work miracles almost automatically. Abolish autocratic rule; remove tyranny, and the innate goodness of mankind will prevail! It was indeed largely a negative faith.

The day of such comfortable thoughts is over. We now know that democracy is dependent on knowledge and wisdom beyond all other forms of government. The grandeur of its aims is matched by the difficulties of their achievement. For democracy is the reign of reason on the most extensive scale. It seeks to prevail when the complexities of life make a demand upon knowledge and understanding never made before, and when the forces inimical to the play of reason have power and subtlety unknown in the past. We have seen the intricate range of problems thrown up by our industrial civilization; the vast body of technical knowledge, more and more beyond the comprehension even of the cultivated, which is required for an analysis of the issues underlying these problems and an exploration of possible remedies. We have also noted the opportunities for arousing passions, confusing judgment, and regimenting opinion that are furnished by chain newspapers, cheap magazines, the movies, and radio. And we now know how slender a reed is reason—how recent its emergence in man, how deep the countervailing instincts and passions, how treacherous the whole rational process. Moreover, the whole tempo of our society is hurried; its atmosphere and appurtenances hostile to reflection. Thus reason is asked to flourish when the conditions for it are least favorable.

Little wonder that, for many, democracy seems ripe for the museum of political institutions. They assess its results as bankruptcy and find its inherent difficulties fatal. The naïve champions of democracy at least built on hope; these latter-day assailants are moved by fear. Both present foes and early friends disregard time and history. The apostles of democracy expected quick results. Those who despair of democracy also lack patience. The former thought they were writing on a clean slate; they forgot the obduracy of the past. Those who concentrate on the defects of democracy are blind to what history discloses of the weaknesses of alternative forms of government.

The answer to the defects of democracy is not denial of the democratic idea. Judged by the most pragmatic tests, democracy has weathered the cataclysm of the World War and extended its rule. It is the worse for wear, but at least it wears. We need not fly from one romantic absolute to another. If we focus attention on the human origin of all government, we shall have a more scientific temper for dealing with its frailties. We shall equally avoid blind attachment and romantic impatience only if we recognize the essentially provisional nature of all political arrangements. Such an attitude will treat government not only as a mechanism for day-to-day adjustments, but also as an hypothesis in action, to be modified by the experience which it adduces.

Democracy has now been submitted to tests of time and stress that call for a reconsideration of its processes and assumptions. Such an examination must build on the new gains of knowledge since modern forms of democracy were evolved, and more especially upon the insight into the dark recesses of man's nature, which pioneers like Freud and Jung are slowly making possible. Acceptance of the democratic idea by no means implies the exhaustion of the forms in which the idea has been clothed. Indeed, we may be sure that the implements and inventions of government have not sufficiently responded to the overwhelming transformation of the external arrangements of society.

If the continuance of our civilization is to be based upon democracy, obviously knowledge and the capacity for judgment must permeate the whole community. But about education, and how to attain it, we are also far less naïve and hopeful than we used to be. The aims and methods of education are to-day as much under fire as are those of government. For its underpinnings, too, have been shaken by new knowledge, and we are far more humble in assuming that wisdom and a conception of the public weal attend learning. Though we are doubtful as to the true nature of education and uncertain how to pursue it, there is no paradox in assuming that effective democracy presupposes a continuous process of adult education. "We must educate our masters," said a British statesman after the Second Reform Bill gave workingmen the vote. Time has only reënforced the deep wisdom of Robert Lowe's dictum. But he overlooked the complementary truth that the people must educate their rulers. At least they must see to it that rulers are educated for the tasks of government.

I am the last person to undervalue the extent to which devotion, intelligence, and technical equipment are enlisted in government. Not political philosophy, not farsighted planning, but the same pressure of circumstances which has made government penetrate into such a wide range of affairs has compelled resort to skill and training in its work. The all too common depreciation of men in public service is at once shallow and cruel. It mocks where it should praise; it debilitates where it should encourage. Publicity headlines the occasional egregious blunder, but the detailed day-by-day achievement is unchronicled. The clash of politics, the friction between executive and legislature, the scrutiny of the press and taste for scandal, tend to make us know when things go wrong in government. It is right that it should be so. The critics of government cannot be too Argus-eyed. But no such conjunction of forces educates the public to a knowledge of the good in government. Virtue is proverbially not news, and an appreciation of achievement in government, except when attained on the colossal scale of a Panama Canal or in the dramatized conflict of foreign relations, is dependent on dull, technical details. The public is therefore surprisingly ignorant of the extent to which its servants contribute to the public good. . . .

But that the public service, except in the highest offices, is so largely without prestige is even more disastrous than that its material rewards are unduly meagre. The whole tide of opinion is against public administration as a career for talent. The enormous rewards which industry offers to able young lawyers, engineers, economists, serve as a powerful attraction to ambitious youth. As against that, there are some, and more than we suspect, who find real satisfaction in work whose aim is the public good. But they have to contend against the whole mental and moral climate of our times—the impalpable but terrific pressure of current standards of achievement. These are overwhelmingly on the side of private gain.

In Great Britain the traditions of public service are as yet powerful enough to enlist the best brains of the country. In its Civil Service is found probably the largest concentration of distinguished talent. Nor is it conceivable that Great Britain would have come through its storms and stresses since the Crimean War without the very high quality of its public administration. The accession of the Labor Party to power in 1924 marked a political revolution in British history. Yet the break with the past involved in a government committed to the principles of socialism was accomplished with a shift in personnel of less than one hundred persons. In large matters of foreign policy one can hardly conceive of more contrasting types than Lord Curzon and Mr. Ramsay MacDonald. Yet, when Mr. MacDonald succeeded Lord Curzon at the Foreign Office, the official who had served Lord Curzon continued as Mr.

MacDonald's private secretary. Perhaps nothing could more pithily reveal how ingrained is the Civil Service in the stuff of English life. Yet the transition from the days when public office was bartered as though it were the private property of politicians to the present system of professional public administration is a surprisingly recent development. It was introduced within the memory of men still living. . . .

The revolutionary movements of 1848 touched the United States only by bringing to our shores liberty-loving rebels from the Continent. While, in England, 1848 led to a searching inquiry into the defects of her government, it renewed America's assurance of the virtues of our system. Moreover, America had no Crimean War, and perhaps no Charles Trevelyan. Besides, we were young and had an abundance of resources. Standards come late, and where there is plenty the temptations to waste are usually not resisted. The key to our history of public administration, as to much else in history, is found in Emerson's quiet observation, "Mankind is as lazy as it dares to be."

In any event, while England was making the beginnings of a change from patronage to public service, the United States was justifying patronage by a political philosophy and establishing it as a public policy. The naked defense of the spoils system was expressed in the classic remarks of Senator Marcy in the debate on Jackson's nomination of Martin Van Buren to be Minister to England:—

It may be, sir, that the politicians of the United States are not so fastidious as some gentlemen are as to disclosing the principles on which they act. They boldly preach what they practice. When they are contending for victory they avow their intention of enjoying the fruits of it. If they are defeated, they expect to retire from office. If they are successful, they claim, as a matter of right, the advantages of success. They see nothing wrong in the rule that to the victor belong the spoils of the enemy.

A hundred years have elapsed since Marcy's engaging candor. But his sentiments are still acted upon and occasionally they survive even in avowal. Woodrow Wilson is the only political scientist who ever occupied the Presidency. Yet it was his Secretary of State who naïvely thought that technical posts requiring high skill and training should be filled by "deserving Democrats." No President has had better reason to know than Mr. Hoover the irrelevance of purely party politics in the discharge of professional duties. And yet in the appointment of judges to the lower Federal courts he has apparently, in some instances, for political reasons departed from the professional standards set by his Attorney General.

Behind the spoils system and all its survivals there is a crude logic of democracy and the versatile energy of the pioneer. Both combined to indoctrinate Americans with a distorted belief in the simplicity of government. Someone has called the British Civil Service the skill department of government. But if public administration can be improvised, if it requires no particular skill, there is no need of special training, no need of the permanence of professionalism, no need of a skill department. That is precisely what Andrew Jackson thought. He practised rotation in office because he thought permanence makes for "corruption in some and in others a perversion of correct feelings and principles." "The duties of all public officers," Jackson wrote in his first message to Congress, "are, or at least admit of being made, so plain and simple that men of intelligence may readily qualify themselves for their performance; and I cannot but believe that more is lost by the long continuance of men in office than is generally to be gained by their experience. I submit, therefore, to your consideration whether the efficiency of the Government would not be promoted and official industry and integrity better secured by a general extension of the law which limits appointments to four years."

There is this much to be said for Jackson's rustic view. Government then was operating within a relatively limited scope. In large measure, it was forbidding conduct; it was not itself an extensive participant in devising complicated arrangements of society and composing the conflict of its manifold interests. But Harding, nearly a hundred years after Jackson, had not even Jackson's excuse. The growing complexity of social organization had compelled a steady extension of legal control over economic and social interests. At first this intervention was largely through specific legislative directions, depending for enforcement generally upon the cumbersome and ineffective machinery of the criminal law. By the pressure of experience, legislative regulation of economic and social activities turned to administrative instruments. The extent and range of governmental participation in affairs, the complexity of its administrative devices, and the intricacy of the technical problems with which they were dealing had never been greater than when Harding came to the Presidency. There never was a more pathetic misapprehension of responsibility than Harding's touching statement, "Government after all is a very simple thing."

I recall the sentence, and it deserves to be remembered, because Harding expressed the traditional American conception of government still deeply inured in American opinion. Until these notions of deluding simplicity are completely rooted out, we shall never truly face our problems of government.

The theoretical defense of the spoils system could hardly withstand its practical results. It was with the moral aspects of political jobbery that the promoters of early civil-service reform, Carl Schurz, George W. Curtis, E. L. Godkin, were mostly concerned. Corruption, not only of individuals, but of the whole democratic process, was involved. "The allurements of an immense number of offices and places exhibited to the voters of the land," wrote Cleveland, "and the promise of their bestowal in recognition of partisan activity, debauched the suffrage and robbed political action of its thoughtful and deliberative character."

But the problem, as we now see, is much more complicated. No doubt democracy is peculiarly dependent on clean and disinterested government. By the very fact of numbers, a corrupt and jaundiced democracy can be most blind and oppressive. But in the modern world the simple virtues of honesty and public devotion are not enough. Indeed, honesty and public zeal without training and a sophisticated judgment may very readily become the unwitting tool of half-truths and misrepresentation. Compelled to grapple with a world more and more dominated by technological forces, government must have at its disposal the resources of training and capacity equipped to understand and to deal with the complicated issues to which these technological forces give rise.

There is a good deal of loose talk

about science in politics. If by "science in politics" is meant the availability of an irrefragable fund of knowledge in the possession of a few wise people who could, out of hand, solve the conundrums of government, it is merely another romantic delusion. But if by science we mean an intellectual procedure and a temper of mind, there must be science in government, because science dominates society. It then becomes a question of how much science government employs and how good it is.

The great political issues of the nineteenth century thrived, in the main, on the levels of feeling and rhetoric. The extension of the franchise, popular elections, the abolition of slavery (apart from its economic aspect), are not matters that yield to statistics or economic learning. But feeling and rhetoric are blind guides for the understanding of contemporary political issues. For the staples of contemporary politics—the organization of industry, the control of public utilities, the well-being of agriculture, the mastery of crime and disease—are deeply enmeshed in intricate and technical facts, and must be extricated from presupposition and partisanship. Such matters require systematic effort to contract the area of conflict and passion and to widen the area of accredited knowledge as the basis of action.

The history of reparations since the Versailles Treaty illustrates the extremely technical basis of political controversies which affect the economic balance of a good part of the world, and the social standards of millions of people. It would not be true to say that reparations presented questions merely for economists. But certainly the political judgments which were involved could only be taken blindly and in passion without an appreciation of those intricate economic factors which Maynard Keynes was the first to elucidate courageously at the bar of public opinion. Similarly, any solid judgment upon public-utility controversies presupposes the capacity to see the meaning of complicated technical data. In both these fields of politics, agitation and advocacy have their place. They are instruments of education, means for making effective the findings of knowledge and the lessons of experience. But the quiet, detached, laborious task of disentangling facts from fiction, of extracting reliable information from interested parties, of agreeing on what is proof and what surmise, must precede, if agitation is to feed on knowledge and reality, and be equipped to reach the mind rather than to exploit feeling.

"It is difficult to realize"—I quote from Graham Wallas—"how short a time it is since questions for which we now rely entirely on official statistics were discussed by the ordinary political methods of agitation and advocacy." But in the United States many of these questions are still anybody's guess—are still the football of political debate. In 1830, the House of Commons wrangled as to the existence of economic distress and its extent. In England these facts —the condition of trade and the state of unemployment—are now as dependably revealed as the barometer registers atmospheric pressure. Debate continues to be anxious and even bitter about modes for relieving unemployment. But at all events search for remedies is not confused and diverted by doubt and denial that anything needs to be remedied. We are still where England was in 1830. Congress still debates whether unemployment really exists, and, if so, where and how much. And we have the extraordinary spectacle of the Secretary of Labor of the United States issuing unemployment estimates which the Commissioner of Labor of the State of New York denies.

Let me take another illustration of the limited application of scientific standards in public administration. Just as in eighteenth-century England it was matter for political controversy whether the population was rising or falling, so in twentieth-century America the homicide or burglary rate in our great cities is a recurring subject for political debate. And this is a very fair index of our whole attitude toward problems of crime. That the level of professionalism, of trained capacity, in our administration of criminal justice is very low, compared with that prevailing in Great Britain and on the Continent, is one of the most patent facts about our system. In saying this I hope I can avoid the appearance of being too simple about crime. I share the conviction of all who have been long immersed in these problems that crime is a true measure of the standards of our civilization. One cannot worry much about these questions without realizing that they touch the motives and purposes and directions of contemporary society. But that our lack of professionalism affects the whole situation hardly admits of doubt. Crime is age-old and ubiquitous, but by common consent it assails in greatest measure the most prosperous country in the world.

No one will deny that problems of crime are at least as difficult as problems of public health and hydraulic engineering. But public health and hydraulic engineering are now as a matter of course made the concern of specialists who give to their problems the devotion of a lifetime. That is the essence of professionalism—men adapted by nature for inquiries for which they are elaborately trained and which they pursue as a permanent career. In regard to crime, this condition on the whole does not obtain. Knowledge of the causes of crime, the ways for its prevention and detection, the modes of its treatment, are widely deemed the common possession of the man in the street. Even where professional training is exacted, namely, from lawyers and judges who at present play such an undue rôle in the administration of criminal justice, merely a general and not a specialized training is required. But even these professionally educated functionaries play their parts for only short terms or discontinuously. In the United States there is no body of highly trained, capable men who are drawn to the enigmas of crime as problems to be solved, who are adequately disciplined for their exploration, and who give the preoccupation of a lifetime to their solution. Broadly speaking, the directing officials are not technically trained for their work before they attain office, and the want of permanent careers through office deprives the community of capitalizing office itself as a school of training. There is thus no professionalism in administration. Partly cause and partly effect, there is equally no professionalism (always broadly speaking) of research into crime, as there is research in medicine and research in the natural sciences. The two indispensable interacting forces in the promotion of knowledge and the control of natural phenomena—to wit, professionalism in inquiry and professionalism in control—are thus lacking as to crime.

There can hardly be room for difference of opinion that indispensable to any effective or candid dealing with crime is the continuous, disinterested, scientific study of its problems. Just as disease has been withdrawn from the realm of quackery and magic, so crime must now be subjected to that systematic, disciplined, continuous attack of reason which we call scientific procedure. Neither crime commissions nor presidential pronouncements will make a lasting dent upon crime unless we can secure acceptance of the standards of professionalism as a postulate of our government, similar to the acceptance by the British of the ideas which underlie their Civil Service.

I am far from suggesting that the conquest of science calls for a new type of oligarchy—namely, government by experts. I mean no such thing. To call the administrative régime of the British Civil Service "the new despotism," as does Lord Hewart, is to use the language of lurid journalism. But the power which must more and more be lodged in administrative experts, like all power, is prone to abuse unless its exercise is properly circumscribed and zealously scrutinized. For we have greatly widened the field of administrative discretion and thus opened the door to arbitrariness. . . .

Undoubtedly ultimate protection is to be found in ourselves, our zeal for liberty, our respect for one another and for the common good—a truth so obviously accepted that its demands in practice are usually overlooked. But safeguards must also be institutionalized through machinery and processes. These safeguards largely depend on very high standards of professional service, an effective procedure (always remembering that "in the development of our liberty insistence upon procedural regularity has been a large factor"), easy access to public scrutiny, and a constant play of alert public criticism, especially by an informed and spirited bar. Moreover, while expert administrators may sift out issues, elucidate them, bring the light of fact and experience to bear upon them, the final determinations of large policy must be made by the direct representatives of the public and not by the experts. Whether, for instance, the government should itself operate Muscle Shoals or lease its water power raises questions beyond the authority of engineer or economist. In the final analysis, we are in the realm of judgment regarding values as to which there is as yet no voice of science. The very notion of democracy implies the right of the public to decide these matters on its own choice.

Government is itself an art, one of the subtlest of arts. It is neither business nor technology, nor applied science. It is the art of making men live together in peace and with reasonable happiness. Among the instruments for governing are organization, technological skill, and scientific methods. But they are all instruments, not ends. And that is why the art of governing has been achieved best by men to whom governing is itself a profession. One of the shallowest disdains is the sneer against the professional politician. The invidious implication of the phrase is, of course, against those who pursue self-interest through politics. But too prevalently the baby is thrown out with the bath. We forget that the most successful statesmen have been professionals. Walpole, Pitt, Gladstone, Disraeli, and Asquith were professional politicians. Beveridge's recent life of Lincoln serves as a reminder that Lincoln was a professional politician. Politics was Roosevelt's profession, Wilson was, all his life, at least preoccupied with politics, and Calvin Coolidge, though nominally a lawyer, has had no profession except politics. Canada emphasizes the professionalism of politics by making the Leader of the Opposition a paid officer of state.

In a democracy, politics is a process of popular education—the task of adjusting the conflicting interests of diverse groups in the community, and bending the hostility and suspicion and ignorance engendered by group interests toward a comprehension of mutual understanding. For these ends, *expertise* is indispensable. But politicians must enlist popular support for the technical means by which alone social policies can be realized. Æ summed it all up when he said, "The expert should be on tap, but not on top." In this country we have been so anxious to avoid the dangers of having the expert on top that we suffer from a strong reluctance to have him on tap. . . .

The difficulties of our social-economic problems will not abate with time. One may be confident that they will become more complicated. They will make increasing demands upon trained intelligence. If government is to be equal to its responsibilities, it must draw more and more on men of skill and wisdom for public administration. As Oxford and Cambridge of old, our institutions of higher learning must be training schools for public service, not through utilitarian courses, but by the whole sweep of their culture and discipline. Above all, the universities must be reservoirs of disinterestedness. For the more contentious issues of politics lie not in the domain of the natural sciences. They depend on the wisdom of the social sciences. But in our generation at least, the social sciences still rest ultimately not upon verifiable and controlled experiments, but, in large measure, upon tentative conclusions and judgments. It is therefore absolutely vital that judgment be as disinterested as possible, that it be not exposed to the undertow of unconscious influences other than those which inhere in our present limited understanding of the workings of the mind. Thinking and reflection in the universities ought not to be guided along the smooth path of material interest or any of its derivatives, in all their subtle forms.

4. The True Conservationist, 1908

CHARLES S. HOWE, "The Function of the Engineer in the Conservation of the Natural Resources of the Country"

The critical importance of technical experts in the definition and prosecution of Progressive reform programs can be seen in the conservation crusade of the early twentieth century. During the late 1800's, in the newly established

From Charles S. Howe, "The Function of the Engineer in the Conservation of the Natural Resources of the Country," *Science*, XXVIII (October 23, 1908), 537-48.

scientific bureaus of the federal government, a group of scientists and engineers had been perfecting the concept of rational and efficient use of our natural resources. When Theodore Roosevelt came to the White House he made conservation a central theme of his program for national reform.

In 1908 he called a conference of technical, industrial, and governmental leaders to meet at the White House and discuss the need for conservation. The technical nature of the problem was clearly understood by the participants, one of whom was Charles S. Howe, President of the Case School of Applied Science and an official representative of the Society for the Promotion of Engineering Education.

The prosperity of a country depends primarily upon its natural resources. The raw material which the farmer and the manufacturer use and the products of which furnish business for the merchant, come from or depend upon timber, fuel, minerals, soil, water. These are the natural resources of any country, and as they exist in large or small quantities, as they are easy of access, as their quality is good or bad, must depend the agricultural and industrial prosperity and success of the nation. Some countries have large supplies of one or more of these natural products and a few are blessed with them all. This country is especially fortunate in that it originally had within its bounds not only all of these natural resources, but large quantities of each of them, and that they were rich in quality and easy of access. When the country was first settled by Europeans, the new inhabitants gave little thought to the question of natural resources except in so far as these directly concerned their daily life. They established themselves where the soil was rich because they wished to pursue agriculture as a vocation, but they made no study of soils further than this. Forests were regarded as an encumbrance to be cleared away as soon as possible, for they interfered

with agriculture, which was the chief business, and they were the lurking places of wild beasts and wilder men. They were useful only for the purpose of furnishing lumber and fuel. A very small amount of forest on each farm was sufficient for these purposes and so the settler did not hesitate to cut down as much as he possibly could. The other natural resources he knew little or nothing about. It was many years before coal came into use, and then only in those sections where it could be dug from the ground near at hand. Precious metals were unknown. The little iron that was used was brought from abroad. The water-ways were used wherever possible and in many sections of the country they were the only avenues of travel and the supply of water was sufficient for the purpose of navigation. Under conditions such as these it was only natural for the inhabitants to suppose that the resources of the country were inexhaustible. They had all they could use and more, and if they had thought of the question of exhaustion, it would have seemed to them that all they had to do was to move to another section, north, south or west, and start over again. While they depended for their livelihood upon one of the natural resources, the soil, they were practically independent of most of the others. And hence they regarded them as of little moment. As the country developed and civilization increased their dependence upon the natural resources increased also, but at first in a scarcely perceptible way. This dependence has grown up to the present time, but it is still difficult to make people see the force of this dependence. Most of the products which come from the natural resources of the country are used at a great distance from the raw material, and hence it is difficult for people to realize the connection between the two and their dependence upon the latter. The natural resources have been so freely drawn upon and often so ruthlessly used that already along some lines they are beginning to disappear to an alarming degree. Investigation has shown that they are in great danger of exhaustion. This is a grave state of affairs and proper steps should be taken so far as possible to prevent it by preserving the natural resources that remain and by carefully and judiciously using them in the future. Unless we can prevent the absolute destruction of the natural resources the ruin of the nation is assured. We should aim to transmit to the generations which are to follow us a country which is better than the one we received from our ancestors and not one which is being rapidly depleted and impoverished. That this can be done has been shown by the work of scientific men during the past few years. Of course some of the natural resources can not be replaced, but their rapid depletion can be stopped and they can be preserved for our use for many centuries. The soil should never be allowed to grow poor. It should grow richer as it is cultivated longer. The forests can be retained through planting at the same time that timber is being cut for use. Fuel and iron can not be replaced, but they can be carefully and economically used. The use of water, either for navigation or power, does not destroy the water and hence does not endanger the waterways system.

With the growth of civilization the wants of men multiply and hence greater demands are made upon nature, for the supply with which these wants are satisfied must come primarily from nature. This will cause a greater drain in the future than in the past. The use of the natural resources has made us a great nation, and if we are to maintain our position among other nations we must be able to use these natural resources in the future, and even to draw upon them to a greater degree. This makes it absolutely essential that the wasteful methods now in use should cease and that a careful and systematic study of the use of the materials we now have be intelligently made. Our land is nearly all taken up. There is remaining in the possession of the government a comparatively small amount excepting that which is useless for cultivation. Nearly all the forests have disappeared; in some sections entirely so, and very little effort has been made to replace them. Our coal and iron are rapidly disappearing and will in time entirely disappear. Our waterways are injured and many of them are entirely useless for navigation or for power. The question of the conservation of our natural resources is then a serious one and deserves careful and mature deliberation. Even with the natural resources not in danger of exhaustion it would seem wise to use them to the best advantages.

On May 13, 14 and 15 there was held at the White House in Washington a conference on the conservation of the natural resources of the country. This conference gathered at the invitation of the President of the United States and was composed of the governors of the states with three delegates from each state appointed by the governor; of the members of the cabinet, the judges of the supreme court, some of the members of congress, and representatives from all the great engineering societies. As president of this society I received an invitation and attended the conference. This meeting was one of the most notable ever held in the country. The President of the United States opened each session and presided at the first and last. At the opening session he delivered a strong address upon the question of conservation which is one that has received his earnest attention for many years. The governors of forty-four states were present. Many members of the cabinet, of the supreme court and of both houses of congress accepted the invitation and attended one or more of the sessions.

Addresses were made upon the subjects of forestry, fuel, mineral products, soil wastage, irrigation and the waterways. Papers were read by Mr. Andrew Carnegie and Mr. James J. Hill, who have taken a great interest in the questions under consideration. Many of the governors and quite a number of the other delegates took part in the discussion. Every one present seemed to be impressed with the importance of the gathering. To many of the governors and their associates the subject seemed to be entirely new. It had never been directly presented to them and they had not, of course, understood its importance, but there was not a dissenting voice as to the necessity of conserving our natural resources and making them

serve the nation as long as possible. A number of the governors stated that upon their return home they would immediately appoint forestry and other commissions which would study these questions within the borders of their states, and that when these commissions made their reports they would do all in their power to carry out the recommendations.

The representatives of the scientific societies probably appreciated the condition of affairs and the momentous possibilities of the questions discussed better than any one else with, perhaps, the exception of the president. Some of them read papers and a number took part in the discussions. At the close of the session a statement of the present condition of affairs and a recommendation as to the proper steps to be taken to conserve the natural resources of the country were adopted as the sense of the convention.

The engineer adapts the forces of nature to the use of men and this adaptation should be done both economically and efficiently. It is not enough to show that a certain force can be made to work when a machine transforms raw into finished product. The work must be done efficiently—that is to say, the greatest amount of good must come from a given expenditure of energy. This makes the machine efficient and shows that it is doing all that it is possible for it to do, and when this is the case it is generally considered that the engineer has successfully performed his duty. If it is a question of using the force or material in some other way, through some other kind of machine; then the engineer may also be concerned and it may be necessary for him to change his methods of work to conform to a new demand—that is, of economy. In some cases the application of the force or the use of material is not economical, for reasons which are beyond the power of the engineer to control, for they may be economic in their character. In the future, waste of raw material should be abhorrent to the engineer and his aim should be to conserve the materials which nature has provided for his use. The agriculturist and the forester, as well as the engineer, are concerned in the conservation of the natural resources, but in a broad sense all may be considered as belonging to the same class. They all develop the natural resources of the country and prepare them for the use of men. I shall speak of these resources separately and try to show in what way the engineer, the forester and the agriculturist may work for their conservation.

FORESTS

I have already stated that in the early days of our history it was the one aim of the settler to destroy the forests because they were in his way. He was an agriculturist and needed to have his land cleared of trees and other obstructions in order that he might harvest the greatest crop. As the country grew the demand for lumber increased and then it became necessary to save the trees in the forest and turn them into lumber, but the supply still seemed inexhaustible and only the finest and best of the trees were used. The destructive use of the forests thus begun has continued ever since, though perhaps not in so great a degree. It takes from thirty to seventy-five years to grow a tree, but the lumbermen only cut those which have grown the straightest and cleanest and only use the best parts of the tree that is cut. The branches and the upper part of the tree are left to decay in the forest. They are not only wasted, but they are scattered over the ground in such a way as to prevent future growth, for the soil is covered with a mat of material through which it is hard for any living thing to penetrate. It is necessary to burn this over in order that a new growth may rapidly start. But the burning over of the forest effectually kills the young trees which were growing among the old ones and thus entails a further loss upon the forest and its owner.

The demand for lumber has increased enormously during the past few years. In 1880 the consumption per capita in the United States was 360 feet, while in 1906 it was 440 feet. The total amount of lumber cut in 1906 was over 40,000,000,000 feet, and this yearly amount will largely increase in the future, both through the increase in population and through the increase per capita, unless some steps are taken to prevent it. No accurate census of the amount of timber in the country has been made, but it is estimated that we have now of standing timber about fourteen hundred billion feet. We are using forty billion feet per year. Upon this basis the present lumber supply will last thirty-five years, but this does not take account of the increase in the amount used per year nor does it take into account the amount of timber which will grow during the next thirty-five years. If nothing is done to increase our forest area we may suppose that these two will balance each other, although it is probable that the lumber cut will increase faster than the growth. But even the more conservative calculation shows that our forests can not last more than thirty-five years on the present basis of cutting. Long before that time the cost of lumber will largely increase and at the end of that period there will be no timber fit to cut. When we consider the extent to which wood is used at the present time, how much it means to all men, this is a most serious question.

The government has tried to check this depletion of our forests by establishing forest reserves in different parts of the country. It is estimated that at present there are in forests about seven hundred million acres, of which twenty per cent. are in national and state hands. This does not mean that all of this land is fully covered with forests, for large sections of it may be totally barren, but surrounded by forests in such a way that it is necessary to call the whole forest land, until a very accurate survey has been made. The National Bureau of Forestry of the United States Department of Agriculture and a number of state departments of forestry have done a great deal towards arousing public interest in the subject and establishing scientific methods of cultivation. Many of the state universities have established departments of forestry which are training foresters to take charge of the development of the forest interests of state and nation.

It is evident that in the future lumber must be considered as a crop to be planted and tended and harvested with the same care that other crops receive. It differs from them only in the methods of cultivation and the length of time necessary for its development. Under this scientific treatment trees will be planted on waste areas or other sections where ordinary crops are not profitable; they will be thinned out until only those which are likely to attain a mature growth are left, and they will be guarded against the destructive ef-

fect of forest fires. When a certain proportion of the crop is ready for harvesting the lumbermen will go in, cut the proper trees, carry away or burn the tops and branches, and then the forester will plant new trees in place of those felled. In a few years another crop will be ready and the same treatment will be repeated. The older forests will be treated in a similar way except that the first stage of planting will not be necessary. In this way the forests will yield a regular crop of lumber once in so often. Under this treatment the forests become profitable to a very much greater degree than under the old method of cutting off all trees large enough for lumber at one time and practically destroying all the young growth.

In some European countries where this method of forestry is in use the entire public expenses of many townships are met by the sale of timber from the public forest lands. Our government reserves now yield but a very small income, but in time, as they are brought under the proper cultivation, they will yield large results. As soon as forest planting is taken up on a large scale by national and state governments and by individuals, the lumber question of the future will be settled. This process, however, is a slow one and we must expect that before that time comes the present forest reserves will be largely exhausted. The danger, however, has been seen and the necessary methods for its correction have been developed. This has been the work of the scientific forester, but the labor can only be done by those agencies which can supply the necessary funds.

The engineer is greatly interested in this question because he needs timber for many of his operations. He also has a hand in the conservation of our forest areas because of the use which he makes of steel and concrete in structural work. The amount of cement manufactured and used in the United States has increased each year until now it has reached vast proportions. Its use will be greatly increased in the future, especially in structural work, as we learn more and more about the strength of concrete reinforced with steel. The United States government, engineering concerns and technical colleges are making an extensive study of this great engineering question and the results of their researches are put into practise as soon as they are published. Every engineer believes that the opportunity for this kind of investigation is very great and that it should be encouraged by both national and state governments.

FUEL

Manufacturing industries depend upon fuel, and cheap fuel is a vital element of our supremacy in the world's markets. The amount used at the present time in the United States is very large. In 1906 the coal mined amounted to four hundred million tons of a value of five hundred and ten million dollars. The petroleum was valued at ninety million dollars; natural gas at fifty million dollars; coke at one hundred and ten million dollars and artificial gas at thirty million dollars. The total value of all fuels, including by-products, was almost one billion dollars.

Coal is found in almost every section of the United States, twenty-nine out of forty-six states having coal beds. Natural gas and petroleum are also found in many of the states. No matter how large the supply of these fuels may originally have been, a yearly drain, such as just mentioned, will inevitably in a few years sadly deplete it, and the amount used is increasing every year and at a very rapid rate. But this is not all; the figures just given are those for the fuel taken from the ground and used, but the amount wasted doubles or trebles this total. Although this latter has not been put to any use, it has been destroyed so far as its future usefulness is concerned.

Natural gas is one of the most perfect fuels in existence. It is found under such pressure that it can be carried long distances and delivered in the factory ready for use. The turning of a cock regulates the supply and there is no dirt or loss. Many wells which yield small amounts are allowed to waste their supply in the air and it has frequently happened that the product of large wells is more or less wasted because proper piping is not at hand or proper precautions have not been taken. In many oil wells there is more or less gas and little if any effort is made to secure this supply. One geologist estimates that at least a billion cubic feet of gas per day are allowed to go to waste in the United States. Only one state, Indiana, has passed stringent laws against this waste. This state found that her supply of natural gas was rapidly being exhausted and that factories formerly dependent upon it were obliged to change to some other form of fuel. After a large part of the supply had been exhausted, laws were passed forbidding operators to open gas or oil wells until precautions had been taken to save all the gas.

The waste in coal mines is very great. Nearly every coal vein has streaks of sulphurous or bony coal mixed with the first-class material. This contains a large amount of carbon, but is not as valuable as some parts of the seam; it is, therefore, left in piles inside the mine or dumped upon the culm bank on the outside. The amount of this low-grade coal varies from ten to fifty per cent. in every mine, and under the present system of mining and of coal using this is an absolute loss. As the roofs of coal mines will not support themselves and as timber is expensive it is the custom to leave great pillars of coal in the mine as supports. As a rule, these pillars are not taken out and so become absolute waste. In most coal mines there are several layers of the coal separated by shale formation. Some of these are narrow and can not be mined to advantage; others are so broken up and dislocated by the mining of adjacent seams that it is impossible to take them out. All of these causes and perhaps some others make up a loss of from forty to seventy per cent. of the coal in the average coal mine of the country. As we obtain only thirty to sixty per cent. of the coal, it is evident that we are exhausting our coal fields twice as fast as the actual amount of fuel used would indicate.

This immense drain upon the coal supply must very soon have an effect. It has been estimated that our anthracite coal can not last more than seventy-five years. The bituminous coal will last much longer, but it will become exhausted in those places where it is now used to the greatest extent. The most important coal vein in the United States is in the Pittsburg belt and is being more rapidly mined than any other. Each acre of land has supplied about eight thousand tons of coal, and at this rate the state geologist of West Virginia estimates that at the beginning of the next century there will be no coal within one hundred miles of Pittsburg. No one can fail to perceive that this

will be a terrible blow to the manufacturing industries of that great industrial center. In many sections of the country where neither anthracite nor bituminous coal is found large deposits of lignite exist. This lignite can be used for heating purposes in houses, but is worthless for manufacturing purposes because the amount of ash is so great that it will not produce steam. In sections of country where this is the only fuel supply it is necessary to bring coal from long distances, which makes it very expensive and puts a great tax upon manufacturing industries.

Our coal measures cover such an extensive area and the supply has seemed so great that the conservation of our fuels has received very little attention until within the past few years. In 1903 the Technologic Branch of the United States Geological Survey was established in St. Louis in connection with the exposition, and since then a very extensive study of the fuel supplies of the country has been carried on. Dr. Holmes, the director of this branch; Professor Lord, of the Ohio State University, in charge of the chemical work; Professor Breckenridge, of the University of Illinois, in charge of the boiler tests, and Professor Fernald, of Case School of Applied Science, in charge of the gas producer and gas engine tests; are all members of this society. The results obtained by these men, all of them engineers, have been of an astonishing character. It has been found that the fine coal, the refuse of mines and breakers, hitherto regarded as of little value and sold at an extremely low price, can be made into briquettes at a comparatively low cost and it is then as valuable as the finest coal that can be obtained. It has also been found that many non-coking coals can, by proper methods, be coked as readily as the best coking coals of Pennsylvania. These two results alone are worth many times as much as this bureau has cost the government, for certain manufacturing industries must have coke for fuel and in some sections it has been necessary to bring the coke from long distances because no coking coal was at hand, although large supplies of other coal were easily obtainable.

But perhaps the most wonderful results from these experiments have come through the investigations in regard to the use of coal in the gas producer and the gas engine. With the old processes we do not obtain on the average more than five per cent. of the heat value of our coals. The steam engine utilizes from four to ten per cent., but the gas producer and the gas engine utilize from eleven to eighteen per cent. Coal converted into gas produces, then, two and one half times as much power as when burned under a boiler. The best Pocahontas coal under a boiler was found to produce .28 H. P. per pound of coal per hour, while with a gas producer the same amount of coal produced .96 H. P., or 3.34 times as much as when used in the ordinary way. A lignite which would produce only .01 H. P. per pound of coal per hour when used under a boiler produced .35 H. P. when used in a gas producer. A still more interesting fact is that the best Pocahontas coal used under a boiler produced .28 H. P. per pound per hour while a lignite in a producer gave .30 H. P. Thus, lignite turned into gas gave more power than the best coal when used under a boiler. These results indicate that there is fuel in all parts of the United States which can be used to produce power through the gas pro-

ducer and gas engine, so that the amount of valuable fuel for power purposes has been increased many fold by the work of the Technologic Branch.

It is true that these results, while they show a great improvement over ordinary methods, look small compared to what should theoretically be obtained. Even the gas engine under the most favorable conditions does not utilize over eighteen per cent. of the heat value of the coal. There is still a great opportunity for the scientific man and the engineer to devise methods by which a larger per cent. of the energy of our fuels can be utilized. And the engineer has an important work to do in connection with the results already obtained. The gas engine has been in use in Europe for a number of years and is now being introduced into this country. There are some installations where the horse power runs into thousands, but these are isolated and are principally in connection with steel plants. The average manufacturer hesitates to install a gas engine because he fears that he can not depend upon it every day as he can upon the steam engine and because he knows that it can not be operated by the same engineer who can operate his steam plant. The steam engine is so simple and has been in use so long that it is very easy to make repairs upon it and it does not take very long comparatively to train a man to use it. The gas engine is more complicated, is not as well understood and at present there are very few men who are experienced in its use. The greater initial cost of the gas plant, the cost of operating and the feeling which the manufacturer has that it is unreliable will retard its use, but if our mechanical engineers, and especially if our engineering colleges, will make the thorough study of this question which it deserves, there is no doubt that within a few years the gas engine will practically supplant the steam engine. The manufacturer wants power and he wants it as cheaply as it can possibly be obtained. If a new form of prime mover will develop two and one half times as much power as the old without too much initial cost or expense of maintenance, the manufacturer will rapidly install the new form. I believe our engineering colleges should install gas plants and make a thorough and systematic study of their use from day to day. In this way their faults can be remedied and through published reports the manufacturer can be made to feel that they are reliable. At the same time it will be of immense benefit to the students in the mechanical engineering departments to have a thorough training in the principles and the use of this new form of engine.

IRON AND STEEL

This is an iron age. A nation's industrial progress is determined by the amount of iron ore it uses. Gold, silver, tin, lead and many other metals, while useful, could be dispensed with, but iron and copper are indispensable at this stage of the world's progress, and of these two iron is by far the more necessary and the more useful. In 1907 fifty-three million tons of iron ore were mined and up to this time seven hundred and fifty million tons had been mined in this country. The total amount of iron ore available in the United States is about as follows: In Lake Superior, one billion five hundred million tons; southern district, two billion five hundred million tons; other parts of the United States, five billion tons; or a to-

tal of about ten billion tons. The highest grade is found in the Lake Superior district and hence 'this ore is in the greatest demand. In 1907 forty-four million tons were mined in this region, and with the present increase in consumption the supply will be completely exhausted by 1940 unless new deposits are discovered. Up to the present time one thirteenth of the original supply of iron ore in the United States has been used. At the present rate of exhaustion the total amount in the whole country will be used up before the end of the present century. This includes, however, only that supply which is of a high enough grade to be worked at the present time. After that it will be necessary to use lower grades of ore or we must do what so many European countries do—import from other places. This, of course, would be a great blow to our material prosperity. We have held our position in the industrial markets for iron and steel products on account of the abundance of our iron and coal and the consequent cheap price of both. When it becomes necessary to import either coal or iron, the cost of manufacture will largely increase, and unless conditions are different from those at present, we shall no longer be an exporting nation. It will be necessary for the engineer to use all of his ingenuity and skill to avert the commercial and industrial disaster which will inevitably come when the supply of iron ore is exhausted. This may be done, perhaps, by new methods which will make it possible to use a lower grade of ore and yet obtain the manufactured product at the same price as at present. New alloys of iron will undoubtedly be discovered by the engineer which will make it possible to obtain the present strength for machines and structures with the use of less material, thus decreasing the amount of ore used. As concrete reinforced by steel takes the place of steel structures, a still greater saving in iron will be the result. This is inevitably coming, for the progress in this direction during the past few years has been astonishing. The engineer is deeply concerned with methods of transportation and by substituting water transportation for rail transportation the saving in steel is very great, for the same load can be carried by the former with one third the steel in the original plant that is necessary when loads are carried by rail.

RECLAMATION OF LAND

The problem of maintaining the fertility of the soil and of enriching the worn-out farming lands of the country is one which belongs to the scientific agriculturist and not to the engineer, but there is one question connected with the agricultural interests of the country with which the engineer is vitally concerned—that is the reclamation of the arid and swampy regions. When the population of a country is sparse people seek the richest farming lands. They use the most exhaustive and least scientific methods of agriculture and the soil is soon depleted, but they are indifferent to this because there are large areas not in use and they can move from the wornout farm to a new section. But as population increases the richest lands are rapidly absorbed, those of second and third grade must then be used and in the end all the fertile soil of the country is under cultivation. After this, if population is to grow, more scientific methods of agriculture must be adopted or the hitherto useless land must be converted into fertile

areas. The useless land consists of mountainous, desert and swampy regions. As a rule, the mountainous districts are not available for agriculture, though they may be for forestry. The desert land can in many cases be reclaimed by irrigation and the swampy land may often be reclaimed by drainage. Both of these processes, irrigation and drainage, are essentially within the province of the engineer and it is due to his efforts that so much fertile soil has been added to our national domain. Eight million acres have already been irrigated and in the next twenty-five years it is estimated that twelve million acres more may be reclaimed. We have in the United States eighty million acres of swampy land, of which twelve million have already been drained and twenty million more may be drained in the future. This will enable us to raise a food supply for many millions of people and hence population can grow to this extent. But the problem of reclamation is only a part of the greater problem of the food supply of the nation and this does not belong to the engineer.

INLAND WATERWAYS

The forests, water power, irrigation and inland navigation are more or less connected. The cutting away of the forests has been the cause of severe floods during certain sections of the year and very low water in the streams during the rest of the year. This has been detrimental to navigation and to the successful use of water power. Some streams are available, both for irrigation and water power and it is a question which of these is of the greatest value. If the water in a stream is used for irrigation it can not be used for water power and hence only one of these methods of utilization is available. Some streams can be used for power and also for navigation. The water which is used for power is not destroyed, but is turned back into the stream after its energy of motion or position has been used. The dams and other works necessary for the utilization of power form an impediment to navigation, but can be overcome by canals. Thus it seems that the question of the use of water must be studied from several standpoints and the final solution of the problem will depend upon a number of different facts.

The United States possesses an unrivaled natural system of waterways. Professor Johnson says that at present we have 25,000 miles of navigable streams and there is as much more that can be made navigable. There are 1,410 miles of navigable waters in the Great Lakes and we have 2,120 miles of canals. There are 2,500 miles of waterways in sounds, bays and bayous on the Atlantic and Gulf coasts. These can all be made into a splendid inland system by the construction of a comparatively few miles of canals. On account of the absence of these canals only a very small part of this natural water route is at present utilized. In view of the importance of our waterways very little has so far been done. We have wasted our natural routes of travel by the destruction of forests, by allowing our streams to fill up with sand, and by our neglect to use those which are still available. It is much cheaper to transport heavy material by water than by rail and the great advantage which comes from the proper use of waterways is shown wherever the government has given the necessary aid. The most striking evidence of the value of work properly directed is seen in the

Great Lakes, where a hundred million dollars has been spent. The water in the lakes is deep enough for the largest vessels, but the rivers and straits connecting them naturally had only from eight to twelve feet of water. This has been increased through government appropriations to twenty-one feet, and now this body of Great Lakes forms one of the grandest pieces of navigable water known in the world. In 1889 twenty-five million tons passed through this system and in 1906 this had increased to seventy-six million tons. In 1907 it was eighty-three million tons and the increase will undoubtedly go on. In the Mississippi Valley two hundred and eight million dollars has been spent, but very little of it has gone for navigation. The larger part has been spent in jetties and dikes and so forth, necessary to prevent the loss of property and of life. So little has been done in the greater part of the Mississippi Valley that the tonnage has decreased during the past twenty years. The Inland Waterways Commission has done a most valuable work in showing the possibilities of our navigable streams, lakes and bays. It is to be hoped that congress will make the appropriations necessary to make this body permanent and that its recommendations will receive favorable consideration. In England, France and Germany the waterways have received far greater attention than here. Although these countries are much smaller than the United States a very much larger proportion of the total tonnage passes through the rivers and canals. We should take a lesson from these nations and learn to give this subject the proper amount of attention. The larger use of our waterways will not decrease the amount of railway traffic. The railways now have more than they can do and they have found great difficulty in raising money sufficient to increase their trackage and their transportation facilities.

Railroad transportation can only take place over a pathway which has been especially prepared and which has been laid with steel rails. Water transportation does not need this. A natural pathway is ready and it is only necessary to provide the vessels to carry the traffic. This makes the cost of transportation by water very much less than that by land. The initial cost is less and the cost of maintenance is less. Navigation has decreased during the past few years in many sections because the streams are shallow and the loads carried have been very small. As the railroads have reached into the districts formerly served by boats, the rapidity of transportation and the possibility of carrying large loads have decreased the cost below that of water service. If these streams, however, can be given the proper depth so that larger vessels can be used and greater loads carried, the transportation by water will be resumed. The whole question of water transportation belongs to the engineer. Whatever has been done in the past has been planned and carried out by him and all improvements in the future must be his work.

CONCLUSIONS

I have presented in a very imperfect way the present state of our natural resources and have suggested some of the steps which should be taken to conserve them. There is nothing original in this. The facts have been gathered from government reports and papers written by experts in each of the several divisions of this question. The point which I had in mind during the preparation of the paper and to which I wish to give especial emphasis is that this work of conservation is the work of the engineer. I am inclined to think that in some cases the statements in regard to the destruction of our natural resources have been overdrawn and that they will not be totally exhausted in as short a period as some seem to believe, but there is no doubt that the question is a grave one and that it should be faced before it is too late. We should try to avoid waste and unnecessary destruction and we should also try to make the best possible use of all of our resources. It will be the work of the engineer to accomplish both of these objects, and it will also be his province to determine new ways of accomplishing results now so wastefully performed. In the past the engineer has been concerned in getting results. If the results were obtained, the waste and destruction of the natural product have scarcely been considered, but in the future, economy of the natural product as well as economy in the final result must receive careful attention. I believe the engineers of the country are capable of solving these problems, and that if they are given the necessary governmental and private aid that the problem of the conservation of our natural resources will be solved.

The engineering colleges of the country will also have a share in this work. They are training the engineers of the future and from now on they must train them with this problem in view. They must not only give them the principles of engineering practise, but they must show them how the work of the engineer can be carried out with a view of transmitting to our posterity the natural resources in, so far as possible, an unimpaired condition. As has been pointed out in this paper, the conservation of some of our natural resources must be accomplished through new inventions. This means that the engineer of the future must be able to do more than the simple engineering work which comes to him from day to day. He must be so thoroughly trained in the principles of science and applied mechanics that he will be able to discover new processes and accomplish old results in new and more economical ways. He must be taught more thoroughly than ever before how to unite theoretical and practical knowledge. In short, he must be able to think along scientific and engineering lines. This is the most difficult thing which the engineering college has to teach. There are so many subjects in the curriculum, so much that is necessary for the engineer to learn, that he has not had the proper time to digest this mass of material. I feel convinced that this problem of teaching the student to think, of giving him the power to solve things for himself, has for many years received the earnest attention of the members of this society, but in view of the problem which I am discussing today, I wish to urge upon all who teach in our colleges the importance of giving it still more attention. Engineering science is progressive, the subjects taught in our engineering schools are alive and not dead. We shall grow, not only in knowledge, but in methods, and we shall accomplish the results we ought to accomplish and solve the problems presented to us.

5. Combinations in Restraint of Waste, 1916

Engineering News

The conservation crusade did not involve only scientists and engineers. Indeed, when Roosevelt left the White House the technicians had to turn to the general public for support. The campaign to sell conservation was carried on in the traditional rhetoric of American reform, and much was said about "the interests" versus "the people." Preservationists, once banned from the ranks (John Muir was not invited to the White House Conference in 1908), were now courted, and the whole movement took a radical swing which alarmed many of its earliest and most stalwart supporters. It became apparent that the experts were not all agreed on what should be done, or by whom.

Eight years ago the attention of the public was effectively directed toward the need of conservation of the Nation's resources, by the famous Conservation Congress held at the White House. That notable meeting, however,

From "Combinations for Conservation of Natural Resources," *Engineering News,* LXXVI (December 14, 1916), 1144-45. Reprinted from *Engineering News-Record,* December 14, 1916, copyright, McGraw-Hill, Inc. All rights reserved.

made only a beginning in the necessary work of public education. Since that meeting, some of the leaders in the conservation movement have diverted it from its original great purpose and concentrated their efforts to oppose grants by the Government to private parties for the use of natural resources still in public ownership. The far greater problem of checking the enormous waste now going on as a result of present methods of utilizing natural resources is almost unheeded.

While the politicans have used the conservation movement for political purposes, engineers, who better than any other class appreciate the vast importance of real conservation to the public welfare, have steadily continued to agitate the subject. The National Chamber of Commerce announces that a referendum vote is about to be taken on the question, "Shall combinations to conserve natural resources be permitted?" The taking of this vote is the result of recommendations by a committee, the chairman of which is a noted engineer and which has in its membership two scientists who may well be ranked as engineers. The committee is made up of W. L. Saunders, past-president of the American Institute of Mining Engineers, chairman; Prof. W. B. Clark, State Geologist of Maryland; John H. Fahey, former president of the National Chamber of Commerce; Charles F. Keith, president of the Southern Pine Lumber Association; and Dr. Charles R. Van Hise, president of the University of Wisconsin.

The recommendation of this committee is that in industries which involve primary natural resources, where co-operative agreements will tend to conserve these resources, to lessen accidents and to promote the public interest, Congress should pass legislation permitting such agreements to be made without infringement of the Sherman law. The committee bases this recommendation on its studies of lumber, coal, oil and ore production.

What the committee points out has been in fact well known to engineers for a considerable time. In coal production, for example, the late Joseph A. Holmes, when head of the Bureau of Mines, pointed out that the strenuous competition and low price at which coal was produced made it impossible for the coal operators in many parts of the country to take out the maximum amount of coal from the seams that they worked. In order to maintain their place in the competitive struggle and keep out of bankruptcy they were practically obliged to take out the most easily mined part of the seam and leave the rest in the ground, to be forever unavailable for the use of humanity.

Practically the same thing has been going on in the lumber industry, as has been repeatedly pointed out by Federal experts in the Forest Service. The intense competition in the lumber business has forced lumbermen to cut from their lands the best timber that can be most readily marketed, leaving the slightly inferior qualities to decay in the forest and furnish a readily available fuel for forest fires.

It is in petroleum and natural-gas production, however, that the most criminal waste is going on, as it has been going on ever since the industry began, notwithstanding the wide public attention called to this waste at the Conservation Congress of eight years ago and notwithstanding repeated demonstrations of the need of effective measures to prevent waste.

At the recent American Mining Congress at Chicago a paper was read by Max W. Ball, of the United States Bureau of Mines, showing that at the present rate of consumption of petroleum the entire petroleum resources of the United States will be exhausted in approximately 30 years. The following extract from Mr. Ball's paper indicates something of the criminal wastefulness with which the natural resources in petroleum and natural gas are being exploited:

Are we practicing conservation? Within the last few weeks I have seen millions of cubic feet of natural gas wasting into the air—gas so rich in gasoline that it dripped from the trees like an April shower. I have seen wells capable of yielding 40,000,000 cu.ft. of gas each being deliberately drowned out by pumping water into the gas sands. Reckless drilling, defective casing, careless plugging are flooding great areas with water and losing forever enormous quantities of oil. It has been testified before the Corporation Commission of Oklahoma that ordinary methods leave from 25 to 85% of the oil in the ground, and this estimate is concurred in by careful engineers and practical oil men.

Nor are these underground losses the only ones. When the oil is brought to the surface before transportation and market are ready for it, it must go into storage. Indeed, in many fields oil has been produced before storage was available, and millions of gallons have gone down the streams or seeped away from earthen reservoirs. Even when the best steel tankage has been provided, evaporation losses still go on. Cushing crude stored in steel tanks for a few months lost approximately a fifth of its gasoline content. The State Mineralogist's office of California has estimated that even with the heavy oils of that state the loss by evaporation represents perhaps 25% of the total value of the production at the well. An official of one of the largest companies in the Midcontinent field recently told me that last year fire destroyed 6% of his company's production.

Just consider these examples; 25 to 85% left underground; 20 to 50% of the value of oil produced lost through evaporation in storage; 6% of stored oil lost by fire! These losses are staggering and are not exceptional! What a small percentage of this wonderful natural resource is saved to run your machine or to deliver goods at your door or to plow the fields from which your food must come!

If we feel these losses in the high prices of the present day, how much more will we feel them five, ten, twenty or thirty years from now? Is it not time we considered them seriously and tried to determine upon some remedy?

Mr. Ball further shows how in the rush to develop a new oil field and the mad competition between the different drillers the natural gas that precedes the oil is frequently allowed to waste itself entirely and the oil deposits are tapped with such haste and carelessness that water often invades the field and drowns out the oil when but a small proportion of that available has been drawn off.

In hearings before the Senate Committee on Public Lands, Jan. 12, 1915, it was shown that the companies which exploited the famous Glenn pool of Oklahoma spent $11,260,000 in drilling wells, when if the whole pool had been exploited by one producer who would have handled the work properly, all the oil could have been obtained for $3,177,000.

Mr. Ball urges that to furnish at least a partial remedy for the appalling waste now going on, the laws should be so amended that oil lands will be divided up into larger tracts, so that producers will not be under the same necessity as now to rush the work of draining off the oil at a sacrifice of all other considerations. Mr. Ball concludes his paper as follows:

If you would prevent waste of oil and natural gas, if you would do away with careless drilling methods, excessive production charges and storage losses, if you would insure the production of the maximum amount of oil at the minimum cost, if you would help to maintain a reasonable price for petroleum and its products in the years to come, then do your part in creating a public sentiment in favor of adequate acreage.

Mr. Ball's recommendations illustrate well the crying need of a better Federal mining law to govern the titles to mineral deposits. To show the active interest that engineers are taking in this aspect of the conservation movement, it may be noted that the Mining and Metallurgical Society of America has just completed a letter ballot of its membership on 33 questions in connection with proposed revision of the Federal mining law. In addition, it has submitted the same questions to a number of other organizations in the mining industry where a similar ballot could be taken.

These illustrations indicate that some engineers, at least, are endeavoring to do their duty in informing public opinion and making it effective toward bringing about intelligent legislation in the public interest. Surely there was never a time within the memory of men now living when the need was more obvious of utilizing without waste the natural resources that furnish the materials necessary for life. It may be hopeless to expect very much remedial legislation at the present short session of Congress, but the work of indicating the direction that legislation should take in order to protect the public interest ought eventually to be effective.

PART X WORLD WAR I

For several decades prior to World War I changes of enormous significance had been taking place in a few scattered, though relatively important, sectors of the nation's economy. Scientific Management, with its emphasis upon productive efficiency; a new respect for science, institutionalized in a growing number of industrial research laboratories; and the increasing willingness of technical experts, especially in the fields of agriculture and resource management, to enter the public service—all of these trends were marked before 1917.

For American technology, the war was a crusade—but not only one to make the world safe for democracy. In this crusade, a great national purpose required national planning; profit was subordinated to production; innovation was applauded rather than fought. It was, in short, a crusade of heroic proportions, one which dwarfed in scale and significance those efforts that had been made against wasteful resource exploitation or municipal corruption.

With large hopes and good hearts the nation's technical men, from draftsmen to engineers to corporation presidents, set about the task of making a better world. Whether as factory inspectors or dollar-a-year men in Washington, they tried to apply on a national scale those technical reforms they had learned in the schools, professional societies, and shops. When the war ended, a scant twenty months after the United States had entered it, much of the technical apparatus created during the emergency was dismantled. What remained were a handful of institutions of potential influence (such as the National Research Council), a certain disillusionment with the politicians and bureaucrats who had somehow failed to be reformed, and a much wider and deeper foundation of acceptance of technology within American industry itself.

1. Preparedness, 1915

Engineering News

On the eve of the American entry into what had hitherto been called the European War, this country's army stood at 200,000 men—half the number of casualties suffered by the British in the single battle of the Somme. Since the sinking of the *Lusitania* in May 1915, and even earlier, there had been speculation about American participation. In such an event the army would have to be expanded tremendously, and a special premium would be placed upon men with special skills. Engineers looked forward to the role they might play, first in preparedness and then in war.

The annual message of the President to Congress proposes an enormous increase in the military and naval establishments of the United States. That the civilian engineers of the country are to play an important part in this preparedness program is a foregone conclusion. There are probably few American engineering societies which have not already listened to talks by military officers on national defense and heard the principles of military engineering explained. Several local societies have gone so far as to seek specific instruction in military science for their members. A committee representing the five great national engineering societies has been working with the War Department for months upon a method of utilizing these organizations in a scheme for national defense, and is soon to report on the legislation it has framed. Evidently, interest is not lacking.

The President proposes to increase the Corps of Engineers by 15 companies. At least 50 additional engineer officers will be required for this force, so it seems probable that civilian engineers may obtain some of these commissions. In the army as a whole about 2,000 additional commissioned officers will be required, and the logical candidates for these commissions, according to what engineering societies are being told, are the younger graduates from the engineering schools.

Moreover it is proposed to build up a volunteer army of 400,000 part-time men, to be raised in groups of 133,000 a year for a period of three years. A large number of volunteer officers will be required for these troops, as well as 750 permanent officers to train them; and here again the technical graduate and engineer are likely to come to the front. It has been publicly stated by responsible army officers that every technical graduate with an elementary knowledge of military science is a potential army officer.

As to the methods by which military training for both regular and reserve officers is to be imparted, three schemes are proposed by the Secretary of War in his annual report. One is to organize a certain number of cadet companies to be attached to the regular army units. These cadets will receive special pay and will engage to serve one year with the cadet corps and five years in the reserve army corps. Their year in the cadet corps will consist of intensive training in all positions in the company from private to commissioned officer. A second scheme is to reorganize the military departments of the various colleges and universities under the direction of army officers, so as to make them in effect officers' training schools. The third method is to commission present officers of the National Guard, technical graduates of military training, civil engineers, railway men and others. It is also proposed to increase the capacity of the Military Academy at West Point to 770 students, which is 146 more than at present.

Additional training for reserve officers may be given in connection with the training of the Continental army or by their assignment for service with the regular army. Officers and men of the reserve force will receive pay on the same basis as the regular army for the time actually occupied in the service.

Repugnant as war and destruction are to every peace-loving American, they are doubly so to the engineer who has ever clung tenaciously to Telford's definition of engineering as "directing the great sources of power in nature for the use and convenience of man." The folly of diverting those sources of power to the destruction of life and property is perhaps more keenly appreciated by the engineer than by any other professional man, for the engineer spends his life in the design and execution of structures for preserving and safeguarding life and property—for such purpose indeed in the last analysis are sewers, water-works, bridges and nearly every other engineering structure which could be named.

Nevertheless engineers well understand that in the event of actual war, engineers everywhere will have to assume great responsibilities. In the European war the pioneers and the miners and the sappers have become the main reliance of the advanced troops. The frontiers of belligerent European countries have been converted into practically continuous lines of trenches under the direction of engineer officers. The engineers charged with the maintenance and operation of lines of transport and communication are as essential to the military operations as the men behind the guns. On the other hand there are engineer troops whose service is wholly destructive; bridges, railways, tunnels, roads, etc., must be demolished behind a retreating army.

If a preponderance of sound public sentiment is for preparedness, engineers will be ready to respond to the patriotic duties asked of them. The military training they receive will have value anyway. Col. William M. Black, Corps of Engineers, U.S.A., has said that the chief fault to be found with civilian engineers in military work is the lack of a sense of proportion—a tendency to give more time and weight to methods and refinement than expediency justifies. For instance, in military topography the engineer must learn to sacrifice a certain amount of accuracy to speed, and yet retain a high degree of accuracy in the essentials for which the topographic survey is to serve. In other words the study of military engineering ought to cultivate judgment, prompt decision, discrimination and foresight—all excellent qualities for any engineer, civil or military, to possess.

2. Jingoists Exposed, 1916

J. McKEEN CATTELL, "Military Preparedness"

Woodrow Wilson campaigned in 1916 on the dubious slogan, "he kept us out of war." There were, nevertheless, a large number of influential Americans who, under the banner of "preparedness," rushed forward to embrace the idea of eventual American participation. The American Association for the Advancement of Science gave some of these men a platform for exploring the connections between science and war. Their enthusiasm and conventional wisdom were questioned by the editor of the *Scientific Monthly*, the psychologist and statesman of science, J. McKeen Cattell.

There is published in the present issue of the Monthly a series of papers on national defense and development presented before the Section of Social and Economic Science of the American Association for the Advancement of Science. It is not clear why one aspect of the subject was emphasized at the meeting, but it is doubtless desirable that the arguments for military preparedness should be represented in this journal, as well as the opposite point of view. An obvious difference exists between the eleven sections of the American Association devoted to the natural and exact sciences and the one devoted to the social and economic sciences. The former are in the main concerned with the discovery of truth, the latter in the main with the expression of opinion, and the same holds for the articles published in this journal. It would not indeed be desirable to include such diverse subjects in the same association and in the same journal, except for the fact that it is one of the most important of all objects to establish the scientific method in belief and in conduct.

It is, however, particularly difficult to make any progress in this direction at a time when the emotions are deeply stirred. The people of each of the Euro-

From "Science and National Strength," *Scientific Monthly*, II (April 1916), 412, 414-16. Reprinted by permission of *Science* and the American Association for the Advancement of Science.

pean nations now at war believe sincerely that they are defending their country and their homes against cruel enemies that have long laid in wait wantonly to attack them. The responsibility for the war and the methods by which it is conducted are judged absolutely differently by Americans of English descent living in Boston and by Americans of German descent living in Milwaukee. It is believed by many that rivalry in armaments and in military and naval preparations intended for defense were the immediate cause of the present war and are likely to be the cause of future wars, yet nearly all the writers of the papers presented before the American Association and printed here argue that this country should increase its armaments and its military establishment in order to maintain peace.

The attempt of Germany to rival the British navy and the increased military preparations of Russia and of France may be regarded as at least among the causes leading to the present war. Nor is it evident that the efficiency for war of the different nations was proportional to their armaments. Their budgets in millions of dollars for the year just preceding the war were as follows:

	Army	Navy
Great Britain	224,300	224,140
France	191,432	119,571
Russia	317,800	122,500
Italy	82,928	51,000
Germany	183,090	111,300
Austria-Hungary	82,300	42,000

Austria-Hungary and Italy about balance, as do also Turkey and Bulgaria, on the one side, and Servia, Belgium and the partial participation of Japan and Portugal, on the other. The expenditure of Great Britain, France and Russia on their armies was about four times that of Germany, but this does not measure their relative efficiency at the outbreak of the war. The militaristic spirit of Germany is in part due to the armaments of the nations surrounding it. A nation may pay for armaments which not only make war more likely but which may help the enemy when war comes. The strength of Germany was its educational, social and industrial organization; its disaster is its military preparedness, which gave power to the military caste and led them to make war when and as they thought it could be waged victoriously. The strength of Great Britain on the seas is in its commerce, of which dreadnaughts are merely a dangerous symbol. The strength of a nation, even when at war, is not in armaments that can be purchased, but in its people and their institutions.

It might have been supposed that a discussion on national defense and development before the American Association for the Advancement of Science would have been concerned chiefly with emphasizing the importance of scientific education, scientific research and scientific organization as leading factors in the maintenance of peace and of national efficiency in case of war. If the battle of Waterloo was won on the playgrounds of the English public schools, it may be that other battles have been lost in the colleges of Oxford. At all events the complaint is made in England that its relative lack of success is due to its neglect of science. The classically trained dilettante, the political doctrinaire, the lawyer politician, the military martinet, are not fit leaders of a nation. The strength of this nation is in its engineers and physicians, in its scientific men, few though they are, in the great mass of the people engaged in productive agriculture and industry. We have shown what we can do in our railways, our automobiles, our telephones, what we can not do in our municipal and state governments, an admixture of success and failure in our schools and in our industrial organization.

A billion dollars spent, as is proposed, on the army and navy, as now organized, would be an incitement to war and would only be of moderate use in a strictly defensive war. The armaments would soon become obsolete and other billions would be called for. A billion dollars spent on scientific education, on scientific research, on public health, or on public works, would be money invested in the way yielding the largest returns, and would accomplish more than armaments to make the nation strong in defense.

As the writer of this note urged before the war, we should have the best army for defense and improved police forces if all local police were soldiers, one twelfth of their wages being paid by the nation and one month annually being spent in camps and drills. Idling in barracks is a method for the promotion of war, drunkenness and disease. The engineering corps, the health service and the commissariat are the most important factors in modern warfare. Engineers, health officers, inspectors of food and others employed by the nation, the states and the municipalities should be at the same time officers in the army and those under them enlisted men. A well-organized and efficient army for defense would thus be maintained at comparatively small expense and be an institution for education instead of for demoralization.

The navy should be converted into a merchant marine, carrying a postal, express, freight and passenger service to every port in the world. At the cost of an idle navy five to ten times as many ships and men could be maintained and employed in useful work. In case of war swift ships and experienced men would win over dreadnaughts. Shipyards and factories for armaments and ammunition should be owned by the nation and manned by officers and enlisted men. The army and the navy can be made self-supporting nearly as easily as the postoffice.

If we had for the past three years employed a large force of men on the Mexican border to build railways and roads, irrigation dams and other public works, it would probably have been a good investment. The net cost would certainly have been less than maintaining there an idle army, and our neighbors would have learned from us the ways of industry and peace instead of being irritated by an apparent threat. There would probably have been no raid; if it had been necessary for us to punish raiders it could have been done more effectively and with less friction than by the army as at present organized.

It might well be wished that instead of listening to Mr. Wise Wood and other frightened gentlemen, it were possible for the American Association for the Advancement of Science to use its influence to teach the president, the congress and the people that education, scientific research and the applications of science in agriculture and in industry, in the promotion of health and the prevention of waste and vice, are the ways to develop the greatness of a nation, to make it potent in maintaining peace, unconquerable in a war of defense.

3. Conflict and Confusion, 1917

GANO DUNN, "The Engineering Societies in the National Defense"

Finally, in April 1917, America did go to war. Engineers, like other groups in America, found that even after two years of "preparedness," they were largely unprepared for actual warfare. Technical people, many for the first time, turned their attention to Washington in an attempt to make an important and unique contribution to the war effort. As they discovered, however, it took more than anxious hearts and willing hands.

Engineers are, indeed, coming into glory and honor—glory in the things we were reading about in yesterday's and today's papers as to the behavior of the very men whom our national engineering societies recruited New York through the agency of the Military Engineering Committee only a few months ago, and honor in the ways that were referred to by your President in his address, in which he mentioned the fact that the engineering profession and the corporate societies representing them are having an ever-growing opportunity to "do their bit" for the Government at this critical time. The spirit, the intelligence, the usefulness of the engineer is a matter of common comment. I have talked with several university presidents who remarked upon the high percentage of enlistments and volunteering for service, particularly of the men in the engineering schools, and Dr. Hollis has not exaggerated the part that engineers are playing, and are yet to play, in respect to the things in this great war which we have only just begun to appreciate and understand.

I should desire this morning to bring to your attention some of the things that are now being done by engineers and engineering societies. Adequately to treat of what the engineers are doing would take days, if not longer, and I can only refer to it. One has only to be in the atmosphere of Washington a short time to see that the whole Government of the United States in respect to its military and naval preparation rests upon a foundation of engineers. My task is encyclopedic, and I beg your indulgence if I but hastily skim over it. I wrote to the representatives of thirty-two different engineering bodies that are now in contact with the Government, asking them to give me authoritatively, although briefly, a résumé of what they were doing in connection with the national defense and with the war. It is beyond our time for me even to go through the replies, but I hope to put them in the record, and they are certainly a scroll of real honor to our credit.

To begin with, there is the Naval Consulting Board. The Naval Consult-

From Gano Dunn, "The Engineering Societies in the National Defense," *Transactions of the American Society of Mechanical Engineers*, XXXIX (1917), 464-73. Reprinted by permission.

ing Board was intended to bring formally to the service of the Government the scientific and technical ability of a group of the best advisers on engineering lines in the country, and the Government had the conception that if it asked the engineering societies to select these advisers the selection would be better made than if it itself attempted to make the selection. Consequently, two representatives from each of the different engineering bodies were nominated, and under that nomination appointed by the Secretary of the Navy, and that board has been doing able service since the time it was appointed, starting with the Committee on Industrial Preparedness, which took an inventory of all the industrial resources of the United States. Later it proceeded to report to the Government on the needs of the experimental development of improved devices, and finally it established connections whereby its services might be made available and useful to the army as well as to the navy.

It now holds an honored position in Washington, where it acts as a Board on Inventions, and substantially all newly invented devices that are brought to the attention of the Council of National Defense, through various channels, are now referred to the Naval Consulting Board to be passed by, or turned down if they are not useful, or given attention if they are valuable. The Naval Consulting Board has offices at 15 Park Row, in New York City, and has a large force of clerks. The devoted services of its members are constantly given to going through thousands upon thousands of suggested devices from engineers, citizens, and others all over the country.

The Naval Consulting Board was created long before the war. The next

body in order was the National Research Council. The National Research Council was started because it was seen that, just as in the Civil War, such help as was given by the National Academy of Sciences, created by President Lincoln, and is now being given, by the national engineering societies, would be again needed. The Government acted, therefore, under the charter of Congress granted in 1864 to the National Academy of Sciences, among the provisions of which were the requirements that the members of the Academy who then represented what we now represent, the engineering as well as the scientific intelligence of the country, serve the Government on request, in whatever direction called upon, without compensation. And they did an unusual amount of service at the time of the Civil War.

Between that time and now, entirely aside from their scientific functions, they have reported on about sixty different questions to the Government. It was seen that this body could be made of great use at this time, and consequently President Wilson requested that it enlarge its scope and bring itself, as it were, down to date, and include the increasing branches of science that were not known in the old days, including engineering, and to do everything to put at the service of the Government the scientific talent of the nation.

In accordance with this request the National Academy of Sciences organized the National Research Council, which may be described as being partly a federation and partly a creation, through which there comes to one single focus every important scientific agency in the United States. It reaches the universities, it reaches the industrial laboratories, it reaches the engineering societies, it reaches the isolated workers in pure science, but the keynote of the National Research Council is science rather than engineering, and engineering plays a part in it only as it deals with pure science and applied science —in short, what we call engineering research.

When the war broke out it was only natural that the Council of National Defense should request a connection to be made between that body, which had existed for nearly a year, and itself, and since the war the National Research Council has almost dropped all other activities and directed its whole efforts to the problems in science that have been handed down to it by the Council of National Defense.

The next body in order of creation was the General Engineering Committee of the Council of National Defense. When the war broke out, our Society, in common with other engineering societies, immediately, and with a patriotic devotion, offered the services of engineers to the United States, directly to the President; and I do not think any of us realized at that time just what we were offering—quite a little confusion has arisen since as to what it was, but I do know that when we made the offer we did not intend to limit it merely to our engineering services, but we meant to go to any lengths that might be necessary.

Later on it came to be obvious that through this offer to the President we had not intended to convey the offer of our military services, and among other things we all remembered then that we were members of an even greater society than The American Society of Mechanical Engineers, we were members of the Society of American Citizenship, and that through membership in that greater society there came to us calls

for military services and other things, and consequently the offer to the President of the services which we made through our Society was regarded as conveying only the offer of engineering services.

The President turned our offer over to the Council of National Defense, and from Dr. Hollis Godfrey, of the Advisory Commission of the Council, an invitation was received to appoint representatives to form an Engineering Societies' Section of the Engineering Committee of the Commission. The Society acted officially upon that invitation and sent representatives to a conference in Washington, who met together with representatives from other societies.

From my point of view, this General Engineering Committee as it stands now is the official connection of our societies with the National Government; but the spirit among the engineers who want to serve the Government in more ways than this Committee renders possible, has caused the springing up on all hands of numerous other committees. I am going to read to you a list of the committees of engineering bodies which were in existence at a time, a short while ago, when outwardly and from the point of view of the Government there seemed to be so many committees that they were crowding each other, overlapping, and in their actual relations to the Government carried with them a certain degree of possible confusion, which was brought to our attention and which some of the members of our societies have been endeavoring to remedy.

These committees or engineering bodies are: Naval Consulting Board, American Engineering Standards Committee, Engineering Committee of the National Research Council, Committee on Gas and Electric Service, Emergency Construction Committee of the War Industries Board, the Intercollegiate Intelligence Bureau, the War Committee of the Technical Societies, the Engineering Council, the American Engineering Service Committee, the Aircraft Production Board, the Aircrafts Standardization Committee, the Aeronautics Committee of the National Research Council, the United Engineering Society, the Engineering Foundation, the American Society of Civil Engineers, The American Society of Mechanical Engineers, the American Institute of Mining Engineers, the American Institute of Electrical Engineers, the American Society for Testing Materials, the American Society of Automotive Engineers, the American Electrochemical Society, the Illuminating Engineering Society, the American Chemical Society, the American Gas Institute, the American Society of Refrigerating Engineers, the American Water Works Association, the National Electric Light Association, and the Association of Edison Illuminating Companies.

The mere enumeration of these engineering bodies itself is a bright light on what the engineers as societies have been doing for the Government. It does not begin to be a token of what engineers as individuals are doing for the Government.

As societies, however, there has been some confusion among the various societies, due to overlapping, and there has been also some lack of distinction between engineering services on the part of individuals and corporate services on the part of societies. For instance, one of the great services which no single individual could render the Government, but which a union of societies could wonderfully render the

Government, is the question of engineering personnel. So great has been the demand in Washington for competent engineers for this, that and the other service that they have not known where to go to find the men. They first went to their personal friends, to the members of the engineering profession already in the departments, and to those whom they were acquainted with, but soon the supply of acquaintances of these men and the men with whom they were in contact was exhausted, and the authorities were simply at the end of their capacity.

It has been very obvious that at least one of the functions that the national engineering societies could perform was to serve as a center to which the Government could go and find an adequate, properly classified roster of all of the men who could render service to the Government, so that the services of these men could be promptly called upon. Through a misconception, the responsibility for which I will not attempt to go into, the General Engineering Committee, which, as I have said, in my view is the official connection of the societies with the Government, declined to furnish the required roster of the personnel. I ought to say that it declined to do it on the recommendation of its chairman, Dr. Hollis Godfrey, who at the time was under some instruction from another branch of the Council of National Defense, which had in view the classifying of engineering service or labor generally, and consequently had in view the grouping and listing of this service in another department of the Council of National Defense, where it was hoped there would be a much broader and more general listing of labor than that which we now usually consider as labor; but be it as it was, the General Engineering Committee declined what, in my opinion, is the principal opportunity to be of service to the Government.

There then sprang up the Intercollegiate Intelligence Bureau for the purpose of making good this deficiency to a certain extent. Its origin was not in the engineering societies, but through an engineer, one of the prominent members of the American Institute of Electrical Engineers, Dr. William McClellan; he organized 170 colleges into a sort of league to supply to the Government men of technical training and engineering qualifications. He went at it through the colleges, because he is president of the Wharton School, and also because he felt that through them he could get in contact with a greater number of engineers and could accomplish better work than in the other direction.

The Engineering Council, which is a body destined to represent not only the great national engineering societies which are members of the United Engineering Society, but all of the great national engineering societies, also took up the question of personnel. It conceived its function to be a very broad one and organized in an endeavor to make certain contacts with the Government, leading up to that through the Naval Consulting Board, through the National Research Council, and through the General Engineering Committee; and there was also created under the Engineering Council the War Committee of the Technical Societies, and also a committee known as the American Engineering Service Committee; Dr. D. W. Brunton is chairman of the former and Mr. George J. Foran, chairman of the latter.

These committees went to work vigorously, headed by Dr. Hollis in the Engineering Council, and from the beginning have seen the importance of a registry of engineers and they actually started to accomplish a registry of that kind. When representations as to what these committees had done and were doing were made to the Government—and now speaking from my own point of view, and with the hope not of producing controversy, but of allaying it—the committees were not fully aware of what had been done already by the Naval Consulting Board, by the National Research Council and by the General Engineering Committee, all of which bodies had been in efficient contact with the Government, contact through channels that had been grooved more or less bright by use; and therefore the newer committees wrote to numerous agencies of the Government and interviewed them, and from the Government point of view canvassed the Government as to what channels they should use in their relations with these various activities.

The confusion that arose, although not serious, required straightening out. For instance, the national engineering societies, as such, had nothing to do with the appointment of the National Committee on Gas and Electric Service of which John W. Lieb, Mem.Am.Soc. M.E., is Chairman. They were more or less unfamiliar with that committee and its work, yet of all the committees in Washington that committee has probably done as much as, if not more than, any other committee in specific and concrete service rendered to the Government. That committee is a committee representing public utilities, or rather it represents the Council of National Defense—it is a committee of the Council of National Defense itself—but it instructs them and knows about the public utilities, and so today is charged with questions of coal supply and of power supply, questions of keeping the industries going that are engaged in munitions manufacture, questions of cantonment inspection and cantonment supplies.

The gist of the matter was that a certain member of our Society, Mr. Swasey, the Father Abraham of the engineering profession, was down in Washington and learned of some of these things. He endeavored to bring about coöperation and understanding among the thirty-two different engineering agencies. He called a meeting of the representatives of these organizations, and they all most promptly responded and met in Washington. That meeting was an eventful one in the history of the relation of the engineering societies of the country to the Government, for the knowledge was there brought out of the vast amount of service that was being rendered to the Government by engineers, and everyone present at that meeting was astounded at hearing how much everyone else had been doing, and the mere getting together of these committees is a thing that is going to solve the temporary and minor difficulty of a unified relation of the engineering societies to the Government.

For instance, at that conference we heard the representative of the Society of Automotive Engineers say what his committee had been doing. That society has been intensely vigorous—it has been of actual, concrete and real service to the Government in a way that cannot be known; in fact, one reason why the members of the societies have felt impatient at their Washington relations is because the work, as such, cannot be dwelt upon in detail among them. The

Government requires that almost all the work of these various committees and societies be confidential and shall be kept to themselves, and that is one reason why the membership of the societies have felt that they were not doing their bit, when in fact they were doing all that the Government so far had called upon them to do.

The status of the matter at present is that that joint meeting in Washington appointed a sub-committee to confer with the Engineering Council and with the governing bodies of the national societies, with a view of reporting back some general plan whereby the chairman of the War Board, for instance, would not be receiving four different letters from engineering bodies, each inviting him to take up problems of a certain kind through that particular committee. It is confusing to that chairman to receive such letters, and, moreover, it shakes his confidence in the ability of the engineers to organize their work effectively and to do the things that they most want to do.

I am afraid I have omitted ninety per cent of the things I wanted to say in regard to the activities of certain of these committees, and I perhaps ought to speak about the War Committee of the Technical Societies. That committee was intended originally to be a vehicle of information between various Governmental activities and the membership of the national societies. It was intended to be of service both ways. It was intended to satisfy this demand on the part of the membership by knowing as far as possible what was going on. It has recently established a connection with the Naval Consulting Board, and the general view of the engineers now interested in the Washington relations is that there never can be too much service in Washington, and that there is room for every committee. Colonel Carty, who presided over the conference called by Mr. Swasey, said that the whole thing is too big to be controlled by any one committee, and it is realized that the more there are of these committees that represent real service, the better it will be, and all that is needed is a little better directive force and a little more inquiry and coöperation before taking up with the Government questions that may have already been settled, in fact, by other agencies.

The situation as it stands now is one in which we may all take great pride. The General Engineering Committee of the Council of National Defense is in the awkward position of being asked by its chairman to resign. This is through, as I understand it, an early interpretation that service on that committee is incompatible with the ruling of the Attorney-General to the effect that men may not serve on committees of the Council of National Defense when they have other business relations with the Government. The business relations of the men in the engineering profession serving the Government are so numerous that if that principle were really carried out in fact, the Government would be deprived of the service of engineers; or, on the other hand, the industries, the engineering projects, and the very great works that are now being accomplished for the Government would be robbed of the directing heads that are producing them. Neither of these alternatives is for a moment conceivably possible.

This opinion of the Attorney-General has been later interpreted by the Secretary of War to mean that no man may sit on a board in Washington when that board is engaged in deliberating upon the award of a contract to a company in which that man is interested. That is only common sense. It has gone one step further, and says that no man may sit on a board when that board is making recommendations to another board, which other board may be empowered to award contracts, except in this case the man is not forbidden to sit on that board, but if he sits he must file with the second board a statement of his complete relation to the contract that is under consideration, and state what other interests he may have with it.

I think one reason for the general resignations that have occurred in the Council of National Defense has gone a good deal further than this technical situation. The Committee has been overgrown, overgrowth indicating rather a lack of authority, which the springing up of so many committees always indicates. The authorities wanted to reorganize the whole matter, and certainly that reorganization is now in force, but whether it will take the form of continuing to ask for the resignations of the members of the General Engineering Committee of the Council of National Defense, or whether that committee can be regarded as an exception, because it is a noncommercial committee, and whether that committee can be permitted to retain its relation there with the Advisory Commission, or establish new relations directly with the Council of National Defense—the same relation that has been established by the National Research Council—is not yet to be known. However, whatever it is, the principal thing which is now to be settled is not the relations of the twenty-eight of the thirty-two committees, whose names I have read; their relations are very satisfactory; they are doing splendid work for the Government;

they are a credit to the societies that have created them and the men who are in them. They are one of the good right arms of the authorities in Washington. Any confusion that may have existed lies in respect to the relations of the engineering societies, as such, to the Government; in other words, our own corporate relations to the Government for those things which we as societies may do, which we as engineers do not do, and under the leadership of Mr. Swasey that general question is now being happily and kindly worked out and thought out in a way which will result in the Government continuing to get not only the service it has been getting, but such increased service as the near future will lead it to demand.

We are not yet really in the war. Times are coming—they are predicting it in Washington—when the service we have so far rendered will be like but a little cloud on the horizon. Our duties will increase; our opportunities will increase. I do not think the patriotism of the engineering societies can increase. It has been at par from the beginning.

But, gentlemen, those of us who felt that because they were not yet called upon they were not going to have a place in this great war; those of us who have felt that because of some defect in the machinery at the top they were not being put in touch with the things they could do; those of us who have felt that way, I think, will soon, and very soon, have a call for everything that they can render. In Washington the views of the authorities are all in one accord as to the patriotism, the usefulness, the distinguished service and the ability of the engineering societies and their representatives in the national service. We have been a credit to ourselves in a big and fundamental way, even if some of our superficial relations have not been quite as orderly as we might have liked to have them. I have been told there is not yet on record a single case where the Government has actually asked an engineer to do a service for it where he has not responded, and that is a badge of honor which for our profession I hold very high.

4. An Inventor and the War, 1917

KARL T. COMPTON, "Edison's Laboratory in War Time"

When the Naval Consulting Board was established in 1915, it was decided to appoint Thomas Edison as chairman so that his great prestige might be used to gain influence for the agency. Unfortunately, Edison, now well advanced

From Karl T. Compton, "Edison's Laboratory in War Time," *Science*, LXXV (January 15, 1932), 70-71. Reprinted by permission of *Science* and the American Association for the Advancement of Science.

in years, preferred to work in his laboratory on specific problems rather than spend his time on administrative details. The following picture of Edison's wartime activities was left by Karl T. Compton, later president of the Massachusetts Institute of Technology.

Immediately following the declaration of war in 1917 Mr. Edison telephoned President Hibben, of Princeton, requesting him to send to his laboratory four scientists as volunteer war workers. I went with three of my colleagues from the department of physics and remained for the months required to bring to a conclusion the problem which was set for me by Mr. Edison.

All through the war the newspapers published frequent stories of Edison's war activities and of the secrecy in which they were carried out. One story which I remember described experiments carried on in the dead of night on the top of a mountain with armed guards posted all around the base. Whether these stories are true or not I do not know, but I do know that Edison's research laboratory was actively at work and that contact with this work gave me a vivid picture of Edison and his methods.

Immediately upon meeting Mr. Edison and barely taking time to say "how do you do," he took out his pencil and began to describe a problem which had been put up to him by the Naval Consulting Board—the problem of increasing the efficiency of the driving mechanism of a torpedo so that a larger amount of explosive could be stored in it without changing its range or size. He gave me a very brief history of the development of the present torpedo, told me the conditions which an improved torpedo would have to satisfy, and told me to come back to see him when I had a solution.

In about three weeks I reported to him that I had found three fuels which seemed to offer possibilities. He disposed of these solutions in three sentences: "Fuel A can only be obtained in Germany. Fuel B has been tried but discarded because of the danger of explosions. Fuel C, which included wood alcohol, is no good because the sailors drink the d— stuff."

So I went back for another couple of weeks and returned with a fourth solution. Mr. Edison took the papers, looked over the calculations, muttering the while to himself, and then said, "When I don't understand work like this I get two men to work at it independently. If they agree, maybe it is all right; if they don't agree, I get a third man. Go up into room—and see whether you agree with a young fellow from Columbia University whom I put to work on the same problem."

On interviewing this Columbia scientist I found that we agreed entirely as to method but disagreed radically as to conclusions. Whereas I had found very few fuels possibly superior to those which the Navy was using, he had found that almost every fuel was superior. On looking over his work, however, I found that he had based all calculations on a formula for alcohol, $C_{12} H_{22} O_{11}$, which is sugar. In other words, he had been actually finding out what fuels would be better than sugar for driving the Navy's torpedoes. When I asked him where in the world he had got that formula for alcohol he said, "You see, I am a mathematician and not a chemist so I went to the library," and with that he showed me an ancient book on chemistry, in which $C_{12} H_{22} O_{11}$ was actually given as the formula for alcohol.

Following this conference, Mr. Edison arranged for me a visit to one of the naval torpedo stations, where the calculations were checked by the torpedo engineer and the work was left in the hands of the Navy, with what results I do not know.

A second investigation illustrated Mr. Edison's great fertility and imagination. There had been numerous demands for the development of a super-sensitive microphone for detecting enemy operations by night or under the ground or beneath the sea. According to Mr. Edison the ordinary carbon granule microphone had too high a resistance, and he wanted to try metal granules, "But," he said, "metal granules are too blamed sluggish. We must make them lighter." He so devised this scheme: First he got a large supply of hog's bristles from a local brush factory; then he plated these hog bristles with a great variety of different metals. Some of them were plated by the electrolytic process, which he used in manufacturing his phonograph records; others were plated by cathode sputtering in a vacuum; and still others by the condensation of evaporated metals. When each of these hog bristles had plated on to it a thin coat of metal, the bristles were cut up into tiny lengths, each about a hundredth of an inch long, by a microtome such as is used in cutting specimens for microscope slides. These tiny little cylinders were then placed in a bath of caustic potash, "the stuff men dissolved their murdered wives in," said Mr. Edison, which dissolved out the hog bristle and left a tiny hollow cylinder of metal,

shaped like a napkin ring, and these were the metal granules which were used in place of carbon for the experimental microphones. How well they worked I do not know, since I did not see the conclusions of the test. My guess would be that they did not work as well as carbon, since scientists think that there is a peculiarity in the structure of carbon which makes it particularly effective for microphonic purposes. It was one of Mr. Edison's characteristics, however, that he would not let his own, or any one else's preconceived ideas stand in the way of making a test. This practice certainly led to many futile experiments, but it is equally true that it led to some successful discoveries which caused the scientists to revise their earlier ideas. Edison was not ignorant of what others had done, even though he often appeared to pay little attention to it. A great reader, frequently, before starting, he read everything which had been published on the subject.

Typical of another method of Mr. Edison's work were experiments on flame throwers and on submarine periscopes. The flame thrower was desired to throw a stream of liquid as far as possible. In order to get the right design of nozzle Mr. Edison instructed one of his helpers to build in his shop a whole series of nozzles with every gradation of angle, length and shape within wide limits, and to pick out the one which threw the stream the farthest.

In the case of the submarine periscope the problem was to prevent the deposit from evaporated salt water spray from rendering the periscope mirror non-reflecting. To prevent this several things were tried, one being to bathe the mirror periodically with materials of very low surface tension, which would prevent the accumulation of water in drops. For this purpose a whole series of liquids was tried and the most satisfactory one selected.

These last two war problems illustrate the method of continual search and trial which underlay much of Edison's work. Notable examples are found in his selection of elements for the Edison storage battery and in his preparation of more than 10,000 double chemical salts in the endeavor to find the most satisfactory fluorescent screen for use with x-rays.

It is a mistake, however, to think that all Edison's work was carried on by this search and trial method. Back of everything which he did or tried there was always an idea. The starting point was always the need of accomplishing some purpose, the second stage seemed to be the suggestion of various ways of accomplishing that purpose, and the final stage consisted in trying out these suggested solutions in as thorough and systematic a manner as possible in order to find the best.

Edison's success lay, I believe, equally in his handling of all three of these stages. He was uncommonly alert to opportunities for supplying a need or presenting an improvement. He was uncommonly ingenious in figuring out ways of designing apparatus to do what he wanted it to do, and he was one of the most patient and persevering men who ever lived in carrying through his ideas to the last stage of comprehensive test.

There are some who think that the day of the inventor of Mr. Edison's type has passed because of the continually greater and greater degree of specialization and scientific background which is demanded. Whether or not this is true, it is certainly true that the talents which Mr. Edison possessed are talents which will always find their outlet in creative service.

5. New Weapons, 1919

WILLIAM L. SIBERT, "Innovations of the Recent War"

Poison gas was among the many innovations made in warfare between 1914 and 1918. The barbarity and futility of gas warfare paralleled the nature of the war itself. At the same time, it also represented one of the increasing number of areas in which only trained technical people could make any real contributions to either offense or defense. The drive to invent and produce poison gases was only one of the stimulants to the rise of an American chemical industry, but it served to highlight that rise for many Americans. General Sibert, then director of the Chemical Warfare Service, spoke on the actual effects of gas warfare in 1919.

From William L. Sibert, "Innovations of the Recent War," *Journal of the Cleveland Engineering Society,* XI (March-May 1919), 273-81. Reprinted by permission of the Cleveland Engineering Society.

This war has brought into existence many innovations, among them of course is the use of gas, and in my talk this evening I purpose to touch upon these innovations, whether chemical or not.

Readers of the progress of the war have undoubtedly been impressed with the fact that in nearly all of these innovations Germany took the lead, not because she had more initiative or more ability, chemical or otherwise, than other nations, but because she had studied these problems in time of peace and was prepared for war. Of course as the war progressed the other nations began to do original things, and even surpassed Germany in those things for which she herself was responsible. The point that I wish to make is that preparation for modern war with its complicated requirements, gives any nation a great advantage for the first eighteen months or two years—time sufficient, in the majority of cases, to win a war. At the time of the armistice this country was just coming into volume production on the absolute essentials of war material, such as guns, projectiles, etc., very little of which ever reached the front, and one can well imagine our fate had no ally been able to supply our needs.

Had not Germany known beforehand how to draw from the air her nitrogen supply, and actually built plants for doing it, her days of resistance would have been limited by her accumulated stocks. What would have been our condition had our communication with Chili been cut, with no reserve supply and no plants for making the essential elements in powder manufacture? Between April, 1917, and November, 1918, 3,644,443 tons of nitrates passed through the Panama Canal. Does it not all emphasize the fact that in modern war chemical preparedness is the most important element of all? A single chemical discovery, with preparations to produce, kept secret until the day of war, might almost determine the victor.

In the beginning of hostilities the first things that appeared out of the ordinary were the extended use of machine guns and the use of longer range, larger calibered guns in the field. This extensive use of machine guns, firing from hastily prepared positions, covered in front by barbed wire, was so destructive to life that it soon became apparent that a position so defended could not be taken by direct infantry attack with the ordinary artillery support. The machine gun has done more to determine the trend of changes in military appliances than any other thing in this war.

This combination of machine gun and barbed wire led to revolutionizing artillery methods. It became necessary to destroy the barbed wire by high explosive shells, and to demolish the trenches and machine gun emplacements by high explosives. Then an infantry attack could be made following closely behind a rolling barrage of artillery, thus holding the enemy in his dugouts until the attacking force was from 50 to 100 yards from such dugouts. This artillery preparation meant expenditures of immense amounts of ammunition; it meant segregating the artillery of many units into an attack on a short part of the front; it meant an advance of only a short distance; it meant local attacks, local objectives, and little progress. This kind of warfare characterized the fighting in general through the year 1917, and was made necessary by the machine gun.

Toward the end of this year, however, a new development received its first serious trial at Cambrai, and that was the tank. This tank could mash down or tear out barbed wire; could carry machine guns and small calibered cannon into the enemy's trenches. This could be done quickly, and thus be a surprise.

The next development, insofar as the tank was concerned, and which development afterwards received general application was the covering of the enemy's front line with smoke so that he could not see the tanks and troops coming forward in the attack. This smoke screen was one of the bigger developments of the Chemical Warfare Service of the belligerent nations. It is a great saver of life. It not only closes the eyes of the infantrymen in the front line, and causes them to shoot at general instead of specific targets, but by it the eyes of the artillerymen are closed by covering their observation stations with smoke, so that they cannot see new targets or control their fire on old ones. . . .

Chlorine was first used in April, 1915, at Ypres, in the form of a cloud emitted from cylinders. It was a complete surprise, and had it been followed closely by infantry attacks the results would have been most disastrous. The German did not appreciate the moral and physical effect of the first gas cloud on unprotected troops, and apparently was not willing to risk his own soldiers in the gassed area soon enough. In many of the inventions that changed the character of fighting in this war, the inventor launched his invention on too small a scale, and hence lost the surprise effect on a scale that might have turned the tide of war. Chlorine is easily stopped. A cloth bandage steeped with sodium hyposulphite placed over the mouth and nose gives fair protection. This, however, gives no protection to the eyes. The Germans knowing this began immediately to develop lachrymators. This led to the gas mask with its eyepieces. The ease with which chlorine was stopped led to the development of other gases more difficult to stop, such as phosgene and chlorpicrin. And thus commenced a struggle between offensive gas and defensive appliances similar to that that has been forever waged between armor-piercing shells and the protective armor of ships.

The research man on the offensive side is continually trying to find some substance that will penetrate the enemy's gas mask, while the research man on the defensive side is trying to find something that will defend the wearer against any new substance that he or anyone else can develop. The result of such a struggle is that as long as both sides use the same kinds of gas, each side will have a mask that will give relatively good protection, if the wearer gets it on in time. That has been the condition for the last year. And, since man's ingenuity will find some protection against anything, if given time, the surprise effect of a new gas or a new tactical use of gas brings the greatest results. . . .

. . . The next great development after the tank, operating in connection with smoke screens, was the tactical, almost strategical use of gas by the Germans in the spring of 1918.

Large quantities of gas had been accumulated during the winter, gases that were well known. The surprise was the unprecedented amount of gas used, and the new tactics adopted in such use. Before the spring of 1918 gas had had only a local use, and had been only a minor element in planning a battle. Its most effective general use had been in forcing the enemy artillery into gas masks.

In a continuous line like that which existed on the Western Front in Europe there are strong points with intermediate weak sections. These strong points are ordinarily high ground, often wooded ground, on which are splendid observation stations, and from which guns can enfilade the weaker parts of the line lying between the strong points. These strong points are the parts of the line that ordinarily hold. They are the key points, and as long as they can deliver their expected fire, the line cannot be taken.

With a large accumulation of gas a plan was adopted by the Germans of saturating with mustard gas these strong points for two or three days before the attack. Mustard gas is a very persistent gas, and soldiers cannot remain many hours where it is present, even though they have good masks, as mustard gas penetrates the clothes. In addition, the road centers five and six miles in the rear, through which the reserves and various supplies would necessarily travel during a battle, were also saturated with mustard gas. The actual attack was made between the strong points, the attacking troops not passing through the areas saturated with mustard gas. In the drive striking at the rear of the English position at Ypres, mustard oil actually ran in the streets of Armentiere. In addition to the above use of a persistent gas, the towns and cantonments occupied by troops on the flanks of the part of the line to be attacked were drenched with gas, rendering the troops largely inert during the attack.

The preliminary bombardment on the parts of the line to be attacked was limited to about six hours, during the first four hours of which high explosive shells and a nonpersistent gas were used, generally phosgene, which gas is ordinarily dissipated in about an hour's time. For the two hours just before the advance high explosive shells only were used, together with a little fake gas without toxicity, thus keeping the Allies in gas masks while the Germans went into the fight unhandicapped by masks. This, in general, was the plan followed in the spring drive of 1918 by the Germans, and came very near succeeding. This was carried out in connection with the smoke screens previously described. The exhaustion of the reserve gas supply of the Germans was one of the greatest elements in turning the war in favor of the Allies. Once turned, the continual addition of American troops maintained a superiority that won.

There are three substances used in producing smoke screens, namely, phosphorus, sulphur trichloride, and titanium tetrachloride. To give an idea of one of the easier problems that was put up to the Chemical Engineer of the United States in well known substances, such as phosphorus, the total production of the United States prior to the war was about 40 tons a month, whereas the finally adopted program for the anticipated campaign in the spring of 1919, involved a phosphorus consumption of about 400 tons a month, ten times the normal production, and everything indicated that the chemical engineering talent of the country would have met the situation. And this was one of the least difficult of the problems to be solved. The chlorine supply was quadrupled. The only thing that came easy was the alcohol needed in making the ethylene used in mustard gas manufacture. Many idle distilleries were available.

To give you a glimpse of some of the minor details, but important in the work of the Chemical Warfare Service, a smoke shell filled with phosphorus, for instance, must have a bursting charge to break open the shell and properly dissipate the phosphorus. If that charge be too great, it throws the phosphorus so high in the air that the cloud is above the ground and fails in its function. If the shell is not properly broken, and the lower half of it remains a cup, it goes on into the ground taking with it about half of the phosphorus.

And, with steel varying with the different manufacturers, and the different heats or runs of the same manufacturer, you can see what a problem the determination of such a little thing as the booster charge of a shell is, and how much experimentation is necessary in order to arrive at the exact specification for the steel of the shell, and the exact amount of the exact kind of explosive material necessary in the booster charge itself. Every gas was a problem in itself in this respect, and the Proving Ground at Lakehurst, New Jersey, was one of the most active fields in the Chemical Warfare Service. This is mentioned in order to show the immense amount of detail work that had to be done before the tactics of gas warfare could be determined, which problem involved finding out the number of shells of each gas needed to produce a lethal concentration in a certain area. This could be done only by tethering goats, dogs and other animals in the area in question, and deduce from the effect the gas had on the animal what effect it would have had on man; the gas shell being fired under war conditions. And I want to say that our Society for the Prevention of Cruelty to Animals stood the test like patriots.

In both its offensive and defensive operations, the policy followed by the Chemical Warfare Service was to devise methods to put into manufacture substances or appliances that the operations in Europe had shown to be satisfactory, and not to embark into a purely experimental field. For instance, the English mask was first adopted with its mouth-piece and its nose-clip. It was known that this mask would give protection. At that time the principal idea seemed to be that if an area were heavily gassed, the principal function of the gas mask was to keep the men in such area alive until the gas was dissipated. So this mask was put into volume production, and work was started to improve it in every line, to improve its charcoal, to improve its fit and to improve every detail of it without stopping volume production.

As the war progressed it became evident that soldiers could not expect to sit quietly during gas attacks, but they must undertake offensive movements through gas. This started a struggle for the best fighting gas mask, one that impeded a man the least and still gave protection.

Extended physical exertion required as small a resistance to breathing as possible, and still keep protection. It required a preservation of the vision, which meant that the eye-pieces must be kept clear; it required that the apparatus worn should interfere least with the man's use of his weapons, etc., etc. This meant extended physiological tests, and practical tests of all kinds, which in the end led to the development of the best fighting gas mask of the war.

One of the leaders in the fundamental and practical research which led to our "fighting gas mask" was Major Roy Gentry Pearce, a physician of your city. He volunteered his services and was afterward commissioned in the Chemical Warfare Service. This mask was just coming into volume production, about 400,000 having been made, at the time of the Armistice. It had no mouth-piece, and no nose-clip, leaving the man free to breathe naturally. It adopted the principle of the French Tissot in that the air was brought inside of the face-piece through tubes which delivered such air immediately behind the eye-pieces, keeping the temperature on both sides of the eye-piece practically the same, and thus preventing fogging and preserving the soldier's vision.

At the time of the Armistice every American soldier was wearing an American-made gas mask. It gave better protection than any other mask in Europe. He would have had the same protection in the best fighting mask in Europe in a few months more.

To look at a simple gas mask one thinks that it could be made without difficulty, but if one would read and study the experiments that were made on one single item, charcoal, in which experiments and investigations our friend Colonel Dorsey here was the leader, the magnitude of the task of the entire mask can be appreciated. I understand that it will take about seven volumes to record the work done by our various research men on charcoal. The material for the charcoal for these masks, as you know, came from all corners of the world, especially the tropical world. The best material available was the cocoanut shells, then came the peach seed, etc. Our scientists were fast working to a synthetic charcoal.

But one little talk cannot go into this great subject fully. It can only be a reconnaissance if applied to the whole field. Those who are especially interested in the particular phases of the work had best consult the monographs that will be printed in all cases where the information is not too secret, and where the industries could profit by the disclosure of such information.

While there was gathered together at the American University probably one of the most competent research organizations that the world has ever seen, and while it was continually delving into new fields of chemical mystery, searching for new substances, the plan was adopted to devise means for making those gases that had actually been used in Europe, the effects of which were well known, before any attempt was made to develop any of the newer ideas and newer discoveries. In connection with the Research Division was a Development Division, the headquarters of which was in Cleveland, and the function of which was to devise quick methods of doing new things on a big scale. In the beginning, the Gas Production Division and the Development Division often worked along the same lines, both having the same object in view. The ingenuity of the American chemical engineer was matched against the ingenuity of the engineer in other Allied countries in devising quickly means of producing in large quantities the standard gases, such as phosgene, chlorpicrin and mustard gas.

Mustard gas was first used in Europe in July, 1917, after we had entered the war. European nations had already commenced the manufacture of other gases, and were already developing chemical appliances that would aid or assist in the manufacture of any gas. Our people started later than any of the Allies, but were producing at the time that the Armistice was signed all the gases, and especially mustard gas, at a far greater rate than any other nation. In fact we were making it at a greater rate than England, France and Germany combined. It is unfortunate that none of our gas was fired at the enemy in our own shells, due to delays, for which the chemists were not responsible, in the development of shells with their booster casing and other parts incident to the use of gas. There was, however, manufactured and shipped to Europe and actually fired at the Germans in shells of foreign make, more American-made gas than the American Army used in its hostile operations against the enemy. The larger part of this gas was sold to the Allies. The output at the time of the Armistice would have been more than doubled by January 1, 1919, and in addition some of our own inventions were just coming into volume production. A wave of disappointment passed over the Chemical Warfare Service when the Armistice came. One always likes to try out a new appliance under the conditions for which it was designed.

The great tactical divisions of gases are persistent and nonpersistent. In the first class mustard is prominent. Its volatility is low, and its effects last especially in woods for several days. It is used in those parts of the line that are not to be immediately traversed by the armies using it. In defensive warfare its use is only limited by the amount available. The non-persistent gas is more toxic in its immediate effect, only lasts a short time, and will dissipate sufficiently to enable troops to go over the area where it is used within an hour or so's time after it is used. There are, in addition to these tactical classes, classifications such as lachrymators, sneeze gases, etc. The research man is of course trying at all times to get as many persistent gases and as many nonpersistent gases as possible, thus obtaining something new, without interfering with the tactical classifications, which, by its surprise effect, will either catch the enemy unawares or with a mask that will not stop the new substance.

A great many people thought that it would not do to hedge the mind of the research chemist by any military restriction, but I have found that some limitation is necessary with the research man. Each thing leads to the hope of something better, something different, and someone must say "this is good enough," "we will put it in manufacture," or "you will have three weeks more to perfect it." The research man quickly appreciated the fact that he was working for this war and not for the next, and he met the situation. . . .

The gas troops in the field had a similar problem presented to them that the chemical engineer had presented in this country, and that was to do something new, and to do it effectively. The first troops organized in the United States for this purpose were known as the "Gas and Flame Troops." The use of the flame projector, however, was so limited in its scope, such a short ranged thing, that it was soon practically abandoned. The work of the gas troops was confined in the beginning to delivering gas to the enemy from cylinders in the form of clouds, and by means of projectors or crude mortars.

The gas cylinders used in the cloud attack, or the crude mortars or projectors that were used, were carried by hand during the night through to the front line trenches. Trenches were dug. Into them these instruments were fitted, the whole position camouflaged during the intervening days and the work prosecuted until the time was ripe for the delivery of the gas to the enemy.

Of course in the case of the gas cloud the wind had to be right in direction and velocity, but in the case of the projectors they were fired as soon as they were ready. These projectors, sometimes as many as two thousand in a bunch, each delivered about 30 pounds of gas and were all fired at once by electricity, which meant the delivery of 30 tons of gas in a flash, and which arrived in such concentration as to kill before gas masks could be put on. These projector attacks were much feared by the enemy. Any indication developed by the aerial photographs as to preparations for a projector-attack or a cylinder attack, resulted in a terrific artillery bombardment that had for its object the complete destruction of the trenches and outfit being installed, showing that the work of the gas troops in the field was exceedingly dangerous and in keeping with that done by his fellow workers in the preparation of the toxic materials at home.

After the operations of war began to change from the trench warfare system to open warfare methods, the infantry going forward greater depths encountered machine gun nests that stopped their progress and which could not be located by the artillery. To meet this situation gas troops again came to the front, going over the top with the infantry, provided with light Stokes mortars and shells loaded with phosphorus, thermite or gas, attacked these machine gun nests, gassing them, covering them with smoke, or terrorizing them with thermite at ranges from 800 to 1600 yards. But like all new services, the transportation needs were not developed beforehand and the work was exceedingly hard, but reports from the front indicate that it was well done.

6. The Philosopher-Kings, 1919

F. H. NEWELL, "Effect of the War on Engineering and Industry"

During World War I the Progressives undertook one of the greatest of their crusades. For moralists the war presented another opportunity to eradicate evil and confirm American virtue; for those who sought to make American society more efficient, it presented an example of how bad conditions were and a unique opportunity for improvement; for engineers, it was a chance to

From F. H. Newell, "The Engineer's Part in After-the-War Problems," *Scientific Monthly*, VIII (March 1919), 239-46. Reprinted by permission of *Science* and the American Association for the Advancement of Science.

apply on the national level of government those techniques of efficient management that were already being applied on the local level of government and in the large industrial plants of the nation.

Technical people came out of the war both disillusioned by the fact that they had been ignored in Washington, and exhilarated by their renewed belief in their own mission. Frederick H. Newell, was a professor at the University of Illinois in 1919, but he had been one of the major architects of the government's conservation program and was one of the great Progressives of the time. He wrote an article for the *Scientific Monthly* on the postwar responsibilities of the engineers.

The engineer—as his designation implies—is the man of ingenuity, the man who has a vision of the future and who, without being visionary, can see and devise methods of producing results by utilizing the forces and resources of nature. His business is to plan and build. During the war his was the task of devising ways of protecting friends and destroying enemies. Now, with peace assured, his task is to make ready and get the machinery of construction and operation into full motion again. His part is also that of the pioneer to explore, to conduct researches into realms beyond our present knowledge and with facts thus secured plan out the safe way for others to follow.

In the countries where war has wrought its destruction, the duty of the engineer is primarily to rebuild, but with us, more fortunately situated, where the disturbance has only been relatively small, our part is to wisely provide for larger and better uses of our resources and prepare for the better communities toward which all of us aspire.

While the war has wrought little destruction to us in Illinois, and in fact has, if anything, increased material prosperity, it has "laid its fearfully vitalizing hand upon our people," and

has served to greatly widen their viewpoint. It has made possible the realization of some of those ideals which a few years ago were regarded as impracticable. In other words, the established order has been so far disturbed as to render it wise to urge improvements which before the war seemed to be out of our reach. This has been stated by Winston Churchill, "If for five years after the war the people devoted the same energy, cooperation and self-sacrifice to reconstruction as have been devoted to the process of destruction, there is no social, industrial or economic problem which could not be conquered."

The question confronts us therefore as to how in this present crisis of world affairs the engineer and organizations of engineers, both individually and collectively, can perform their largest service. What are the steps to be taken in order that we may do our full duty as citizens?

It is desirable to emphasize the fact that engineers as a class owe a larger duty to the public than almost any other group. They have been educated largely at public expense and given the opportunity of enjoying a wider outlook upon the forces and activities of nature than have most of our fellows. Because of this fact there rests upon them the obligation to utilize these advantages in the most efficient manner for the general good. They have already shown what they can do under the stimulus of war. Now under peace conditions—which should be even more inspiring—it is for them to demonstrate their continued value to humanity. The question is as to how this can best be performed.

1. *Diffusion of Information.*—Under our form of government any notable advance or improvement must be made largely through the support of the majority of the thinking people. To secure wise action it is obviously necessary that the public be well informed as to the objects to be attained and relative costs and benefits involved. The engineers in short should do everything in their power to diffuse information regarding the matters in which they are skilled in order that the public may be able to act intelligently.

In the past, it must be acknowledged, engineers as a body, particularly as represented by our larger societies, have been remiss in taking the public into their confidence regarding the facts and conclusions to be drawn regarding many important engineering matters. In fact, we have rather prided ourselves upon this condition and upon our close adherence to narrow technical detail. As a consequence not only the public has suffered but the engineering profession even more so in being regarded as technicians; the engineer has been classed in the same group with the engine runner or fireman but without enjoying anything like the influence on public affairs had by the latter.

Our first and foremost part in the after-the-war or reconstruction problems is obviously that of aiding the public through the diffusion of information as to the nature of these problems and their solution since most of them rest upon matters which come mainly within the cognizance of the engineer.

2. *Research.*—Closely connected with the duty of diffusing information is that of encouraging in every practicable way the acquisition of additional information regarding natural resources of the country and the methods of utilizing these. While much is already known there lie in every direction innumerable unanswered or partly answered questions to which it is necessary to obtain complete and satisfactory replies in order that progress may be made. Here engineers individually and collectively have a duty, namely, that of stimulating continued study and research into those conditions which are often assumed by the public to be facts and yet concerning which comparatively little definite information can be had. Most of these present-day problems relate to transportation and its control, to the movement of persons and goods, to better methods of road construction and maintenance, the restoration of navigation, better water supply for towns and industrial establishment. There are innumerable lines in which the engineers and their organizations should be actively at work either directly or in stimulating others.

3. *Preparation of Plans.*—In connection with the diffusion of information and stimulation of research it is incumbent upon the engineers to use the experience and ingenuity with which they are endowed to make general plans and bring before the public the possibilities of larger health, comfort and prosperity. It is true that the details can only be worked out with safety after adequate funds have been provided, but it is

nevertheless possible to outline the picture in a broad way and to keep continually before the people or communities concerned a conception as to what may be done by the use of information possessed by the engineer or which may be had by further study. In reply it may be urged that the busy engineer immersed in the details of his daily work has little time for such matters. Nevertheless, reflection will show that even the busiest must have a certain relaxation and that he will be improved mentally and morally, and possibly gain in a financial way if occasionally he lifts his eyes from his desk and permits his mental vision to take in the larger aspects of the things with which he is familiar. Moreover, the contact with his fellow men in the direction of their vision to the wide scope of engineering possibilities must have a beneficial effect in counteracting the narrowing influences of professional detail.

Reconstruction Problems.—But what are these after-the-war or reconstruction problems? How do they differ from the ordinary routine? In many ways these do not differ but are the culmination and grouping together of many questions which have been before us for a generation but which are now demanding early attention. They take in the whole range of human activity, but may be classified for convenience into three groups in the order of their immediate insistence.

(*a*) Men or man power.

(*b*) Materials or natural resources.

(*c*) Ideals or plans.

(*a*) *Men.*—The immediate and vital question following the war is that of demobilization of the army, providing employment for returning soldiers and war workers and the reconstruction of the crippled or injured men. The latter

is being given attention by the War Department and theoretically at least no man is discharged from the army until he is equipped as far as humanly possible to make a living at some suitable occupation.

This reconstruction of men is the first and most pressing duty, one in which the time element is vital. It began with first aid to the wounded and was continued not merely through hospital service but through reeducation activities or vocational training such that the man injured in the service of his country is restored as completely as possible to health and rendered self-supporting through the use of artificial limbs supplied to him. He is aided by the acquisition of a training in vocational or even in engineering occupations which enables him to become a self-supporting and self-respecting citizen after he has done his part in winning the war.

More than this the reconstruction plans involving the return to industry, in the quickest and best way, of the munitions workers and others who have been employed more or less directly in connection with the war and to do this in such a way as not to interfere with the earnings or proper enjoyment of others who have taken their former places in industry.

The present problem is that of finding work immediately for these men and women who are returning to the industries which have been discontinued or which have not yet come into active operation. Here is demanded not charity nor political discussion but immediate practical action. This can come about in many ways.

1. By urging that each and every employer take on as many people as he can and in spite of present high prices

incur every reasonable business risk in getting his operations under way.

2. In urging public officers and persons having control of expenditures of public or private organizations to undertake at once the works which have been planned or contemplated such as highways, waterways, water supply, drainage systems, public buildings, parks and all those things which benefit the public. In opposition it is urged that there is scarcity of material and prices are high. Even though this be true, it is often possible to substitute materials; even though the prices may be high it is a matter of public economy in the long run that the work be performed now and that an outlet be afforded for labor on things which are ultimately of use.

(b) *Materials.*—In the reconstruction problems having to do with materials there is a far wider diversion of interests and of methods; the first and most vitally important are those things which have to do with food production and transportation. Next in importance are the fuel problems and then the other natural resources such as raw materials needed in manufacturing. Fortunately, the study of these resources, their distribution and best employment in industry has been the subject of investigation by a group of conservationists and engineers who during the past decade aroused interest in these matters. Due to their systematic efforts there has been made by various federal bureaus a beginning upon the systematic collection of data.

Each and every business man and agency needs to be stimulated to larger efforts and to a consideration of the practicability of putting to full use all of his resources whether of raw materials, agricultural products, manufactured articles, or of human or man power. To do this effectively there must be an agreement upon the larger ideals or underlying principles which result in well-considered plans of action.

(c) *Ideals of Reconstruction.*—No far-reaching result can come about from the planning of the use of man power or of raw materials until there has been a general agreement upon fundamental principles. It is true that the working out of these to a form where they will be generally agreed upon may not be accomplished for some months. In the meantime certain details involving employment of men and use of materials may be satisfactorily entered upon. There should be an immediate discussion of ideals even though agreement on the statements of them may not be reached for some time.

On most of the fundamental ideals there will probably be sharp division between two great parties, representing opposing social or political beliefs; it is well that this should be so, and that each ideal should be submitted to the hot fires of discussion.

There are almost innumerable agencies, more or less directly concerned in the practical working out of these ideals. The banking and related industrial interests in general are on the one side—on the other the labor organizations. Each is urging from its own standpoint the adoption of certain policies with reference to the utilization of man power and of materials. Between them is the engineer who must make the plans to put into effect the line of action needed to produce the desired result. He should not be content to be merely the go-between but should guide and direct as may be possible from his relatively disinterested standpoint.

Under the head of ideals or plans

may be grouped many problems whose solution depends upon the policy to be adopted by public and private bodies concerned with labor, commerce, industry, education and economics. These ideals and the problems dependent upon them afford a wide range of speculation or of idealism, but among these needs that of a national labor policy stands prominent as the prime requisite for reconstruction; and next to this, land, taxation and raw materials.

Dean Davenport has well stated that we are to address ourselves to the evolution of a real democracy.

This evolution will submit to society for progressive solution, a series of detailed problems—every one difficult and every one coordinated with every other one, but all conditioned by the one object—the highest possible development of the human race. These issues will include such difficult problems as (a) an adequate land policy, (b) sanitary and comfortable housing, (c) good and abundant food, (d) public insurance against preventable or curable diseases for public reasons, (e) universal and free education that really educates, (f) economic opportunity, (g) industry and thrift either optional or enforced, (h) adequate provision for the helpless, (i) a clean public service, (j) a rational conception as between the individual and state, and between public and private ownership.

There are a thousand related questions, local, national and international that will thrust themselves upon us for adjustment and more than that for readjustment, for we shall have the power to see only a little way at a time along the road that we shall then be traveling.

Each of these policies is usually considered by the persons interested as a separate entity and one which may be discussed by itself. This is where danger lies to the country as a whole, namely, in that with lack of full information, there is inability on the part of the public to mentally visualize the relative proportions of each topic. For example, the settlement of soldiers upon reclaimed lands, important in itself, may lead to the obscuring of larger needs and to divert attention to the detriment of the best interests of the country as a whole. It is exceedingly important, therefore, that all of these problems be catalogued together and be viewed as a whole—as well as in detail.

It is the engineer who must supply many of the facts and conclusions upon which the policies may be based. Some of the subjects above enumerated fall entirely within his cognizance, especially those pertaining to land, to housing and to the discovery and use of the natural resources.

Without the intelligent direction of the engineer, little progress can be made. The great war has awakened Americans to the fact that in their somewhat complacent attitude of mind they had permitted European nations, especially Germany, to far outstrip them, with the result that when war came suddenly upon us, we were compelled to lose time, and directly or indirectly sacrifice thousands of lives and millions of dollars in accumulated wealth because of our short-sighted policy with reference to engineering and to scientific research along engineering lines.

The whole subject of raw materials is also one which can be attacked successfully only by the engineer, including with these materials not only iron, copper, clay, petroleums and other substances from the earth, but also the fuels and other sources of power, such as from the flowing waters.

The engineer's problems of to-day also include that of transportation, not merely the building and operating of railroads, waterways and highways, and the cars or boats moving on these, but also the navigation of the air and all of the matters which lead up to successful performance.

Next in importance comes the means of communication—the telephone, the telegraph, the wireless, and closely connected with these the rapidly increasing number of public utilities, founded primarily on engineering plans and methods. It has been the fashion to leave the larger control of these to business men and lawyers, but the time is arriving when the engineer is appreciated to be the chief factor in their success.

In agriculture also the engineer has entered, and with the increasing demand for food, his skill is being more and more called upon, not only in developing agricultural machinery, but in building irrigation and drainage systems, in clearing lands, and in directing operations in a large way. In housing problems the engineer, as well as the architect, must direct affairs. Even in education and the diffusion of intelligence, the operations are becoming more and more closely connected with the principles of engineering.

In all of these matters which pertain to the conservation and use of the resources of the country, both material and human, and the development of ideals, the engineer should be active; while his profession may not include

the direct control of capital and credit, of foreign and domestic trade, of agricultural distribution, and of many purely business questions, yet he is, or should be, such a factor in the fundamentals of these that his knowledge and skill can not safely be neglected.

Assuming that the above statements of the engineer's part in after-the-war problems are approximately correct, then comes the question as to what he and his organization should do in the present crisis of world affairs. The reply seems obvious that as an individual he should take an active part in these world problems. Every engineering society should have its committee on reconstruction, charged with the duty of arranging for effective presentation of one or another of these great subjects of employment of labor, research, study of raw materials, or fuels, power, transportation, public utilities and other matters, all of which are undergoing radical changes. The trend of these should be studied and the influence of the engineer as an individual should be wisely used.

Each society under this conception has a great duty and responsibility to its members and through them to the public. The standing of the engineering profession in the near future must be determined largely by the wisdom of the action taken now in approaching these great problems of reconstruction.

PART XI THE BUSINESS DECADE

Science and engineering rose to new heights of achievement during the 1920's. In part this was because of the record they had made during the war. In part it was because they were able to identify themselves closely with the nation's business interests, which were also enjoying an era of unprecedented dominance. Scientists and engineers took great pains to demonstrate that it was they who were, in large part, responsible for the prosperity of the decade.

They could make a good case. Whole industries, the chemical, petroleum, and electrical industries, among others, were absolutely dependent upon technical people for both production and product innovation. In these and other major industries, such as the automobile industry, the technologies involved were so complex and sophisticated that only highly trained technicians could keep them operating. Some industries owed their very inception to scientific technology; many more depended upon research laboratories to produce innovations; most found an increasing need for trained engineers to work out production methods.

At the same time, America was virtually being rebuilt. The burgeoning automobile industry stimulated the federal and state governments to launch a massive road-building program which was to provide the country, for the first time, with an adequate system of highways. During these same years the downtown areas of many American cities were transformed by the erection of skyscrapers, and in the suburbs housing tracts and the first of the shopping centers were built. It was a decade in which men who "got things done" were looked up to.

Although a few intellectuals worried about the fact that the Western frontier was closed, the nation's scientists and engineers were busily exploiting the frontiers of technology—building the roads and the cities, and bringing electrical power and tractors to the farms and a vast flood of intricate consumer goods to the homes of America. If men like President Herbert Hoover, who had a degree in mining engineering, looked forward to perpetual growth and prosperity, it was because they saw technology creating new frontiers of economic opportunity as each old frontier was tamed.

1. An Infant Industry, 1918

ROBERT HILTON, "The Maintenance and Preservation of
Our Dyestuff Industries"

One of the most dramatic industrial effects of World War I was the growth of the American chemical industry. While it would be inaccurate to say that there had been no such industry in this country prior to 1914, the need to replace German chemicals (cut off by the British blockade) gave American manufacturers an incentive to expand and diversify their production, especially of dyestuffs. The industry was hardly an "infant" in 1919, but it was loath to give up the virtual monopoly on the domestic market that it had held during the war.

The eventually successful campaign to win a high protective tariff for chemicals was supported even by those professional societies which normally shied away from "politics" and concentrated on purely technical questions. A high tariff on chemicals was finally provided by the Fordney-McCumber tariff, passed by the business-oriented Republican Congress in 1922.

So much has already been written about the preservation of our Chemical Industries that I doubt if I can add anything new: But there are certain phases of the situation that may bear emphasis. As my interest and experience lie directly in the Dyestuff Industry I will confine my remarks to this branch of chemical manufacture.

I take it that we all agree on the premise that the dyestuff industry in the United States must be conserved at all cost. We are familiar with Germany's attitude towards the establishment and growth of the dyestuff industry outside of Germany. We know something about her post-war plans, her combination, for a period of 50 years, of all her dyestuff industries and her determination to dominate the world markets. We recognize the immense advantages Germany enjoys as

From Robert Hilton, "The Maintenance and Preservation of Our Dyestuff Industries," *Transactions of the American Institute of Chemical Engineers*, XI (1918), 281-84. Reprinted by permission.

the result of her forty years of activity in this field. We sense deeply the Prussian spirit which will do everything and anything, regardless of morality, to bring about the ends she seeks and we know that Germany will not meekly give up without a great fight an industry that has netted her millions of dollars every year.

How are we to meet this situation? we who are rooted to the individualistic idea in industry and our laws forbidding combinations while our German competitors are compelled to operate as a unit. If the dyestuff industry were a much less complicated one, involving few products and a limited capital, we would not be at this great disadvantage. The dyestuff industry is of such a nature that I doubt if a number of individual manufacturers without a sanctioned governmental agreement as to prices, output, etc., could exist in the long run and build up a great industry.

In my opinion outside help is therefore necessary and this help can come only from our government.

The first necessary step would be to shut out the German products by high tariff and by the system of licensing advocated by Great Britain.

The framing of adequate tariff legislation has proven to be so difficult, owing to the divers and complicated processes of dye manufacture, that Great Britain has about given up this idea and has concentrated its efforts on a licensing system which would shut out the importation of all such dyes that are made in Great Britain, but would allow the importation of dyes not made at home and those of which an insufficient amount is produced. Furthermore Great Britain, through its Board of Trade, intends to make considerable loans at favorable rates for the building up of the industry.

Let us consider for a moment what has been done here in the States to help our industry. The recent slight tariff increase on dyes brought about by a Democratic administration in itself is noteworthy and commendable, but it will in no way help the industry because it is absolutely inadequate, especially so if undervaluation for tariff purposes is allowed to go on as it has in the past. An increase in the tariff rate, unless it be so high as to amount to prohibition, will do but little good. In my opinion the example set by Great Britain is the one to follow and every effort should be made to have Congress recognize the soundness of the licensing principle.

Prof. Taussig, in his talk before the Dyestuff Manufacturer's Association, warned the manufacturers not to place before Congress any radical measures, such as the Licensing System may be considered, for fear that such proposals would not be received with favor. With all deference to Prof. Taussig, it seems to me that the dyestuff situation here in the States is in a precarious condition and radical methods must be adopted to save a key and pivotal industry necessary to the welfare of the nation, an industry in which over $100,000,000 has been invested and which indirectly controls the labor of over 2,000,000 men.

A negative attitude on the part of the Tariff Commission for fear that a necessary radical measure may not carry does not inspire confidence and tends to bring about defeat. The licensing system, in the minds of some of our best thinkers, gives greater promise than any form of tariff legislation and besides this we have Great Britain's example. May we not therefore suggest to our Tariff Commission a more positive stand

and advocate a radical measure where a radical measure is absolutely necessary. Congressmen are human and are actuated by good impulses of a positive nature, but a wavering, fearsome and negative attitude will never bring results. The suspension, or at least the modification, of the Sherman Anti-Trust Law, allowing trade agreements and the fixing of prices under government control, would do much to stabilize the industry. It is hard to reconcile the fact that products made under Trust or Kartel control are allowed to be sold in competition with products manufactured in the United States when our laws prohibit Trusts and Kartels. If Congress would pass a law prohibiting the importation of articles manufactured under Trust control it would do much to place our dye industry on a firm basis. To my mind this suggestion has not been exploited enough, commensurate with its obvious importance to industry.

If Congress in its wisdom should decide to put up the necessary barriers to the importation of dyestuffs, it should still further protect the industry by prohibiting German firms from engaging in the manufacture of dyestuffs here in the United States, and assume the same attitude that Germany has taken in her own courts in not allowing any industry to thrive there which may work counter to her national welfare.

The fear has been expressed that if the United States would put up a tariff wall against Germany, Germany would discriminate against us in the matter of potash, the monopoly of which she has enjoyed for many years. France, since her acquisition of Alsace-Lorraine, is now in a position to supply us with all the potash we may want at favorable rates and the German potash monopoly

no longer exists. In this respect the restitution of Alsace to France concerned deeply all the Allies and not France alone.

It has been said that science knows no frontiers. This would be true as an absolute proposition, leaving contingencies out of account, and it would have been true if the lust of military autocracy, of conquest, and of the absorption and subjection of other nations had not made of science an instrument of abuse, of despotism, and of violence in the hands of a predatory race. The Central Empires have naturally distorted the spirit and the mission of true science, the mother of progress. Under the name of "Kultur" they have associated it with unbridled barbarism, making it an accomplice of the worst excesses.

To the true American there must be a complete severance from Germany in all relations and we must look to our government to bring this about, not only as punishment for their hideous crimes, but as a mark of respect and honor to the men who have given up their lives to the cause of freedom.

If the dye industry in the United States, through the help of the government, may develop itself to the extent that fair profits would result, the means would be at hand for scientific research, the value of which we as chemists fully recognize in the upbuilding of any industry. The American chemist will put the same pep into research that the manufacturers have put into their methods of production, but we must first be assured of the necessary profits to furnish the means for the cost of research work.

The Webb-Pomerene Bill will undoubtedly do much to help our export trade. An extension of the provisions of this bill, allowing collective buying as well as collective selling, may be of great help to certain chemical industries.

The revision of our Patent Laws should be taken up at once so that the practice of preventing the development of discoveries can no longer be possible.

In conclusion let me emphasize the fact that legislation for the welfare of a key industry necessary to the well-being of a nation should not be considered as a political measure in opposition or in accord with the principles of either of the great parties—it should be looked upon wholly and solely as a means for the preservation of our nation.

2. Science Aids Industry, 1913

ARTHUR D. LITTLE, "Industrial Research in America"

Late in the nineteenth century, the chemical and electrical industries—and, indeed, all the industries that had developed from the scientific discoveries of the preceding century—began to concentrate on systematic industrial research. This linking of science and technology has been largely responsible for the dramatic technical innovations of this century; innovations so sweeping that it almost might be said we are going through a second industrial revolution.

On the eve of World War I, the nation that seemed to understand the usefulness of science best was Germany. But institutions were already forming in the United States to bring science to the service of industry—universities, government, and above all, industrial research laboratories. Arthur D. Little, who had established his research-for-hire firm as far back as 1886, was an acknowledged leader in the crusade to spread the gospel of research in this country.

Germany has long been recognized as preeminently the country of organized research. The spirit of research is there imminent throughout the entire social structure. This is not the time nor place, however, nor is it necessary before this audience, to refer in any detail to the long record of splendid achievement made by German research during the last fifty years. It is inscribed in lumi-

From Arthur D. Little, "Industrial Research in America," *Science*, XXXVIII (November 7, 1913), 643-45, 648-53, 655-56. Reprinted by permission of *Science* and the American Association for the Advancement of Science.

nous letters around the rock upon which Germany now stands secure among the nations of the world.

The virility and range of German research were never greater than they are to-day. Never before have the superb energy and calculated audacity of German technical directors and German financiers transformed so quickly and so surely the triumphs of the laboratory into industrial conquests. Never has the future held richer promise of orderly and sustained progress, and yet the pre-eminence of Germany in industrial research is by no means indefinitely assured. A new competitor is even now girding up his loins and training for the race, and that competitor is strangely enough the United States—that prodigal among nations, still justly stigmatized as the most wasteful, careless and improvident of them all.

To one at all familiar with the disdain of scientific teaching which has characterized our industry, and which still persists in many quarters, this statement is so contrary to the current estimate that its general acceptance can not be expected. It will have served its purpose if it leads to a consideration of the facts which prove the thesis.

The country of Franklin, Morse and Rumford; of McCormick, Howe and Whitney; of Edison, Thomson, Westinghouse and Bell; and of Wilbur and Orville Wright, is obviously a country not wholly hostile to industrial research or unable to apply it to good purpose. It is, however, not surprising that with vast areas of virgin soil of which a share might be had for the asking; with interminable stretches of stately forest; with coal and oil and gas, the ores of metals and countless other gifts of nature scattered broadcast by her lavish hand, our people entered upon this rich inheritance with the spirit of the spendthrift, and gave little heed to refinements in methods of production and less to minimizing waste. That day and generation is gone. To-day, their children, partly through better recognition of potential values, but mainly by the pressure of a greatly increased population and the stress of competition among themselves and in the markets of the world, are rapidly acquiring the knowledge that efficiency of production is a sounder basis for prosperity than mere volume of product, however great. Many of them have already learned that the most profitable output of their plant is that resulting from the catalysis of raw materials by brains. A far larger number are still ignorant of these fundamental truths, and so it happens that most of our industrial effort still proceeds under the guidance of empiricism with a happy disregard of basic principles. A native ingenuity often brings it to a surprising success and seems to support the aphorism "Where ignorance is profitable, 'tis folly to be wise." Whatever may be said, therefore, of industrial research in America at this time is said of a babe still in the cradle but which has nevertheless, like the infant Hercules, already destroyed its serpents and given promise of its performance at man's estate. . . .

The name of Edison is a household word in every language. The Edison method is a synonym for specialized, intense research which knows no rest until everything has been tried. Because of that method and the unique genius which directs its application, Italian operas are heard amid Alaskan snows and in the depths of African forests; every phase of life and movement of interest throughout the world is caught, registered, transported and reproduced that we may have lion hunts in our drawing-rooms and the coronation in a five-cent theater. From his laboratory have come the incandescent lamp, multiple telegraphy, new methods of treating ores and a thousand other diverse inventions, the development of a single one of which has sometimes involved millions.

The development of the automobile, and especially of the low-priced American car, is a thing of yesterday. Today a single manufacturer turns out two cars a minute, while another is expanding his output to 500 cars a day. Every 23 days the total engine horsepower of new cars of one small type equals the energy of the entire Mississippi river development at Keokuk. Every 46 days this engine output rises to the total energy development at Niagara Falls. The amount of gasoline consumed upon our roads is equal to the water supply of a town of 40,000 inhabitants, and its cost on Sundays and holidays is $1,000,000.

It goes without saying that any such development as that of the automobile industry in America has been based upon and vitalized by an immeasurable amount of research, the range and influence of which extends through many other industries. It has accelerated the application of heat treatment more than any other agency. One tire manufacturer spends $100,000 a year upon his laboratory. The research department organized by my associates for one automobile company comprised within its staff of experts in automobile design, mathematics, metallography and heat treatments, lubrication, gaseous fuels, steel and alloys, paints and painting practise, in addition to the chemists, physicists and assistants for routine or special work.

The beautiful city whose hospitality has so greatly added to the pleasure and success of the present meeting of our society is the home of two highly scientific industries of which any community may well be proud. The Bausch & Lomb Optical Company, through its close affiliation with the world-famed Zeiss works at Jena, renders immediately available in this country the latest results of German optical research. The Eastman Kodak Company is perhaps more generally and widely known than even the Zeiss works, and in capital, organization, value of product and profit of operation will bear comparison with the great German companies whose business is applied science. Like them, it spends money with a lavish hand for the promotion of technical research and for the fundamental investigation of the scientific bases on which its industry rests. As you have happily been made aware, this work is carried on in the superb new research laboratories of the company with an equipment which is probably unrivalled anywhere for its special purposes. The laboratory exemplifies a notable feature in American industrial research laboratories in that it makes provision for developing new processes first on the laboratory scale and then on the miniature factory scale. . . .

Chemistry in America is essentially republican and pragmatic. Most of us believe that the doctrine science for science's sake is as meaningless and mischievous as that of art for art's sake, or literature for literature's sake. These things were made for man, not for themselves, nor was man made for them. Most of us are beginning to realize that the major problems of applied chemistry are incomparably harder of solution than the problems of pure chemistry, and the attack, moreover, must often be carried to conclusion at close quarters under the stress and strain induced by time and money factors. Under these circumstances it should not excite surprise that a constantly rising proportion of our best research is carried on in the laboratories of our great industrial corporations, and nowhere more effectively than in the research laboratory of the General Electric Company under the guidance of . . . Dr. Whitney. As to the laboratory method Dr. Whitney says in a personal letter:

We see a field where it seems as though experimental work ought to put us ahead. We believe that we need to get into the water to learn to swim, so we go in. We start back at the academic end as far as possible, and count on knowing what to do with what we find when we find it. Suppose that we surmise that, in general, combustible insulation material could be improved upon. We try to get some work started on an artificial mica. May be we try to synthesize it and soon come to a purely theoretical question; *e. g.*, is it possible to crystallize such stuff under pressure in equilibrium with water vapor corresponding to the composition of real mica? This may lead a long way and call in a lot of pure chemistry and physical chemistry. Usually we just keep at it, so that if you haven't seen it on the market we're probably at it yet.

In striking contrast to the secrecy maintained between individual workers in large German research laboratories, is the almost universal custom in America to encourage staff discussion. In the General Electric Laboratory, as in many others, the weekly seminars and constant helpful interchange of information has developed a staff unity and spirit which greatly increases the efficiency of the organization and raises that of the individual to a higher power.

Many evenings could profitably be spent in discussing the achievements of this laboratory. Their quality is well indicated by the new nitrogen tungsten lamp, with its one half watt per candle, which combines the great work of Dr. Coolidge on ductile tungsten with the studies of Langmuir and others of the staff on the particular glass and gas and metal which are brought together in this lamp.

Any attempt to adequately present the enormous volume of research work, much of which is of the highest grade, constantly in progress in the many scientific bureaus and special laboratories of the general government or even to indicate its actual extent and range, is of course utterly beyond the limits of my attainments or of your patience. The generous policy of the government toward research is unique in this, that the results are immediately made available to the whole people. Heavy as some of the government reports are, they can not be expected to weigh more than the men who write them. Some, like the "Geochemistry" of F. W. Clarke, are of monumental character. A vast number are monographs embodying real and important contributions to scientific knowledge or industrial practise. Some, as would be expected, are little more than compilations or present the results of trivial or ill-considered research.

The United States is still essentially an agricultural country and agriculture is, in its ultimate terms, applied photochemistry. The value of our farm property is already over $42,000,000,000, and each sunrise sees an added increment of millions. Even small advances in agricultural practise bring enormous monetary returns. The greatest problem before the country is that of developing rural life. While our people still crowd into already congested cities, some are beginning to realize that Long Acre Square is not a wholly satisfying substitute for Long Acre Farm, and to question whether the winding, fern-fringed country roads of Vermont may not be a better national asset than the Great White Way.

Chief, therefore, among the government departments, in the volume of industrial research is of course the Department of Agriculture, which includes within its organization ten great scientific bureaus, each inspired by an intense pragmatism and aggressively prosecuting research in its allotted field. The magnitude of these operations of the department may be inferred from the fact that it spent for printing alone during the fiscal year just ended $490,000. The activities of its army of agents literally cover the earth, and its annual expenditure runs to many millions. The Bureau of Soils, the Bureau of Plant Industry, the Bureau of Animal Industry and the Forest Service have to do with the very foundations of our national existence and prosperity, and their researches have added billions to the national wealth. The Bureau of Chemistry, through its relation to the enforcement of the pure food law and the inspection of meats before interstate shipment, is as ubiquitous in its influence as the morning newspaper and touches the daily life of the people almost as closely. The consumer is by no means the only one benefited by its activities. Manufacturers are protected from the unfair competition of less scrupulous producers. The progress of research is stimulated not only by investigation within the bureau, but by their reaction upon the manufacturers of food prod-

ucts who are rapidly being brought to establish laboratories of their own. The food work of the bureau is supplemented and extended by the laboratories of the state and city boards of health, of which that of Massachusetts has been notable for productive research. Special laboratories within the bureau carry its influence and investigations into other fields as in case of the paper and leather laboratory.

The office of Public Roads of the department, mindful of the fact that less than ten per cent of the total road mileage of the country has ever been improved, maintains a large organization of engineers, chemists and other scientists to conduct investigations and compile data, the ultimate purpose of which is to secure efficiency and economy in the location, construction and maintenance of country roads, highways and bridges.

The research work of the Department of Agriculture is greatly augmented and given local application through the agency of 64 state agricultural experiment stations established for the scientific investigation of problems relating to agriculture. These stations are supported, in part, by federal grants, as from the Hatch and Adams funds, and for the rest by state appropriations. Their present income exceeds $3,000,000. All are well equipped; one of them, California, includes within its plant a superb estate of 5,400 acres with buildings worth $1,000,000.

The station work is organized upon a national basis but deals primarily with the problems of the individual states. The efficiency of their work is stimulated by the requirement of the Adams Fund that appropriation shall be confined to definite projects. The number of such projects during 1910 was 335 and during 1911, 290. The reduction in number in no way implies diminished activity, and is due to more careful selection and preparation, with elimination of trivial and merely demonstrational projects. While the work of the stations necessarily covers a wide range of subjects, many of which would not be regarded as chemical in nature, a notable proportion has to do directly with chemical projects. . . .

The Bureau of Mines of the Department of the Interior was established to conduct in behalf of the public welfare fundamental inquiries and investigations into the mining, metallurgical and mineral industries. Its appropriation for the current fiscal year is $662,000, of which $347,000 is to be devoted to technical research pertinent to the mining industry. The bureau has revolutionized the use of explosives in mines. Over $8,000,000 worth of coal is now bought on the specification and advice of the bureau while more than 50 of the larger cities, a number of states and many corporations have adopted the bureau plan of purchase. . . .

Perhaps no better evidence could be adduced of the present range and volume of industrial research in America than the necessity, imposed upon the author of such a general survey as I am attempting, of condensing within a paragraph his reference to the Bureau of Standards of the Department of Commerce. Its purpose is the investigation and testing of standards and measuring instruments and the determination of physical constants and the properties of materials. To these objects it devotes about $700,000 a year to such good effect that in equipment and in the high quality and output of its work it has in ten years taken rank with the foremost

scientific institutions in the world for the promotion of industrial research and the development and standardization of the instruments, materials and methods therein employed. Its influence upon American research and industry is already profound and rapidly extending. The bureau cooperates with foreign governments and institutions, and is constantly consulted by state and municipal officials, technical bodies, commissions and industrial laboratories as a court of highest appeal.

I can not better conclude this cursory and fragmentary reference to governmental work in applied science than with the words of the distinguished Director of the Bureau of Standards:

If there is one thing above all others for which the activities of our government during the past two or three decades will be marked it is its original work along scientific lines, and I venture to state that this work is just in its infancy.

In view of the evidence offered by Germany of the far-reaching benefits resulting from the close cooperation which there obtains between the university laboratory and the industrial plant, it must be admitted with regret that our own institutions of learning have, speaking generally, failed to seize or realize the great opportunity confronting them. They have, almost universally, neglected to provide adequate equipment for industrial research, and, what is more to be deplored since the first would otherwise quickly follow, have rarely acquired that close touch with industry essential for familiarity and appreciation of its immediate and pressing needs. There are happily some notable exceptions. Perhaps foremost among them stands the Massachusetts Institute of Technology with its superb engineering and testing equipment, its Research Laboratory of Applied Chemistry and the meritorious thesis work of its students in all departments. The biological department has been especially active and successful in extending its influence into industrial and sanitary fields, while unusual significance attaches to the motor vehicle studies just concluded and the more recently inaugurated special investigations in electricity, since both were initiated and supported by external interests. About two years ago the institute brought vividly before the community the variety and extent of its wide-spread service to industry by holding a Congress of Technology, at which all of the many papers presented recorded the achievements of institute alumni.

The Colorado School of Mines, recognizing that $100,000,000 a year is lost through inefficient methods of ore treatment, has recently equipped an experimental ore dressing and metallurgical plant in which problems of treatment applicable to ores of wide occurrence will be investigated. The Ohio State University has established an enviable reputation for its researches in fuel engineering. Cornell has been especially alive to the scientific needs of industrial practise, and a long experience with technical assistants enables me to say that I have found none better equipped to cope with the miscellaneous problems of industrial research than the graduates of Cornell. It may in fact be stated generally that the quality of advanced chemical training now afforded in this country is on a par with the best obtainable in Germany, and that home-trained American youth adapt themselves far more efficiently to the requirements and conditions of our industries than do all but the most exceptional

German doctors of philosophy who find employment here.

Several of the great universities of the middle west, notably those of Wisconsin and Illinois, have placed themselves closely in touch with the industrial and other needs of their communities and are exerting a fundamental and growing influence upon affairs. In the east, Columbia has recently established a particularly well equipped laboratory for industrial chemistry and is broadening its work in this department.

The universities of Kansas and of Pittsburgh are carrying forward an especially interesting experiment in the operation of industrial research fellowships supported by the special interests directly concerned. These fellowships endow workers for the attack of such diverse subjects as the chemistry of laundering, the chemistry of bread and baking, that of lime, cement and vegetable ivory, the extractive principles from the ductless glands of whales, the abatement of the smoke nuisance, the technology of glass, and many others. The results obtained are intended primarily for the benefit of the supporters of the individual fellowships but may be published after three years. The holder of the fellowship receives a proportion of the financial benefits resulting from the research, and the scale of sums allotted has progressively risen from $500 a year to $2,500 and even to $5,000. While some doubt may reasonably be expressed as to the possibility of close individual supervision of so many widely varying projects, the results obtained thus far seem entirely satisfactory to those behind the movement, which has further served to strongly emphasize the willingness of our manufacturers to subsidize research.

The present vitality and rate of progress in American industrial research is strikingly illustrated by its very recent development in special industries. It has been said that our best research is carried on in those laboratories which have one client, and that one themselves.

Twenty-five years ago the number of industrial concerns employing even a single chemist was very small, and even he was usually engaged almost wholly upon routine work. Many concerns engaged in business of a distinctly chemical nature had no chemist at all, and such a thing as industrial research in any proper sense hardly came within the field of vision of our manufacturers. Many of them have not yet emerged from the penumbra of that eclipse and our industrial foremen, as a class, are still within the deeper shadow. Meantime, however, research has firmly established itself among the foundation stones of our industrial system, and the question is no longer "What will become of the chemists?" It is now, "What will become of the manufacturers without them?"

In the United States to-day, the microscope is in daily use in the examination of metals and alloys in more than 200 laboratories of large industrial concerns.

An indeterminate but very great amount of segregated research is constantly carried forward in small laboratories which are either an element in some industrial organization or under individual control. An excellent example of the quality of work to be credited to the former is found in the development of cellulose acetate by Mork in the laboratory of the Chemical Products Company, while a classic instance of what may be accomplished by an aggressive individualism plus genius in research is familiar to most of you

through the myriad and protean applications of bakelite. The rapidity of the reduction to practise of Baekeland's research results is the more amazing when one considers that the distances to be traveled between the laboratory and the plant are often, in case of new processes and products, of almost astronomical dimensions.

Reference has already been made to the highly organized, munificently equipped and splendidly manned laboratories of the du Pont Company, the General Electric Company and the Eastman Kodak Company. There are in the country at least fifty other notable laboratories engaged in industrial research in special industries. The expenditure of several of them is over $300,000 each a year; the United States Steel Corporation has not hesitated to spend that amount upon a single research; the expenses of a dozen or more probably exceed $100,000 annually. The limits of any address delivered outside a jail unfortunately preclude more than the merest reference to a very few. One of the finest iron research laboratories in the world is that of the American Rolling Mills Co. Equally deserving mention from one aspect or another are the laboratories of the Fire Underwriters, the National Carbon Co., the Solvay Process Co., the General Bakelite Co., Parke, Davis & Co., the Berlin Mills Co., the United Gas Improvement Co., the National Electric Lamp Association, Swift & Co., the Pennsylvania Railroad and many others. . . .

There are in the country many analytical, testing and commercial laboratories, and, in most of these, special researches are conducted for clients, often with gratifying results. It is to be regretted, however, that there is not a more general appreciation among commercial chemists of the scale and quality of equipment and organization essential for really effective industrial research. As this broader viewpoint is attained, and the engineer's habit of mind acquired, we may expect a great extension of independent research, and the cessation of complaint regarding the trend of prices for analysis.

Among the relatively few private or incorporated laboratories with highly organized staff, and adequate special equipment, should be mentioned those of the Institute of Industrial Research at Washington, which has done notable work on the corrosion of metals, paint technology, canning, road material, cement and special mill problems; the electrochemical laboratories of FitzGerald and Bennie at Niagara Falls, which have so successfully specialized on the construction and operation of electric furnaces to meet the requirements of special processes and products; the ore sampling and treating plant of Ricketts and Banks, and the Pittsburgh Testing Laboratory.

Industrial research is applied idealism: it expects rebuffs, it learns from every stumble and turns the stumbling block into a stepping stone. It knows that it must pay its way. It contends that theory springs from practise. It trusts the scientific imagination, knowing it to be simply logic in flight. It believes with F. P. Fish, that, "during the next generation—the next two generations—there is going to be a development in chemistry which will far surpass in its importance and value to the human race, that of electricity in the last few years. A development which is going to revolutionize methods of manufacture, and more than that, is going to revolutionize methods of agriculture," and it believes with Sir William Ramsay that "The

country which is in advance in chemistry will also be foremost in wealth and general prosperity."

With these articles of faith established in our thought, let us consider where they lead us. Within the last few days Frank A. Vanderlip, than whom no one speaks with more authority upon financial matters, has told the assembled representatives of the electrical industries that they are facing a capital requirement of $8,000,000 a week for the next five years—a total within that period of $2,000,000,000. As chemists, we are ourselves entering upon an era in which the capital demands of industries now embryonic or not yet conceived will in the not distant future be equally insistent and even more insatiable. Have we as chemists given a thought to this aspect of the development of our science, or planted the seeds of the organization which may some day cope with it? In the electrical and other established engineering professions, it is significant that the great industrial applications of the sciences involved have been in large part due to the activities of firms and organizations like Stone and Webster, J. G. White & Co., Blackwell, Viehle & Buck and the United Gas Improvement Co., which, by an orderly but inexorable evolution, passed from the status of engineers to that of engineers and bankers. Our own profession has not yet evolved the chemist and banker, but such an evolution, or at least the close alliance of chemistry and banking is a fundamental prerequisite if the results of industrial research are to find their full fruition in America. Let me add that no field within the purview of the banker is more ripe for tillage or capable of yielding a richer harvest.

We need, however, to lead the banker

to the chemical point of view, and even more do we ourselves require to be taught the financial principles involved in the broad application of chemistry to industry. To the ideals of service which inspire our profession, and which are so finely exemplified in Cottrell and made effective in the research corporation, we should add a stronger impulse to direct personal initiative in affairs. We shall need for years to prosecute a vigorous campaign for a better understanding by the general public of what chemistry is and what research is. The popular imagination is ready to accept any marvel which claims the laboratory as its birthplace, but the man in the works still disbelieves that two and two in chemical nomenclature make four. We need a multiplication of research laboratories in special industries, each with an adequate staff of the best men obtainable and an equipment which gives full range to their abilities. In nearly every case this equipment should include apparatus of semi-commercial size in which to reduce to practise the laboratory findings. Nothing is more demoralizing to an industrial organization, and few things are more expensive, than full-scale experimentation in the plant.

These laboratories should each be developed around a special library, the business of which should be to collect, compile and classify in a way to make all instantly available, every scrap of information bearing upon the materials, methods, products and requirements of the industry concerned. Modern progress can no longer depend upon accidental discoveries. Each advance in industrial science must be studied, organized and fought like a military campaign. Or, to change the figure, in the early days of our science, chemists patrolled the shores of the great ocean of the unknown, and seizing upon such fragments of truth as drifted within their reach, turned them to the enrichment of the intellectual and material life of the community. Later they ventured timidly to launch the frail and often leaky canoe of hypothesis and returned with richer treasures. To-day, confident and resourceful, as the result of many argosies, and having learned to read the stars, organized, equipped, they set sail boldly on a charted sea in staunch ships with tiering canvas bound for new El Dorados.

3. Official Blessings, 1928

CALVIN COOLIDGE, "Address of President Coolidge in Honor of Mr. Edison"

The two men who captured the spirit of the 1920's best were the nation's President, Calvin Coolidge, and its greatest inventor, Thomas Edison. Coolidge took long naps in the White House after lunch; he likened the factory to a cathedral where men worshiped with their work. It was said that

"Address of President Coolidge in Honor of Mr. Edison," *Science*, LXVIII (October 26, 1928), 389-90. Reprinted by permission of *Science* and the American Association for the Advancement of Science.

Edison never slept—he was always on the go, confounding the intellectuals on his staff while he concentrated on his inventions. Both men emphasized no-nonsense practicality and were enthusiastic over what the businessmen of the day called "service." On October 20, 1928, Congress presented Edison a gold medal in recognition of his distinguished service as an inventor, and President Coolidge congratulated him over the radio, a broadcast which was proudly "relayed to forty-eight stations."

A person of high character and remarkable achievement holds a fascination for all mankind. It is literally true that the world will make a beaten path to his door. Such persons are the leaders who by their example and their wisdom stimulate their fellow men to better things and are in the main responsible for human progress. They are the pioneers in opening up new territory in our physical surroundings and in the domain of thought. Not only the United States, but other regions in the far-off ends of the earth are pausing to-night to pay their tribute of respect and reverence to such a figure, while he is still with us, in appreciation of what he has done to advance the cause of civilization.

The life of Thomas Alva Edison, master of applied science, has been represented as a romance. He has been called a genius, a wizard. While these terms may well be used to describe his great abilities, yet this remarkably modest man has constantly refused to attribute such qualities to himself. In his blunt and homely way he is quoted as having said that genius is made up of one per cent. inspiration and ninety-nine per cent. perspiration. Even if not literally true, this expresses an important idea, which he has not failed to apply. Carrying on the same thought he is said to have made an adaptation of the well-known maxim to the effect that every-

thing comes to him who hustles while he waits. Rather than to any mysterious power, he attributes his success to intelligent and persistent hard work along the practical lines of applied science.

That Edison was endowed at birth with that rare intellect and wisdom given to those who have helped shape our destinies, few will deny. But, when asked on his seventy-seventh birthday for his philosophy of life, the reply was: "Work—bringing out the secrets of nature and applying them for the happiness of man." His goal always has been some useful objective. Rarely has he wasted his energies. Having carefully determined what needed to be accomplished, he has gone ahead with unerring instinct of a seeker after truth, with an indomitable spirit for accurate research, with an infinite capacity for taking pains. Temporary failure has only spurred him to renewed activity. Few men have possessed to such a striking degree the blending of the imagination of the dreamer with the practical, driving force of the doer. In the record of his inventions and improvements rests the unimpeachable testimony that he has brought things to pass.

I have been interested in his account of a visit to the White House in 1878 to exhibit his newly developed phonograph. He relates that he came at 11 o'clock in the evening upon the invitation of President Hayes, who, with Mrs.

Hayes and their guests, became so engrossed in the marvelous device that the inventor did not get away until 3:30 A.M. But we know that Edison has never made a practice of retiring early.

The field of electricity will be most closely associated in future years with the name of Edison. It has been asserted somewhere that there is scarcely an electrical process or instrument of to-day which does not reflect in some way changes wrought by his researches. Steinmetz, who should be an authority, said Edison had done more than any other man to promote the art and science of electrical engineering. In his invention of the incandescent lamp and in the perfection of means for developing and distributing electrical energy he literally brought light to the dark places of the earth. Through these and other products of his genius old industrial processes have been revolutionized, new ones developed, and our daily lives have been made easier, our homes pleasanter and more comfortable.

Although Edison belongs to the world, the United States takes pride in the thought that his rise from humble beginnings and his unceasing struggle to overcome the obstacles on the road to success well illustrate the spirit of our country. We are happy to share his achievements as our contribution to progress. He represents the finest traditions of our citizenship. At the request of the Secretary of the Navy in 1915 he became president of the Naval Consulting Board, which looked into inventions and devices designed to aid us in preparedness and later in our participation in the world war. From 1917 to 1919 his entire time was at the disposal of the government. Not only by his own discoveries, but by training in his laboratories men who have gone out to important places in the scientific and industrial world and by encouraging countless others to renewed efforts in applied science and invention, he has made a notable contribution to education.

This is my message to Mr. Edison: Noble, kindly servant of the United States and benefactor of mankind, may you long be spared to continue your work and to inspire those who will carry forward your torch.

4. A New Co-operation, 1927

HERBERT HOOVER, "The Nation and Science"

Herbert Hoover was known to his legion of admirers as The Great Engineer. After graduating from Stanford University with a degree in mining engineering, he accumulated a fortune as a consultant. During World War I his honesty and efficiency as a dollar-a-year man led to his appointment under Presi-

From Herbert Hoover, "The Nation and Science," *Science*, LXV (January 14, 1927), 26-29. Reprinted by permission of *Science* and the American Association for the Advancement of Science.

dent Harding as Secretary of Commerce. In that post he supervised the work of the Patent Office, the Bureau of Standards, and other government bureaus concerned with science. He was also a member of the National Academy of Sciences, where he came to meet the best of the academic scientists of the country.

From both sources Hoover gained an appreciation of the fact that, in spite of an unprecedented national enthusiasm for the fruits of applied science, there was also a national tendency to neglect the investigation of nature in those areas where no immediate reward was visible. Although the border between "pure" and "applied" research was not as clear as Hoover implied, the problem he described was not really attacked until after World War II.

I should like to discuss with you for a few moments certain relationships of pure- and applied-science research to public policies, and above all the national necessity for enlarged activities in support of pure-science research.

Huxley was perhaps not the first, but at least he was the most forceful in his demand that preliminary to all understanding and development of thought there should be a definition of terms. Men in the scientific world will have no difficulty in making a distinction between the fields of pure and applied science. It is, however, not so clear in industry nor in our governmental relations, and sometimes even in our educational institutions.

At least for the practical purpose of this discussion I think we may make this definition: that pure-science research is the search for new fundamental natural law and substance, while applied science is clearly enough the application of these discoveries to practical use. Pure science is the raw material of applied science. And the two callings depart widely in their motivating impulses, their personnel, their character, their support, and their economic setting. And these differences are the root of our problem.

As a nation we have not been remiss in our support of applied science. We have contributed our full measure of invention and improvement in the application of physics, in mechanics, in biology and chemistry, and we have made contributions to the world in applied economics and sociology.

Business and industry have realized the vivid values of the application of scientific discoveries. To further it, in twelve years our individual industries have increased their research laboratories from less than 100 to over 500. They are bringing such values that they are increasing monthly. Our federal and state governments today support great laboratories, research departments, and experimental stations, all devoted to applications of science to the many problems of industry and agriculture. They are one of the great elements in our gigantic strides in national efficiency. The results are magnificent. The new inventions, labor-saving devices, improvements of all sorts in machines and processes in developing agriculture and promoting health are steadily cheapening cost of production; increasing standards of living, stabilizing industrial output enabling us to hold our own in foreign trade; and lengthening human life and decreasing suffering. But all these laboratories and experiment stations are devoted to the application of science, not to fundamental research. Yet the raw materials for these laboratories come alone from the ranks of our men of pure science whose efforts are supported almost wholly in our universities, colleges, and a few scientific institutions.

$200,000,000 SPENT ANNUALLY IN AMERICA IN APPLIED-SCIENCE INVESTIGATIONS

We are spending in industry, in government, national and local, probably $200,000,000 a year in search for applications of scientific knowledge—with perhaps 30,000 men engaged in the work.

I should like to emphasize this differentiation a little more to my non-scientific audience. Faraday in the pursuit of fundamental law discovered that energy could be transformed into electricity through induction. It remained for Edison, Thomson, Bell, Siemens, and many score of others to bring forth the great line of inventions which applied this discovery from dynamo to electric light, the electric railway, the telegraph, telephone, and a thousand other uses which have brought such blessings to all humanity. It was Hertz who made the fundamental discovery that electric waves may traverse the ether. It was Marconi and DeForest who transformed this discovery into the radio industry. It was Becquerel who discovered the radioactivity of certain substances, and Professor and Madame Curie who discovered and isolated radium. It was Dr. Kelly who applied these discoveries to the healing art and to industrial service. It was Perkins who discovered the colors in coal-tar by-products. It was German industrial chemists who made the inventions which developed our modern dye industry. It was Pasteur who discovered that by the use of aniline dyes he could secure differentiation in colors of different cells, and this led to the discovery of bacilli and germs; and it was Koch and Ehrlich who developed from this fundamental discovery the treatment of disease by antitoxins.

And so I could traverse at great length these examples of the boundaries and the relations of these fields of pure and applied science.

There is a wide difference in the mental approach of the men engaged in these two fields of scientific work. The men in pure science are exploring the frontiers of knowledge and they must necessarily do so without respect to reward or to its so-called practical benefits, whereas the men engaged in applied-science research have long since demonstrated that it pays in immediate returns. It brings such direct rewards as to generate its own steam mostly through the Patent Office. There is seldom any direct financial profit in pure-science research, although its ultimate results are the maintenance of our modern civilization and are the hopes for the future.

For all the support of pure-science research we have depended upon three sources—that the rest of the world would bear this burden of fundamental discovery for us, that universities would carry it as a by-product of education, and that our men of great benevolence would occasionally endow a Smithsonian or a Carnegie Institution or a Rockefeller Institute. Yet the whole sum which we have available to support pure-science research is less than $10,000,000 a year, with probably less than 4000 men engaged in it, most of them dividing their time between it and teaching.

PURE-SCIENCE ACTIVITIES OF COUNTRY HAVE DIMINISHED DURING THE LAST DECADE

Some months ago our leading scientists in reviewing the organizations of pure science of the country were discouraged to find that their activities had been actually diminished during the last decade, whereas if these laboratories are to furnish the increasing vital stream of discovery to our nation and our normal part of the world, they should have been greatly enlarged. Moreover, they discovered that the pressures of poverty in Europe were taking a worse toll of pure science abroad.

The causes in the United States are not far to seek. They arise from two directions: First, 80 per cent of the men devoted to pure-science research with us are in our scores of universities and colleges. Our universities have doubled in the number of their students. Their prewar endowments and income have been depreciated by the falling dollar. New resources have been given many of them, but not enough to handle their new burdens of teaching. All of this has led them to more and more curtailment and the suppression of expansion in pure-science research in order that they might attend to the immediate problem of education. Thus the four or five thousand men in the United States who have demonstrated their ability for research of this character are not applying themselves in this direction so much as they are applying themselves to the education of the youth. Teaching is a noble occupation, but other men can teach, and few men have that quality of mind which can successfully explore the un-

known in nature. Not only are our universities compelled to curtail the resources they should contribute in men and equipment for this patient groping for the sources of fundamental truth because of our educational pressures, but the sudden growth of industrial laboratories themselves and the larger salaries they offer have in themselves endangered pure science by drafting men from the universities. This is no complaint against our great industries and their fine vision of the application of science. It simply means we must strengthen the first line of industrial advancement—pure-science research.

These men of pure science are the most precious assets of our country, and their diversion to teaching and applied science reduces the productivity which they could and should give to the nation. It is no fault of their own, but it is the fault of the nation that it does not give to them and to the institutions where they labor a sufficient support.

There is no price that the world could not afford to pay these men who have the originality of mind to carry scientific thought in steps or in strides. They wish no price. They need but opportunity to live and to work. No one can estimate the value to the world of an investigator like Faraday or Pasteur or Millikan. The assets of our whole banking community today do not total the values which these men have added to the world's wealth.

Some scientific discoveries and inventions have in the past been the result of the genius struggling in poverty. But poverty does not clarify thought, nor furnish laboratory equipment. Discovery was easier when the continent was new. Discovery nowadays must be builded upon a vast background of scientific knowledge, of liberal equipment. It is stifled where there is lack of staff to do the routine work and where valuable time must be devoted to tending the baby or peeling potatoes, or teaching your and my boys. The greatest discoveries of today and of the future will be the product of organized research free from the calamity of such distraction.

DAY OF THE GENIUS IN THE GARRET, IF IT EVER EXISTED, HAS PASSED

The day of the genius in the garret has passed, if it ever existed. The advance of science today is by process of accretion. Like the growth of a plant, cell by cell, the adding of fact to fact some day brings forth a blossom of discovery, of illuminating hypothesis, or of great generalization. He who enunciates the hypothesis, makes the discovery, or formultes the generalization, and thus brings forth the fine blossoms of thought, is indeed a genius, but his product is the result of the toil of thousands of men before him. A host of men, great equipment, long, patient scientific experiment to build up the structure of knowledge, not stone by stone but grain by grain, is now our only sure road of discovery and invention. We do have the genius in science—he is the most precious of all our citizens. We cannot invent him; we can, however, give him a chance to serve.

And the more one observes, the more clearly does he see that it is in the soil of pure science that are found the origins of all our modern industry and commerce. In fact, our civilization and our large populations are wholly builded upon our scientific discoveries. It is the increased productivity of men which has come from these discoveries that has defeated the prophecies of Malthus. He held that increasing population would constantly lower the standard of living among men until the pressure of subsistence upon population would limit its number by starvation. But since his day we have seen the paradox of the growth of population far beyond anything of which he ever dreamed, coupled with a constantly increasing standard of living. This result would be impossible but for the men of fundamental scientific research and discovery. In fact, there is for the future but one contestant in the race with the principle of Malthus, and that is pure science. If we would have our country increase in its standards of living and at the same time accommodate itself to an increasing population at the rate of more than 15 million each decade, we must maintain the output of our pure-science laboratories.

The wealth of the country has multiplied far faster than the funds we have given for these purposes. And the funds administered in the nation today for it are but a triviality compared to the vast resources that a single discovery places in our hands. We spend more on cosmetics than we do upon safeguarding this mainspring of our future progress.

AVENUES ALONG WHICH MORE LIBERAL SUPPORT TO PURE-SCIENCE RESEARCH MUST BE SOUGHT

But to return to my major theme—How are we to secure the much wider and more liberal support to pure-science research? It appears to me that we must seek it in three directions: First, from the government, both national and state; second, from industry, and third from an enlargement of private benevolence. We have long since accepted the obligation upon the state to provide universal and free education. We have advanced it further than any nation in the world. Yet the obvious function of education is to organize and transmit our stock of knowledge—it is not primarily concerned with the extension of the borders of knowledge except in so far as the process is educational. It seems to me that we must accept the fact that the enlargement of our stock is no less an obligation of the state than its transmission. As a nation we must have this enlargement of stock if we would march forward. And the point of application is more liberal appropriations to our national bureaus for pure-science research instead of the confinement as today of these undertakings to applied-science work. And we must have the more liberal support of pure-science research in our state universities and other publicly supported institutions.

Our second source of support must come from business and industry. You are aware of the appeal in this particular from the National Academy of Sciences of a year ago—that they might be entrusted with a fund largely for the better support of proved men now engaged in such research in our universities and elsewhere. It is no appeal for charity or benevolence. It is an appeal to self-interest, to insurance of every business and industry of its own future. That appeal has been met generously by some of our largest industries; it is under consideration by others; it has been refused by one or two largely because they have not grasped the essential difference between the applied-science investigations upon which they are themselves engaged and the pure science which must be the foundation of their own future inventions. A nation with an output of fifty billion annually in commodities which could not be produced but for the discoveries of pure science

could well afford, it would seem, to put back a hundredth of one per cent as an assurance of further progress.

Nor is the interest of a particular industry confined to the science research which appears on its face to be directly in the line of that industry. Practically all industry and all business gains by scientific discovery in any direction. The discoveries which led to the invention of the internal-combustion engine and thus to the automobile have benefited every industry and every business in the United States. Business and industry have an interest in the common pool of scientific research irrespective of its particular field. Those fundamental discoveries of the germ basis of disease, with the load of mortality they have lifted from the race, have lowered the rates of insurance and thus contributed directly to business.

From benevolence we have had the generous support of some individuals to our universities and scientific institutions, but this benevolence has come from dishearteningly meager numbers, as witness the discouraging results of recent appeals from the Smithsonian—the father of American science—and the failure of appeals from some of our universities. In a nation of such high appreciation of the value of knowledge, and of such superabundance of private wealth, we can surely hope for that wider understanding which is the basis of constructive action.

NO GREATER CHALLENGE SINCE
WORLD WAR THAN THAT OF
SCIENTIFIC MEN IN THEIR DEMAND
FOR GREATER FACILITIES

And there is something beyond monetary returns in all this. The progress of civilization, as all clear-thinking historians recognize, depends in large de-gree upon "the increase and diffusion of knowledge among men." Our nation must recognize that its future is not merely a question of applying present-day science to the development of our industries, or to reducing the cost of living, or to eradicating disease and multiplying our harvests, or even to in-creasing the general diffusion of knowl-edge. We must add to knowledge both for the intellectual and spiritual satis-faction that comes from widening the range of human understanding, and for the direct practical utilization of these fundamental discoveries. If we would command the advance of our material and, to a considerable degree, of our spiritual life, we must maintain this earnest and organized search for truth. I could base this appeal wholly upon moral and spiritual grounds: the unfold-ing of beauty, the aspiration after knowledge, the ever-widening penetra-tion into the unknown, the discovery of truth, and finally, as Huxley says, "the inculcation of veracity of thought."

No greater challenge has been given to the American people since the Great War than that of our scientific men in the demand for greater facilities. It is an opportunity to again demonstrate in our Government, our business, and our pri-vate citizens the recognition of a re-sponsibility to our people and the na-tion greater than that involved in the production of goods or in trading in the market.

5. The Old Deal Defended, 1931

VERNON KELLOGG, "Herbert Hoover and Science"

Seldom has so much been expected of any President as of Herbert Hoover, and never have events and personal limitations so conspired to disappoint those hopes. Scientists and engineers had a special reason for expecting an exceptional administration. He was the first President with technical training (unless one wanted to count George Washington, who had surveying ex-perience). He was a member of the National Academy of Sciences, and he had had experience administering the scientific activities of the Department of Commerce.

And yet all this experience did not seem to add up to any new departure for government science, or any new relationship between the government and civilian technologists. When the crash came in the fall of 1929, Hoover

From Vernon Kellogg, "Herbert Hoover and Science," *Science*, LXXIII (February 20, 1931), 197-99. Reprinted by permission of *Science* and the American Association for the Advancement of Science.

responded by cutting deeply into government spending, and scientific and engineering activities were among the most heavily curtailed. Yet, even as his administration ended in disaster, some technical people stepped forward to praise his record.

As a boy preparing for college Herbert Hoover decided to go to a university which paid especial attention to science. He went to Stanford University, took major courses there in geology and mining, graduated in 1895, and began at once a successful career as mining engineer. This lasted up to the beginning of the World War, when he gave it up and became known to all the world as relief worker, Food Administrator, Secretary of Commerce, and President of the United States. In all these capacities he has shown a notable appreciation of science and the scientific method, and he has helped materially to support and extend scientific knowledge.

As mining engineer in charge of very large enterprises in Australia, China, Burma, the Ural Mountains, Mongolian Siberia, South Africa and elsewhere he attacked with success various scientific mining and metallurgical problems. Most notable, perhaps, was his success in Australia in advancing the flotation process and in working out means of profitably recovering the zinc content from low-grade silver ores.

In the prosecution of his large mining operations he successfully met important social problems arising from the gathering together of communities of thousands of workmen and their families in parts of the world distant from civilized regions. His great Kyshtim project in the Ural Mountains, for example, maintained a community of 70,000 people who were lifted by him through his scientific and social work from poverty and squalor to a high state of comfort and prosperity.

He is the author (with specialist collaborators) of "Economics of Mining," published by the *Engineering and Mining Journal,* New York City, 1905; also of "Principles of Mining," 199 pp., 1909, McGraw-Hill Book Company, used in mining schools; also of "De Re Metallica," by G. Agricola, founder of the modern science of mineralogy, translated by Mr. Hoover and his wife from the first medieval Latin edition of 1556. To the original text the translators added an important biographical introduction and an invaluable host of annotations and appendices about the development of mining law and mining and metallurgical methods from the earliest times to the sixteenth century. He also is the author of numerous addresses and papers published in mining and engineering magazines and elsewhere. He has lectured on engineering at Stanford and Columbia Universities, and has been president (1920-1921) of the American Institute of Mining and Metallurgical Engineers; president (1920-1921) of the American Engineering Council (federated American engineering societies); chairman of the Advisory Committee of the Food Research Institute, Stanford University (1921-   ); president (1927) of the International Radiotelegraph Conference; trustee (1920-   ) of the Carnegie Institution of Washington; trustee (1912-   ) of Stanford University, and officer or member of various other major national engineering and scientific societies and organizations.

He has been given honorary academic degrees by twenty-five universities, and has been awarded the following medals for scientific merit:

1914—Mining and Metallurgical Society of America—gold; jointly with Lou Henry Hoover for "distinguished contribution to literature of mining." ("De Re Metallica.")

1920—National Academy of Sciences—for "eminence in the application of science to the public welfare."

1928—American Institute of Mining and Metallurgical Engineers—for "achievement in mining."

1929—John Fritz Gold Medal—awarded jointly by the American Society of Civil Engineers, the American Institute of Mining and Metallurgical Engineers, the American Society of Mechanical Engineers and the American Institute of Electrical Engineers for notable scientific or industrial achievement.

In 1902 he was elected member of the American Association for the Advancement of Science, and fellow in 1915. On the occasion of the meeting of the association in Philadelphia in December, 1926, Mr. Hoover made a notable and largely attended public address ("The Nation and Science") in which he emphasized energetically the importance to the nation of science, and urged strongly the support by the people of this country of "pure" or fundamental science as a necessary basis for continuing advance in applied science.

No greater challenge has been given to the American people since the great war than that of our scientific men in the demand for greater facilities. It is an opportunity to again demonstrate in our government, our business, and among our private citizens the recognition of a responsibility to our people and the nation greater than that involved in the production of goods or trading in the market.

He delivered a similar address ("The Vital Need for Greater Financial Support to Pure Science and Research") before the American Society of Mechanical Engineers in December, 1925. In this address he made the following statement:

The far-sighted leaders of industry fully recognize the dependence of their progress upon advances in science, and emphasize their belief that fundamental research should be much more greatly aided. . . . We have prided ourselves on our practicality as a nation. Would it not be a practical thing to do to give adequate organized financial support to pure science? If, by chance, we develop a little contribution to abstract learning and knowledge, our nation will be immensely greater for it.

In 1922 he was elected member of the National Academy of Sciences, and in November, 1925, accepted the active chairmanship of a special board of eminent scientific men and outstanding men of public affairs set up by the National Academy to attempt to establish a National Research Fund of several million dollars for the support of work in fundamental science. Mr. Hoover took an active personal part in the work of obtaining pledges for this purpose from large industrial organizations and wealthy men of this country. The amount already pledged is at least five million dollars, with contingent possibility of another five.

As Secretary of Commerce and President he has made an impressive record in bringing about ever increasing support and extension of the work of the government's scientific divisions and bureaus. He became Secretary of Commerce in March, 1921. In the past ten years the appropriations for the support of the (primarily) scientific bureaus of the department have increased as follows: Bureau of Standards, from $1,354,-

632 to $3,485,671; Bureau of Fisheries, $1,291,810 to $2,640,560; Bureau of Mines, $1,302,642 to $2,729,480; Coast and Geodetic Survey, $2,316,317 to $3,020,104.

It was as a result of his vigorous championship that the establishment of a great National Hydraulic Laboratory ($350,000) at the Bureau of Standards was brought about.

He has been active in having formulated, adopted and enforced various important fish conservation measures based on careful studies by leading scientific fisheries experts of the country. In this connection have been established, under his active sponsorship, an Upper Mississippi River wild life and fish refuge; a Northern Pacific Halibut Convention with Canada, and a generous five-year construction and maintenance program for the Bureau of Fisheries, with special support for its strictly scientific work. He also obtained, after an active struggle, authority for the Secretary of Commerce to say when, where and how salmon and other fishes were to be taken in the waters of Alaska. In exercising this authority, Mr. Hoover placed great dependence on the advice of the late Dr. C. H. Gilbert, one of the country's greatest fishery scientists, as well as his assistant in charge of salmon research, Dr. W. H. Rich.

The Bureau of Mines, transferred in 1925 from the Department of the Interior to the Department of Commerce, was enabled, with the active sponsorship of the Secretary of Commerce, to expand materially its scientific investigations of fundamental problems in the extraction of shale oil and in the extraction of potash from ores occurring in the various parts of the United States.

Mr. Hoover's special interest in aeronautics led to large expansion of the scientific work of the aeronautics branch of the Department of Commerce. The total appropriation for the work of this branch in the year 1927 was $500,000, while in the year 1929 it was over $5,-000,000. With this large increase in funds available, the division was able to develop a comprehensive and far-reaching constructive research program.

While Mr. Hoover was Secretary of Commerce, radio broadcasting was begun. He took great interest in the scientific development of radio and realized the future possibilities of broadcasting. He presided over four national radio conferences and took a lively interest in the proceedings of the International Radio-Telegraph Conference held in Washington in 1927.

In 1925 Mr. Hoover negotiated the transfer of the seismological investigations from the Weather Bureau of the Department of Agriculture to the Coast and Geodetic Survey in the Department of Commerce. A direct attack is being made by the survey on the problem of obtaining complete information about all earthquakes occurring in the United States or regions under its jurisdiction, and special investigations are being conducted to discover fundamental facts which may be made available to engineers and builders in connection with building for earthquake resistance. The Coast and Geodetic Survey undertook a survey of the Mississippi River area from Cairo to New Orleans, thus making available basic data touching fundamental problems of flood control.

Mr. Hoover has shown his special interest in promoting scientific care of child health and protection by his organization in 1922 of the American Child Health Association, of which he was the first president, and by the organization of the White House Conference on Child Health and Protection.

But a catalogue of the scientific undertakings encouraged and materially supported by Secretary and, later, President Hoover would be a long one—much too long a one to print here.

As Secretary of Commerce and President, Mr. Hoover's relation to scientific work has been that of encourager, supporter and administrator, necessarily not that of laboratory or field man. As such supporter and administrator of science he has made much and great scientific work possible; and for this he should have the gratitude of scientific men.

What President Hoover said of Dr. W. H. Welch in his impressive address at the celebration, in April, 1930, of Dr. Welch's eightieth birthday may well be said of Mr. Hoover:

Our age is marked by two tendencies, the democratic and the scientific. In Dr. Welch and his work we find an expression of the best in both tendencies. He not only represents the spirit of pure science but constantly sees and seizes the opportunities to direct its results into the service of humankind.

PART XII   THE GREAT DEPRESSION

The golden years of the 1920's were cut off with savage abruptness when the stock market crashed in October 1929. From the dizzying heights of optimism and good times the nation slid precipitously into a decade of pessimism and despair. At first many refused to believe that the end had really come, then they were at a loss to explain it, and finally there was a general search for scapegoats. President Hoover fixed the blame on the Depression in Europe, while some congressmen launched an investigation to demonstrate that the communists were at fault.

Science and technology were particularly vulnerable targets. Agricultural researchers had bragged for a decade that they were making two blades of grass grow where only one had grown before. Was this not at least part of the cause of agricultural overproduction and disastrously low prices? Industrial engineers had taken credit for the new machines and products that were at the base of the nation's prosperity. Were not these engineers therefore at least partly to blame for the replacement of workers by new laborsaving machines?

In short, scientific and technical research had been oversold during the 1920's. Researchers, by identifying themselves with the business prosperity of the 1920's, had made themselves vulnerable to the charge that they were equally to blame for the Depression that followed. There were demands—made by only a few people but given wide publicity—that a moratorium be called on any further research or development of science and technology, at least until the social sciences had developed to the place where the physical sciences might be controlled.

Scientists and engineers were as quick to deny blame for the bad times as they were to take credit for the good. Indeed, some launched a counterattack, claiming that the cure for a little science was a great deal more of the same. If the automobile had put buggy-whip makers out of work, the building of dams would give them new employment. If genetics made wheat a glut on the market, organic chemistry would find a way to convert surplus wheat into new and useful industrial products. If technology was lifting the burden of labor from the masses, it was also increasing their leisure by that same amount. The failure was not in technology, which created abundance, but in political and economic systems that were unable to cope with abundance.

Although few radically new social arrangements were adopted in the 1930's, many of the old ones were so badly undermined by the Depression that they could not be restored. Scientists, engineers, politicians, and academicians argued about the proper relationships between science and society, the social responsibilities of the engineer, and the responsibility of the state to foster research. It was a period of academic debates and ad hoc solutions, but it prepared the way for the unprecedented changes of the coming war years.

1. Unemployed Engineers, 1932

J. P. H. PERRY, "The New York Engineers' Successful Efforts
to Relieve Unemployment"

For many engineers the central fact of the Depression was their own unemployment. In some industrial centers the problem was acute; it has been estimated that by 1932 some 112,000 engineers, perhaps half the profession, were without jobs. There was a great deal of talk about increasing job opportunities by stimulating public works and about limiting the number of engineers through smaller college enrollments and strict licensing. But for the unemployed the immediate problem was solved by direct relief.

In the February issue of Civil Engineering *there appeared an article outlining the organization, aims, and activities of the Professional Engineers Committee on Unemployment up to the middle of January 1932. It is believed that members of the Society in general, as well as the various committees scattered over* *the country that have been organized to deal with the relief of unemployed civil engineers, may be interested in this latest report of the work of the Professional Engineers Committee on Unemployment of the four Founder Societies in the New York Metropolitan District, known locally as the "P.E.C.U."*

From J. P. H. Perry, "New York Engineers' Successful Efforts to Relieve Unemployment," *Civil Engineering*, II (June 1932), 404-7. Reprinted by permission of the American Society of Civil Engineers.

The organization of the P.E.C.U. has been changed but very slightly from that described in my article in the February issue of *Civil Engineering*. The work has gone on steadily and fairly successfully. Up to May 14, 1932, our organization had registered unemployed members of the four Founder Societies and non-members to a total number of 2,689.

Of this total registration, 526 were not regarded as active applicants for relief since 139 had stated on a reclassification that they were definitely interested only in permanent engineering jobs, not in relief, and 249 had not replied to a series of letters asking if they still desired assistance, thereby indicating to the P.E.C.U. that they were no longer interested, while 138 had registered for educational courses.

DISTRIBUTION OF REGISTERED UNEMPLOYMENT

Of the active registrants, totaling 2,163 men, P.E.C.U. has made 1,389 placements divided as follows:

On P.E.C.U. payrolls 307
Receiving other relief, such as that given by the Gibson, Bliss, and general public committees in the Metropolitan District of New York 879
In permanent engineering jobs 203

The division among society members and non-members, both for registrations and placements, is as follows:

The Division Among Society Members and Non-members

Society	Registered	Percentage of total registration	Placed	Percentage of total placed	Percentage of registered placed
American Society of Civil Engineers	239	11.0	184	14.9	77.0
American Institute of Mining and Metallurgical Engineers	35	1.6	31	2.8	88.6
American Society of Mechanical Engineers	345	15.9	248	20.2	71.9
American Institute of Electrical Engineers	210	9.6	157	12.7	74.8
Western Society of Engineers	4	0.2	4	0.3	100.00
Non-Members	1,339	61.7	603	49.1	45.03
	2,172	100.0	1,227	100.0	
Duplicate Memberships	9		7		
	2,163		1,220		
Men placed more than once			169		
TOTAL			1,389		

The analyses of registration and placements by married and single classifications and also by groupings of salaries received by the registered man in his last employment, are shown in the following tabulations:

Marital Status	Registered	Placed
Single	648	228
Married	1,431	964
Widower	33	18
Divorced	29	10
	2,141	1,220
Unaccounted for	22	Replacements 169
Totals	2,163	1,389

Salary	Registered	Placed
$6,000 or better	127	92
$3,600–$6,000 ..	505	352
$2,400–$3,600 ..	1,016	576
$2,400 and below	493	200
	2,141	1,220
Unaccounted for	22	Replacements 169
Totals	2,163	1,389

TYPES OF RELIEF PROVIDED

The average relief afforded the individual unemployed engineer through the P.E.C.U. has been $19.05 per week. This sum has varied somewhat depending upon where the relief was obtained. The average under different conditions varied as follows:

For those paid direct through
P.E.C.U.'s payroll $18.82
For those who obtained relief
through the Gibson, Bliss, and
other relief committees $21.50
For those who got engineering jobs
through the P.E.C.U. and other
sources $32.50

There have been 73 loans granted in amounts in excess of $15, totaling $3,355, and averaging $45.18 per man. There have been 60 emergency loans granted in amounts less than $15, totaling $248 and averaging $4.13 per man.

These loans were on demand notes without interest. The expectation is that ultimately a considerable percentage of

the borrowers will repay them. The notes are made payable to the United Engineering Trustees, Inc., the official treasurer of the P.E.C.U. Should these loans be repaid, the funds collected will be reserved in a permanent fund to be managed by the presidents of the four local sections of the four Founder Societies for the relief of destitute engineers, or they will be held in reserve to meet another business depression.

The relatively small number of loans made and the meager sums of money required surprised those active in the P.E.C.U. At the inception of our organization the forecast was that the loaning of money would be one of our chief activities. Apparently engineers (especially our members) are extremely loath to apply for loans. They much prefer wages from made work or even direct relief from city bureaus. Also, a loan meets only the momentary emergency, whereas a wage, even at a trifling rate, makes possible the planning of one's life. Loans, to be satisfactory, must be at a continuing rate, and this is impossible, in our experience, to contemplate.

In addition to its other activities, the P.E.C.U. has been very active in using the influence of its personnel to persuade the gas and electric light companies to forebear as far as possible enforcing routine orders to discontinue their services to destitute engineers who were being aided in other ways by the P.E.C.U. In some instances it has been possible to persuade holders of mortgages to be more lenient in the terms on which they extended or renewed them. Occasionally money has been loaned to pay interest on mortgages.

A legal aid department has been established, whose function has been to give free legal advice to registered unemployed whose circumstances were such that they required such advice. Similarly, an agency has been set up to assist registered unemployed who had developed inventions or processes possibly warranting patents. Occasionally the P.E.C.U. has been of help through various hospitals in the city in getting special terms or special admittance for its registered unemployed.

It has been found that many unemployed engineers lack the knack of writing suitable and effective letters applying for jobs. Engineers seem to have difficulty in "selling" themselves. Therefore the P.E.C.U. organized a little department, the function of which has been to help registered men prepare letters outlining their past experience in a way to interest the prospective employer. This has been supplemented with a mimeographing service to produce multiple copies of such letters.

Another way of stating P.E.C.U.'s accomplishments is that through February, March, and April it was responsible for building up a payroll of about $21,000 a week for unemployed engineers. Of this, about $4,000 was met directly by the P.E.C.U. from its own funds; the balance, by public or other agencies.

As regards clothing, in the early winter the McGraw-Hill Company generously donated floor space in its building on West 42d Street. Two unemployed engineers were set to work to operate this clothing bureau. To date 203 men, 61 women, and 58 children have been provided with clothing, which has been contributed largely through the kind efforts of the Engineering Woman's Club of New York. This clothing has been a godsend to many unemployed men, who, if they had not had the clothing from the P.E.C.U., in many cases could not have taken the positions which were found for them.

The Engineering Woman's Club not only did a splendid work in collecting and distributing clothing but also initiated and managed in a fine way a charity bridge party which was held in the rooms of the Engineering Societies Building. Some 700 tickets were sold at $2 apiece, and between 400 and 500 members of the Founder Societies played bridge one evening. The result was that a net contribution of $1,160 was made to the funds of the P.E.C.U. This report would not be complete without including words of warm appreciation and gratitude to the officers and members of the Engineering Woman's Club for their active assistance to the P.E.C.U. throughout the past winter.

Another successful activity of the P.E. C.U. was that of certifying unemployed engineers to Columbia University so that they could attend classes without academic credit and without expense. Early in the campaign it was felt that in addition to affording financial relief to unemployed men, we must do something to sustain the morale of those who were not as yet in dire need of financial relief. Columbia University responded very generously to the suggestion, and to date we have sent there 138 men, who made 564 registrations in 163 different courses for the winter and spring terms. The subjects elected by these men cover a wide range. They may be summarized briefly as embracing architecture, chemistry, civil engineering, electrical engineering, industrial engineering, geology, mechanical engineering, mathematics, languages, metallurgy, mining, physics, accounting, finance, industrial relations, and economics.

Another important committee which was recently established is known as the Committee on Industrial Opportunities. This committee endeavors to place engineers outside the profession. It has prepared a list of some 800 industrial concerns which in its judgment could use engineers for cost studies and in other ways where their technical training and mathematical ability would make them more useful than the ordinary layman. This committee plans to continue its work all summer, and has been reinforced by two other groups who will solicit positions of a permanent nature.

Advertisements in the daily and technical press are being posted on a bulletin board in the Engineering Societies Building, and, as has been mentioned, assistance is being rendered in preparing letters of application. . . .

Another committee, known as the Committee on Construction Legislation, under the able leadership of Malcolm Pirnie, John P. Hogan, and R. C. Marshall, Members Am. Soc. C.E., has been active in Washington and Albany in endeavoring to persuade Congressmen and other legislators that the cutting out of construction enterprises from Federal, state, and municipal budgets is fallacious economy, results in great increase in unemployment, and is particularly distressing to engineers. It is believed that the work done by this committee has been, or will be, fruitful in part.

Reviewing the activities of the past seven months, the greatest accomplishment of the P.E.C.U. has been to convince the semi-public relief agencies in the Metropolitan District of the desirability, from their point of view, of using unemployed engineers in supervising capacities or as key men in directing the 35,000 or 40,000 individuals to whom these agencies have had to give unemployed relief in the form of made work or as direct relief in New York this past winter. Extreme care was taken in certifying P.E.C.U. registrants to these public bodies, notably to the Gibson and Bliss Committees, to make certain that the candidates sent down for employment were qualified for the job in question.

A large part of the work of the Registration Committee, ably led by Ernest S. Holcombe, as a part of the General Relief Committee under the fine management of George L. Lucas, M. Am. Soc. C.E., has been to classify all registrants as to their prior experience and their fitness for different types of work. In other words, it was a "selling proposition" and we had to be sure that the goods we were offering were satisfactory. Our care along these lines in the early stages of our activities has been rewarded many times over. The fact that wages paid by these relief agencies to our unemployed engineers totaled $307,119 is distinctly "proof of the pudding."

Although the raising directly by P.E.C.U. of $107,841.69 may be regarded as satisfactory, it is only proper to call attention to the fact that this has come from only 3,286 men out of over 12,000 members of the four Founder Societies in the Metropolitan District, to say nothing of an estimated non-membership of at least 10,000 more. This estimate is based on the fact that our registrations indicate that the division between members and non-members among unemployed engineers is almost exactly half and half. It is also distressing to report that in spite of four letters of appeal, over 5,000 members of the societies failed to reply in any way. Some 4,000 members who did not contribute did accord the P.E.C.U. the courtesy of acknowledging its appeals and giving reasons why they could not contribute. In most cases the reason for non-contribution was loss of job or extreme outside relief burdens to which the member was committed.

PLANS FOR THE FUTURE

As to the immediate future, the Relief Committee after mature study submitted a written report to the Executive Committee, which in turn, after consideration, made a written recommendation to the General Committee to the effect that registration of unemployed engineers should cease April 9. The General Committee unanimously approved the recommenation. The branch offices of the P.E.C.U. in New Jersey and in Westchester and Nassau counties in New York State were closed on the same date. A nucleus of the normal staff of some 60 paid and volunteer P.E.C.U. workers on registration, classification, vital statistics, certification of unemployed to vacant jobs, and other work will be maintained until October 1 to the number of about 16.

Announcements were sent out giving two weeks' notice to unemployed non-members that they were to go off the P.E.C.U. payrolls on April 15; a month's notice was given to married non-members and unmarried members that they would go off the P.E.C.U. payroll on May 1; and a month's notice was given to married members other than those falling within Class A destitution that they would go off the payroll on May 15.

A reserve of money to start up the activities of the P.E.C.U. on October 1 was set aside and the remainder of its funds were held to take care of married members in Class A destitution from May 15 to October 1. The general feeling of those active in the P.E.C.U. is that the problem of relief for unemployed engineers will be more serious in the

winter of 1932-1933 than in the past winter and that the number of members of the four Founder Societies falling within Class A destitution will increase throughout the summer months, not only because of the tapering off of direct relief from the P.E.C.U. but also because of the laying off of the engineers placed through the P.E.C.U. with other relief agencies in New York City, notably with the Gibson and Bliss committees, which began to occur in April and will continue throughout the summer, and further because of the continued loss of employment by engineers throughout the summer months.

It was felt that above all the P.E.C.U. must keep itself in such financial condition that it can take care of all married members of the four Founder Societies whose situation now places them, or may place them within the next few months, within our Class A destitution. To be in Class A destitution a man must have three or more dependents, must have exhausted all personal resources and all personal credit. He may be briefly described as one with his back to the wall.

Starting in October 1931, the P.E. C.U., on instructions from the four Founder Societies, rendered assistance to members and non-members without discrimination. About February 8, when we had more knowledge of the problem confronting us, the Executive Committee, with the support of the General Committee, reached the conclusion that inasmuch as substantially 90 per cent of the money contributed to the P.E.C.U. had come from members of the four Founder Societies and yet more than 50 per cent of its registrations and more than 50 per cent of its placement of unemployed engineers had been of non-members of the Societies, it was necessary from that date on to use the funds contributed to the P.E.C.U. only for the assistance of members or former members of the four Founder Societies. We continued, however, to place our registered men with public or semi-public agencies without discrimination between members and non-members. In the face of present conditions, the decision has been made that the P.E.C.U. will use its own funds only for the relief of members of the Founder Societies. In deciding for the present to relieve only Class A destitute married members, we interpret the word "married" to include a single man with dependents. We also interpret "members" to include former members of the Founder Societies whose membership ceased because of their loss of position and inability to pay dues.

In concluding this report, on behalf of the General Executive Committees of the Professional Engineers Committee on Unemployment, I desire to make public our gratitude to the rank and file of our organization, including particularly the committee chairmen, who have done such spendid work and have given of their time and energy so unselfishly and with such splendid results. I believe that the thanks of the four Founder Societies are also due to all these men.

2. A Call for Subsidy, 1934

Report of the Science Advisory Board

With the advent of Franklin Roosevelt's New Deal in March 1933, a few scientists and engineers, most of whom were connected with the National Research Council, saw an opportunity not only to bring relief to their colleagues but also to help bring technology to bear upon the nation's problems. After prevailing upon the White House to establish a Science Advisory Board (1933-35), they then proposed a plan for massive federal subvention of scientific research. It was never clear whether relief and research were compatible goals, and the plan did not receive Roosevelt's backing. It remained merely evidence that at least a few men saw what science might have done to aid the nation's recovery.

Believing that scientific research is an essential element of any far-sighted and comprehensive program for planning and improving the national prosperity, and that failure to nourish and encourage American scientific activity will re-

From "Proposal of a Recovery Program of Science Progress," *Report of the Science Advisory Board: July 31, 1933 to September 1, 1934* (Washington, D.C., 1934), pp. 269-74, 282-83.

sult in failure to realize the nation's best economic advantages and standards of living, the undersigned representatives of the leading scientific and engineering organizations of America request consideration of the proposal to organize and support a Recovery Program of Science Progress under the National Industrial Recovery Act.

Such a program of research would give sorely needed employment to scientists, engineers, mechanics, assistants and apparatus makers. It would yield knowledge essential to future improvements in public works as well as to the creation of new industries and activities, and to the protection of American industry against competition arising from foreign discovery or invention. It should therefore be "self-liquidating" in a most significant way, as regards ultimate beneficial returns to the country. Through cooperation with existing research agencies, notably with the National Research Council with its affiliated scientific and engineering organizations, and with the universities, it could be organized rapidly and administered with a minimum of overhead expense.

THE PROPOSAL

It is proposed that $16,000,000 be appropriated for expenditure during six years in support of research in the natural sciences and their applications, the expenditures being contemplated approximately as set forth in a following section entitled "Planning and Administration."

Among the fields of research eligible to support from this fund should be the following:

(1) Investigations which may reasonably be expected to lead to improvement or extension of public works, as usually interpreted, e. g., transportation, communication, sanitation, building construction, etc. *Examples:* Intensive meteorological study of atmosphere up to 20,000 ft. elevation at 20 selected localities looking toward permanent improvement of weather forecasting, especially as regards air navigation; determination of physical properties of undisturbed samples of soils from important construction areas, in order to permit application of an improved method of designing foundations and earth works and calculating their future performance; intensive scientific and engineering study of sewage disposal from chemical and bacteriological viewpoints.

(2) Study and survey of natural resources in their economic, social and political relations, and particularly in regard to conservation, which call for a wide variety of special investigations and which are immediately necessary for intelligent national planning. *Examples:* Mapping of marginal lands with reference to degrees of agricultural risk, with consideration of location, long and short-range climate, soil, ground-water, plant life, etc.; study of effect of deforestation and of modes of reforestation on economic value of land.

(3) Determination of physical and chemical properties of materials which may be useful in industry and engineering, e. g., physical-chemical properties of matter at extreme temperatures, plasticity of materials of construction, electrical and thermal insulation, etc. *Example:* Measurement of heat capacities of substances at temperatures near absolute zero, supplying data needed for calculating yields in chemical industrial processes at high temperatures, as in fixation of nitrogen, or hydrogenation or cracking of hydrocarbons.

(4) Research in biology, medicine

and food technology directed ultimately toward public health and comfort. *Examples:* Development of more economical equipment for radiation therapy of cancer by recently improved methods; bacteriological study of frozen foods and their handling.

(5) Research in important fields which may lead to knowledge applicable to the satisfaction of human desires, the creation of new industries or the extension and improvement of established industries, including manufacture and agriculture, and the creation of wholesome recreational opportunities. *Examples:* Creation of an organic chemistry of the newly discovered "heavy hydrogen" and investigation of its possible applications to medicines, dyes, etc.; development of a practical method for transmission of electric power which is free from present limitations of cost and distance and which has met preliminary laboratory tests.

(6) Research on mechanization in relation to employment and costs. *Example:* Study by economists and engineers of the types of mechanization which are socially most advantageous in their effects on employment and costs, and an attempt to devise a plan for the best social and economic new uses of machinery.

Several examples of the types of projects which can be included in this program are explained in more detail in the Appendix.

In any such program of research, it is important that the limitations be not interpreted too rigidly, and also that discretion be exercised to eliminate proposals which involve the routine of research but which are uninspired and not directed toward significant results.

Furthermore, such a program supported by the Government, should give preference to research work whose results may reasonably be expected to be of general benefit, rather than of benefit to one special manufacturing or industrial group, since in the latter case such groups themselves should see the advantage and take the initiative in carrying on the research. Nothing is more reasonable, however, than that the Federal Government should foster investigations of general value, which have no powerful self-interested backers, yet which it is obviously important to have done.

The present time, with its subnormal employment of scientifically and technically trained men and diminished resources of universities and foundations which might otherwise support such investigations, is *the* time, if ever, for the Government to step in and support a temporary program which will give employment and at the same time will give results of immediate and permanent general value.

EMPLOYMENT

Unemployment among scientifically and technically trained men has been, and is, acute. The plight especially of the technically trained young men, who have received an expensive education and who are essential to the future life of the country, is pathetic. This has arisen from general decrease in engineering activity, and has been accentuated by the reduction of research and the dropping of research personnel for emergency budgetary reasons by large industries and by universities. The present drastic reduction in the scientific work of the Government bureaus, in order to balance budgets, has added significantly to this unemployment, and places upon the Government a considerable responsibility to extend its measures for emergency unemployment relief to scientific workers. The program here proposed would afford such emergency relief, without setting up a situation which, like a Government Bureau, is likely to become a more or less permanent drain on the Treasury.

It is important that this class of useful citizens should receive encouragement at this time. Unless it is done there will be two unfortunate results: first, these men will drift down into the more unskilled labor class or the competitive business class, increasing the distress in these classes; second, ambitious and able young men will be discouraged from entering a career in science or engineering, thus paving the way for great economic and intellectual loss in the near future.

It is appropriate also to emphasize the value of a large, able and well equipped body of scientific and technical men as perhaps the nation's chief asset for defense in time of war or for economic progress in time of peace. It is highly important that the morale and effectiveness of these groups be supported in this emergency, which has struck them as severely as any other group.

It is respectfully submitted that wise statesmanship demands some such form of governmental aid, in such a time of emergency, to the great group of productive scientists and engineers on whom depends so much of the future welfare of the country. Fortunately certain activities under the National Industrial Recovery Act are already giving employment to certain technical groups, notably civil engineers, naval constructors and agricultural experts. The proposed program would extend this stimulation of activity to all branches of science.

SELF LIQUIDATION

Desirable as it is that every project sponsored by the Emergency Public Works Administration be self-liquidating in the literal sense that all money advanced by the Federal Government be subsequently repaid to the Government, it is also realized, as a practical matter, that this ideal will be difficult, if not impossible, completely to attain in a program involving such large and rapid expenditures as are necessary to attain the other and principal objective of the Administration, viz., the quick stimulation of business activity combined with a healthy and useful relief of unemployment.

The National Industrial Recovery Act, Section 202, gives the Administrator broad powers to support work which will benefit a community permanently and socially, which can be undertaken promptly and which will not involve the Federal Treasury in recurring expenses. The Administrator has already acted favorably upon certain projects such as road construction, control of soil erosion, improvement of Government technical services and the construction of war ships, which are not self-liquidating in the literal sense, but which were approved as in the public interest and at the same time providing needed employment. We would therefore urge a strong claim for the research program here proposed, a program designed to promote the peaceful arts and the future prosperity of the country, while at the same time conserving and encouraging the scientific talent so badly needed for both the present and the future.

RELATIONSHIP WITH OTHER PROGRAMS

The chief advantages of administering such a program through the National Research Council are (1) the facility with which all elements of the program may be correlated with each other and with all other scientific work in the country and (2) the means which exist for marshalling the best talent of the country, within and without governmental circles, for planning and executing the work. Such cooperation and broad vision are impossible if each scientific or technical project is planned, presented and executed by a particular group with a viewpoint which is necessarily restricted to the interests and experience of the group.

The present program is directed primarily toward the solving of important problems rather than to the providing of work for particular groups of men in governmental, university or professional circles. However, the execution of the program would, in its various aspects, call for cooperation of men drawn from all these groups and provide employment for them.

If this project is approved, the Board charged with its administration could be called upon by the Administrator, at his discretion, to advise or assist in connection with any other projects of a scientific or technical character, in order to avoid duplication and to promote wise planning and effective cooperation.

PUBLIC APPROVAL

It is believed that support of this program under the National Industrial Recovery Act would meet with universal approval on such grounds as the following:

All can recognize the arguments, for example, for providing useful employment on a large scale for unskilled labor in the Civilian Conservation Corps, or for maintaining the shipyards and the national defense by the great program of naval construction, with its attendant employment and stimulation of business, or for the construction of useful roads and structures. Among thoughtful people, however, there will be sensed a lack of proper balance in any program which devotes several hundred millions of dollars to preparedness for war while at the same time restricting expenditures for the most effective and constructive enjoyment of peace through increased knowledge and its applications.

We believe that the proposed program would have the maximum freedom from any suspicion of undue opportunities for private profit or political advantage, since the work would be principally carried out and the moneys expended by non-profit institutions operated solely for public service, such as the universities and the national scientific and technical societies centered in the National Research Council, with cooperation in certain phases by governmental bureaus.

We believe further, that such a program would be enthusiastically welcomed by the best thought of the country as one that is unique, not only designed to correct an important element of unemployment, but also constructive in the best sense.

PLANNING AND ADMINISTRATION OF THE PROGRAM

The most effective planning and economical administration of such a program would be through the National

Research Council, which unites the national scientific and engineering societies including representatives of the technical services of the Government, for organized cooperative effort. Established and operated effectively as a civilian agency to cooperate with the Government during war time, it has continued to perfect its organization, and gain experience in fostering and directing research programs in the whole realm of pure and applied science. It has also had experience in administering numerous special research funds, including an annual general fund for "grants-in-aid-of-research" supplied by the Rockefeller Foundation.

To expedite action and insure prompt adoption and application of policies, it is suggested that a small board of scientists and engineers, including the Chairman of the National Research Council, be appointed with authority and responsibility directly under the Board of the Emergency Public Works Administration, to operate through the National Research Council. This board may, in fact, be a special committee of the National Research Council, analogous to the Science Advisory Board, appointed for the purpose.

It is probable that the National Research Council would, as in the past, set up a special planning and supervisory committee on each individual research project so as to enlist for each project the best advisory scientific and engineering talent in the country.

By carrying out the research activities as far as possible in university and engineering school laboratories, overhead expenses for quarters, supervision and administration can be reduced to a minimum, so that the funds will go where they are most needed and will be most effective. It is suggested also that,

in such a cooperative program for public good, manufacturers may be induced to supply equipment at or near actual cost of production.

In carrying out the proposed program, three factors are important in determining the most favorable schedule: These are the urgency of immediate action as a relief measure, the time required to get the program into full swing and the desirability of bringing the program to a gradual rather than an abrupt conclusion in order to distribute the period of absorption into permanent employment of the personnel engaged in the program. For these reasons, and having in mind the time limitations specified in the National Industrial Recovery Act, we suggest that the fund of $16,000,000 be appropriated in such a manner that the funds may be available for expenditure approximately according to the following schedule:

Balance of 1933	....	$1,000,000
1934	....	5,000,000
1935	....	4,000,000
1936	....	3,000,000
1937	....	2,000,000
1938	....	1,000,000
Total	....	$16,000,000

. . .

The present combination of available funds, available personnel and urgent need for the information should make this a peculiarly appropriate subject for support from the Emergency Public Works fund.

SOCIAL PROBLEMS OF MECHANIZATION

Technical progress has two principal industrial results: it creates new industries and new employment; it displaces labor by machines. This latter result has both good and bad effects. The problems thus created are of enormous social import. Much half-baked and sensational discussion has centered around these problems in the past few years. There can be no doubt, however, but that mechanization of industry will continue, and this presents a challenge to our best engineering and social talent to devise a method of handling mechanization so as to minimize its ill effects while enjoying its advantages.

It is submitted that intelligent planning should yield better results than unplanned operation in this, as in other fields. Various suggestions have been made, and some of them tried in particular industries. These include such policies as a temporary tax on new labor displacing machinery, the proceeds of which supply work for the displaced labor for a limited period, or the maintenance of personnel and wages subsequent to introduction of labor saving machinery until a new employment equilibrium is reached, or cooperation between industries to absorb labor in new activities whenever it is displaced by machinery, or reduction in working hours, or a combination of such policies.

Industrial management engineers and sociologists should make a thorough study of the results of such plans, and give consideration to new suggestions, in the hope of working out a feasible method of handling the problems of industrial mechanization on a large scale. A number of individuals are already studying these problems. It is proposed to engage them in a cooperative study, with assistance by trade associations and large industries. It is conceivable that it may eventually be desirable to incorporate the results of such a study into industrial codes.

GRANTS IN AID OF RESEARCH IN BASIC SCIENCES

Most of the preceding examples are applications of science to attain some desirable practical objective. It should not be forgotten that back of applied science must be continual progress in pure science. Consequently any well balanced program of research should provide for continued productive activity in the fundamental sciences. It is suggested therefore, that some portion of the funds here discussed be made available for such research, with particular consideration of important programs already in progress in institutions, which have had to be dropped or curtailed in the present financial emergency.

In conclusion it may be pointed out that several national organizations, such as the great engineering societies, have already assembled lists of important investigations of general public benefit, which can be undertaken as soon as funds are available.

The preceding examples illustrate the type and scope of the work which could be carried on under the proposed program. If this application is favorably acted upon, the Board would proceed at once to select the most important and promising projects and set up competent committees to outline and organize them and supervise their execution.

3. Technocracy, 1936

HOWARD SCOTT, "A Rendezvous With Destiny"

Although the subsidization of civilian research by the federal government seemed a radically dangerous idea to many, it was relatively conservative when compared with some of the other proposals which won an audience in the Depression years. One controversial figure was Howard Scott, who for a brief time gained support for his idea of Technocracy. Even though he was soon discredited, his organization still exists; it remains one of the relics of a period when radical conditions seemed to call for radical solutions.

Civilization has moved ever westward. In 7000 years of recorded social history along this westward movement mankind has evolved many forms of government around a single technic of social administration.

Governments of yesterday and today have produced many variations in their structures but have succeeded only in embellishing the basic technic common to all previous theories of governance.

All government of our social history has been the imposition of a conscious regulatory control on the functional procedure of the means whereby people live. This conscious regulatory control or government has always been extraneous to the functional sequences necessary for man's social livelihood upon which it was imposed.

All governments have had to depend for their economic maintenance upon a subtraction of a portion of the productive output of the individual citizen. The result has been the same whether the individual government achieved it through taxes, tithes, or forced levies. It is significant to note that governments in their extractions of their economic income from the individual citizen have in no case guaranteed any standard of livelihood to their citizens. That governments have been wise or unwise, judicious or tyrannical in the administration of their national affairs is irrelevant to the scope of this inquiry.

In any consideration of governments, past and present, the dominant significance is the relationship of government to the methods of production and distribution and to all physical processes necessary for the conduct of human affairs.

In all social systems the standard of living of the citizens of any particular one is the direct result of energy applied to the natural resources for the satisfaction of the wants of man.

In all civilizations previous to the modern age the only energy that could

From Howard Scott, "A Rendezvous With Destiny," reprinted from *Technocracy* in *American Engineer*, VI (October 1936), 8-10, 24. Reprinted by permission of *American Engineer*.

be degraded and consumed in the social process of living was the physical effort of the citizenry.

It was human toil that built the pyramids at Ghizeh, the walls and gardens of Babylon, the Parthenon of Athens, the temple at Luxor, the Roman highways, the irrigation ditches of Assyria and Nineveh, the castles and cathedrals of medieval Europe, and the palaces of the pre-Power Age.

All governments have regulated the lives of their citizenries more or less—regulations instituted chiefly for the primary purpose of perpetuating more government. Governments have "guaranteed" their citizens and subjects many things. They have promised their citizens peace and safety from attack; they have promised them war and possible loot; they have promised them freedom and liberty; they have promised them heaven when they die, equality here on earth, and equality with the angels.

All governments have imposed upon their citizens the obligation of service and surrender, the obligation of serving their country and their countrymen, and the obligation of surrendering a portion of their economic wherewithal for the perpetuation of government, and their obligations.

In these 7000 years of scarcity economy no government has ever been obliged to maintain a maximum standard of living in the area under its administration. No government has ever been charged by its citizenry with the responsibility of conducting all operations.

Every government of a scarcity economy has striven to avoid the assumption of any such responsibility, and if it has acted at all it has only been in moments of extreme national emergency. The citizens of all previous economies of scarcity were compelled to expend their time and effort in human toil from sunrise to sunset by the ever present threat of starvation; therefore the government of any previous economy of scarcity had internally only the minor problem of maintaining civil order among its underfed citizens. In 7000 years of scarcity economy no government has ever faced the social problem that arises from a new method of producing physical wealth. Hitherto ninety-nine percent of all citizens have burned out their lives in exhaustive human toil, providing the benefactions of leisure to a dominant minority while compensating themselves with a meager sustenance rendered more palatable by the slaven morale of their wish-fulfillment psychology.

Today, in 1936, the national political entities on the North American Continent are confronted with a problem never faced by any previous government of man. The two chief national entities on this Continent cannot avoid the imminent solution of the problem of producing all physical wealth with the minimum of human effort.

The United States and Canada are being compelled by the technological march of events to meet this fundamental issue in advance of every civil government of the world. The governments of the United States and Canada will be compelled in spite of their reluctance to meet this epochal issue in the march of civilization—an issue that has but one possible ending, the defeat and abolition of every political government on the Continent of North America.

No political administration of any economy of scarcity, however competent, can, by the very nature of its structure, usher in an economy of abundance.

An economy of abundance on the

North American Continent is only possible when political government has been abolished.

The death of the American Price System and its political government will be a far, far greater event to the citizens of this Continent than any of its living acts.

Amid the raucous din of the political circus, the hilarity of the Technocrats over the predicament of this Price System and its political administrators is the one healthy note.

Technology marches on. The political governments of the United States and Canada are beseeching Providence for economic absolution for the sins of the Price System, and Providence tenders them droughts and floods and even more technological equipment.

The political governments of the United States and Canada are part and parcel of the Price System of this Continent. They are the purveyors of scarcity, the merchandisers of national debt and the sowers of national dissolution. They are the ballyhooers of public confidence and the salesman of sucker bait to their citizens.

The political governments of the United States and Canada are the institutional blockades to social progress. They are the strong-arm squads of the merchants of debt and death.

These political governments of debt and dissolution, of scarcity and slaven morale, and unconsciously and unknowingly engaged in stampeding their respective citizens into a national rush— headed for the last roundup.

With all the resources of the national treasuries at their command, these political governments are flooding their respective countries with high-powered propaganda exhorting their citizenries to enter the national political contest for the reward of the more abundant life.

This national propaganda on the part of both countries is a deliberate conspiracy to deceive and defraud the citizens of the United States and Canada from receiving their natural heritage of Continental abundance by delaying the arrival of the New America.

There are clamorings on the part of political parties in the United States and Canada for the revision and amendment of the Constitution and the British North America Act. Technocracy in previous literature has very clearly pointed out that installation of an era of abundance on the North American Continent involves a basic change in the economic channelization of the means whereby the people live.

No basic change in the economic channelization of these two countries is possible under any form of political government. Both the British North America Act and the Constitution of the United States are contractural agreements between the Provinces and the Dominion, the States and the Federal Government. These contractural agreements are national indentures guaranteeing in perpetuity that chiselling shall be the sole prerogative of the merchants of debt.

These documents are the scarecrows of scarcity, the anachronism of a Red River cart or prairie schooner trying to pull a hundred horsepower automobile. They are the antiquities of the poverty of a hand-tool age. They were written with the sickle and the scythe, the spade and the hoe. They sufficed well enough during the primitiveness of a pioneer America; but in this Power Age there is just one last fitting service that modern technology can bestow upon them, that they be wrapped in celophane and preserved in a museum as evidence of social ascent.

The Constitution of the United States and the British North America Act of Canada are the last legal refuges of the Bourbonism of our Price System. The debt merchants of the Price System are seeking to preserve these two blanket permits as the last guarantee of the prerogative of national chiselling; but, alas and alack! when these documents were conceived and perpetrated it was for the purpose of regulating and controlling the privileges of exploiting human effort in creating the values of property. Modern technology was not anticipated by the founding fathers. Wise as the statesmen of our past may have been, the totality of their knowledge would in this Power Age be but a ticket to national stupidity. All social institutions and political documents conceived out of and originated by the experience of men prior to the Power Age are totally useless in solving the problems of the Continental technology that are daily mounting in the social progression of this age of power and machinery.

The ward and the county are the foundation stones in the political structure of the United States and Canada. The 5600 counties in the United States are that many separate divisions in 48 sovereign powers. Within these 5600 counties and 48 States there exist in excess of 162,000 separate and distinct political units charged with the political responsibility of administering the United States under this Price System.

In view of this complicated obsolescent structure of national administration, the absurdity of any political solution to the national problems of the United States—and similarly Canada— becomes immediately apparent.

In the United States a two-thirds majority of the 48 States is required in order to enact a fundamental political change. Can you imagine, Mr. Citizen, the predicament of any political party in either of these countries if it should become sufficiently powerful to be assured of representing the will of the people to the extent of acquiring a two-thirds majority? Mr. Citizen, can you imagine any political party, upon achieving that power, voting itself and its millions of office holders out of existence for the good of the people?

In the United States there are 17,-500,000 telephones, 22,500,000 automobiles, 49,000,000 horsepower of industrial prime movers, 240,000 miles of railroad. These are but part of the productive and service equipment whose daily operation is required in the processes of living for its 127,000,000 citizens.

The United States has in excess of 1,600,000,000 horsepower of installed prime movers necessary to drive the equipment in its total operation. This totality of equipment is consuming in excess of 153,000 kilogram-calories per capita per day—a consumption of energy per capita per day which is not only the highest in the world, but, exclusive of Canada, is not even approached by any other country. This energy is produced from our natural resources of coal, oil, gas, and hydroelectric power. More will be produced from these sources each succeeding year. The continued increase in the conversion of extraneous energy will automatically force a further decline in the consumption of total man-hours in the national economy. The consumption of this extraneous energy is increasing in excess of 5 per cent per annum.

The social operation of the United

States will become increasingly critical as the total consumption of extraneous energy approaches 200,000 kilogram-calories per capita per day. This critical total of energy conversion per capita per day is only 30 per cent greater than the present total of 153,000. It is therefore obvious that at the rate of growth of 5 per cent per annum the United States will be brought to the critical figure on or before 1942. It is significant that the efficiency of all energy consuming devices tends to increase proportional to the rate of increase in the total energy consumption.

The combination of increasing energy consumption and greater efficiency will result in higher speed, less floor space, reduced plant area, greater production in less hours, faster transportation, and quicker turnover, and bring the final resultant of a greater total productive capacity for the country as a whole with less employment, and consequently less purchasing power, in the form of salaries and wages.

The competitive practices of corporate enterprise in this Price System is compelling the installation of more efficient equipment. The so-called "modernization" of industry in the United States is proceeding by leaps and bounds. The machine tool industry is enjoying a boom almost equal to that of 1929; but its output is two to five times faster and more efficient than that of 1929.

The coal mining industry in the United States is spending 365 million dollars in new coal mining equipment. Coal mining in three years will have no resemblance to the coal mining of today. The new equipment ranges from open pit power-shovels of 50 tons per bucketload to underground loaders capable of loading 8 tons per minute. The world's record for underground coal mining is held by the Orient Mine, in Illinois—an average of 10,000 tons per eight hours with 600 men. It has reached a peak of 15,314 tons in eight hours with the same staff. And this is only the beginning! Technology in the coal industry has merely started. Modern technology, fully applied, is capable in the coal industry of mining 30,000 tons of coal in 24 hours with less than 20 men by the practical development and application of the continuous milling long wall process.

The United Mine Workers of America are on their way to join the glass-blowers and the cigar makers in labor's oblivion.

No human being ever acquired social prestige mining coal.

The steel industry of the United States is pouring over 300 million dollars into the modernization of its plants. The United States Steel Corporation, the sleeping giant of the steel industry, has at last been forced by the technology of its competitors to rush into the most extensive rebuilding of steel plants that the industry has ever known. This is the corporation which in the heyday of its prosperity had such a huge capital account that it could obtain its business mainly by financial pressure and not by the metallurgical advancement of ferrous technology.

The United States Steel Corporation, since its inception, has been so powerful financially that it has enjoyed the enviable position of never having made a single contribution to the technology of ferrous metallurgy. It has been rich in dollars and poor in sense, but is now being compelled—like the United States Supreme Court—to bow grudgingly to the technology of this Power Age. It is a little late, but its program of modernization bulks large on the horizon of steel. Technocracy, Inc., is deeply grateful for its unconscious advancement of Technocracy's social objective for the North American Continent.

By September, 1937, practically all of the modernization of the sheet and strip divisions of the steel industry will have been completed and over 60,000 men now employed in the steel industry will no longer be required.

God is good and God is kind. God provided this Continent with the greatest natural resources. God has had a lot of trouble with human beings. In Napoleon's day He was on the side of the heaviest artillery, but in this Power Age, with millions of human beings more capable than they have ever been before, God in His kindness is on the side of the greatest technology.

When the buffalo roamed the western plains and the prairie sod was thick, the water table was high, providing a vast pasturage. The American plains at that time were in biologic equilibrium. The buffalo and the prairie sod have disappeared. Land speculation and farm development by the railroads, the States, the Provinces, and private corporations opened up millions of acres of prairie land. The United States Department of Agriculture assisted corporate enterprise by showing the farmer how to raise crops on the western plains by dry farming. Millions of farms were made and the country was settled. Cities and towns sprang up and it was all deemed part and parcel of American initiative, thrift and industry. Individually, it required hard work, stamina, and ability. It brought the result of a glorious temporary success. But once farming in those areas became widespread (in the last thirty years) its very extensiveness spelled its doom, for agri-

culture cannot be maintained there over any period of time except in particular locations where water is available for irrigation or the maintenance of the subsoil water table. The widespread agricultural development of dry farming in these areas has lowered the water table from 20 to 40 feet in the last two decades. The present droughts are accessories after the fact. The individualistic, anarchic development of agriculture in these areas has been a cumulative process that can have but one end, the desertizing of the great plains of the United States and Canada —unless the process is controlled by a Continental agronomy and a Continental hydrology.

God is good and God is kind. Floods and droughts are the warnings of Providence that we citizens of this Continent had better mend our sinful ways. Agrotechnology is on the march with its Faraday Fluid Feeding Process or tank farms. Droughts will force the further economic liquidation of farmers in the United States and Canada.

This forcing is a providential blessing, for it simultaneously compels the introduction on a commercial scale of agrotechnology, by which man for the first time in his history will no longer be dependent upon the fertility of soil and the vagaries of the weather. Technocracy wishes to express its thanks for this providential aid.

It would like to point out that no human being ever acquired social prestige following the plow.

The Faraday Fluid Feeding Process will provide no place for the plow or the harrow, the sickle or the hoe, the cultivator or the combine. It is a process whereby chemical plant food, dissolved in water, feeds the roots descending through a seed bed of tar-treated excelsior, stationary or on a travelling belt. A maximum of biologic growth is attained—a maximum undreamed of by the tillers of the soil—and a growth so fast that even the bugs have but a slight chance. This agrotechnology does not require cultivation; neither are there any weeds. Agricultural child labor won't be a basic requirement of the small farmer.

The Faraday Fluid Feeding Process grows Burley tobacco 13 feet high, 2,-500 to 3000 bushels of potatoes per acre of surface, and tomato vines 35 feet high with a tremendous increase in yield.

This agrotechnology will solve the food problem of any area that can convert sufficient extraneous energy and has the requisite water and mineral resources for the plant food of the particular agrotypes necessary for its food consumption. Farming and farmers are the last great upholders of human toil. Agrotechnology as it advances will consign them to oblivion.

In the face of these progressions on the Continent of North America, every political platform, every political gesture is but an expression of national idiocy. For the issues of this country and this Continent will not be met by any political party, radical or conserv-

ative, liberal or reactionary. Both autocracy and democracy are defunct, and will go out with the human toil of the ages of scarcity.

President Roosevelt, in his acceptance speech at Philadelphia, made only one significant statement. His other statements were irrelevant, incompetent, and immaterial. That statement was, "This generation of Americans has a rendezvous with destiny."

This Continent has a rendezvous with destiny and in that destiny lies the future of civilization. That destiny will not tolerate the politician and poverty, the economic pestilence of this Price System.

This Continent has no choice but to lead the march of civilization. The opportunity is given to no other Continent. The twentieth century belongs to North America. This Continent's destiny, its task, is the elimination of human toil and the installation of security and abundance. This Continent will have its rendezvous with destiny within the next decade, and upon this generation of Americans will fall the competent and orderly achievement of a new civilization. This generation of Americans has the technology, the men, the materials, and the machinery for its accomplishment.

4. A Difference of Opinion, 1936

Science

If many scientists and engineers tended to doubt the wisdom and good will of politicians, not all public officials were willing to exonerate technology of

From "The Responsibility of Engineering," *Science*, LXXXIV (October 30, 1936), 393-94. Reprinted by permission of *Science* and the American Association for the Advancement of Science.

all responsibility for the Depression. Powerful spokesmen for the Two Cultures addressed each other in 1936 when Karl T. Compton, President of the Massachusetts Institute of Technology and former chairman of the Science Advisory Board, and President Roosevelt exchanged polite letters on the subject of "The Responsibility of Engineering."

President Roosevelt has addressed to Dr. Karl T. Compton, president of the Massachusetts Institute of Technology, and to the heads of other schools of technology and engineering an open letter that reads:

Events of recent years have brought into clearer perspective the social responsibility of engineering.

In respect of wise use of natural resources such reports as those of the Mississippi Valley Committee, the National Resources Committee and the Great Plains Drought Area Committee have brought out the facts impressively. The enclosed report, "Little Waters," presents in miniature many of the social-engineering problems of soil and water conservation.

In respect of the impact of science and engineering upon human life—social and economic dislocations as well as advance in productive power—the facts are revealed with distressing clearness in public records of unemployment, bankruptcies and relief. The responsibility of scientists has been analyzed in noteworthy addresses such as, among the most recent, those presented at the Tercentenary Celebration of Harvard University and the meeting of the British Association for the Advancement of Science.

The design and construction of specific civil engineering works or of instruments for production represent only one part of the responsibility of engineering. It must also consider social processes and problems, and modes of more perfect adjustment to environment, and must cooperate in designing accommodating mechanisms to absorb the shocks of the impact of science.

This raises the question whether the curricula of engineering schools are so balanced as to give coming generations of engineers the vision and flexible technical capacity necessary to meet the full range of engineering responsibility.

I am calling this matter to the attention of educators of high administrative authority in the hope that it may be thoroughly explored in faculty discussions and in meetings of engineering, educational and other pertinent professional associations.

To this letter President Compton made on October 23 the following reply:

In response to your challenge to educators to give students the necessary "vision and flexible technical capacity," and to engineers to "cooperate in designing and accommodating mechanisms to absorb the shocks of the impact of science," I am sure you will be pleased to know that these are already matters to which progressive educators and engineers have been giving most earnest and constructive attention through their schools and professional organizations. To this end, for example, increasing emphasis is being placed upon fundamentals rather than specialties in undergraduate engineering education, and there has been a notable increase in attention to the study of economics and social science.

I can not but wonder why your exhortation has been directed specifically toward engineers, for surely we would agree that similar breadth of knowledge and training is also urgently desirable among business leaders, economists and politicians—as is also thorough training in fundamentals. For example, there is a tendency in some quarters to make science the major scapegoat of our social ills, from which social planners will rescue us. What are the facts?

Just before the advent of the machine age, social planners were devising resettlement projects and model industrial communities based upon a scheme to employ labor of all children above the age of four years. This was their best solution of the desperate struggle of the masses of the people for the bare necessities of life. Since that time science and engineering have so increased productive power that it has been possible for enlightened public leaders to inaugurate a great program of social security, including child labor laws, universal education, moderate hours of labor, pensions, insurance and unemployment relief on a large scale. These are superimposed on an enormously improved general standard of comfort, health and interest in living. Such achievements of science dwarf into insignificance the "social and economic dislocations" to which you refer, unfortunate as these are and much as these merit the attention which you recommend.

One significant fact is generally unrecognized by those who are chiefly impressed by the fact that science, through machine production, has displaced human labor. It is that such machines are, by and large, products of a relatively old branch of science, mechanics, whereas the present day activities in science are principally in electricity, chemistry, metallurgy, biology and such newer branches as lead to new knowledge, new products, new industries, new employment and improved health and material welfare.

There are two basic methods of dealing with "unemployment, bankruptcies" and similar dislocations which you mention, one palliative and the other curative. Both may be needed. The former includes relief, emergency work, and regulation, and operates immediately; the latter aims at creation of new employment, new wealth and new values, and is a longer range program. It is primarily to the latter that engineers and scientists are devoting their major attention, since both logic and past experience demonstrate its social effectiveness, and since it can only be carried on through their type of knowledge and training. Quite properly and of necessity it is the first method which has been the chief concern of the government, since the emergency called for swift action.

We engineers and scientists, however, are disturbed lest the palliative measures be mistaken for the cure, and lest the attention and money devoted to relief and regulation should interfere with simultaneous adequate attention and support to the basic contributions which our sciences can certainly make if given a chance.

As illustrations of our cause for concern, and of the need for broader understanding by political leaders as well as engineers, I would respectfully refer to four events. (1) The engineering and scientific organizations of the country combined to urge that a small portion of the public works expenditures be devoted to research aimed at better designs and materials for public works for the future, in accordance with all enlightened industrial policy. (2) Your Science Advisory Board of prominent engineers and scientists recommended that attention be given to development of scientific knowledge on which can be built the new industries, so urgently desired by your administration to provide employment. (3) Various groups urged that the present efforts to aid the farmer be supplemented by a really adequate attempt to create new markets for farm products through discovery of new industrial uses for these products through research. None of these recommendations was acted upon. (4) Your letter to us calls attention of the public to the "dislocations" produced by science, and quite properly calls on us to try to cure them, but it does not indicate interest in the creative work and permanent values which engineers and scientists continue to regard as their chief contributions to social welfare.

My colleagues and I will do everything in our power to deal with the situations which you have called to our attention: reciprocally we most respectfully urge you and your colleagues in the government to put science to work more effectively for the national welfare, and to encourage its activities in all three of its principal settings—in governmental bureaus, in industry and in educational institutions.

Since your letter was received through the press, it is evidently your desire to call these issues to the attention of the public generally. I assume, therefore, that there is no impropriety in my replying *via* the same route.

5. Technological Trends, 1937

The role of science and technology in the progress or disruption of society continued to be a major question both within and without the government. One agency which was particularly concerned with such questions was the Science Committee of the National Resources Committee. The Science Committee was made up of representatives from both the physical and social sciences, as well as from the field of education. In 1937 they made a pioneer report on the problem, of which William F. Ogburn, Professor of Sociology at the University of Chicago, was a major architect.

FOREWORD

BY THE SCIENCE COMMITTEE

Anticipation of the future is the key to adequate planning for the best use of our national resources. It is, however, more difficult to look forward without the aid of precise instruments, than it is to look backward, with the aid of memory and records. Though this report attempts to deal with the future, it is fully realized that the future grows out of the past and hence that past trends must be studied to determine future trends.

Planning is usually carried on in relation to a specific task, for a definite time, in a limited territory; but changes coming from without these limits may upset the best laid programs. Thus the chemical inventions making substitutes of wool and cotton from cellulose, gasoline from coal, and rubber from coal and chalk, may affect cotton, coal, and timber production, and no doubt poli-

cies in regard to other natural resources. So closely interrelated is the mechanism of modern civilization that a change occurring in one part, say in industry, will produce an effect in a quite different and unexpected part, as for instance, in the schools, or the use of natural resources. Hence we need a view of the general causes, types, and trends over a broad front, since any specific program may be affected by forces originating elsewhere.

Invention is a great disturber and it is fair to say that the greatest general cause of change in our modern civilization is invention; although it is recognized that social forces in turn encourage or discourage inventions. Certainly developments in technology cause a vast number of changes in a great variety of fields. A banker once defined invention as that which makes his securities insecure. Hence a study of the trends of inventions furnishes a broad perspective of many great movements

From *Technological Trends and National Policy, Including the Social Implications of New Inventions, June 1937*, Report of the Subcommittee on Technology to the National Resources Committee (Washington, D.C., 1937), pp. vi-viii, 3, 8-9, 12-14.

of change and basic general information for any planning body, however general or specific their plans may be. . . .

Findings

1. The large number of inventions made every year shows no tendency to diminish. On the contrary the trend is toward further increases. No cessation of social changes due to invention is to be expected. It is customary to speak of the present age as one of great change, as though it were a turbulent transition period between two plateaus of calm, but such a conclusion is illusory. Though the rate of change may vary in the future there is no evidence whatever of a changeless peace ahead.

2. Although technological unemployment is one of the most tragic effects of the sudden adoption of many new inventions (which may be likened to an immigration of iron men), inventions create jobs as well as take them away. While some technological changes have resulted in the complete elimination of occupations and even entire industries, the same or other changes have called into being new occupations, services, and industries.

3. No satisfactory measures of the volume of technological unemployment have as yet been developed, but at least part of the price for this constant change in the employment requirements of industry is paid by labor since many of the new machines and techniques result in "occupational obsolescence." The growth and decay of industries and occupations caused by technological progress necessitate continuous and widespread—and not always successful—readjustments and adaptations on the part of workers whose jobs are affected by these changes.

4. The question whether there will be a large amount of unemployment during the next period of business prosperity rests only in part on the introduction of new inventions and more efficient industrial techniques. The other important elements are changes in the composition of the country's production (such as appreciable changes in the proportion which service activities constitute of the total), the growth of population, changes in the demands for goods and services, shift in markets, migration of industry, hiring age policies of industries, and other factors discussed in the body of the report. For instance, even if industrial techniques remained the same, the volume of production would have to be greater in the future than in 1929 in order to absorb the increase in the working population and keep unemployment to the level of that date. If the productivity of 1935 (the latest year for which figures are available) continues the same in 1937, and the composition of the nation's total product remains unchanged, production would have to be increased 20 percent over that of 1929 to have as little unemployment as existed then. Failing this there will be more unemployment and if labor efficiency is increased by new inventions or otherwise, then the production of physical goods and services must be more than 120 percent of what it was in 1929.

5. Aside from jobs, subtracted or added, new inventions affect all the great social institutions; family, church, local community, State, and industry. The Committee finds that in all the fields of technology and applied science which were investigated there are many new inventions that will have important

influences upon society and hence upon all planning problems. Particularly impressive were new inventions in agriculture, communication, aviation, metallurgy, chemistry, and electrical tools and appliances.

6. A large and increasing part of industrial development and of the correlated technological advances arises out of science and research. Invention is commonly an intermediate step between science and technological application, but this does not make less important the point that the basic ideas upon which these programs are developed come out of scientific discovery or creative activity.

7. Advance of many aspects of industry and the correlated technologies is dependent upon scientific research and discovery. This fact is made clear by the increasing importance of research laboratories in the great industries. The research conducted is not only well organized but it is carried forward with the cooperation of investigators having high rank in the field of science. If the contribution of research were to be reduced, the industries would tend to freeze in a particular pattern.

8. Though the influence of invention may be so great as to be immeasurable, as in the case of gunpowder or the printing press, there is usually opportunity to anticipate its impact upon society *since it never comes instantaneously without signals.* For invention is a process and there are faint beginnings, development, diffusion, and social influences, occurring in sequence, all of which require time. From the early origins of an invention to its social effects the time intervals averages about 30 years.

9. While a serious obstacle to considering invention in planning is lack of precise knowledge, this is not irremediable nor the most difficult fact to overcome. Other equally serious obstacles are inertia of peoples, prejudice, lack of unity of purpose, and the difficulties of concerted action.

10. Among the resistances to the adoption of new inventions and hence to the spread of the advantages of technological progress there is specially noted those resistances arising in connection with scrapping equipment in order to install the new. Better accounting methods and greater appreciation of the rate of inventional development facilitates the spread of improved capital goods. The rate of capital obsolescence is especially a major problem under monopolistic conditions, which probably favor the adoption of technological improvements less than do conditions of keen competition.

11. The time lag between the first development and the full use of an invention is often a period of grave social and economic maladjustment, as, for example, the delay in the adoption of workmen's compensation and the institution of "safety first" campaigns after the introduction of rapidly moving steel machines. This lag emphasized the necessity of planning in regard to inventions.

Recommendations

1. The reports herewith presented reveal the imminence of a few very important inventions that may soon be widely used with resultant social influences of significance. Since these inventions may deeply affect planning it is recommended that a series of studies be undertaken by the planning agencies herein recommended or by existing planning boards, with the aid of such

natural and social scientists as may be needed, on the following inventions: the mechanical cotton picker, air conditioning equipment, plastics, the photoelectric cell, artificial cotton and woolenlike fibres made from cellulose, synthetic rubber, prefabricated houses, television, facsimile transmission, the automobile trailer, gasoline produced from coal, steep-flight aircraft planes, and tray agriculture.

2. A special case of the influence of invention is technological unemployment. It is recommended that a joint committee be formed from the Department of Labor, the Department of Commerce, the Department of Agriculture, Bureau of Mines, Interstate Commerce Commission, Social Security Board, and the Works Progress Administration with such other cooperation as may be needed, for the purposes of keeping abreast with technological developments and ascertaining and noting the occupations and industries which are likely to be affected by imminent technological changes and the extent to which these inventions are likely to result in unemployment. It is recommended that such information be made available through the appropriate departments to the industry and labor likely to be affected.

3. In view of the findings regarding the importance of technology and applied science, it is recommended that the Federal government develop appropriate agencies for continuous study of them; and more specifically that there be set up in the respective departments science committees with the definite function of investigating and reporting at regular periods on the progress and trends of science and invention and the possible and economic effects flowing therefrom as they affect the work of the departments and of the agencies to whom they render service. Copies of such reports should be supplied to the National Resources Board and it is recommended that insofar as is feasible they be made available to the various city, county, and State planning boards, and to the public.

4. Since the patent laws have considerable influence on the rate of technological progress, it is recommended that the whole system be reviewed by a group of social scientists and economists. This review, unlike others dealing with specific reforms, technical operations, scientific aspects, or ethical implications should be concerned with the articulation of the patenting process with the fundamental processes of human progress and the types of economic systems. From such basic relationships the better adaptation of the system to changing conditions can be worked out in the necessary detail.

5. It is recommended that the Science Committee of the National Resources Committee, with the cooperation of other scientists that may be needed, make an investigation of the adequacy of the reporting of inventions and of discoveries in applied science and advise on the feasibility (a) of more balanced coverage, (b) of selecting those more socially significant, and (c) of assembling of such data in some central location or locations.

6. The most important general conclusion to be drawn from these studies is the continuing growth of the already high and rapidly developing technology in the social structure of the Nation, and hence the hazard of any planning that does not take this fact into consideration. This pervasive interrelationship so clearly manifest throughout the pages of this report points to one great

need, namely, a permanent over-all planning board. Such a board is needed to give breadth of consideration to the variety of factors which affect specific plans. This board would take its place in the governmental pattern as coordinator for the many special planning boards, of which there are now 47 State boards, 400 county boards, and 1,100 city boards. The Technology Committee, therefore, makes to the National Resources Committee, as a major recommendation of this report, the creation of a National Resources Board, as recommended by the President's Committee on Administrative Management in their report of January 8, 1937. . . .

NATIONAL POLICY AND TECHNOLOGY
BY WILLIAM F. OGBURN

When conditions are changing rapidly, policies for national welfare are especially in need of guiding principles. To this end, knowledge of probable technological trends is, in modern times, of very great help. This idea which is the subject of this section of the report of the National Resources Committee may be set forth briefly in a paragraph.

In an age of great change, anticipation of what will probably happen is a necessity for the executives at the helm of the ship of state. A study of invention offers a very good clue to future social conditions and problems of a nation. For, of four material factors that determine the economic well-being of nations, to wit, invention, population, natural resources, and economic organization, the first changes the most frequently in the modern world and hence is most often a cause. Thus, there are 50,000 patents a year and some of them have great influence. For instance, the airplane will change the nature of na-

tional defense in case of war. In this case the growth of the airplane precedes the development of national defense. This sequence is common. The scientific achievement comes first and the social effects later. The fact that there is a lag makes invention a social barometer. The production curve of automobiles forecasts the growth of suburbs. Furthermore, since it requires a quarter of a century more or less for an invention to be perfected and to be put into wide use, it is possible to anticipate their results some years ahead. Whether the social effects of inventions can in practice be read off this barometer with sureness is doubtful in the present stage of the advancement of social science. But that inventions are an indicator seems clear though it may require special education so to use them. The usefulness of scientific discovery as a guide for national policy is also strengthened because of (a) the great variety of inventions and (b) the number of points of contact between a modern government and the affairs of its citizens. It follows, then, that whether plans are made and executed or not, trying to anticipate is an endeavor of prime importance, unless drifting is to be the course.

These conclusions were at the basis of the recommendations of the President's Research Committee on Social Trends appointed by President Hoover in the autumn of 1929 and which reported their findings 3 years later in their report, Recent Social Trends. In discussing the vast complexity of problems that confront our Nation, that committee found ". . . that the clue to their understanding as well as the hope for improvement lies in the fact of social change. Not all parts of our organization are changing at the same speed, or at the same time. Some are rapidly moving forward and others are lagging. These unequal rates of change in economic life, in government, in education, in science and religion make zones of danger and points of tension. . . . Scientific discoveries and inventions instigate changes first in the economic organization and social habits which are most closely associated with them. . . . The next set of changes occurs in organizations one step further removed, namely, in institutions such as the family, the government, the schools, and the churches. Somewhat later as a rule come changes in social philosophies and codes of behavior. . . ."

Thus the analysis in the Committee's report, which is here quoted because of its significance for national policies, was based upon a recognized lack of balance in civilization occasioned by unequal rates of change in the different parts of the social organism, beginning in point of time with mechanical invention and scientific discovery. Thus invention and discovery become guides to future changes, though, of course, not the only ones; nor are they infallible.

This report of the National Resources Committee then begins where the President's Committee on Social Trends left off. The development proceeds from this point in the sections which follow. . . .

Technology and National Welfare

The United States is greater today than were the Indian tribes that lived here before the sixteenth century, in part, at least, because of a superior technology. With the Indians it was relatively crude. The difference was not due to natural resources, for they were the same for both peoples. England's prestige and power during the nineteenth century rested in part upon her early acquisition of the machines and transportation agencies over the neighboring powers who still used the handicrafts. Germany has been in the vanguard in industrial chemistry, which has greatly added to her power.

But this investigation is not concerned with technology as such nor national power in general, but rather with the influences of specific technological developments, as may affect various national interests. Thus poison gas is a scientific discovery that places a powerful weapon of attack in the possession of an enemy, and affects the balance of powers among nations giving advantage to bold offensive states. Similarly, in an earlier age, the use of gunpowder was a powerful factor in breaking down the system of life built around the feudal lord and his castle. It is well known that the use of steam in connection with machinery made of hard metals has greatly changed family life, taking industrial production from the home and somewhat later a proportion of married women too, eventually aiding the extension of suffrage and encouraging the entrance of women into political life. The automobile has changed the problem of the apprehension of the criminal and was a factor in the assumption of new police responsibilities by the Federal Government. Sometimes relatively simple technological developments may raise profound problems. Thus discoveries in regard to methods of birth control are affecting the relative strength of military establishments of different nations, and are objects for suppression by the most aggressively warlike powers. On the other hand, the differential diffusion of these methods leads to a contribution of one-half the population of the next generation by one-quarter of the present generation, and that one-quarter is made up disproportionately of those with low income.

It is clearly seen then that scientific discoveries in applied science and invention do have important social consequences that greatly affect public policies. The subject is then important, not because there may be isolated cases of influential technologies as might be inferred from the few illustrations cited, but because the technological equipment is of such great magnitude, a fact which calls for a brief discussion.

The Volume of Technological Change

Our times have been called the machine age, because of the almost inconceivable variety and number of inventions and discoveries affecting every field of human endeavor. Not all those inventions are of the order of the airplane nor do they all have the far-reaching effects of the automobile. But there are several that do; with many more less significant ones exerting smaller social influences. To conceive of the role of technology one must think of the influence of any one invention, or of a manageable number multiplied many thousands of times.

The magnitudes are difficult to appreciate; but it is commonly said that a greater part of all social changes of modern times are precipitated by technological changes. Indeed it is not easy to think of a single social problem whose present nature is not influenced in part by one or more inventions of recent times.

For instance, the problem of social security can readily be related to a number of inventions without undertaking any extensive analysis. The large proportion of elders insecure in their old age is affected by various inventions, such as those making possible a smaller proportion of children, by urban factories and agricultural machinery which increased the population of cities, by transportation inventions which move sons and daughters to various parts of the United States and even to other lands, and by machines the tending of which employers prefer young persons to old ones. Thus new inventions bring insecurity to the aged. There is also the problem of security of employment. The large numbers of unemployed are in part due to machines taking jobs away and in part to business depressions which do not last long in civilizations not based on machines. The insecurity of the sick is occasioned in part by the high cost of medical service resulting from the development of science in medicine which gives rise to expensive specialists and to a technological medical equipment which means a large capital outlay for the physician, necessitating a charge of high prices to pay interest on the investment. The modern problem of workmen's compensation is directly traceable to whirling steel.

Even problems that are common to all societies and hence are not caused by changing technologies, as war, crime, divorce, disease, take on new forms or new degrees of expression under the impact of changes precipitated by technology.

The environment of modern men is to a surprising degree made up of machines, much as the environment of wild animals is made up of fauna, flora, wind, rain, and temperature. Even those men and women who do not work on a machine for a living are only once removed from it or its products.

Modern man's problem of adaptation to his machine-made environment is different from the problem of primitive man in adapting to nature because the machine-made environment is rapidly changing, and this is not the case with nature.

How Scientific Achievements Produce Social Changes

An invention usually affects first the persons using it directly. If it be a producer's goods such as a farm tractor, it means at once the replacement of horses or mules, the purchasing of gasoline, and changes in various other farm practices. If it be a consumer's goods such as an air conditioning unit in a home, it affects the construction and use of the house, but of course the units must be fabricated and hence, for that purpose, factories must be created, marketing machinery set up, etc. All such results are called the primary influences of the new technology.

These primary effects may flow out in different directions. Thus the X-ray is used for purposes of diagnosis in medicine and in dentistry. At the same time it is used in therapy as in the treatment of endocrine glands. It is also used in industry to detect minute flaws in the interior of steel castings or other solid objects. Indeed, manufacturers of the X-ray apparatus have noted some sixty different uses of the X-ray.

Similarly there are many different influences of radio. Some 150 were reported in the study of inventions in Recent Social Trends. Radio waves are used in guiding ships to port, as danger signals when a navigator is in distress, in flying airplanes, in program broadcasting, in point-to-point telephoning, in medicine, and in exterminating parasites.

These primary effects are not all exerted at once. Just as it sometimes requires 30 or 40 inventors working over a long number of years to evolve a complex major invention, and just as it may require hundreds of thousands of improvements spread out over time after the invention has been produced; so it requires a long time for the various uses of an invention to be determined. The phonograph was early used for recording dictation. Only later did it evolve into a musical instrument. Indeed, Edison, the inventor, did not think much of the possibility for the phonograph as a musical instrument, but thought it might have some use as a toy, and for recording the last words of dying persons. One does not yet know what may be the possible uses of the cathode ray.

Each of these primary effects may, in turn, produce derivative effects. Thus, as the tractor replaces animals on the farms there follows as a derivative influence less need for horse feed, which means that the land used for growing such feed is turned to other uses. This is a secondary effect. As land formerly used for stock feed yields other crops, the quantity is increased of other agricultural products, which tends to lower their prices. These lower prices are, in turn, mirrored in land values, perhaps in demands for tariff protection. Thus, these various derivative influences occasion effects secondary, tertiary, and so on. Each effect follows the other much like links in a chain, except that the succeeding derivative effects become smaller and smaller in influence. The effect of the tractor on lobbying for a higher tariff is very slight in comparison with other forces. A derivative effect in another direction is the stimulation the tractor brings to the cooperative movement in various ways, but especially in the purchase of gasoline.

In general, the first primary effect of an invention is found in (a) the economic practices of production and (b) in the habits of the consumers using the finished product. The economic organization as a whole may be the secondary influence if the technologies concerned are important ones. Thus, the tractor has the influence of making farms larger because on the smaller farms a tractor will not pay. Time is required to purchase additional land and to consolidate farms. In other ways tractors influence the agricultural economic organization. They make the adjustment to a business depression more difficult than in the case of horses and mules, for in a depression it is easier to raise feed than to buy gasoline. The tractor also moves the farmer a bit closer toward specialized commercial farming as contrasted to subsistence farming. Very many of the great inventions following the so-called Industrial Revolution have been machines affecting industrial and economic life, namely, gasoline engines, motors, steamboats, chemical and metallurgical inventions. Very often, then, the first great social institution affected by these changes has been the economic organization.

Later derivative effects impinge on other social institutions, such as family, government, church. Thus, the great economic changes that followed the power inventions modified the organization of the family. Women went to work outside the home. Children were employed in factories. The home gradually lost its economic functions. The father ceased to be much of an employer or manager of household labor, at least in cities and towns. There followed a shift of authority from father and home to industry and State. In cities homes became quite limited as to space. More time was spent outside by the members of the family. In general, then, these changes in industry reacted on the family life. . . .

While the delay between the origin of an invention and its various social consequences may be quite long and thus allow time for the anticipation of these social consequences, planned action may not necessarily follow even a successful anticipation, for planning means choice and a decision to act on the plans. Thus it becomes desirable to extend the discussion of technology with its delayed social effects into considerations of planning.

Policy, Planning, and Technology

One important lag in connection with the policy of society toward invention lies in the rate of adoption of new invention in the place of existing machinery. A conspicuous trait of the dynamic age in which we live is to be seen in the rapid pace at which existing capital equipment is made obsolete by technical inventions and other innovations in the design and construction of consumption and capital goods. Economists and business men have always been aware of the effects of this rapid rate of change in bringing capital obsolescence. But special attention has been focused on the obsolescence of capital equipment by the industries making new equipment. Trade journals and industry associations have stimulated study and collected data on the extent of obsolescence. In 1934, the trade journal Power made a study of 454 "better-than-average" industrial power plants constituting nearly 10 percent of industrial primemover capacity and found 62 percent of the equipment was over 10 years old while 25 percent was over 20 years. Some of the older equipment was presumably used as standby plant for emergencies, but the bulk of the older equipment was regarded as obsolete to such an extent that, by replacing it by facilities of the most advanced design, 50 cents could be saved, on the average, out of each dollar spent in the older plants for industrial power. In 1935 the American Machinist made a study of the obsolescence of metalworking equipment, concluding that, because of the rapid improvement in machine design, metal working equipment was as a rule obsolete if not produced within the last 10 years. It took an inventory of the age of such machinery and found that 65 percent of all the metal-working equipment in the country was over 10 years old and presumably obsolete. The Interstate Commerce Commission records indicate that 61 percent of the steam locomotives in the country were built over 20 years ago. These figures suggest the magnitude of capital obsolescence.

Further light on the magnitude of capital obsolescence is thrown by the estimates of the potential machinery requirements of all industry made in 1935 by the Machinery and Allied Products Institute. This institute made an extensive survey, sampling the requirements of industries covering over 85 percent of all industry, and on the basis of this survey estimated that the potential machinery requirements of all industry amounted to over 18 million dollars worth. Of this amount over 10 billion consisted of new equipment to replace old equipment which was for the most part obsolete.

Obsolescence surveys like the ones above referred to clearly indicate the magnitude of capital obsolescence. Yet the social implications of capital obsolescence have received very little study and a whole series of questions are waiting to be answered. When equipment becomes obsolete and therefore loses value who suffers a loss? Does obsolescence involve a social cost or only a business cost? Is capital obsolescence a cause of industrial maladjustment? Does the existence of extensive obsolete equipment prevent the using of better industrial techniques? Can the risks of capital obsolescence be reduced without impeding the use of better techniques? Should the losses due to capital obsolescence be distributed throughout industry? So little is known of the actual impact of capital obsolescence on industrial activity that no answer can be given to these questions. Yet they are questions forced on us by our rapidly improving technology and deserve the most careful study. Capital obsolescence and all that it involves needs to be extensively studied if the full social implication of current trends of improving technology are to be appreciated and the problems presented by improving technology are to be met.

But after inventions are adopted, the social effects do not come immediately as has been shown in the preceding section. There would thus seem to be time to consider the social implications of inventions. The difficulties in planning lie in other directions.

One of these difficulties is the unwillingness to admit the great role which so material a thing as technology plays in causing problems in society. It is only recently that one would admit that a man was unemployed because a machine had destroyed his job. The explanation, all but universal, was that a man was out of work because he wouldn't work. The forces of society were wholly moral. The driving forces that changed things were great ideas. With the requisite great men and the proper leadership, all problems could be solved. Solutions were seen in terms of moral conduct, the proper choices and the necessary will power. That a nation could not be a great power without coal and iron was not readily admitted for it posited a materialistic limitation. But with machines all about us during our daily life in this the great machine age, their great influence cannot be gainsaid. Such an awareness of material things makes no denial of the power of ideas, of ethics, of will power, of great leaders. But it does insist on the necessity of taking into consideration in planning the great influence of machines and scientific discoveries. The planned use or distribution of natural resources of any nation are of little value without knowledge of what uses technologies will make of them. Will oil be made from coal? Will plastics take the place of wood? Will alcohol be used as a motor fuel? Will more food stuffs be produced chemically? These questions suggest the importance of a knowledge of scientific development in any planning in regard to natural resources.

Social institutions as well as natural resources are affected by technology as has been shown. The home was changed because a steam engine and the machines it drove were too large for a dwelling. Now there has come a new source of power readily available for home use, electricity. Will it restore to family life something of its former glory before steam reduced its functions? Another illustration is war, a function of all states in the past. It is affected by the discoveries of poison gases as a weapon of military offense particularly their distribution among civilian populations by airplanes. Such technological developments must be considered by governments for they affect the very life and death of states.

Granting that sound plans must be based on technological knowledge, and granting that technological development is sufficiently slow to permit time for study and planning, the task still remains very difficult. Also the task of forecasting a trend within a limited period, say the next 20 years, is a more difficult assignment than to have an unlimited time. And since plans are expected to be carried out in a definite time, what is needed is not to say that something will occur in the future, but within a definite time limit.

The difficulties in forecasting the social influences of mechanical inventions and scientific discoveries and the status of the effort at this time should not be considered as obstacles so great as to make the method useless for the very practical task of governmental planning. Indeed, the experience gained from this first attempt at describing the technological trends of the near future is such as to give confidence that further efforts will be more fruitful and that much information increasingly reliable can be made available for governmental executives and legislators.

What, of course, is needed is a group of thinkers who will make it their business to devote a continuing study of some duration to future trends, and whose work will be given adequate recognition. The movement to study future trends would be furthered by the aid of new scientific journals devoted to this field or else by the granting of adequate space in the existing scientific publication media for studies of forecasting of both technological and social trends. In the world of social change of today, such a division of labor and specialization is altogether reasonable. Indeed it is more, it is essential for adequate attack upon the problems ushered in by social change. A decade of organized effort devoted to such inquiries into future trends would result in contributions of the utmost value to the formation of governmental policies and plans.

How the governments will act on the basis of such contributions is another question. For presenting conclusions is different from acting on the basis of those conclusions. Plans of action involve policies which are based often on values and choices. Governments are very often at the crossroads of important decisions. Government is not a passive agent molded by the forces evolving from technology.

For these reasons the effect of invention on the State is often longer delayed than is the case with other social organizations. For instance, it is obvious that modern transportation carries its freight and passengers across State boundary lines much more frequently than in the early history of the Nation. Los Angeles is now as close to New York as Philadelphia was at the time the Supreme Court was founded. Industry transcends State lines and the market for most economic goods is Nation-wide. Though these things be true, yet the people and the Government are not decided as to just what policy to follow in regard to the reduction of distances by the transportation inventions. There are some who would try to keep business small and within bounds manageable by the 48 different States. But

there are others who feel the need of one strong centralized government to deal with industries, so many of which it is claimed are extending in influence beyond the boundaries of any one State. This illustration shows that though the growth of transportation is well recognized and that its effect on State boundary lines and local government may be seen, yet decisive action on the part of Government may be delayed.

In other words, even though changing technology may give information about future social conditions which may be used as the basis of planning, such knowledge may not be acted upon. For successful planning rests upon other factors than knowledge, particularly unanimity of purpose, the will to act. The place which a knowledge of technological trends occupies in planning is only to furnish information without which plans are likely to be uncertain. Even though unanimity of purpose exists and the will to act is present, without knowledge as to what is likely to happen in the future, such plans as may be made will be to that extent defective.

At the beginning of the twentieth century it was shown that the Nation stood on the threshold of a great development of important inventions, such as the telephone, the airplane, the radio, the motion picture, the automobile, and the manufacture of artificial fibers which were to affect profoundly all phases of national life. The Nation faces now the second third of the twentieth century. What may be expected in technological development?

How far reaching will be the effects of the mechanical cotton picker? Will the surplus labor of the South flood the northern and western cities? Will the governments plan and act in time, once the spread of this invention is certain? The influence on Negroes may be catastrophic. Farm tenancy will be affected. The political system of the southern States may be greatly altered.

In another field, science has gone far on the road to producing artificial climate in all its aspects, which may have effects on the distribution of population, upon health, upon production, and upon the transformation of the night into day.

Then again television may become widely distributed, placing theaters into millions of homes and increasing even more the already astounding possibilities of propaganda to be imposed on a none too critical human race.

Talking books may come as a boon to the blind, but with revolutionary effects upon libraries and which, together with the talking picture and television, may affect radically schools and the educational process.

The variety of alloys gives to metals amazing adaptabilities to the purposes of man.

The use of chemistry in the production of new objects in contrast to the use of mechanical fabrication on the basis of power continues to develop with remarkable rapidity, in the production of oil, of woolen-like fibers, of substitutes for wood, and of agencies of destruction.

So the immediate future will see the application of new scientific discoveries that will bring not only enticing prospects but uncertainties and difficulties as well.

6. Revolution on the Farm, 1940

Technology on the Farm

Technological change was exceptionally rapid in agriculture. Partly because of the power revolution initiated at the beginning of the century with the gasoline tractor, and partly through the scientific research carried on by the state and federal governments, productivity in agriculture was rising dramatically. The result, both in surplus crops and surplus rural population, showed the social influence of technical change more clearly here than in any other sector of the national economy.

THE PROBLEMS OF CHANGE

Technology is science, art, and invention. It is tractors, combines, corn pickers. It is the testing and breeding of animals and the conquest of diseases. It is hybrid corn, new kinds of wheat, soybeans, kudzu, and lespedeza. It is ways to feed cows, plants, and men. It is road building and rural electrification. It is

From *Technology on the Farm: A Special Report by an Interbureau Committee and the Bureau of Agricultural Economics of the United States Department of Agriculture* (Washington, D.C., August 1940), pp. 3-5, 42-43, 77-80.

contour plowing, conservation of soil, management of forests, protection of wildlife. It is marketing and distribution. It is a race between insect pests and ways to kill them. Technology is in the workshop, in the laboratory, barn, grove, field, and home. It is a social and economic force that challenges thought and ability to plan, because its many-sided nature combines the intricate in fluences of getting and spending, savings and debts, employed leisure and unemployed relief.

Technology may be a paradox. Scientists discover that the cross-breeding of two highly developed strains of corn gives a productive and healthy hybrid: Within two short decades hybrid seed corn is used on 24 million acres; the estimated increase in yield in that time is 100 million bushels. The force of the change is still unspent. Not all the corn can be used; prices drop; farmers worry.

Mechanization has changed American agriculture so swiftly and so surely that between 1915 and 1940 the tractor, truck, and automobile eliminated the need for the labor of thousands of men and caused a reduction of nearly 10 million in the number of horses and mules.

Science learns more about the needs of soils. Engineers perfect labor-saving machinery. New ways to preserve food come from laboratories. Plant innovations, ways to control insects and disease, new uses for agricultural products, more knowledge of breeding practices and marketing, and countless other developments bring higher productivity, better living for town and country folk, improved nutrition and health, and the widening of markets. They also bring problems.

No end is seen to these products of science, genius, or accident. Technical progress has given us many farm commodities, some of which we have been unable to distribute to those who need them. It has given farmers equipment that can increase each worker's output, and the machine may become more important than the man. Set in motion are forces that affect all people, rural and urban, and show the need for programs to improve agricultural conditions.

It is not that these scientific advances in themselves are to be blamed; the troubles, if any, arise from the inequality of adjustments and responses in agriculture and industry to such advances.

Why the Study Is Important Now

These forces have existed for centuries, and have helped or troubled men for a long time. But several factors give especial urgency to the problems now, and make important a study of technological changes and their effects on national production, regional specialization, displaced manpower, and loss of income by some farm groups.

American agriculture has gone through a period of attempts to recover from the bad effects of expansion demanded by the World War. Many of these efforts augmented the volume of goods marketed at a time when farmers' capacity to produce exceeded any expected demands, both foreign and domestic. In other words, the tendency of technology to increase production just adds to agricultural pressures rooted in other causes—wars and threats of war since 1935, a consequent loss of foreign markets, slow industrial recovery, social problems, and others.

The short-term effects on agriculture of new wars seem to be in the direction of reducing further the export outlets for most of our agricultural products. A prolonged conflict might alter temporarily this prospect, but it would only accentuate the problem at the end of the war.

Increased volume, without a corresponding increased demand, brings lower prices, and the economic benefits of greater efficiency go to the consumer, rather than the farmer. Mechanization reduces the amount of labor needed in agriculture. This means less need for hired labor, or perhaps a shift from tenants and sharecroppers to wage hands. Thus undesirable effects, appearing perhaps temporarily as a result of the change from the old to the new, bear most heavily on the groups that are already at a disadvantage in American agriculture. To him that hath is given, and from him that hath not is taken away.

An Ever-Widening Circle

If we want to develop ways of meeting immediate and undesirable effects of technology we must understand better how new processes are introduced into our economy and their probable long- and short-term consequences. Farmers adopt innovations in the expectation that they can increase the volume of production, improve the quality of the product, lower unit costs, reduce the actual amount of labor needed, or lessen the fatigue and tedium of farming.

The fulfillment of these aims releases productive power for other uses. When mechanization reduces the labor needed to produce 100 bushels of wheat, for example, the displaced labor is available to grow more wheat, to do other work, or to take advantage of increased leisure. When the use of hybrid seed increases yields 15 to 20 percent, as much corn as before can be grown on 13 to 17 percent less land, and that land can be used for other crops or for more corn. Or, the displaced men and acres may remain idle.

Once, our constantly expanding economy assured new industrial jobs for workers displaced by agricultural improvements and for young people from farms. The growing industrial population, with constant recruits from farms, and large foreign markets (made especially accessible before the World War through our position as a debtor nation) caused few doubts about finding outlets for an expanding volume of wheat, cotton, corn, oats, tobacco, meat.

But the situation has changed. Our population is growing slowly. Industry lags. And industry, more than agriculture, can withhold improvements that might augment production and employment. Industry also can emphasize innovations that cut costs but require little increase in investments that would add to employment. The volume of industrial output and employment has not kept pace with the increase in the productivity of labor. . . .

When the prices of industrial goods do not reflect the decreases in costs resulting from a worker's increased productivity, purchasing power may be unused, so that employment suffers in other sectors of our economy, unless new investment and new production are undertaken. Workers supplanted by technological advances in one field cannot readily find employment in other fields unless industrial output expands sufficiently to use those workers and the ones who enter the labor market each year.

The Dilemma of Unemployment

Here is a dilemma. Scientific advances in agriculture constantly release labor at a time when employment opportunities are no longer open in urban industry. In fact, industry has an unemployment problem of its own; and the service and professional occupations are limited by the inadequate purchasing power of consumers of these services. Lacking other alternatives, the surplus hired men of agriculture swell the ranks of migratory farm workers, apply for direct relief, or find some shelter in subsistence farming, too often in the poorer localities.

The difficulty is made worse by differences in the birth rate, which is higher among farmers than among urban groups: Each year young workers, who formerly would have gone into industrial occupations, are seeking their livelihood in agriculture. A jump in industrial production (in armament industries, for example) might change briefly this situation but—on the basis of a long perspective—might not permanently solve it.

This increased manpower in agriculture naturally results in a pressure to increase the production of agricultural products, even when markets will absorb the commodities only at much lower prices, and farm people, who have no choice but to remain in farming, get lower incomes.

Desirable Paths for Technology

But surely improvements that lessen the physical burden of farm work, or that increase crop yields without appreciably increasing expenses, can be guided into paths that are socially desirable. Historically, technology makes possible greater production along many lines, and thus contributes to the higher levels of living. Cultural advancement would surely be a boon to the farm population, provided it could be properly distributed among different groups and could be obtained without too great a sacrifice of a purchasing power that is badly needed for other things.

The urgent need is to develop methods of directing technological change into socially desirable paths. Technical progress that creates jobs should be stressed in these methods. Opportunities for wisely used leisure should be properly distributed.

Even within agriculture, new products may be developed to widen market outlets for farm production. New regional Federal laboratories and older research units give promise of performing this task in time. Perhaps new markets can be found for old products, or maybe we can devise ways and means of encouraging the consumption of those foods most needed in the national diet.

We also need to concentrate on new ways and means of conserving our agricultural resources—both physical and human. Our goal is to develop new techniques that will aid rather than hinder progress of the groups already disadvantaged in American agriculture. . . .

A SUMMARY OF PRIMARY CHANGES

Profit and loss largely motivate the adoption of new machines and techniques, but an economic consideration like that furnishes an incomplete picture. For a full understanding of agricultural technology, one needs more: An appreciation for the human factors involved and a knowledge of the roots and tendrils of farm welfare that are intertwined economically with industry and culturally with city life. Technology may alter or emphasize these relationships.

We can determine easily the effects of some developments. We can observe directly the displacement of farm workers by tractors. But an analysis of the effects must be broad enough to include the problems that such displacement may create among all groups of our population. The displaced laborers may join the ranks of migratory workers, who already represent a social problem of national significance.

Not all developments that affect agriculture are obvious. Not all of them even occur in agriculture. The substitution of a synthetic fiber for Japanese silk might lead to smaller sales of cotton to Japan, because the purchasing power derived by Japan from the sales of raw silk to the United States would disappear. Thus, the purchase of American products by Japan would become more difficult. A reduction in the sales of cotton and other goods to foreign countries might start further changes that would react on agriculture. This illustrates the widespread and intimate interrelationship of technological change with all phases of economic life, and shows the difficulty of tracing its consequences.

The rate of adoption of new techniques in agriculture fluctuates. Low farm prices and low incomes in the past have kept many farmers from making adjustments; for example, few tractors were sold in the depression years of 1932-34. On the other hand, scarcity of labor and high prices of farm products encourage adjustments such as the use of tractor power. The degree of farm prosperity should be expected to influence decidedly the rate of adoption. There are a number of developments of outstanding importance whose effect can be estimated with sufficient confidence to draw some conclusion with respect to their influence on the volume of production, labor and capital requirements, prices, costs, income, the size of farm units, and, finally, the farm population.

Looking forward from 1940, some of the important technological developments that have been discussed seem reasonably certain to lead to the following primary changes:

1. A continued rapid increase in adoption of tractors, especially the small general-purpose tractor with rubber tires.

2. A further use of small combines, corn pickers, and other harvesting and tillage equipment operated with tractors.

3. A rapid extension of rural electrification, especially if support of the Rural Electrification Administration is continued as in 1940.

4. A slow but constant improvement in the productive efficiency of livestock; and progress in the correction of nutritional deficiencies and in disease control.

5. A tendency toward considerable increases in corn production as a result of further adoption of hybrid seed.

6. Some increase in wheat and oats production as a result of wider adoption of new disease-resistant varieties.

7. Greater acreages of soybeans for seed production, resulting partly from better seed-yielding varieties, partly from improved methods of harvesting, and from development of new industrial outlets.

8. Extension of flax and grain sorghums into new producing areas as a result of breeding cold-resistant and hardy varieties.

9. Continued shifting from small-grain and tilled crops to forage and pasture in the interest of soil conservation; also, continuation of the shift from low-yielding to high-yielding hays.

10. Greater use of cover crops and other cultural and engineering conservation practices.

11. Some increase in production of corn and cotton as a result of greater use of cover crops in the South.

12. Expansion in the use of domestic wood-pulp and increased attention to forests and wood lots as sources of supplementary income for farmers.

13. Greatly increased use of frozen packing of farm products.

14. Continued advances in the production of synthetic textile fibers.

15. Wider outlets and use of both the edible and the drying oils.

16. Possible development of starch production from sweetpotatoes on a commercially important scale.

17. Some development of plastics and other industrial products from cellulose and protein—using mostly wood as the source of cellulose, and soybeans and casein as sources of protein. . . .

TECHNOLOGY AND THE FARM PROBLEM

Changes of the kind and magnitude indicated in the preceding pages obviously cannot take place without serious consequences to agriculture and the nation. Probably the basic problem will be that of providing employment and security to the displaced and underprivileged people who are most adversely affected by these developments.

Expected shifts in tenure and income raise difficult questions, for they entail loss of position and income and a progressive piling up at the lower end of the social scale, and that effect is most likely in areas of lowest agricultural productivity where the existing population is already in excess.

This intensification of population pressure is bound to accelerate population movement. There will be an increased tendency to migrate between rural areas and between rural and urban areas. Furthermore, machines alone are expected to displace 350,000 to 500,000 additional farm workers.

The important (but not new) problem of maintaining farm prices and income will be intensified by the expected technical developments.

Significant increases of corn, soybeans, small grains, hay and forage, cotton, and other crops and livestock through improvements in varieties and strains, in conservation and cultural practices and in insect and disease control, and through changes in feed supplies and prices, cannot come without serious repercussions upon costs, prices, and income of all farmers, but especially commercial producers.

These changes, furthermore, will not take place uniformly throughout the country. Fluctuations in costs as a result of mechanization will be most pronounced in areas where machine methods can best be used. Similarly, changes in costs and prices will take place first in localities best adapted to the new strains, varieties, and new methods of processing, but they soon will spread and produce varying effects in other parts of the country. They will have some significant effects upon regional specialization and will intensify the problem of interregional competition. It is clear, therefore, that the extent and magnitude of these changes will be such as to render extremely difficult the task of maintaining farm prices and income at reasonable levels.

Technological developments also raise important questions of significance to the several national agricultural programs, which at many points are closely related to technological changes. Many of the problems these programs are trying to meet, in fact, are intensified by the developments.

The Agricultural Adjustment Administration, for example, in addition to its acreage allotment and conservation practice program, strives through these efforts and through loans and marketing quotas to keep supplies in line with the effective demand of the market so as to maintain farm prices and income at reasonable levels. To keep the supplies of the principal basic commodities at legally defined, normal levels, the acreage allotments are varied each year, depending upon the situation with respect to carry-over, yields, domestic and export demand, etc. Loans and marketing quotas are provided when supplies and prices reach stated levels, but the latter come into operation only when supplies reach rather extreme heights.

Obviously under this adjustment procedure anything which materially increases yields of a particular crop, even assuming domestic and export demand are constant, will decrease the acreage allotment necessary to maintain the supply at normal levels. It is just at this point that technological changes come into the picture and affect the result.

We have already pointed out the rapid strides that are taking place with respect to the development and adoption of hybrid corn in the Corn Belt. Such changes in yields and production, even assuming a reasonably active domestic and export demand, would be difficult to absorb without depressing prices and income. With the domestic and foreign demand in prospect as a result of the present general unemployment situation and the maladjustments that will be accentuated by the war, the problem will be much more difficult.

Because of these factors and a rapidly increasing carry-over, the Agricultural Adjustment Administration put through a 20-percent downward adjustment in the corn acreage allotment in 1939 and has requested an additional downward adjustment of approximately 10 or 12 percent in 1940. With the changes in prospect that have been noted, it seems clear that further downward shifts in acreage will be necessary if supplies are to be maintained at reasonable levels, unless adverse weather conditions interfere to cut the crop or domestic and foreign demand unexpectedly improve greatly.

Growing out of these downward adjustments in acreage is another problem of increasing significance both to the Agricultural Adjustment Administration and to the Farm Security Administration. Reference is made to the growing practice of "bonus" renting, whereby share tenants are forced to pay cash rent for perquisites, buildings, crib space, meadows, pasture, and the like in addition to the usual share of the crop.

Technological developments accentuate this problem in two ways. The first effect comes about through increasing yields which necessitate further downward adjustments in acreage to maintain a given supply. As the acreage of depleting crops is decreased, the released acreage simply swells the total of the acreage of other crops upon which "bonus" rents may be charged.

Another effect is due to the influence of mechanization upon size of farm and the relation of this to the availability of farms for tenants. A few years ago, a farmer upon retirement would go to a town and rent his farm as a unit to a bona fide tenant, but now he is more than likely to stay on the farm and rent it by fields to his neighbors, who thus increase the size of their operating units. Machines help them operate the additional acreage practically as efficiently as if it were a definite part of their home tracts. They stand to enlarge their operations and incomes thereby, but there is one less farm for some other tenant.

This situation apparently is developing to the point where there are more tenants looking for farms than there are farms available; obviously the tenants bid against each other for a farm, and the landlord, with a definite advantage in bargaining, can demand and receive the "bonus" rents. Any such additional charges lower the tenant's income and standard of living.

Because of such situations, the Farm Security Administration is encountering increasing difficulty in finding farms for its tenant-purchase and rehabilitation-loan clients. The problem of the Agricultural Adjustment Administration also is made more difficult, because these "bonus" rents often take the form of "by-agreements" and raise problems very difficult to identify and correct.

Closely related to this development is the influence of mechanization and acreage adjustments upon the shift from a position as tenant and sharecropper to one as wage hand. These shifts have taken place to a considerable degree in the intensive cotton areas of the South, where mechanization has increased markedly. Many people attribute the shift in cropper status primarily to this factor. Others lay it also to a landlord's desire to adjust his labor force to his reduced cotton acreage and to get a larger share of the benefit payments. But regardless of the causes, the fact remains that it is a serious human problem and deserves careful consideration.

The problem may become even more intensified in the next few years ahead. The trend toward increased mechanization is very likely to continue. This shift will further displace man labor. Even if it does not cause complete physical displacement, it is likely to result in further "economic" displacement, which comes about because of the tendency of certain landlords to keep a large supply of labor on the plantation for the seasonal peak load tasks of chopping and picking.

Instead of giving the croppers the usual acreage of share cotton, however, they will give them only "nominal" allotments of cotton and use them the rest of the time as wage hands. The consequences are less income for the croppers from the smaller acreages, less wage work, some idleness, a smaller annual income, and inevitably a lower standard of living.

Note must be taken also of another problem due to technological developments of significance to the national programs—particularly to the Agricultural Adjustment Administration. This is the decrease in unit costs (resulting from increased efficiency, etc.) and their bearing upon parity payments and the loan program. The question will have to be faced sooner or later whether under conditions of supply, demand, and prices in prospect, the level of parity prices as now calculated is one that reasonably can be attained, or whether it may be necessary to recalculate it on a more recent basis so as to take into account these new developments.

In such a calculation, technological and other changes in nonagricultural industries also would come into the picture. In fact, as we have indicated previously, these changes have equalled, (and in some industries have exceeded) those in agriculture, hence the net result might continue to indicate a relationship between agricultural and industrial prices not greatly different from the existing one. But even so, we still would face the difficult administrative problem of how to attain such levels.

Similar questions arise with respect to the loan program, whether the present loan levels be maintained, or if not, at what levels they can be made with a reasonable assurance of repayment. There is also the question of the relation of the loan and resulting price level on feed grains to the elasticity and efficiency in feeding.

These changes and their effects cannot be disassociated from the existing situation, either in agriculture or industry. In fact, they really intensify an already bad situation, which has had its roots in part in other causes, but also to which past technological developments have contributed.

It is generally recognized that the situation at present, in both agriculture and industry, is characterized by depressed conditions, reduced national and individual incomes, excessive unemployment and relief. It also must be evident that further technological progress either in agriculture or industry simply will add to, and accentuate, these conditions unless we find some way greatly to expand our domestic and foreign markets and absorb the already large army of unemployed.

If some permanent improvement were foreseen in these prospective economic conditions, we could be much more optimistic about the social and economic effects of technology. But unfortunately there is little basis for such optimism. During the next few years, at least, industrial opportunities are not likely to be of such magnitude as to absorb anything like the present industrially unemployed, to say nothing of absorbing the large excess of manpower on the farm.

In 1937 we succeeded in employing about 35 million persons in nonagricultural pursuits. By the end of 1939, when industrial production finally, but temporarily, exceeded the 1929 peak, total nonagricultural employment reached only about 34 million persons, nearly a million fewer than in 1937 and approximately 2 million fewer than in 1929.

There are, at present, probably 42 million to 44 million nonfarm persons available for work, of whom perhaps 2 million are on Government work projects and about 2 million normally would be unemployed in prosperity years. Every year probably 500,000 are added to this available working force. Although the tremendous sums that are being employed for defense undoubtedly will speed up business activity and give employment to considerable numbers of unemployed people the next year or so, the effect is likely to be temporary and not on a scale sufficient to meet the problem we are discussing.

Nor are the prospects much brighter for the years ahead. A prolonged European war might alter this prospect, but only temporarily. A short war, on the other hand, might make it even darker. Even when peace is declared it will require a period of years to overcome the maladjustments resulting from the war. There will be extreme competition among all nations for world markets. Because of the major importance of foreign markets to the prosperity of the bulk of our agricultural producers, it appears that agriculture as a whole will be affected particularly by this situation.

Agriculture will be benefitted, however, to the extent that our domestic industrial economy can be made to function more effectively through expanded production, lower prices, and increased employment. But changes in this direction, as we have seen, probably will be slow, so slow, in fact, that agriculture likely will have to take care of not only as many but probably more people than has been the case during the 1930's.

There were in 1937, according to the unemployment census, more than 1,-

500,000 males living on farms who either were totally or partially unemployed or only had emergency employment. It does not appear that this unemployment situation has improved or will improve much in the next few years, since nearly 400,000 farm males are reaching maturity each year and only about 110,000 farmers are dying each year, with possibly as many more retiring or leaving for other occupations.

Unless there is an unexpected increase in net migration, therefore, the total population in agriculture in 1950 will be higher even than today, when it is the highest on record. Indications are that it may reach a total of 34 million persons, approximately 2 million more than today.

In the South during the 1930's, for example, 275 white persons reached 15 years of age for every 100 persons over 15 who died or reached 65 years. In other words, for every 100 vacancies there were 275 applicants. Among the Negro population comparable figures indicate that there were 210 applicants for every 100 vacancies. Consequently, there must be a material migration from southern farms or there will result a substantial increase in an area where farm population pressure is already acute.

When it is realized further that there are 3 million farm families in the United States today receiving gross farm incomes averaging only $615 and more than a million and a half males of working age living on farms who are totally or partially unemployed, it is obvious that the further expected displacement of 350,000 to 500,000 workers during the next ten years, because of mechanization alone, will create an extremely bad situation and will make imperative the adoption of remedial measures to meet it.

PART XIII WORLD WAR II

In the spring of 1940, a decade of debate over the proper role of science and technology in society was suddenly made academic. Throughout the New Deal period demands for a closer relationship between the two had been fought by government officials who saw no likely return commensurate with the spending of tax monies, and by a technical community which feared the government control that in some form would go along with the money.

With the German blitzkreig, however, most of this antagonism was either dissipated or ignored. Suddenly the government realized that without the aid of science and technology it might not be able to maintain itself in the face of foreign threats. The technical community, for their part, realized that both self-interest and patriotism demanded that they lend their talents to accomplishing public as well as private goals. Prompted by the war emergency, and able to draw upon a rich heritage of precedent and experience, technical men like Vannevar Bush put together a series of organizations that co-ordinated the American sciences—and these organizations worked in government, educational institutions, industry, and private foundations.

This research establishment bore the characteristics with which we are now familiar. The federal government remained at the center of the enterprise, providing both funds and purposes. The actual research was carried on primarily in institutions which were formally private, though they could and often did rely solely upon federal patronage for their support. The devices which made possible this bridging of the gap between private and public were the grant and the contract, carried over from normal procurement procedures but adapted to meet the needs of the research process. The major virtue of the system, the factor which made it so effective, was that it brought together and co-ordinated both the assets and goals of so many disparate elements—government bureaucrats, academic scientists, industrial engineers, corporation presidents, and military officers. All were used, and all were served.

383

This very virtue was also a great danger. Scientific and academic freedoms were gravely compromised. Federal controls did in fact tend to go along with federal funds. It was practical in war to compromise interests for defense; it was not easy when peace came to bring the system to bear upon domestic problems. And, finally, in seeking out the best laboratories and technicians, the research establishment tended to perpetuate the severe inequalities which already separated the scientific institutions of the country. It was a system conceived to accomplish the narrow purposes of war, and it succeeded—but at a social cost which has yet to be measured.

1. The Scientists Organize, 1940

JAMES P. BAXTER 3RD, *Scientists Against Time*

The story of research and development in the United States during World War II revolves around one man, Vannevar Bush, and the organization he led, the Office of Scientific Research and Development. Beginning with the National Defense Research Committee in June 1940, Bush and his associates from the educational, governmental, and industrial sectors of American science set themselves the task of co-ordinating and sponsoring research in weapons and medicine. The following description of the founding of the NDRC is from the official history of that organization.

When the Germans attacked Poland in 1939, there were grave shortcomings in the organization of science for war in Great Britain and the United States. In both countries the Government had developed important service laboratories, such as the Naval Research Laboratory at Anacostia, D.C., founded in 1923. These institutions, however, were always in danger of being swamped as soon as war broke out by demands for routine testing, and thereby diverted from any fundamental research they

might have under way. Few outstanding scientists, moreover, were attracted to government service in time of peace, for the conditions as to both pay and freedom are far less favorable than those of industry or the academic life.

The shadow under which Great Britain had lived for some years prior to 1939 had turned the thoughts of many scientists of the first order to problems of national defense. Her skies and her shores were so close to the German menace and were for so long an actual battle

From James P. Baxter 3rd, *Scientists Against Time* (Boston, 1946), pp. 11-25.

front that close and fruitful contacts developed early between her civilian scientists and her fighting services. The British, it is true, never created as simple an organization of science for war as that established in the United States in 1940 and 1941, but it is one of their qualities which have stood them in good stead that they can operate, under pressure, what seems to us an enormously complicated structure and get results which elsewhere could be hoped for only from simpler and better co-ordinated administrative machinery.

The organization of American science for war in 1939 was neither simple nor well co-ordinated. The services had not learned yet, as American industry had, that it is fatal to place a research organization under the production department.

Basically, research and procurement are incompatible. New developments are upsetting to procurement standards and procurement schedules. A procurement group is under the constant urge to regularize and standardize, particularly when funds are limited. Its primary function is to produce a sufficient supply of standard weapons for field use. Procurement units are judged, therefore, by production standards. Research, however, is the exploration of the unknown. It is speculative, uncertain. It cannot be standardized. It succeeds, moreover, in virtually direct proportion to its freedom from performance controls, production pressures and traditional approaches. . . . To be effective, new devices must be the responsibility of a group of enthusiasts whose attentions are undiluted by other and conflicting responsibilities.

Human nature being what it is, the union of the research and procurement functions has another unfortunate consequence. A procurement unit that also is responsible for research tends to think all its geese are swans.

The result is to slow down the adoption of devices which first appear or are first suggested outside of the procurement unit. This may be particularly serious when we remember that modern weapons may either draw their components from or be, at least in part, the responsibility of several competing procurement units—each of which is in a position to retard or advance the progress of the other.

What was required was the reorganization of the scientific establishments within the services which has thus far been only partially effected, and the creation of means to mobilize civilian science and link it effectively with the war effort. No existing organization was adequate for this task. The National Academy of Sciences had been created by Act of Congress in 1863 as a completely independent self-perpetuating body bound to give, without compensation, the best scientific advice of which its members were capable whenever requested by any department of Government. It has always operated through committees or boards, a majority of whose members have not been members of the Academy. President Wilson requested the President of the National Academy in 1916 to set up a National Research Council, which was perpetuated by the Executive Order of May 11, 1918, "to stimulate research in the mathematical, physical and biological sciences, and in the application of the sciences" alike to peace and war. Committees of the National Research Council were to render important service in the national war effort, but the Council lacked funds, was not a government agency supported by the Congress and reporting directly to the President, and the proceedings of its committees were often slow and cumbrous. They were set up to deal with every sort of problem in a large field of science, and were therefore not designed to focus attention on such relatively narrow portions of the field as those concerned with instrumentalities of war. To make the Academy and Council adequate to direct war research would have required drastic changes and a new Act of Congress.

A more effective organization, partly because it operated over a much narrower field, was the National Advisory Committee for Aeronautics, established by the Congress in 1915 "to supervise and direct the scientific study of the problems of flight." Generous Congressional appropriations had enabled the Committee to construct laboratories and wind tunnels, to develop a research staff under Civil Service, and to make a limited number of contracts with educational institutions for studies and reports. The results have been of incalculable importance in the development of civil aircraft, in which we are the acknowledged leaders of the world, and in the production of military and naval aircraft as well. The presence of the heads of the Army and Navy Air Forces on the Committee ensured close co-operation with the armed services. By order of the President in June 1939, the NACA was to become a consulting and research agency for the Joint Army and Navy Aeronautical Board at the outbreak of a national emergency.

For some years prior to the German attack on Poland the members of the NACA had been acutely conscious that they were living in a prewar, not in a postwar, period. It was quite natural that from the chief of this group should come the idea of providing as efficient an organization of American science for all other war purposes as had already been effected in the field of flight. Dr. Vannevar Bush, a Cape Cod Yankee of wide experience as Professor of Electrical Engineering, and an inventor with business experience, had been appointed to the NACA in 1938, and be-

came its chairman a year later, not long after he had resigned the vice-presidency of the Massachusetts Institute of Technology to become President of the Carnegie Institution of Washington, the operating agency for the far-flung scientific activities financed by the late Andrew Carnegie. Bush was well known to scientists the country over for his contributions in applied mathematics and electrical engineering, especially for his extraordinary creation, the differential analyzer. The Army and Navy officers were familiar with his work in ballistics and in a more secret field.

After the outbreak of the war in Europe, Bush's thoughts turned more and more to the need for an over-all organization of science for war. He discussed this project with his former chief, President Karl T. Compton of the Massachusetts Institute of Technology, and with two groups who helped to catalyze his thinking, his colleagues at NACA and the members of a Committee on Scientific Aids to Learning, on which he was serving with President James B. Conant of Harvard and Frank B. Jewett, the President of the Bell Telephone Laboratories and of the National Academy of Sciences. It was John Victory, the Secretary of NACA, who proposed that the organization taking form in Bush's mind be named the National Defense Research Committee. At Bush's direction Victory prepared in May 1940 the draft of an Act of Congress setting up an organization

to co-ordinate, supervise, and conduct scientific research on the problems underlying the development, production, and use of mechanisms and devices of warfare, except scientific research on the problems of flight.

The National Defense Research Committee of not more than twelve members appointed by the President, and serving without compensation, was to include two members each from both the War and the Navy Department and from the National Academy of Sciences. It was to be authorized to contract with educational institutions, individuals, and industrial organizations for scientific studies and reports.

The sweep of the German armies across France precipitated American action. Bush saw President Roosevelt early in June, 1940, and convinced him that a new agency was needed. It was to be set up by executive action with funds of its own to be allocated from the substantial sum the Congress was about to place at the President's disposal. From the outset the President took a keen interest in the proposed Committee. As Bush outlined it, it was to be similar in form to NACA, but empowered

to correlate governmental and civil research in fields of military importance outside of aeronautics.

It should form a definite link between the military services and the National Academy. It should lean on the latter for broad scientific advice and guidance. It should supplement, and not replace, activities of the military services themselves, and it should exist primarily to aid these services. . . .

If it were welcomed and supported by the War and Navy Departments and by the National Academy of Sciences, it would

also be able to enlist the support of scientific and educational institutions and organizations, and of individual scientists and of engineers, throughout the country.

The President agreed to write to the Secretaries of War and the Navy and to the President of the National Academy of Sciences, requesting their support of the new agency.

In the next few days Bush talked the matter over in greater detail with Harry Hopkins at the White House and submitted to the President the names of

Jewett, as President of the National Academy of Science, and Conway P. Coe, Commissioner of Patents, both to serve ex officio, Conant, Compton, and Richard C. Tolman of the California Institute of Technology. Tolman, who like Conant had been early convinced that the United States would soon be drawn into the war, had come to Washington in June 1940 to offer his services, and like the other civilian members had taken part in the discussions out of which the NDRC took shape. Things were moving so rapidly that Bush obtained on the telephone the consent of these men to serve. Conant asked only two questions: "Is it real?" and "Are you to head the committee?" Assurance on those points was enough. On June 15 the President signed the letters of appointment, naming Bush as chairman and indicating that the War and Navy Departments would be represented by officers of distinction and would each detail a liaison officer to the chairman's office.

Bush had already called on General George C. Marshall and Admiral Harold Stark, who were both very cordial. In view of the prospect that their research establishments would soon be swamped with problems of immediate procurement, and that the Army would probably have more research allotments in the next fiscal year than it could use under the new situation, General Marshall expressed pleasure at the prospect that the National Defense Research Committee could take over some current Army research and his willingness to transfer funds for the purpose. General H. H. Arnold took Bush with him to Wright Field on June 17 to explore the possibility of transferring some of the research under way there, outside the field of NACA, to educational and scientific establishments under NDRC contracts. . . .

Bush determined to leave his own hands free but to assign to each of his colleagues supervision of one class of problems he was especially qualified to handle. Tolman was to serve as chairman of Division A, dealing with armor and ordnance; Conant of Division B, bombs, fuels, gases, and chemical problems; Jewett of Division C, communications and transportation; Compton of Division D, detection, controls, and instruments; and Coe, Division E, patents and inventions. Each division was to have one or more vice-chairmen and was to consist of several sections, which it was assumed would be "the real working groups."

Compton's first assignment was to list the military research projects under way in government laboratories, especially those likely to be curtailed in favor of work on production, and also the projects not under way which the services considered desirable. It would then be possible to determine what programs the Committee wished to supplement. Meanwhile Jewett and Conant undertook to explore the possible assistance that might be had from the academic world. As President of the National Academy of Sciences Jewett wrote to the heads of 725 colleges and universities asking for information as to their facilities and their staff in the various fields of science. Conant followed this up with a letter to fifty academic institutions with extensive facilities for advanced research, explaining that the most immediate work of the NDRC would lie in the fields of physics and chemistry, civil, electrical, and mechanical engineering, and metallurgy. He asked that each of the institutions approached supply an outline of its special facilities and personnel for research in the fields within which NDRC would be working, "indicating only those in which your institution is exceptionally qualified," and that a description be included "of specific research projects in which your staff are now engaged which may have an application in devices or mechanisms of warfare." On the basis of the replies received by Jewett and Conant, Wilson compiled by early August a "Report on Research Facilities of Certain Educational and Scientific Institutions" which proved of much service, and was familiarly known as "the Bible."

Meanwhile the agency came formally into existence when the President approved on June 27 an order of the Council on National Defense establishing the National Defense Research Committee. At the first regular meeting held on July 2, 1940, Tolman was elected vice-chairman and resolutions were adopted asking the co-operation of the National Academy of Sciences and the National Research Council.

In the normal pattern of Washington life at that time a new executive agency might be expected to obtain a broad grant of power, stretch that authority to the limit, and become involved in jurisdictional disputes with other agencies proceeding in similar fashion. From this type of controversy the lot of NDRC has been free. From the outset Bush preferred to stay in his own field, work as far as possible though existing agencies, and construe narrowly the terms "instrumentalities, methods and materials of war." Although it had first been intended to entrust NDRC with the heavy burden of evaluating the projects of inventors, he welcomed and indeed supported the movement which led to the establishment by the Secretary of Commerce of the National Inventors' Council as a separate agency on July 11. Procedures were developed to sift and bring to the attention of NDRC such inventors' projects as were of promise so that, if the Army or Navy wanted further research done on them, the Committee might arrange for it. The tie-in with the Inventors' Council was facilitated by the fact that the Commissioner of Patents was a member of both bodies. No friction developed between NDRC and NACA, not merely because of the clear definition of their respective fields, but because Bush retained his membership on the latter, while relinquishing the chairmanship, in June 1941, to Professor Jerome C. Hunsaker, of the Massachusetts Institute of Technology. The two agencies collaborated fruitfully in certain problems of jet propulsion.

Many proposals were soon received for research in borderline fields, especially with regard to strategic materials. An early ruling established the principle that no such work be undertaken without a specific request from the Advisory Commission. Bush's interpretation of the order under which he was operating ruled out, for example, research on steelmaking practice in general, synthetic rubber, and tung oil substitutes. Two members of this Committee, Conant and Compton, did serve with Bernard M. Baruch in the summer of 1942 in preparing the celebrated Rubber Report. But the standing policy of the Committee was to leave this type of research to other agencies, and Bush warmly supported the establishment of the Office of Production Research and Development under Dr. Harvey Davis in November 1942.

Money was never a limiting factor although at the outset the expectations were extremely modest. When Bush suggested at a breakfast conference in June 1940 that operations might reach $5,000,000 the first year, some thought the figure very high. By July 8, however, he was asking the Bureau of the Budget for an allocation of ten millions, of which he got six and a half. As the agency grew, Congress proved unfailingly generous. A temporary emergency developed in July 1941 when the passage of the annual appropriation acts was delayed, but this flurry was of short duration. The Executive Committee of the Trustees of the Massachusetts Institute of Technology agreed at that time to underwrite the salaries of the key men at the Radiation Laboratory to the extent of half a million dollars, and when it appeared that this sum might be insufficient, President Compton went to Mr. John D. Rockefeller, Jr., who agreed to underwrite personally a second half million. Congressional funds were, however, soon available, and thereafter were provided in ample measure.

Manpower, not money, constituted in the long run the limiting factor. The efforts of the NDRC to utilize to the full the resources of the academic world became therefore of prime importance. There was no disposition to slight industrial contractors or to minimize the immense contribution they could make to war research. But it was apparent from midsummer of 1940 that American industry was about to be called on for production of weapons in unprecedented amounts. Aware of the heavy load piling up on the shoulders of American business, the Committee determined not to make too heavy initial demands on scientists in industry but rather to obtain widespread support from the academic world.

The original idea was to decentralize research and leave the scientist free to work on his home grounds. This appealed to most of them and to university presidents who wished to keep their staff together. As late as December, 1941, Bush described the agency as one which conducted "research through cost-basis contracts with academic institutions and industrial companies which in most cases permit scientists to work in their own laboratories with the least disruption to other defense and training activities."

In mobilizing academic scientists the Chemistry Division got off the mark first. Its survey of Army and Navy needs and of the facilities available was pushed with such rapidity that the Committee approved on August 29, 1940, the placing of contracts with nineteen different institutions. As the latter were willing to proceed at once without waiting for contracts to be drawn, work was well under way on campuses from coast to coast by the beginning of the September term. At the University of Nebraska a contract was placed for the preparation of certain organic arsenicals needed in chemical warfare, the work to be undertaken by a member of its faculty who had done the most recent important American work in this field. Again, at a meeting of the Division held in Washington on October 3, it was pointed out that the Navy needed a portable instrument to be used on aviation oxygen-breathing equipment for measuring and indicating the partial pressure of oxygen in a mixture of gases. Linus Pauling, who came on from California to attend this meeting, thought about the problem for several days, put to himself the question, "What physical property of oxygen distinguishes it sharply from other common gases?" concluded that it was the magnetic susceptibility, and proceeded to devise an instrument which utilized this distinguishing property. This ingenious and successful device was promptly developed under a contract signed with the California Institute of Technology.

In the Chemistry Division a great effort was made for many months to avoid the development of central laboratories and leave the scientists at their home institutions. But as the volume of work increased it became more and more difficult to bring the workers together for consultation with sufficient frequency or to visit them often enough to keep them posted on advances in the same or adjacent fields. The benefits to be derived from teamwork of sizable groups were too great to be neglected. The organic chemist, for example, has mastered an art as well as a science. His knowledge and his techniques, no matter how eminent and versatile he may be, cover but a small portion of a vast and rapidly expanding science. When the organic chemist works in a central laboratory he is in constant contact with other men with special skills in other portions of the field, and out of the resultant pooling of knowledge and techniques great gains are derived. Sizable central establishments were therefore developed at the University of Illinois, Chicago, Northwestern, Carnegie Institute of Technology, and George Washington University.

The need of large central laboratories was immediately apparent when work was projected on radar and rockets. For both of these, ready access to airfields was indispensable. Rocket development required appropriate firing ranges and facilities for experimentation with explosives in considerable quantities. Out of such considerations grew the great rocket development at the California Institute of Technology.

There was great variety in the contracts with academic institutions. In some cases the contractor provided only space and management, as in the Johns Hopkins University contract to operate an important laboratory at Silver Spring, Maryland, later transferred to the Navy. More typical was the arrangement by which a university furnished space, management, and a portion of the scientific personnel. Sometimes these included the chief figures in the undertaking, sometimes not. The director of the Radio Research Laboratory at Harvard, Dr. F. E. Terman of Stanford University, had six hundred on his staff in 1945, of whom there were more from California institutions than from Harvard. At the giant Radiation Laboratory at Massachusetts Institute of Technology, of which Dr. Lee A. DuBridge of the University of Rochester was director and Dr. F. Wheeler Loomis of the University of Illinois associate director, only one M.I.T. professor was a member of the Steering Committee at the close of the war. By 1945 there were an extraordinary number of displaced persons in the academic world. These scientists worked full time on some sector of an NDRC contract, and had no other relation to the academic institution which now paid for their services. They were not receiving a grant-in-aid of pure research of the type now under discussion for the advancement of science in the postwar period. They were hired to hit an assigned target in an organized effort to create new instrumentalities of war. The government money which paid them was not expended to advance pure science or to aid the institutions from which they came or at which they worked, but to speed the day of victory.

Scores of institutions the country over released their scientists to work elsewhere on special projects. Harvard, Columbia, Princeton, and other institutions with research programs of their own released many of their men to work on other projects. Sixty-nine different academic institutions were represented on the staff of the Radiation Laboratory in 1945. For the scientists who moved to these large establishments it was an opportunity for rapid development,

though often narrow and not usually in their chosen field. For the institutions which released them and then scoured the country for suitable replacements it represented real sacrifice.

California, Columbia, Harvard, and the Woods Hole Oceanographic Institution operated major laboratories for the study of underwater sound and underwater explosives. Princeton specialized in ballistics; the Franklin Institute of Philadelphia in airborne fire control; Penn State in hydraulic fluids.

The California Institute of Technology constructed and operated the longest known torpedo tube, while Harvard built for its studies in acoustics the quietest room in the world. Many academic institutions were called on to produce by "crash programs" some actual equipment for use in the field. The California Institute of Technology went much farther. Not only was it our chief center for rocket research, but the Institute found itself producing rocket motors by the thousand and special powders to propel them.

Some of the most interesting work was done by institutions which made few or no additions to their staff or facilities. This was true of Michigan in explosives and Rochester in optics. Other notable work was accomplished at Stanford, at the State Universities of New Mexico, Texas, Iowa, and Florida, at Ohio State, Duke, and at Rensselaer Polytechnic Institute.

However versatile or broadly trained the academic scientists might be, most of them now found themselves working on problems of which they had previously known little or nothing. Psychologists developed methods of selecting and training the operators of countless new Army and Navy devices. Mathematicians and biologists mastered the intricacies of fire control and bombing techniques and staffed the operational analysis groups of the armed forces. Chemists made their contributions in chemical warfare or in research on penicillin, insecticides, and antimalarials. Werner Bachmann relates that ·when Conant and Roger Adams asked him to work on explosives his heart sank. Unfamiliar though he was with this type of work, he was destined within a year to develop in his laboratory at the University of Michigan a new process which saved the Government more than one hundred million dollars.

The college and university at war had their dormitories and classrooms filled with Army and Navy trainees and their laboratories turned over to war research of a secret character. This involved them, like the industrial contractors, in the complexities of a first-rate security system of which armed guards were the outward and visible sign and painstaking indoctrination the most important component. No one could start work for NDRC without a careful check by the Government's investigating authorities and until he had taken an oath and signed a statement that he had read the Espionage Act. From the outset the principle was established that no officer or employee of NDRC or of its contractors was entitled to any classified information whatever unless it was necessary for the performance of his duties. For instance, after Bush and Conant turned the contracts concerning atomic power over to the Corps of Engineers in May 1943, only they and one other member of their agency, Tolman, were cleared for this top secret project. If an OSRD employee were authorized to receive secret or confidential information, he was then furnished copies of the applicable Army or Navy regulations regarding classified matter. The record as to security has been admirable, proving

that intelligent and patriotic civilians, carefully indoctrinated as to the importance of security, can maintain secrecy as effectively as members of the armed services. Had not this been true, decentralization of information and operations would have been as hazardous as an open flame in a powder magazine.

The task of the administrator in applying science to war was to find first-rate talent, assign it to the right jobs, and create the conditions under which the task could best be performed. Above all it was to save time. Irvin Stewart devised a streamlined system of processing contracts which enabled the ordinary ones to move rapidly along while the more difficult cases were receiving special handling. But the fact that NDRC could make contracts quicker than large government agencies was in the nature of things. The contracting officer, Bush or Stewart, was always available for a quick decision which in a large department might have taken a fortnight before all the necessary concurrences were obtained.

Streamlined contract procedures helped a great deal, but effective liaison with the armed services was still more important. The better the teamwork between the services, the academic contractors, and the industrial contractors, the more time could be saved. Great effort was required to get the scientists the information they needed with the minimum of delay; and to avoid the regimentation which so hampered the German effort. It is not an easy thing in wartime to afford full scope to inventiveness. Yet where scientific manpower and imagination are the limiting factors the creation of conditions favorable to prompt and original solutions is the crux of the problem.

It must not be imagined that the liaison established with the services was perfect or that it functioned without difficulty. In wartime the Army and Navy are immense and complex organizations in a constant state of flux. The first problem of the civilian scientist is to find the right people to work with. If his assignment has to do with aerial gunnery he may not know at the outset that though the Navy Bureau of Aeronautics is responsible for turrets the Bureau of Ordnance supplies the gunsights. When he has found the right people at the right level in the right bureaus his problem is not solved. The next time he calls, one of the men may have been ordered to sea duty and another to the European theater. In England it was much easier for the scientist to get in close contact with men just back from the front than it was in the United States. In both countries the scientist was sorely handicapped unless he could work closely both with his opposite numbers in the research and production branches of the various bureaus, and with operations officers as well. He also needed permission to use Army and Navy facilities for his experiments, which might require anything from airplanes and blimps to detroyers and submarines.

When the civilian scientists had demonstrated conclusively how good their work was and how well they could keep secrets, their liaison with the services became increasingly better, but it varied from bureau to bureau. The Army and Navy each had a representative on the National Defense Research Committee, and one or both services detailed at least one officer to each project. The success of these liaison officers varied in accordance with their knowledge of the work and the length of time they served before their transfer to other duties. Under Major General Clarence C. Williams, a former Chief of Ordnance, the War Department Liaison Office which had been set up to handle relations with NDRC became a very effective instrument. The Office of the Co-ordinator of Research and Development, under Dr. Jerome C. Hunsaker from July to December 1941, and Rear Admiral Julius A. Furer from that date until May 1945, worked wonders in handling NDRC liaison with the Navy Department. Fully posted on the needs of the Navy and alive to the possibilities of civilian contributions, these tactful and imaginative co-ordinators exerted a powerful influence over the whole field of Navy-OSRD collaboration. . . . They acted as catalysts in many developments of outstanding importance. "That your group would contribute brilliant ideas and achievements to the war effort was expected," wrote Admiral Furer to Bush, "but that you would be so versatile, and that the scientists and the Navy would find themselves so adaptable to each other's way of doing business, was unexpected by many."

2. The Atomic Bomb, 1945

HENRY DEWOLF SMYTH, *Atomic Energy for Military Purposes*

The greatest single technological development of World War II was, of course, the atomic bomb. In the Manhattan District, basic and applied science and engineering, foreign and American scientists, civilians and the military, academic and industrial personnel—all possible institutions of research—were brought together to build the ultimate weapon. Some of the men involved at a high level were already well known: Vannevar Bush and James B. Conant, for example. Others, like J. Robert Oppenheimer, became national heroes because of their work on the bomb. The following document was the War Department's press release on the New Mexico test of the atomic bomb, July 16, 1945.

Mankind's successful transition to a new age, the Atomic Age, was ushered in July 16, 1945, before the eyes of a tense group of renowned scientists and military men gathered in the desertlands of New Mexico to witness the first end results of their $2,000,000,000 effort. Here in a remote section of the Alamogordo Air Base 120 miles southeast of Albuquerque the first man-made atomic explosion, the outstanding achievement of nuclear science, was achieved at 5:30 a.m. of that day. Darkening heavens, pouring forth rain and lightning immediately up to the zero hour, heightened the drama.

Mounted on a steel tower, a revolutionary weapon destined to change war as we know it, or which may even be the instrumentality to end all wars, was set off with an impact which signalized man's entrance into a new physical world. Success was greater than the most ambitious estimates. A small amount of matter, the product of a chain of huge specially constructed industrial plants, was made to release the energy of the universe locked up within the atom from the beginning of time. A fabulous achievement had been reached. Speculative theory, barely established in pre-war laboratories, had been projected into practicality.

This phase of the Atomic Bomb Project, which is headed by Major General Leslie R. Groves, was under the direction of Dr. J. R. Oppenheimer, theoretical physicist of the University of California. He is to be credited with achieving the implementation of atomic energy for military purposes.

Tension before the actual detonation was at a tremendous pitch. Failure was an ever-present possibility. Too great a success, envisioned by some of those present, might have meant an uncontrollable, unusable weapon.

From Henry DeWolf Smyth, *Atomic Energy for Military Purposes: The Official Report on the Development of the Atomic Bomb under the Auspices of the United States Government, 1940-1945* (Princeton, 1945), pp. 247-54.

Final assembly of the atomic bomb began on the night of July 12 in an old ranch house. As various component assemblies arrived from distant points, tension among the scientists rose to an increasing pitch. Coolest of all was the man charged with the actual assembly of the vital core, Dr. R. F. Bacher, in normal times a professor at Cornell University.

The entire cost of the project, representing the erection of whole cities and radically new plants spread over many miles of countryside, plus unprecedented experimentation, was represented in the pilot bomb and its parts. Here was the focal point of the venture. No other country in the world had been capable of such an outlay in brains and technical effort.

The full significance of these closing moments before the final factual test was *not* lost on these men of science. They fully knew their position as pioneers into another age. They also knew that one false move would blast them and their entire effort into eternity. Before the assembly started a receipt for the vital matter was signed by Brigadier General Thomas F. Farrell, General Groves' deputy. This signalized the formal transfer of the irreplaceable material from the scientists to the Army.

During final preliminary assembly, a bad few minutes developed when the assembly of an important section of the bomb was delayed. The entire unit was machine-tooled to the finest measurement. The insertion was partially completed when it apparently wedged tightly and would go no farther. Dr. Bacher, however, was undismayed and reassured the group that time would solve the problem. In three minutes' time, Dr. Bacher's statement was verified and basic assembly was completed without further incident.

Specialty teams, comprised of the top men on specific phases of science, all of which were bound up in the whole, took over their specialized parts of the assembly. In each group was centralized months and even years of channelized endeavor.

On Saturday, July 14, the unit which was to determine the success or failure of the entire project was elevated to the top of the steel tower. All that day and the next, the job of preparation went on. In addition to the apparatus necessary to cause the detonation, complete instrumentation to determine the pulse beat and all reactions of the bomb was rigged on the tower.

The ominous weather which had dogged the assembly of the bomb had a very sobering affect on the assembled experts whose work was accomplished amid lightning flashes and peals of thunder. The weather, unusual and upsetting, blocked out aerial observation of the test. It even held up the actual explosion scheduled at 4:00 a.m. for an hour and a half. For many months the approximate date and time had been set and had been one of the high-level secrets of the best kept secret of the entire war.

Nearest observation point was set up 10,000 yards south of the tower where in a timber and earth shelter the controls for the test were located. At a point 17,-000 yards from the tower at a point which would give the best observation the key figures in the atomic bomb project took their posts. These included General Groves, Dr. Vannevar Bush, head of the Office of Scientific Research and Development and Dr. James B. Conant, president of Harvard University.

Actual detonation was in charge of Dr. K. T. Bainbridge of Massachusetts Institute of Technology. He and Lieutenant Bush, in charge of the Military

Police Detachment, were the last men to inspect the tower with its cosmic bomb.

At three o'clock in the morning the party moved forward to the control station. General Groves and Dr. Oppenheimer consulted with the weathermen. The decision was made to go ahead with the test despite the lack of assurance of favorable weather. The time was set for 5:30 a.m.

General Groves rejoined Dr. Conant and Dr. Bush, and just before the test time they joined the many scientists gathered at the Base Camp. Here all present were ordered to lie on the ground, face downward, heads away from the blast direction.

Tension reached a tremendous pitch in the control room as the deadline approached. The several observation points in the area were tied in to the control room by radio and with twenty minutes to go, Dr. S. K. Allison of Chicago University took over the radio net and made periodic time announcements.

The time signals, "minus 20 minutes, minus fifteen minutes," and on and on increased the tension to the breaking point as the group in the control room which included Dr. Oppenheimer and General Farrell held their breaths, all praying with the intensity of the moment which will live forever with each man who was there. At "minus 45 seconds," robot mechanism took over and from that point on the whole great complicated mass of intricate mechanism was in operation without human control. Stationed at a reserve switch, however, was a soldier scientist ready to attempt to stop the explosion should the order be issued. The order never came.

At the appointed time there was a blinding flash lighting up the whole area brighter than the brightest daylight. A mountain range three miles from the observation point stood out in bold relief. Then came a tremendous sustained roar and a heavy pressure wave which knocked down two men outside the control center. Immediately thereafter, a huge multi-colored surging cloud boiled to an altitude of over 40,000 feet. Clouds in its path disappeared. Soon the shifting substratosphere winds dispersed the now grey mass.

The test was over, the project a success.

The steel tower had been entirely vaporized. Where the tower had stood, there was a huge sloping crater. Dazed but relieved at the success of their tests, the scientists promptly marshalled their forces to estimate the strength of America's new weapon. To examine the nature of the crater, specially equipped tanks were wheeled into the area, one of which carried Dr. Enrico Fermi, noted nuclear scientist. Answer to their findings rests in the destruction effected in Japan today in the first military use of the atomic bomb.

Had it not been for the desolated area where the test was held and for the co-operation of the press in the area, it is certain that the test itself would have attracted far-reaching attention. As it was, many people in that area are still discussing the effect of the smash. A significant aspect, recorded by the press, was the experience of a blind girl near Albuquerque many miles from the scene, who, when the flash of the test lighted the sky before the explosion could be heard, exclaimed, "What was that?"

Interviews of General Groves and General Farrell give the following on-the-scene versions of the test. General Groves said: "My impressions of the night's high points follow: After about an hour's sleep I got up at 0100 and from that time on until about five I was with Dr. Oppenheimer constantly. Naturally he was tense, although his mind was working at its usual extraordinary efficiency. I attempted to shield him from the evident concern shown by many of his assistants who were disturbed by the uncertain weather conditions. By 0330 we decided that we could probably fire at 0530. By 0400 the rain had stopped but the sky was heavily overcast. Our decision became firmer as time went on.

"During most of these hours the two of us journeyed from the control house out into the darkness to look at the stars and to assure each other that the one or two visible stars were becoming brighter. At 0510 I left Dr. Oppenheimer and returned to the main observation point which was 17,000 yards from the point of explosion. In accordance with our orders I found all personnel not otherwise occupied massed on a bit of high ground.

"Two minutes before the scheduled firing time, all persons lay face down with their feet pointing towards the explosion. As the remaining time was called from the loud speaker from the 10,000-yard control station there was complete awesome silence. Dr. Conant said he had never imagined seconds could be so long. Most of the individuals in accordance with orders shielded their eyes in one way or another.

"First came the burst of light of a brilliance beyond any comparison. We all rolled over and looked through dark glasses at the ball of fire. About forty seconds later came the shock wave followed by the sound, neither of which seemed startling after our complete astonishment at the extraordinary lighting intensity.

"A massive cloud was formed which surged and billowed upward with tremendous power, reaching the substratosphere in about five minutes.

"Two supplementary explosions of minor effect other than the lighting occured in the cloud shortly after the main explosion.

"The cloud traveled to a great height first in the form of a ball, then mushroomed, then changed into a long trailing chimney-shaped column and finally was sent in several directions by the variable winds at the different elevations.

"Dr. Conant reached over and we shook hands in mutual congratulations. Dr. Bush, who was on the other side of me, did likewise. The feeling of the entire assembly, even the uninitiated, was of profound awe. Drs. Conant and Bush and myself were struck by an even stronger feeling that the faith of those who had been responsible for the initiation and the carrying on of this Herculean project had been justified."

General Farrell's impressions are: "The scene inside the shelter was dramatic beyond words. In and around the shelter were some twenty odd people concerned with last-minute arrangements. Included were Dr. Oppenheimer, the Director who had borne the great scientific burden of developing the weapon from the raw materials made in Tennessee and Washington, and a dozen of his key assistants, Dr. Kistiakowsky, Dr. Bainbridge, who supervised all the detailed arrangements for the test; the weather expert, and several others. Besides those, there were a handful of soldiers, two or three Army officers and one Naval Officer. The shelter was filled with a great variety of instruments and radios.

"For some hectic two hours preceding the blast, General Groves stayed with the Director. Twenty minutes before the zero hour, General Groves left for his station at the base camp, first because it provided a better observation point and second, because of our rule that he and

I must not be together in situations where there is an element of danger which existed at both points.

"Just after General Groves left, announcements began to be broadcast of the interval remaining before the blast to other groups participating in and observing the test. As the time interval grew smaller and changed from minutes to seconds, the tension increased by leaps and bounds. Everyone in that room knew the awful potentialities of the thing that they thought was about to happen. The scientists felt that their figuring must be right and that the bomb had to go off but there was in everyone's mind a strong measure of doubt.

"We were reaching into the unknown and we did not know what might come of it. It can safely be said that most of those present were praying—and praying harder than they had ever prayed before. If the shot were successful, it was a justification of the several years of intensive effort of tens of thousands of people—statesmen, scientists, engineers, manufacturers, soldiers, and many others in every walk of life.

"In that brief instant in the remote New Mexico desert, the tremendous effort of the brains and brawn of all these people came suddenly and startlingly to the fullest fruition. Dr. Oppenheimer, on whom had rested a very heavy burden, grew tenser as the last seconds ticked off. He scarcely breathed. He held on to a post to steady himself. For the last few seconds, he stared directly ahead and then when the announcer shouted 'Now!' and there came this tremendous burst of light followed shortly thereafter by the deep growling roar of the explosion, his face relaxed into an expression of tremendous relief. Several of the observers standing back of the shelter to watch the lighting effects were knocked flat by the blast.

"The tension in the room let up and all started congratulating each other. Everyone sensed 'This is it!' No matter what might happen now all knew that the impossible scientific job had been done. Atomic fission would no longer be hidden in the cloisters of the theoretical physicists' dreams. It was almost full grown at birth. It was a great new force to be used for good or for evil. There was a feeling in that shelter that those concerned with its nativity should dedicate their lives to the mission that it would always be used for good and never for evil.

"Dr. Kistiakowsky threw his arms around Dr. Oppenheimer and embraced him with shouts of glee. Others were equally enthusiastic. All the pent-up emotions were released in those few minutes and all seemed to sense immediately that the explosion had far exceeded the most optimistic expectations and wildest hopes of the scientists. All seemed to feel that they had been present at the birth of a new age—The Age of Atomic Energy—and felt their profound responsibility to help in guiding into right channels the tremendous forces which had been unlocked for the first time in history.

"As to the present war, there was a feeling that no matter what else might happen, we now had the means to insure its speedy conclusion and save thousands of American lives. As to the future, there had been brought into being something big and something new that would prove to be immeasurably more important than the discovery of electricity or any of the other great discoveries which have so affected our existence.

"The effects could well be called unprecedented, magnificent, beautiful, stupendous and terrifying. No man-made phenomenon of such tremendous power had ever occurred before. The lighting effects beggared description. The whole country was lighted by a searing light with the intensity many times that of the midday sun. It was golden, purple, violet, gray and blue. It lighted every peak, crevasse and ridge of the nearby mountain range with a clarity and beauty that cannot be described but must be seen to be imagined. It was that beauty the great poets dream about but describe most poorly and inadequately. Thirty seconds after, the explosion came first, the air blast pressing hard against the people and things, to be followed almost immediately by the strong, sustained, awesome roar which warned of doomsday and made us feel that we puny things were blasphemous to dare tamper with the forces heretofore reserved to the Almighty. Words are inadequate tools for the job of acquainting those not present with the physical, mental and psychological effects. It had to be witnessed to be realized."

3. The Nuclear Future, 1945

HENRY DeWOLF SMYTH, *Atomic Energy for Military Purposes*

Some of the implications of the atomic weapons were obvious almost immediately. Within weeks after the dropping of the two bombs on Japan, the government published an official report on the Manhattan District, written by one of the physicists involved. Perhaps never before had a new technology been loosed upon an unprepared society with such dramatic and potentially disastrous results. The efforts to develop the proper institutions (not to mention ethics) to cope with the nuclear threat began in those same weeks following the end of the war.

As the result of the labors of the Manhattan District organization in Washington and in Tennessee, of the scientific groups at Berkeley, Chicago, Columbia, Los Alamos, and elsewhere, of the industrial groups at Clinton, Hanford, and many other places, the end of June 1945 finds us expecting from day to day to hear of the explosion of the first atomic bomb devised by man. All the problems are believed to have been solved at least well enough to make a bomb practicable. A sustained neutron chain reaction resulting from nuclear fission has been demonstrated; the conditions necessary to cause such a reaction to occur explosively have been established and can be achieved; production plants of several different types are in operation, building up a stock pile of the ex-

From Henry DeWolf Smyth, *Atomic Energy for Military Purposes*, pp. 223-26.

plosive material. Although we do not know when the first explosion will occur nor how effective it will be, announcement of its occurence will precede the publication of this report. Even if the first attempt is relatively ineffective, there is little doubt that later efforts will be highly effective; the devastation from a single bomb is expected to be comparable to that of a major air raid by usual methods.

A weapon has been developed that is potentially destructive beyond the wildest nightmares of the imagination; a weapon so ideally suited to sudden unannounced attack that a country's major cities might be destroyed overnight by an ostensibly friendly power. This weapon has been created not by the devilish inspiration of some warped genius but by the arduous labor of thousands of normal men and women working for the safety of their country. Many of the principles that have been used were well known to the international scientific world in 1940. To develop the necessary industrial processes from these principles has been costly in time, effort, and money, but the processes which we selected for serious effort have worked and several that we have not chosen could probably be made to work. We have an initial advantage in time because, so far as we know, other countries have not been able to carry out parallel developments during the war period. We also have a general advantage in scientific and particularly in industrial strength, but such an advantage can easily be thrown away.

Before the surrender of Germany there was always a chance that German scientists and engineers might be developing atomic bombs which would be sufficiently effective to alter the course of the war. There was therefore no choice but to work on them in this country. Initially many scientists could and did hope that some principle would emerge which would prove that atomic bombs were inherently impossible. This hope has faded gradually; fortunately in the same period the magnitude of the necessary industrial effort has been demonstrated so that the fear of German success weakened even before the end came. By the same token, most of us are certain that the Japanese cannot develop and use this weapon effectively.

As to the future, one may guess that technical developments will take place along two lines. From the military point of view it is reasonably certain that there will be improvements both in the processes of producing fissionable material and in its use. It is conceivable that totally different methods may be discovered for converting matter into energy since it is to be remembered that the energy released in uranium fission corresponds to the utilization of only about one-tenth of one per cent of its mass. Should a scheme be devised for converting to energy even as much as a few per cent of the matter of some common material, civilization would have the means to commit suicide at will.

The possible uses of nuclear energy are not all destructive, and the second direction in which technical development can be expected is along the paths of peace. In the fall of 1944 General Groves appointed a committee to look into these possibilities as well as those of military significance. This committee (Dr. R. C. Tolman, chairman; Rear Admiral E. W. Mills (USN) with Captain T. A. Solberg (USN) as deputy, Dr. W. K. Lewis, and Dr. H. D. Smyth) received a multitude of suggestions from men on the various projects, principally along the lines of the use of nuclear energy for power and the use of radioactive by-products for scientific, medical, and industrial purposes. While there was general agreement that a great industry might eventually arise, comparable, perhaps, with the electronics industry, there was disagreement as to how rapidly such an industry would grow; the consensus was that the growth would be slow over a period of many years. At least there is no immediate prospect of running cars with nuclear power or lighting houses with radioactive lamps although there is a good probability that nuclear power for special purposes could be developed within ten years and that plentiful supplies of radioactive materials can have a profound effect on scientific research and perhaps on the treatment of certain diseases in a similar period.

During the war the effort has been to achieve the maximum military results. It has been apparent for some time that some sort of government control and support in the field of nuclear energy must continue after the war. Many of the men associated with the project have recognized this fact and have come forward with various proposals, some of which were considered by the Tolman Committee, although it was only a temporary advisory committee reporting to General Groves. An interim committee at a high level is now engaged in formulating plans for a continuing organization. This committee is also discussing matters of general policy about which many of the more thoughtful men on the project have been deeply concerned since the work was begun and especially since success became more and more probable.

We find ourselves with an explosive which is far from completely perfected. Yet the future possibility of such explosives are appalling, and their effects on future wars and international affairs are of fundamental importance. Here is a new tool for mankind, a tool of unimaginable destructive power. Its development raises many questions that must be answered in the near future.

Because of the restrictions of military security there has been no chance for the Congress or the people to debate such questions. They have been seriously considered by all concerned and vigorously debated among the scientists, and the conclusions reached have been passed along to the highest authorities. These questions are not technical questions; they are political and social questions, and the answers given to them may affect all mankind for generations. In thinking about them the men on the project have been thinking as citizens of the United States vitally interested in the welfare of the human race. It has been their duty and that of the responsible high government officials who were informed to look beyond the limits of the present war and its weapons to the ultimate implications of these discoveries. This was a heavy responsibility. In a free country like ours, such questions should be debated by the people and decisions must be made by the people through their representatives. This is one reason for the release of this report. It is a semi-technical report which it is hoped men of science in this country can use to help their fellow citizens in reaching wise decisions. The people of the country must be informed if they are to discharge their responsibilities wisely.

4. Innovations on the Home Front, 1945

Wartime Technological Developments

One of the major policies of the Office of Scientific Research and Development, and one which was important in its success, was that of resisting the temptation to become involved in research and development in areas other than weapons. Even the Manhattan District, because of its enormous scale, was passed on to a more appropriate agency, the Army Engineers. While this policy of self-denial allowed the OSRD to concentrate its efforts, it left certain technical areas without a central co-ordinating body. This deficiency was especially felt in the area of industrial production.

Faced with shortages of skilled workers, adequate tools, and strategic raw materials, such agencies as the War Production Board sorely needed technical innovation to help in expediting the flow of war materials. Some changes did take place, despite the lack of over-all planning. They tended to be conservative and unconnected, but their cumulative effect posed problems for the postwar economy.

Since 1940, when our armament program began, the national output has advanced steadily and rapidly. Confronted with an urgent need for war equipment, the Nation has expanded its production to an extent which seemed inconceivable a few years ago.

The magnitude of the expansion of economic activity in response to war needs is indicated roughly by the change in the gross national product—the total value of currently produced goods and services flowing to Government, to business for gross capital formation, and to consumers. Department of Commerce estimates show an increase of 75 percent between 1939, the last year unaffected by war changes, and the year 1943; expressed in terms of 1939 prices, the gross national product rose from 89 billion dollars to 155 billion between the 2 years. War expenditures of the Federal Government, which amounted to only 1.4 billion dollars in 1939, comprised 44 percent of the total gross national product in 1943. During the first half of 1944, both gross national product and war expenditures were somewhat above the average levels for 1943.

Despite the remarkable war production record, there has been no sharp reduction in the quantity of goods available for current civilian use. The manufacture of many types of consumers' durable goods—for example, automobiles, radios, and refrigerators—has been, of course, virtually discontinued. Most

From U.S. Congress, Senate Committee on Military Affairs, Subcommittee on War Mobilization, *Wartime Technological Developments*, 79th Cong., 1st sess. (May 1945), pp. 1-5, 28-29.

essential consumers' goods, however, have been available in reasonably satisfactory quantities. Indeed, according to the Department of Commerce, consumers' expenditures, expressed in 1939 prices, increased from a total of 62 billion dollars in 1939 to 71 billion in 1943.

To meet the production goals of the war economy, the Nation has attempted to mobilize to the best possible advantage all of its resources—natural wealth, capital equipment, labor, and technical skill. Although the advance of production to peak levels has been beset with many difficulties and, although numerous problems still remain, there is general agreement that the record thus far represents a creditable accomplishment.

Within the limits set by available natural resources, the total volume of production may be considered to depend principally on two factors—the amount of labor expended and the efficiency with which it is used. One of the more important factors tending to raise efficiency in our munitions industries has been technological development. The need for rapid volume production of munitions has resulted in the development, within a few years, of numerous innovations in industry which otherwise would have been achieved only over a much longer period, if at all. Increased research into manufacturing techniques made possible great progress in welding methods, in the fabrication of the light metals, in heat treating, in inspection methods, and the like. Critical shortages of materials which arose because of the curtailment of imports or because of increased requirements have encouraged the development of new materials. In addition, the need for materials to serve new purposes has also stimulated technical improvements in the production of basic materials. Thus, outstanding advances have been made in techniques for producing or fabricating materials particularly required for war use—for example, synthetic rubber, aviation gasoline, aluminum, magnesium, and plastics.

Perhaps even more striking than the contribution of technology to manufacturing efficiency has been its role in improving the effectiveness of the implements of war and in developing new types of munitions. Constant research has been devoted to the improvement of combat matériel. Thus, to cite only a few examples, designs of planes have been improved steadily, jet propulsion has been developed, superior models of aircraft instruments have been introduced, and tremendous progress has been made in the development of radar and other electronic devices.

Contributions to the wartime technical progress have been made by public and by privately supported research agencies, by the technical staffs of producing plants, and by other plant employees. A surprisingly large proportion of the developments reported have been made by plant employees themselves, under employee suggestion systems worked out by labor-management committees, rather than by technicians. Agencies of the Federal Government have been active, throughout the war period, in conducting industrial research or in promoting such research. In June 1941 the Office of Scientific Research and Development was created to provide for research on the processes used in the production of the instruments of war and on the development of improved war implements. The Office of Production Research and Development was established in the War Production Board, in November 1942, to do similar work with respect to war materials. In addition, the War and Navy Departments have conducted much technical research themselves and other agencies of the Government have continued or expanded their peacetime research activities. Few of the wartime developments are completely new or attributable to any one individual or organization. Most current developments can be traced to achievements made over a considerable period in the past. The war emergency, however, resulted in a great acceleration of the pace at which progress was made.

Nevertheless, there has not been a consistent acceleration of technical progress throughout the whole economy during the war period. Attention has been directed primarily to the production of munitions goods and materials for munitions goods. Industries producing goods chiefly for civilian use have had their normal peacetime progress interrupted. Technicians have been drawn into war work and the general shortage of manpower and materials has made impossible the introduction of new production processes or new types of products.

Technological developments—if the term is defined to include only genuinely new advances in industrial science —are of the greatest long-term importance. Basically new products or new types of production processes have a continuing effect on the economy. They encourage investment and the production of new capital equipment. They give rise to new enterprises and to entire new industries. Technological advances thus provide an important basis for an expanding economy. The development of the automobile, for example, resulted not only in the creation of an industry which employed 450,000 workers by 1929, but also in great stimulus to other manufacturing activities—the production of machinery, petroleum refining, and the manufacture of tires. In ad-

dition, the automobile brought about a vast amount of road construction and gave rise to important service industries —for example, garages and repair shops, filling stations, and tourist courts.

Since improvements in production techniques frequently involve a decline in the total amount of labor required for a given volume of output, they are sometimes described as labor-displacing innovations. If production methods are improved and production volume is not expanded, there may be a net decline in employment opportunities. Similarly, if a new product is developed which competes with and replaces an older product, there may be a decline in labor requirements, if the number of man-hours needed to produce a unit of the new product is smaller than for the old and if total production is not expanded. Nevertheless, discussions of technological changes as simply labor displacing are incomplete and may be extremely misleading. Comparisons of labor requirements under differing methods of production for the same volume of goods are of little significance, since the volume of production is clearly not independent of the techniques of manufacture. Some industries which have experienced very rapid increases in productivity, rayon manufacture, for example, have nevertheless expanded employment because cost savings and improved quality have led to greatly increased markets and production.

Because of the interdependence of our industries, the relationship between technological change and productivity, or output per man-hour, is complex. Although new techniques frequently make possible gains in output per man-hour in the industries adopting the new methods, such developments do not necessarily involve a corresponding decline in the amount of labor required for the final product. The new method may, for example, involve increases in labor requirements for the production of materials or capital equipment, which offset in part the reductions in labor requirements in the final operations. Most important is the impetus given by rapid technological change to replacement of capital equipment. If technical changes result in a rapid rate of obsolescence for equipment, they may imply an increase rather than a decrease in the total amount of labor required for a given volume of production. On the other hand, some developments involve declines in labor requirements for the final product which may not be reflected in any statistics of output per man-hour as they are conventionally prepared. They may, for example, permit savings in the cost of raw materials through the reduction of waste or the use of new materials. Such changes will not be reflected in measures of output per man-hour for the industries adopting the changed processes or for the industries producing the raw materials.

The important fact is that technological change exerts a continuing impetus to increased productivity. As new goods are produced on a larger scale, productivity usually increases rapidly in their manufacture and improvements also occur in industries providing the necessary materials and capital equipment. Similarly, the introduction of new materials encourages research in the development of better methods for the production of the materials and for their fabrication. Increased use of new production techniques also stimulates technical improvements in the industry instituting the changes as well as in allied industries.

While technological change is the most important factor making for long-term increases in productivity, output per man-hour may change within short periods because of a variety of influences. In the munitions industries the most important element has been the adoption of mass production methods which were not new advances but which were already well established in American industry. Designs were standardized, line production systems were developed, prefabrication, and subassembly were increasingly employed, special-purpose machinery was introduced, and numerous other improvements were made in production methods. Line production systems have been adopted in the manufacture of many war items, notably aircraft, aircraft engines, ordnance, tanks, and other military vehicles. They are particularly applicable to the assembly of many parts into identical complex products to be manufactured in great quantity. The production process is divided into successive small operations, usually simple in themselves, and there is a regular, continuous flow of materials through the various stages of fabrication. Not the least important aspect of line production is the ability it confers to use large numbers of inexperienced workers after brief training on parts of a job which, taken in its entirety, is complex in the extreme. In heavy construction industries, prefabrication is analogous to line assembly methods, since it makes possible the mass production of standardized sections which can be rapidly assembled. In shipbuilding, the use of prefabrication has permitted great savings in the time required between keel laying and delivery and has contributed to striking declines in labor requirements as successive ships have been built.

In peacetime new technological developments usually gain general adoption only over a considerable period of years and they may influence productivity only slowly. Their importance depends, therefore, on the rate at which they are adopted. Even if no new advances in techniques occur, productivity depends very greatly on the rate at which capital equipment is replaced, since the average age of equipment in use in most industries is high.

Numerous other factors have a pronounced effect on the level of output per man-hour at any time. Changes in the quality of the resources and materials used may result in changes in productivity. In mining operations, particularly, the nature of the deposits worked is of the utmost importance. Where "indirect" labor constitutes a large proportion of total labor required, productive efficiency may depend greatly on the degree of utilization of capacity. The skill and experience of the labor force and the quality of management also have their influence on the level of output per man-hour. During the war period some of these nontechnical factors have become of increased importance and various aspects of labor utilization have received greater emphasis—recruitment and training, turn-over, absenteeism, hours and shift arrangements, working and living conditions, morale and labor relations, production planning. All of these factors may result in short-term fluctuations in productivity in individual plants and industries.

Nevertheless, over long periods the chief impetus for improved efficiency is technological development. During the war technical advances in certain fields have been made at a far more rapid rate than in peacetime. While many of these wartime developments will not be applicable to peacetime production, others will be adopted for a variety of peacetime uses. To the extent that we integrate them into the economy without creating dislocations, they will contribute to higher standards of living and to greater leisure. . . .

When peace returns, the Nation will have an expanded industrial plant, a larger labor force, and increased technical knowledge. Together, these provide the technical basis for a high standard of living. The industries which make up the normal civilian economy will resume the progress which was interrupted during the war. New equipment will be installed, new techniques will be introduced, and new products will be developed. In this process, wartime technical achievements will make no small contribution. The development of new civilian products will be speeded by wartime research and by the experience gained in the production of war goods. The existence of a large capacity for the manufacture of many relatively new materials —for example, magnesium, synthetic rubber, and plastics—will stimulate the increased use of these materials in civilian products. Processes especially developed for war production, particularly in metal working, will find many applications in the manufacture of goods for peacetime use.

Of course, many of the innovations made during the war period will find no uses in the post-war economy. Some techniques developed specifically to speed up the manufacture of guns, bombs, and ammunition, for example, may be of no importance in the manufacture of civilian goods. Moreover, many of those techniques which are transferrable from war to peace production will not be adopted immediately. Ordinarily, new products or new processes gain general acceptance only over a period of many years. The influence of wartime technical progress, therefore, will not be fully reflected in the economy during the first post-war years. Technological development during the war period has been concentrated in the metal-producing, metal-fabricating, and chemicals industries. Many important civilian industries, therefore, will not be in a position to benefit immediately or directly from war experience, particularly industries producing textiles, leather, apparel, and similar products. Nevertheless, rapid technical progress may be made in these industries after the war. A considerable amount of equipment will have to be replaced and production levels will probably be high. These factors will doubtless result in an accelerated rate of technical change for several years following the end of hostilities.

Technological progress is not the only aspect of the war economy which will affect the rate of technical change in the post-war period. Many other factors will have significant, although sometimes indirect, influences. There will be a large volume of savings and a large demand for consumers' durable goods which have not been available during the war, notably automobiles, radios, and refrigerators. The large markets which will exist for these products may make possible rapid introduction of new types of goods—for example, frequency modulation receivers, television receivers, etc. On the other hand, since manufacturers will wish to resume production of these goods at the earliest possible date, initial models may be essentially the same as those produced before the war. Thus, automobile manufacturers are apparently planning that their first post-war offerings will be very much like the 1942 models. The existence of a large capacity for the production of many materials may also influence the pace of technical change in the post-war period. It appears clear that facilities for the production of synthetic rubber, aluminum, and magnesium, for example, will be greater than necessary to supply civilian markets for some time to come. Processes for the manufacture of these materials were selected rapidly to meet the needs of the war-production program, and the manufacturing techniques now in use may be "frozen" after the war. As a consequence, some of the benefits obtainable through continued experimentation and slow growth may be lost. Similarly, there will be large stocks of standard machine tools after the war. If new production is small for several years following the war, improvements in design may be few.

New tastes acquired during the war will also play their part in determining which types of products will gain popular acceptance. The training in flying received by men in the armed forces, for example, is expected to contribute to the demand for planes for private use and to popular acceptance of commercial air transportation. On the other hand, the market for dehydrated and other processed foods may suffer if military personnel have acquired prejudices against such foods.

In the final analysis, the pace of technical progress in the post-war period will depend greatly on the general level of economic activity. Only if manufacturers can look forward to a sustained large volume of output will there be substantial investment in new types of equipment or the manufacture of new types of products. A post-war depression, or even the expectation of a depression, would limit the incentives toward technical progress. An economy of expansion will stimulate constant improvements in products and in production methods.

5. A New Relationship, 1945

VANNEVAR BUSH, *Science—The Endless Frontier*

The wartime mobilization of the nation's scientific and technical resources, imperfect as it was, was unprecedented in our history. During the Depression there had been a good deal of talk about increased government involvement in science and technology, but little had been accomplished, and many felt that government interference would be unwise. During the war most of the doubts, on both sides, were swept away. The government found that it needed science and technology to survive, and technical men discovered just how much they could do with the new magnitude of funds available to them. By the end of the war most close observers of the situation were agreed that the federal government would play a new and more vigorous role in stimulating and using scientific and technical innovations in the postwar years. •

Two men in particular took the responsibility for drawing up the ground rules and planning the institutions for such a new relationship. In the Senate, Harley Kilgore of West Virginia held long and detailed hearings on the subject. In the Office of Scientific Research and Development, Vannevar Bush studied the problem from the vantage point of a working scientist. His report served to focus the debate and action taken in the immediate postwar period. When the National Science Foundation was finally established in 1950, its mission was less comprehensive than that envisioned by Bush five years before. Nevertheless his general arguments proved effective.

SCIENTIFIC PROGRESS IS ESSENTIAL

Progress in the war against disease depends upon a flow of new scientific knowledge. New products, new industries, and more jobs require continuous additions to knowledge of the laws of nature, and the application of that knowledge to practical purposes. Similarly, our defense against aggression demands new knowledge so that we can develop new and improved weapons. This essential, new knowledge can be obtained only through basic scientific research.

Science can be effective in the national welfare only as a member of a team, whether the conditions be peace or war. But without scientific progress no amount of achievement in other directions can insure our health, prosperity, and security as a nation in the modern world.

For the War Against Disease

We have taken great strides in the war against disease. The death rate for all diseases in the Army, including overseas forces, has been reduced from 14.1 per thousand in the last war to 0.6

From Vannevar Bush, *Science—The Endless Frontier: A Report to the President* (Washington, D.C., 1945), pp. 1-7, 12-17, 25-28.

408

per thousand in this war. In the last 40 years life expectancy has increased from 49 to 65 years, largely as a consequence of the reduction in the death rates of infants and children. But we are far from the goal. The annual deaths from one or two diseases far exceed the total number of American lives lost in battle during this war. A large fraction of these deaths in our civilian population cut short the useful lives of our citizens. Approximately 7,000,000 persons in the United States are mentally ill and their care costs the public over $175,000,000 a year. Clearly much illness remains for which adequate means of prevention and cure are not yet known.

The responsibility for basic research in medicine and the underlying sciences, so essential to progress in the war against disease, falls primarily upon the medical schools and universities. Yet we find that the traditional sources of support for medical research in the medical schools and universities, largely endowment income, foundation grants, and private donations, are diminishing and there is no immediate prospect of a change in this trend. Meanwhile, the cost of medical research has been rising. If we are to maintain the progress in medicine which has marked the last 25 years, the Government should extend financial support to basic medical research in the medical schools and in universities.

For Our National Security

The bitter and dangerous battle against the U-boat was a battle of scientific techniques—and our margin of success was dangerously small. The new eyes which radar has supplied can sometimes be blinded by new scientific developments. V-2 was countered only by capture of the launching sites.

We cannot again rely on our allies to hold off the enemy while we struggle to catch up. There must be more—and more adequate—military research in peacetime. It is essential that the civilian scientists continue in peacetime some portion of those contributions to national security which they have made so effectively during the war. This can best be done through a civilian-controlled organization with close liaison with the Army and Navy, but with funds direct from Congress, and the clear power to initiate military research which will supplement and strengthen that carried on directly under the control of the Army and Navy.

And for the Public Welfare

One of our hopes is that after the war there will be full employment. To reach that goal the full creative and productive energies of the American people must be released. To create more jobs we must make new and better and cheaper products. We want plenty of new, vigorous enterprises. But new products and processes are not born full-grown. They are founded on new principles and new conceptions which in turn result from basic scientific research. Basic scientific research is scientific capital. Moreover, we cannot any longer depend upon Europe as a major source of this scientific capital. Clearly, more and better scientific research is one essential to the achievement of our goal of full employment.

How do we increase this scientific capital? First, we must have plenty of men and women trained in science, for upon them depends both the creation of new knowledge and its application to practical purposes. Second, we must strengthen the centers of basic research which are principally the colleges, universities, and research institutes. These institutions provide the environment which is most conducive to the creation of new scientific knowledge and least under pressure for immediate, tangible results. With some notable exceptions, most research in industry and in Government involves application of existing scientific knowledge to practical problems. It is only the colleges, universities, and a few research institutes that devote most of their research efforts to expanding the frontiers of knowledge.

Expenditures for scientific research by industry and Government increased from $140,000,000 in 1930 to $309,-000,000 in 1940. Those for the colleges and universities increased from $20,-000,000 to $31,000,000, while those for the research institutes declined from $5,-200,000 to $4,500,000 during the same period. If the colleges, universities, and research institutes are to meet the rapidly increasing demands of industry and Government for new scientific knowledge, their basic research should be strengthened by use of public funds.

For science to serve as a powerful factor in our national welfare, applied research both in Government and in industry must be vigorous. To improve the quality of scientific research within the Government, steps should be taken to modify the procedures for recruiting, classifying, and compensating scientific personnel in order to reduce the present handicap of governmental scientific bureaus in competing with industry and the universities for top-grade scientific talent. To provide coordination of the common scientific activities of these governmental agencies as to policies and budgets, a permanent Science Advisory Board should be created to advise the executive and legislative branches of Government on these matters.

The most important ways in which the Government can promote industrial research are to increase the flow of new

scientific knowledge through support of basic research, and to aid in the development of scientific talent. In addition, the Government should provide suitable incentives to industry to conduct research, (a) by clarification of present uncertainties in the Internal Revenue Code in regard to the deductibility of research and development expenditures as current charges against net income, and (b) by strengthening the patent system so as to eliminate uncertainties which now bear heavily on small industries and so as to prevent abuses which reflect discredit upon a basically sound system. In addition, ways should be found to cause the benefits of basic research to reach industries which do not now utilize new scientific knowledge.

WE MUST RENEW OUR SCIENTIFIC TALENT

The responsibility for the creation of new scientific knowledge—and for most of its application—rests on that small body of men and women who understand the fundamental laws of nature and are skilled in the techniques of scientific research. We shall have rapid or slow advance on any scientific frontier depending on the number of highly qualified and trained scientists exploring it.

The deficit of science and technology students who, but for the war, would have received bachelor's degrees is about 150,000. It is estimated that the deficit of those obtaining advanced degrees in these fields will amount in 1955 to about 17,000—for it takes at least 6 years from college entry to achieve a doctor's degree or its equivalent in science or engineering. The real ceiling on our productivity of new scientific knowlege and its application in the war against disease, and the development of new products and new industries, is the number of trained scientists available.

The training of a scientist is a long and expensive process. Studies clearly show that there are talented individuals in every part of the population, but with few exceptions, those without the means of buying higher education go without it. If ability, and not the circumstance of family fortune, determines who shall receive higher education in science, then we shall be assured of constantly improving quality at every level of scientific activity. The Government should provide a reasonable number of undergraduate scholarships and graduate fellowships in order to develop scientific talent in American youth. The plans should be designed to attract into science only that proportion of youthful talent appropriate to the needs of science in relation to the other needs of the nation for high abilities.

Including Those in Uniform

The most immediate prospect of making up the deficit in scientific personnel is to develop the scientific talent in the generation now in uniform. Even if we should start now to train the current crop of high-school graduates none would complete graduate studies before 1951. The Armed Services should comb their records for men who, prior to or during the war, have given evidence of talent for science, and make prompt arrangements, consistent with current discharge plans, for ordering those who remain in uniform, as soon as militarily possible, to duty at institutions here and overseas where they can continue their scientific education. Moreover, the Services should see that those who study overseas have the benefit of the latest scientific information resulting from research during the war.

THE LID MUST BE LIFTED

While most of the war research has involved the application of existing scientific knowledge to the problems of war, rather than basic research, there has been accumulated a vast amount of information relating to the application of science to particular problems. Much of this can be used by industry. It is also needed for teaching in the colleges and universities here and in the Armed Forces Institutes overseas. Some of this information must remain secret, but most of it should be made public as soon as there is ground for belief that the enemy will not be able to turn it against us in this war. To select that portion which should be made public, to coordinate its release, and definitely to encourage its publication, a Board composed of Army, Navy, and civilian scientific members should be promptly established.

A PROGRAM FOR ACTION

The Government should accept new responsibilities for promoting the flow of new scientific knowledge and the development of scientific talent in our youth. These responsibilities are the proper concern of the Government, for they vitally affect our health, our jobs, and our national security. It is in keeping also with basic United States policy that the Government should foster the opening of new frontiers and this is the modern way to do it. For many years the Government has wisely supported research in the agricultural colleges and the benefits have been great. The time has come when such support should be extended to other fields.

The effective discharge of these new responsibilities will require the full attention of some over-all agency devoted to that purpose. There is not now in the permanent Governmental structure receiving its funds from Congress an agency adapted to supplementing the support of basic research in the colleges, universities, and research institutes, both in medicine and the natural sciences, adapted to supporting research on new weapons for both Services, or adapted to administering a program of science scholarships and fellowships.

Therefore I recommend that a new agency for these purposes be established. Such an agency should be composed of persons of broad interest and experience, having an understanding of the peculiarities of scientific research and scientific education. It should have stability of funds so that long-range programs may be undertaken. It should recognize that freedom of inquiry must be preserved and should leave internal control of policy, personnel, and the method and scope of research to the institutions in which it is carried on. It should be fully responsible to the President and through him to the Congress for its program.

Early action on these recommendations is imperative if this nation is to meet the challenge of science in the crucial years ahead. On the wisdom with which we bring science to bear in the war against disease, in the creation of new industries, and in the strengthening of our Armed Forces depends in large measure our future as a nation.

Scientific Progress Is Essential

We all know how much the new drug, penicillin, has meant to our grievously wounded men on the grim battlefronts of this war—the countless lives it has saved—the incalculable suffering which its use has prevented. Science and the great practical genius of this nation made this achievement possible.

Some of us know the vital role which radar has played in bringing the United Nations to victory over Nazi Germany and in driving the Japanese steadily back from their island bastions. Again it was painstaking scientific research over many years that made radar possible.

What we often forget are the millions of pay envelopes on a peace-time Saturday night which are filled because new products and new industries have provided jobs for countless Americans. Science made that possible, too.

In 1939 millions of people were employed in industries which did not even exist at the close of the last war—radio, air conditioning, rayon and other synthetic fibers, and plastics are examples of the products of these industries. But these things do not mark the end of progress—they are but the beginning if we make full use of our scientific resources. New manufacturing industries can be started and many older industries greatly strengthened and expanded if we continue to study nature's laws and apply new knowledge to practical purposes.

Great advances in agriculture are also based upon scientific research. Plants which are more resistant to disease and are adapted to short growing seasons, the prevention and cure of livestock diseases, the control of our insect enemies, better fertilizers, and improved agricultural practices, all stem from painstaking scientific research.

Advances in science when put to practical use mean more jobs, higher wages, shorter hours, more abundant crops, more leisure for recreation, for study, for learning how to live without the deadening drudgery which has been the burden of the common man for ages past. Advances in science will also bring higher standards of living, will lead to the prevention or cure of diseases, will promote conservation of our limited national resources, and will assure means of defense against aggression. But to achieve these objectives—to secure a high level of employment, to maintain a position of world leadership—the flow of new scientific knowledge must be both continuous and substantial.

Our population increased from 75 million to 130 million between 1900 and 1940. In some countries comparable increases have been accompanied by famine. In this country the increase has been accompanied by more abundant food supply, better living, more leisure, longer life, and better health. This is, largely, the product of three factors—the free play of initiative of a vigorous people under democracy, the heritage of great natural wealth, and the advance of science and its application.

Science, by itself, provides no panacea for individual, social, and economic ills. It can be effective in the national welfare only as a member of a team, whether the conditions be peace or war. But without scientific progress no amount of achievement in other directions can insure our health, prosperity, and security as a nation in the modern world.

Science Is a Proper Concern of Government

It has been basic United States policy that Government should foster the opening of new frontiers. It opened the seas to clipper ships and furnished land for pioneers. Although these frontiers have more or less disappeared, the frontier of science remains. It is in keeping with the American tradition—one which has made the United States great—that new frontiers shall be made accessible for development by all American citizens.

Moreover, since health, well-being, and security are proper concerns of Government, scientific progress is, and must be, of vital interest to Government.

Without scientific progress the national health would deteriorate; without scientific progress we could not hope for improvement in our standard of living or for an increased number of jobs for our citizens; and without scientific progress we could not have maintained our liberties against tyranny.

Government Relations to Science— Past and Future

From early days the Government has taken an active interest in scientific matters. During the nineteenth century the Coast and Geodetic Survey, the Naval Observatory, the Department of Agriculture, and the Geological Survey were established. Through the Land Grant College Acts the Government has supported research in state institutions for more than 80 years on a gradually increasing scale. Since 1900 a large number of scientific agencies have been established within the Federal Government, until in 1939 they numbered more than 40.

Much of the scientific research done by Government agencies is intermediate in character between the two types of work commonly referred to as basic and applied research. Almost all Government scientific work has ultimate practical objectives but, in many fields of broad national concern, it commonly involves long-term investigation of a fundamental nature. Generally speaking, the scientific agencies of Government are not so concerned with immediate practical objectives as are the laboratories of industry nor, on the other hand, are they as free to explore any natural phenomena without regard to possible economic applications as are the educational and private research institutions. Government scientific agencies have splendid records of achievement, but they are limited in function.

We have no national policy for science. The Government has only begun to utilize science in the nation's welfare. There is no body within the Government charged with formulating or executing a national science policy. There are no standing committees of the Congress devoted to this important subject. Science has been in the wings. It should be brought to the center of the stage—for in it lies much of our hope for the future.

There are areas of science in which the public interest is acute but which are likely to be cultivated inadequately if left without more support than will come from private sources. These areas—such as research on military problems, agriculture, housing, public health, certain medical research, and research involving expensive capital facilities beyond the capacity of private institutions—should be advanced by active Government support. To date, with the exception of the intensive war research conducted by the Office of Scientific Research and Development, such support has been meager and intermittent.

For reasons presented in this report we are entering a period when science needs and deserves increased support from public funds.

Freedom of Inquiry Must Be Preserved

The publicly and privately supported colleges, universities, and research institutes are the centers of basic research. They are the wellsprings of knowledge and understanding. As long as they are vigorous and healthy and their scientists are free to pursue the truth wherever it may lead, there will be a flow of new scientific knowledge to those who can apply it to practical problems in Government, in industry, or elsewhere.

Many of the lessons learned in the war-time application of science under Government can be profitably applied in peace. The Government is peculiarly fitted to perform certain functions, such as the coordination and support of broad programs on problems of great national importance. But we must proceed with caution in carrying over the methods which work in wartime to the very different conditions of peace. We must remove the rigid controls which we have had to impose, and recover freedom of inquiry and that healthy competitive scientific spirit so necessary for expansion of the frontiers of scientific knowledge.

Scientific progress on a broad front results from the free play of free intellects, working on subjects of their own choice, in the manner dictated by their curiosity for exploration of the unknown. Freedom of inquiry must be preserved under any plan for Government support. . . .

Relation to National Security

In this war it has become clear beyond all doubt that scientific research is absolutely essential to national security. The bitter and dangerous battle against the U-boat was a battle of scientific techniques—and our margin of success was dangerously small. The new eyes which radar supplied to our fighting forces quickly evoked the development of scientific countermeasures which could often blind them. This again represents the ever continuing battle of techniques. The V-1 attack on London was finally defeated by three devices developed during this war and used superbly in the field. V-2 was countered only by capture of the launching sites.

The Secretaries of War and Navy recently stated in a joint letter to the National Academy of Sciences:

This war emphasizes three facts of supreme importance to national security: (1) Powerful new tactics of defense and offense are developed around new weapons created by scientific and engineering research; (2) the competitive time element in developing those weapons and tactics may be decisive; (3) war is increasingly total war, in which the armed services must be supplemented by active participation of every element of civilian population.

To insure continued preparedness along farsighted technical lines, the research scientists of the country must be called upon to continue in peacetime some substantial portion of those types of contribution to national security which they have made so effectively during the stress of the present war. . . .

There must be more—and more adequate—military research during peacetime. We cannot again rely on our allies to hold off the enemy while we struggle to catch up. Further, it is clear that only the Government can undertake military research; for it must be carried on in secret, much of it has no commercial value, and it is expensive. The obligation of Government to support research on military problems is inescapable.

Modern war requires the use of the most advanced scientific techniques. Many of the leaders in the development of radar are scientists who before the war had been exploring the nucleus of the atom. While there must be increased emphasis on science in the future training of officers for both the Army and Navy, such men cannot be expected to be specialists in scientific research. Therefore a professional partnership between the officers in the Services and civilian scientists is needed.

The Army and Navy should continue to carry on research and development on the improvement of current weapons. For many years the National Advisory Committee for Aeronautics has supplemented the work of the Army and Navy by conducting basic research on the problems of flight. There should now be permanent civilian activity to supplement the research work of the Services in other scientific fields so as to carry on in time of peace some part of the activi-

ties of the emergency war-time Office of Scientific Research and Development.

Military preparedness requires a permanent independent, civilian-controlled organization, having close liaison with the Army and Navy, but with funds directly from Congress and with the clear power to initiate military research which will supplement and strengthen that carried on directly under the control of the Army and Navy.

Science and Jobs

One of our hopes is that after the war there will be full employment, and that the production of goods and services will serve to raise our standard of living. We do not know yet how we shall reach that goal, but it is certain that it can be achieved only by releasing the full creative and productive energies of the American people.

Surely we will not get there by standing still, merely by making the same things we made before and selling them at the same or higher prices. We will not get ahead in international trade unless we offer new and more attractive and cheaper products.

Where will these new products come from? How will we find ways to make better products at lower cost? The answer is clear. There must be a stream of new scientific knowledge to turn the wheels of private and public enterprise. There must be plenty of men and women trained in science and technology for upon them depend both the creation of new knowledge and its application to practical purposes.

More and better scientific research is essential to the achievement of our goal of full employment.

The Importance of Basic Research

Basic research is performed without thought of practical ends. It results in general knowledge and an understanding of nature and its laws. This general knowledge provides the means of answering a large number of important practical problems, though it may not give a complete specific answer to any one of them. The function of applied research is to provide such complete answers. The scientist doing basic research may not be at all interested in the practical applications of his work, yet the further progress of industrial development would eventually stagnate if basic scientific research were long neglected.

One of the peculiarities of basic science is the variety of paths which lead to productive advance. Many of the most important discoveries have come as a result of experiments undertaken with very different purposes in mind. Statistically it is certain that important and highly useful discoveries will result from some fraction of the undertakings in basic science; but the results of any one particular investigation cannot be predicted with accuracy.

Basic research leads to new knowledge. It provides scientific capital. It creates the fund from which the practical applications of knowledge must be drawn. New products and new processes do not appear full-grown. They are founded on new principles and new conceptions, which in turn are painstakingly developed by research in the purest realms of science.

Today, it is truer than ever that basic research is the pacemaker of technological progress. In the nineteenth century, Yankee mechanical ingenuity, building largely upon the basic discoveries of European scientists, could greatly advance the technical arts. Now the situation is different.

A nation which depends upon others for its new basic scientific knowledge will be slow in its industrial progress and weak in its competitive position in world trade, regardless of its mechanical skill.

Centers of Basic Research

Publicly and privately supported colleges and universities and the endowed research institutes must furnish both the new scientific knowledge and the trained research workers. These institutions are uniquely qualified by tradition and by their special characteristics to carry on basic research. They are charged with the responsibility of conserving the knowledge accumulated by the past, imparting that knowledge to students, and contributing new knowledge of all kinds. It is chiefly in these institutions that scientists may work in an atmosphere which is relatively free from the adverse pressure of convention, prejudice, or commercial necessity. At their best they provide the scientific worker with a strong sense of solidarity and security, as well as a substantial degree of personal intellectual freedom. All of these factors are of great importance in the development of new knowledge, since much of new knowledge is certain to arouse opposition because of its tendency to challenge current beliefs or practice.

Industry is generally inhibited by preconceived goals, by its own clearly defined standards, and by the constant pressure of commercial necessity. Satisfactory progress in basic science seldom occurs under conditions prevailing in the normal industrial laboratory. There are some notable exceptions, it is true, but even in such cases it is rarely possible to match the universities in respect to the freedom which is so important to scientific discovery.

To serve effectively as the centers of basic research these institutions must be strong and healthy. They must attract our best scientists as teachers and investigators. They must offer research opportunities and sufficient compensation to enable them to compete with industry and government for the cream of scientific talent.

During the past 25 years there has been a great increase in industrial research involving the application of scientific knowledge to a multitude of practical purposes—thus providing new products, new industries, new investment opportunities, and millions of jobs. During the same period research within Government—again largely applied research—has also been greatly expanded. In the decade from 1930 to 1940 expenditures for industrial research increased from $116,000,000 to $240,000,000 and those for scientific research in Government rose from $24,000,000 to $69,000,000. During the same period expenditures for scientific research in the colleges and universities increased from $20,000,000 to $31,000,000, while those in the endowed research institutes declined from $5,200,000 to $4,500,000. These are the best estimates available. The figures have been taken from a variety of sources and arbitrary definitions have necessarily been applied, but it is believed that they may be accepted as indicating the following trends:

(a) Expenditures for scientific research by industry and Government—almost entirely applied research—have more than doubled between 1930 and 1940. Whereas in 1930 they were six times as large as the research expenditures of the colleges, universities, and research institutes, by 1940 they were nearly ten times as large.

(b) While expenditures for scientific research in the colleges and universities increased by one-half during this period, those for the endowed research institutes have slowly declined.

If the colleges, universities, and research institutes are to meet the rapidly increasing demands of industry and Government for new scientific knowledge, their basic research should be strengthened by use of public funds.

Research Within the Government

Although there are some notable exceptions, most research conducted within governmental laboratories is of an applied nature. This has always been true and is likely to remain so. Hence Government, like industry, is dependent upon the colleges, universities, and research institutes to expand the basic scientific frontiers and to furnish trained scientific investigators.

Research within the Government represents an important part of our total research activity and needs to be strengthened and expanded after the war. Such expansion should be directed to fields of inquiry and service which are of public importance and are not adequately carried on by private organizations.

The most important single factor in scientific and technical work is the quality of personnel employed. The procedures currently followed within the Government for recruiting, classifying and compensating such personnel place the Government under a severe handicap in competing with industry and the universities for first-class scientific talent. Steps should be taken to reduce that handicap.

In the Government the arrangement whereby the numerous scientific agencies form parts of larger departments has both advantages and disadvantages. But the present pattern is firmly established and there is much to be said for it. There is, however, a very real need for some measure of coordination of the common scientific activities of these agencies, both as to policies and budgets, and at present no such means exist.

A permanent Science Advisory Board should be created to consult with these scientific bureaus and to advise the executive and legislative branches of Government as to the policies and budgets of Government agencies engaged in scientific research.

This board should be composed of disinterested scientists who have no connection with the affairs of any Government agency.

Industrial Research

The simplest and most effective way in which the Government can strengthen industrial research is to support basic research and to develop scientific talent.

The benefits of basic research do not reach all industries equally or at the same speed. Some small enterprises never receive any of the benefits. It has been suggested that the benefits might be better utilized if "research clinics" for such enterprises were to be established. Businessmen would thus be able to make more use of research than they now do. This proposal is certainly worthy of further study.

One of the most important factors affecting the amount of industrial research is the income-tax law. Government action in respect to this subject will affect the rate of technical progress in industry. Uncertainties as to the attitude of the Bureau of Internal Revenue regarding the deduction of research and development expenses are a deterrent to research expenditure. These uncertainties arise from lack of clarity of the tax law as to the proper treatment of such costs.

The Internal Revenue Code should be amended to remove present uncertainties in regard to the deductibility of research and development expenditures as current charges against net income.

Research is also affected by the patent laws. They stimulate new invention and they make it possible for new industries to be built around new devices or new processes. These industries generate new jobs and new products, all of which contribute to the welfare and the strength of the country.

Yet, uncertainties in the operation of the patent laws have impaired the ability of small industries to translate new ideas into processes and products of value to the nation. These uncertainties are, in part, attributable to the difficulties and expense incident to the operation of the patent system as it presently exists. These uncertainties are also attributable to the existence of certain abuses, which have appeared in the use of patents. The abuses should be corrected. They have led to extravagantly critical attacks which tend to discredit a basically sound system.

It is important that the patent system continue to serve the country in the manner intended by the Constitution, for it has been a vital element in the industrial vigor which has distinguished this nation.

The National Patent Planning Commission has reported on this subject. In addition, a detailed study, with recommendations concerning the extent to which modifications should be made in our patent laws is currently being made under the leadership of the Secretary of Commerce. It is recommended, therefore, that specific action with regard to the patent laws be withheld pending the submission of the report devoted exclusively to that subject.

International Exchange of Scientific Information

International exchange of scientific information is of growing importance. Increasing specialization of science will make it more important than ever that scientists in this country keep continually abreast of developments abroad. In addition a flow of scientific information constitutes one facet of general international accord which should be cultivated.

The Government can accomplish significant results in several ways: by aiding in the arrangement of international science congresses, in the official accrediting of American scientists to such gatherings, in the official reception of foreign scientists of standing in this country, in making possible a rapid flow of technical information, including translation service, and possibly in the provision of international fellowships. Private foundations and other groups partially fulfill some of these functions at present, but their scope is incomplete and inadequate.

The Government should take an active role in promoting the international flow of scientific information.

The Special Need for Federal Support

We can no longer count on ravaged Europe as a source of fundamental knowledge. In the past we have devoted much of our best efforts to the application of such knowledge which has been discovered abroad. In the future we must pay increased attention to discovering this knowledge for ourselves particularly since the scientific applications of the future will be more than ever dependent upon such basic knowledge.

New impetus must be given to research in our country. Such new impetus can come promptly only from the Government. Expenditures for research in the colleges, universities, and research institutes will otherwise not be able to meet the additional demands of increased public need for research.

Further, we cannot expect industry adequately to fill the gap. Industry will fully rise to the challenge of applying new knowledge to new products. The commercial incentive can be relied upon for that. But basic research is essentially noncommercial in nature. It will not receive the attention it requires if left to industry.

For many years the Government has wisely supported research in the agricultural colleges and the benefits have been great. The time has come when such support should be extended to other fields.

In providing Government support, however, we must endeavor to preserve as far as possible the private support of research both in industry and in the colleges, universities, and research institutes. These private sources should continue to carry their share of the financial burden.

The Cost of a Program

It is estimated that an adequate program for Federal support of basic research in the colleges, universities, and research institutes and for financing important applied research in the public interest, will cost about 10 million dollars at the outset and may rise to about 50 million dollars annually when fully underway at the end of perhaps 5 years. . . .

New Responsibilities for Government

One lesson is clear from the reports of the several committees attached as appendices. The Federal Government should accept new responsibilities for promoting the creation of new scientific knowledge and the development of scientific talent in our youth.

The extent and nature of these new responsibilities are set forth in detail in the reports of the committees whose recommendations in this regard are fully endorsed.

In discharging these responsibilities Federal funds should be made available. We have given much thought to the question of how plans for the use of Federal funds may be arranged so that such funds will not drive out of the picture funds from local governments, foundations, and private donors. We believe that our proposals will minimize that effect, but we do not think that it can be completely avoided. We submit, however, that the nation's need for more and better scientific research is such that the risk must be accepted.

It is also clear that the effective discharge of these responsibilities will require the full attention of some over-all agency devoted to that purpose. There should be a focal point within the Government for a concerted program of assisting scientific research conducted outside of Government. Such an agency should furnish the funds needed to support basic research in the colleges and universities, should coordinate where possible research programs on matters of utmost importance to the national welfare, should formulate a national policy for the Government toward science, should sponsor the interchange of scientific information among scientists and laboratories both in this country and abroad, and should ensure that the incentives to research in industry and the universities are maintained. All of the committees advising on these matters agree on the necessity for such an agency.

The Mechanism

There are within Government departments many groups whose interests are primarily those of scientific research. Notable examples are found within the Departments of Agriculture, Commerce, Interior, and the Federal Security Agency. These groups are concerned with science as collateral and peripheral to the major problems of those Departments. These groups should remain where they are, and continue to perform their present functions, including the support of agricultural research by grants to the Land Grant Colleges and Experiment Stations, since their largest contribution lies in applying fundamental knowledge to the special problems of the Departments within which they are established.

By the same token these groups cannot be made the repository of the new and large responsibilities in science which belong to the Government and which the Government should accept. The recommendations in this report which relate to research within the Government, to the release of scientific information, to clarification of the tax laws, and to the recovery and development of our scientific talent now in uniform can be implemented by action within the existing structure of the Government. But nowhere in the Governmental structure receiving its funds from Congress is there an agency adapted to supplementing the support of basic research in the universities, both in medicine and the natural sciences; adapted to supporting research on new weapons for both Services; or adapted to administering a program of science scholarships and fellowships.

A new agency should be established, therefore, by the Congress for the purpose. Such an agency, moreover, should be an independent agency devoted to the support of scientific research and advanced scientific education alone. Industry learned many years ago that basic research cannot often be fruitfully conducted as an adjunct to or a subdivision of an operating agency or department. Operating agencies have immediate operating goals and are under constant pressure to produce in a tangible way, for that is the test of their value. None of these conditions is favorable to basic research. Research is the exploration of the unknown and is necessarily speculative. It is inhibited by conventional approaches, traditions, and standards. It cannot be satisfactorily conducted in an atmosphere where it is gauged and tested by operating or production standards. Basic scientific research should not, therefore, be placed under an operating agency whose paramount concern is anything other than research. Research will always suffer when put in competition with operations. The decision that there should be a new and independent agency was reached by each of the committees advising in these matters.

I am convinced that these new functions should be centered in one agency. Science is fundamentally a unitary thing. The number of independent agencies should be kept to a minimum. Much medical progress, for example, will come from fundamental advances in chemistry. Separation of the sciences in tight compartments, as would occur if more than one agency were involved, would retard and not advance scientific knowledge as a whole.

Five Fundamentals

There are certain basic principles which must underlie the program of Government support for scientific research and education if such support is to be effective and if it is to avoid impairing the very things we seek to foster. These principles are as follows:

(1) Whatever the extent of support may be, there must be stability of funds over a period of years so that long-range programs may be undertaken.

(2) The agency to administer such funds should be composed of citizens selected only on the basis of their interest in and capacity to promote the work of the agency. They should be persons of broad interest in and understanding of the peculiarities of scientific research and education.

(3) The agency should promote research through contracts or grants to organizations outside the Federal Government. It should not operate any laboratories of its own.

(4) Support of basic research in the public and private colleges, universities, and research institutes must leave the internal control of policy, personnel, and the method and scope of the research to the institutions themselves. This is of the utmost importance.

(5) While assuring complete independence and freedom for the nature, scope, and methodology of research carried on in the institutions receiving public funds, and while retaining discretion in the allocation of funds among such institutions, the Foundation proposed herein must be responsible to the President and the Congress. Only through such responsibility can we maintain the proper relationship between science and other aspects of a democratic system. The usual controls of audits, reports, budgeting, and the like, should, of course, apply to the administrative and fiscal operations of the Foundation, subject, however, to such adjustments in procedure as are necessary to meet the special requirements of research.

Basic research is a long-term process—it ceases to be basic if immediate results are expected on short-term support. Methods should therefore be found which will permit the agency to make commitments of funds from current appropriations for programs of five years duration or longer. Continuity and stability of the program and its support may be expected (a) from the growing realization by the Congress of the benefits to the public from scientific research, and (b) from the conviction which will grow among those who conduct research under the auspices of the agency that good quality work will be followed by continuing support.

Military Research

As stated earlier in this report, military preparedness requires a permanent, independent, civilian-controlled organization, having close liaison with the Army and Navy, but with funds direct from Congress and the clear power to initiate military research which will supplement and strengthen that carried on directly under the control of the Army and Navy. As a temporary measure the National Academy of Sciences has established the Research Board for National Security at the request of the Secretary of War and the Secretary of the Navy. This is highly desirable in order that there may be no interruption in the relations between scientists and military men after the emergency wartime Office of Scientific Research and Development goes out of existence. The Congress is now considering legislation to provide funds for this Board by direct appropriation.

I believe that, as a permanent measure, it would be appropriate to add to the agency needed to perform the other functions recommended in this report the responsibilities for civilian-initiated and civilian-controlled military research. The function of such a civilian group would be primarily to conduct long-range scientific research on military problems—leaving to the Services research on the improvement of existing weapons.

Some research on military problems should be conducted, in time of peace as well as in war, by civilians independently of the military establishment. It is the primary responsibility of the Army and Navy to train the men, make available the weapons, and employ the strategy that will bring victory in combat.

The Armed Services cannot be expected to be experts in all of the complicated fields which make it possible for a great nation to fight successfully in total war. There are certain kinds of research—such as research on the improvement of existing weapons—which can best be done within the military establishment. However, the job of long-range research involving application of the newest scientific discoveries to military needs should be the responsibility of those civilian scientists in the universities and in industry who are best trained to discharge it thoroughly and successfully. It is essential that both kinds of research go forward and that there be the closest liaison between the two groups.

Placing the civilian military research function in the proposed agency would bring it into close relationship with a broad program of basic research in both the natural sciences and medicine. A balance between military and other research could thus readily be maintained.

The establishment of the new agency, including a civilian military research group, should not be delayed by the existence of the Research Board for National Security, which is a temporary measure. Nor should the creation of the new agency be delayed by uncertainties in regard to the postwar organization of our military departments themselves. Clearly, the new agency, including a civilian military research group within it, can remain sufficiently flexible to adapt its operations to whatever may be the final organization of the military departments.

National Research Foundation

It is my judgment that the national interest in scientific research and scientific education can best be promoted by the creation of a National Research Foundation.

PART XIV   THE POSTWAR YEARS

No one now doubts that we are living in a technological age. Innovation is constant and accepted with hardly a murmur. Large firms derive their entire income from the manufacture and sale of products unknown only a decade ago. We expect miracle drugs to be developed as a matter of course. We are surrounded by machines, most of which serve some useful purpose in making life easier or richer for someone. We have come to believe that technical solutions to our problems, if they are not always the best ones, are frequently the easiest. By and large, Americans rejoice in technology.

At the same time, we are increasingly aware that there is a social cost for every step forward, and it is not always clear whether that cost is billed to the same people who reap the social benefit from progress. We sanitize the agony of war by a careful attention to the canons of good taste and broadcast it into our homes for dinner time viewing, thus reducing human sacrifice to triviality and anesthetizing us against human suffering. We spend over three trillion dollars for national security, and discover that we have less security now than we did at the end of World War II, so successful have been the innovators of military hardware. Although automobiles are so much improved each year that we must buy a new one, and although air speeds are constantly increased, we find that our national transportation network is less flexible and less satisfactory today than it was a generation ago. We have created a technological society that promotes and feeds upon an ever-increasing Gross National Product, but have failed to remember that the GNP includes the cost of such items as funerals for those killed by defective automobiles.

We are discovering, in short, that technology is not a panacea—that the difficult problems are still those involving human values and conflicting interests. Our technological society serves some interests well—it remains to be seen whether it can serve all interests equally well.

1. Keeping the Economy Strong, 1963

J. HERBERT HOLLOMON, "Science, Technology, and Economic Growth"

In the years since World War II, the federal government has poured unprecedented amounts of money into the stimulation of technological development. Nearly all of this money, however, has been directed into the two areas of national defense and space. The justification for this has been national survival and prestige, but the hope has been expressed that technological innovations beneficial to the civilian sector of the economy would "spin off" from projects undertaken for quite different ends. By the time John F. Kennedy came to the White House, this hope was proving to be less than substantial. Kennedy's Secretary of Commerce, Luther Hodges, and his Assistant Secretary for Science and Technology, J. Herbert Hollomon, suggested the direct stimulation of civilian technology through a large federal program of research and development.

The relationships between science and technology and economic growth are not at all clear to many of those engaged in science or to those who participate in the business of "growing" the economy. It is a strange paradox that, although the human intellect has been capable of great achievements in science and its pursuit, the translation of science to use by society is not well understood. Indeed, the glittering successes of science have dimmed our perception of the details of the complex process by which man's understanding of the universe finally enters the world of industry and commerce.

That there is misunderstanding is clear from the frequent claims that the large research and development expenditures and the large commitment to science in our country lead inevitably to national prosperity and well-being. Consider for a moment our recent expenditures for research and development and the rate of growth of our gross national product. The enormous increases in funds for science and for the development of technology have not been followed by a corresponding increase in the rate of growth of our economy. Indeed, nearly the reverse has been true. In the period 1947 to 1954, the average annual rate of growth was 3.7 percent. From 1954 to 1960, the average rate dropped to 3 percent. All this occurred during the period when our expenditures for R&D tripled and the percentage of our gross national product spent for R&D doubled (rising from 1.4 to 2.8 percent). During this time, there have been loud and strident claims of the great social benefits that were to come from this large commitment to science and to research and development.

However, the enormous increase in R&D was stimulated mainly by the requirements of national programs not

From J. Herbert Hollomon, "Science, Technology, and Economic Growth," *Physics Today*, XVI (March 1963), 38-40, 42, 44, 46. Reprinted by permission of the author and *Physics Today*.

particularly directed toward the increase of industrial productivity or toward innovation in civilian technology, both of which are so important in increasing our rate of economic growth or in improving the variety of our society. Moreover, the people, institutions, and environment necessary for the health of technology pertinent to the civil needs have not been well supported.

The development of technology is clearly influenced by the pressures and demands of the times. Even science has its fads, encouraged by the interests, needs, and amusements of its patrons. Solid-state physics claims its practical application to materials, and much of the justification of nuclear physics derives from the awesome power of the atom.

Of the annual R&D expenditure of 2.8 percent of our gross national product, about 2 percent is spent for space, defense, and atomic-energy purposes, with only 0.8 percent for all other purposes, including those to increase productivity and stimulate innovation. Other major industrial countries, such as Japan, West Germany, the Netherlands, and Sweden, spend an average of about 1.25 percent of their gross national product for R&D, little of it aimed at military or space objectives. In terms of manpower, 0.4 percent of the West German labor force are scientists and engineers devoted directly to activities that either relate to science itself or are pertinent to the development of industry and commerce. The comparable figure for the United States is 0.2 percent. While it is evident that economic growth depends upon many factors other than research and development, during recent times the rate of growth of almost all the industrial nations of the world exceeded our own. This gives cause for serious concern about the effectiveness of the use of science and of the resources we apply to the

development of civilian technology. The United Kingdom and Canada, the other industrialized countries having relatively low rates of economic growth, are also concerned about the development and use of scientific and technical resources for their own national objectives.

The rate of growth of the Soviet gross national product was 6 to 7 percent in the 1950's, and is expected to reach 8 percent in the 1960's. In terms of productivity, the Soviet gross national product per man-year in this decade is expected to grow at 4 per cent per year, almost double ours. Here it is important to note that, despite large space and military programs, the Soviet Union has enjoyed a high productivity growth rate by committing nonmilitary and nonspace R&D to the development of basic heavy industry rather than to the development of consumer goods and services.

It is clear that the effort to break the way technologically may be greater and the risks higher than they are for the adaptation of demonstrated accomplishment to the needs of another society or circumstances. Thus, as the front runner, our relative effort should be much greater than that of other nations.

We must be concerned not only with how our economy and our society use science but also that the means for its use are healthy and effective. In the long term, the development of science depends upon the support of the society in which it flourishes. As Bacon said, "The true and lawful goal of science is that human life be endowed with new powers and inventions." If the economy is not healthy, science itself cannot be healthy. If science claims too much or is misused, it may not be able to demand the conditions of free inquiry and healthy support that it needs. Thus, it is important to understand the relationship of science and technology to the growth of the economy, and to examine those things that need to be done to insure that our scientific and technical houses are in order and that the best use is being made of the rare resources and capabilities of unusual people.

You know well that science is international. A scientific discovery made in the United States—or in Britain or France— is more quickly communicated, and its significance more swiftly appreciated, throughout the international scientific community than it is to those who use it for practical ends. The knowledge of the great discoveries of biophysics and biochemistry concerning the structure and character of living matter and the discoveries of the nature of atomic forces spread quickly through the "open" society of science. Science is common property available to all nations with even a modest scientific effort.

Science is free to all. The economy or our way of life benefits only after someone puts science to work for the practical benefit of man. Modern myth says that science, through some magic, converts itself into useful products of society. The great achievements of science in changing the modern world and broadening the character of our society have obscured the activity that is engaged in its use. The activity that puts science to use to meet the needs of society proceeds almost independently of the advancing science. The technology of the Gothic period did not use science, nor does the construction of modern shelter depend much on the immediate advances in atomic, quantum, or nuclear physics.

It is also true that the knowledge and understanding that are associated with the technology of pertinence to our civilian economy and to the improvement of the character of society are not necessarily the same as those which are thought to be needed for our military or space efforts. The science of possible pertinence to the improvement of housing or to the elimination of air pollution is not likely to be the same as that related to space travel. Nor does the activity through which science is made useful happen by itself. It requires a special environment, people with a special education and outlook, and institutions that encourage invention, innovation, and the diffusion of technology. Basic to the art of invention and the technique of innovation is the art of design and synthesis, using science, economics, practice, and lore. The two activities are symbiotic— advances in science benefit the development of technology, and the tools developed from new technology open new vistas for the advancement of science.

However, economic progress stems from increased productivity based on new technology; then, the resulting increased income provides the purchasing power for new products and new services. The broadening of the economic choice and the improvement in our way of life that are made possible by increased productivity come from the introduction of new goods and services. More frequently than not, the introduction of these new goods awaits the ability of the society to purchase them. The sale of washing machines to Nigeria is not limited by technology, nor was the sale of automobiles that recently increased so rapidly in the Netherlands.

The process by which science is used to benefit the economy occurs by an extraordinarily complex process of the development and diffusion of new technology throughout the whole of industry and commerce. It depends upon a close interaction between the known and the unique demands of the times. The mechanics of technological change require perceptive and technically trained management to comprehend the potential of the new technology and to know about the interaction among production, science, marketing, distribution, and technology.

It is often assumed that the spectacular results of atomic energy (which have so radically changed concepts of national defense), the transistor (which led to miniaturization and the reliability so important to space vehicles), and radar (so crucial to modern travel) have made substantial contributions to our economy. Actually, their contribution to gross national product has been small, and they have not as yet made substantial contributions to an increased efficiency in the use of capital and of labor. Probably the greatest recent impact of technology on our economy has come from the increase in agricultural productivity. The most fundamental change in the character of our society in the last five decades has been the change from an agricultural to an industrial economy —from a rural to an urban society.

The rise in agricultural productivity provided the increased income to allow the purchase of products and services other than those which fulfill the simple necessities. Just as in agriculture, the great force that will further increase our economic growth, improve the environment for science, and lead to new products and services for the consumer, is the increase in the productivity of industry and commerce. Last year only about 10 percent of the huge total of $15 billion spent on research and development was devoted to improving productivity.

In our society, innovation is often first introduced by industries and enterprises that can afford the high costs of modern technical resources and can appreciate and exploit the results of new science and the opportunities provided by advancing technology. But the society generally benefits only when these techno-

logical improvements diffuse rapidly to the less efficient firms. This rate of adaptation depends on an effective means of rapidly diffusing technical knowledge. Japan and Russia, for example, appreciate the importance of this diffusion as basic to the development of their economy, and seek to exploit the best practices of others and use their own technical resources for their own special needs.

This problem of diffusion is critical to our effective use of science and to the growth of the economy. Of the 300,000 manufacturing companies in the United States, about 300 perform 80 percent of industrially sponsored research and development. The same 300 companies account for 60 percent of the sales of all manufacturing companies and 61 percent of total manufacturing employment. They also spend about 2.75 percent of their sales on research and development, while the remainder of the 300,-000 spend 0.9 percent, about one-fifth as much. This disparity reduces the ability of the smaller enterprises to compete in the world economy. As companies become less profitable, they spend less on research and development. This tends to make them comparatively less productive and still less profitable.

The ability of the small company either to undertake innovation on its own, or to take advantage of the innovations of large companies, is determined first by the availability of new technology, and second by the facility with which the small company can profitably exploit the possibilities it provides. Unlike the diffusion of agricultural technology, which was effectively accomplished by land-grant colleges and extension services, there is no special mechanism of assuring the diffusion of technology to the 3.3 million industrial and commercial firms in America, even though that figure means there are almost as many individual companies as there are now farms.

Let us look at another aspect of the relationship of scientific and technical effort to the economy. Reassuring justification of the enormous federal programs for research and development is that there will be results deriving from it that will be of substantial direct benefit to private industry and the public. The argument runs something like this: We don't have to worry about our economy since the results of the government-supported technical effort will be so useful to civilian technology that they justify the huge expenditures. These efforts to develop military equipment, atomic power plants, and space vehicles may well be providing the basis for a whole new technology of complex systems made up of highly reliable parts, but the translation of this technology to the economy through industry and commerce is neither direct nor cheap—nor inevitable. In fact, the translation requires specially trained people with a special point of view and an industry that understands and appreciates the possibilities of the new technology and can afford to use it. These people come from the same pool of scientists and engineers who provide the advancing technology to meet the threat to our national security.

Government-sponsored activity is becoming increasingly dependent on a sophisticated science and technology peculiarly suited to very specialized military and space objectives, and thus more and more unlikely to be of important direct benefit to the economy, to the improvement of our transportation system, to urban development, to food, shelter, and clothing, or to education. Moreover, the results that can be used require further research and development to adapt them for civilian needs. Essential to that adaptation process are technically competent people able to carry out the additional research and development and institutions to produce and distribute the resulting product in a competitive market at a profit. It is also well to recognize that technically competent people are required to develop a market for a product as well as to develop the product itself. The establishment of an efficient service organization or the determination of the need of an industrial customer for new products are examples.

Crucial to the development and use of science for any of our social, economic, or national needs is an adequately growing supply of scientists and engineers, and the technicians that work with them. We, in our country, have not made a sufficient commitment to education. Our unemployed are those of our people who are the least skilled and with the least education. An earlier investment in education would have made them available to fill the openings so widely advertised for teachers, nurses, technicians, engineers, and scientists. We are also failing to provide the people for research and development, particularly in fields important to our civilian economy.

The 1963 increase in the supply of scientists and engineers engaged in research and development is expected to be almost 30,000. But the increase in support for research and development for space alone will require about the same number, and that number is equivlent to 20 percent of the total now doing research and development supported by industry, and equivalent to half the total of those doing research and development in universities.

The number of engineering graduates this year declined to an annual average of 35,000. Yet it is the engineer that conceives, designs, builds, launches, and controls the complex space vehicles that orbit the earth and reach for the moon. And, it is the technician who backs up the engineer who backs up the scientists. For lack of adequately trained technicians, we waste the talent of both scientists and engineers. For lack of engineers to implement the results of scientific research, we delay the practical benefits from scientific discovery.

The education of engineers to carry on the development and advancement of technology today is inadequate. Few of our schools provide the enthusiastic challenge that the big problems of our time pose, nor do many show the young man the opportunities for applying science to the civilian economy. There are few schools in the country that provide a professional graduate education for engineers or recognize that the art of design and the understanding of social need and opportunity are basic to engineering while providing the science and mathematics that are the engineers' working tools.

The overwhelming concentration of research and development on space and defense projects, the relatively small amount done for private industrial purposes, and the even smaller fraction designed to increase productivity, determine the distribution of our technically trained manpower. With the demand for that scarce resource exceeding the total supply, we must make more efficient use of our technical people, or increase the supply, or modify our national goals.

Increasing the supply depends upon the capacity of our educational institutions, both in physical plant and teachers, the financial rather than scholastic ability of students to stay in school, and the encouragement of careers in science and engineering without starving the other disciplines.

If we are to improve the supply, we must increase the proportion of baccalaureates going on to graduate study. In whereas the increase of personnel in gineering, the most critical fields to

many of our national aspirations, only 3000 PhD's are graduating each year, and of these, only 1000 are engineers. If scholastic ability were the limiting factor, there could be ten times as many in engineering, five times as many in mathematics, and twice as many in the physical sciences. The chief obstacle to further study seems to be money—either a lack of funds to pay for the additional education, or the decision to increase immediate income by taking a full-time job.

Redistribution of the current activity is a complex matter. Of the 1.4 million scientists and engineers in America, 400,000 are doing research and development, most of them (280,000) on government-sponsored projects such as space and defense. The remaining 120,000 work in industry for civilian objectives.

The enormous increase in federal support for research and development has already brought about a significant redeployment in technical manpower. There is little doubt that scientists and engineers have been diverted from such fields as teaching, management, supervision, and production to work in research and development. For example, the annual increase in scientists and engineers is about 6 percent a year, but the increase in the number engaged in research and development is 10 percent, whereas the increase of personnel in other areas of activity is only 3 percent.

Educational institutions and government are finding it increasingly difficult to recruit and to hold competent technical people. The fraction of technical people who manage the vast government-sponsored technical programs—who influence policy decisions involving science and technology—the fraction of these with PhD's is declining. The fraction of college science teachers with PhD's is also decreasing.

We need to recognize that there are

some fundamental steps required to improve the health of the economy and provide the adequate and proper support for science. Concerted action by physicists as individuals and through their professional institutions is required to insure public understanding and the political force to meet the problems of our time.

First, we must urge that all aspects of education be strengthened. College and postgraduate training is as important today as secondary-school education was 50 years ago, and deserves and needs the same public support.

Support for education at all levels and in all fields is probably the most important national investment that can be made. Future generations will be better equipped intellectually to cope with the enormously complex technical and social problems, an ability indispensable to the survival of democracy in this technological age. This investment in education is the capital for future economic growth.

This support must be provided directly both to individuals and to institutions for education itself, and not limited to the indirect route of research grants and contracts. This latter form of support, coming largely from the military and space agencies, has biased our teaching and learning toward their special needs.

Secondly, we must recognize that after two centuries of emphasizing the practical and the pragmatic, we are now in great danger of over-reacting. Not only are we neglecting the pragmatic aspects of society but we teach our best students to look down upon practical or useful activities as being intellectually demeaning or inferior. We must provide the climate and the support for work in universities related to the broad practical needs of our civilian economy and society.

Thirdly, we must encourage the establishment of the institutions and the environment that most effectively puts science to practical use, diffuses the results of technology throughout the society, and encourages even higher levels of innovative activity. What is needed is additional support for research and teaching in those fields and in those disciplines that undergird the civilian industrial needs and the technical requirements that an increasingly urbanized life demands. Means must also be found to provide support and stimulation to increase the technological work required for better productivity and the development of new products and services for our people. Industry is aware of the need for this work and has knowledge of its pertinence. In some cases, however, industry either cannot afford (or consists of units too small) to support adequately the development and spread of the technology. Support must be made available for industry, probably through associations, to do work of broad application.

Fourthly, those of us with technical training have a particular responsibility to understand and explain the complex relationship among the elements and factors involving science, technology, invention, and innovation, on the one hand, and the social, economic, political, and cultural needs of our society, on the other. A worthwhile precedent is the important contribution made by physicists after World War II in explaining the physical, social, and political implications of atomic energy.

In summary, we must address ourselves to the task of providing the climate and support required both for science and for that separate activity which puts science to use. Science cannot prosper nor can our nation be secure without a healthy, growing economy based upon a system of free enterprise.

2. Partners in Prosperity, 1963

FREDERICK E. TERMAN, "The Newly Emerging Community of Technical Scholars"

Technology has always been an important factor in economic growth, and since the turn of the century, science has had an increasing role in stimulating innovation in industry. It is only recently, however, that science and technology have moved to the very center of our economic and industrial life. Although a few underdeveloped states in America still hope to attract investment by advertising low taxes and freedom from labor union activity, an increasing number of communities realize that today prosperity is based upon brains, and that brains are more attracted by good schools than by a docile population.

Whether one views the growth of education in technical research as a simple extension of the traditional obligation of American schools to provide public services or as a new and dangerous complicity in the military-industrial complex, the fact remains that scientific and technological research now form the basis for much of the economic growth in the nation. The author of this article was vice-president, provost, and professor of electrical engineering at Stanford University.

In medieval times scholars tended to concentrate in locations where the principal attraction was the presence of other scholars. Where there were scholars, there came students. The presence of students as an audience and potential disciples naturally increased the attractiveness to other scholars who came with their followers, and this in turn drew still more scholars and students, and so on. In this way, the medieval center of learning, or *universitas*, came into being.

In the beginning this was all very informal. There were no curricula, admissions procedures, grade-point averages, degrees, or even typewriters. Individuals set themselves up as scholars and offered lectures as they pleased. If they could attract students who were able to pay fees, they prospered and could become famous, influential, and even well off financially. Some of these *communities of scholars* became famous as centers of learning, and many great universities of present-day Europe are their descendants. Examples are Oxford, Bologna, Heidelberg, Salamanca, Paris, Gottingen, and Cambridge.

A new counterpart of these medieval communities of scholars has in recent years begun to take form in our modern society. These consist of universities

From Frederick E. Terman, "The Newly Emerging Community of Technical Scholars," *Colorado and the New Technological Revolution: Proceedings of The University-Industry Liaison Conference, 1963* (Boulder, Colo., 1963), pp. 43-53. Reprinted by permission of the author.

431

which have strong programs in engineering and science, surrounded by companies emphasizing research and development, under conditions where there is continual interaction among all of the components—some formal, some informal, some organized, others unorganized.

These companies emphasizing research and development are commonly referred to as growth companies, or science companies. They are concerned with such things as electronics, nucleonics, missiles, instrumentation, computers, space, etc., and many of them have had remarkable records of growth. This growth is in the main the result of new products made possible by recent advances in science and technology. These growth industries are research oriented and they commonly live close to the frontiers of knowledge. In such companies the founders, board members, presidents, and general managers often have Ph.D. degrees in engineering or science. Another feature of these growth companies is their very extensive use of highly trained men whose formal education has extended beyond a bachelor's degree, often to the doctorate. This advanced training is required to understand the complicated processes and devices that are involved and to make contributions to their continued development.

The modern version of the medieval community of scholars consists of a concentration of such growth companies in association with a strong educational influence. This modern version of a community of technical scholars is still embryonic in character, having developed only in the last 20 or so years. However, the trend toward concentration of the research and development industries in such centers is clearly present and is becoming more definite with each year that passes. Industry is finding that, for activities involving a high level of scientific and technological creativity, a location in a center of brains is more important than a location near markets, raw materials, transportation, or factory labor.

The largest and best defined such community of technical scholars in the United States is in the Boston area. Here, one has the Massachusetts Institute of Technology and Harvard in a community that includes many growth companies—some large, many small. Also included are a number of large research and development laboratories, supported by the government, which add further stimulation and diversity to the community.

Another example is on the San Francisco Peninsula around Stanford University. This particular community of technical scholars is especially noteworthy in that there had been almost no war research at Stanford, and at the end of World War II in 1945 there was almost no industry of the growth type there. Yet in 18 years this area has become one of the liveliest and most creative centers in the country. The development around Stanford has been widely publicized because of its spectacularly rapid emergence in the national scene, the clearly visible relationship with the educational activities at Stanford University, and the encouragement Stanford has provided through the development of the Stanford Industrial Park on Stanford-owned lands adjacent to the academic campus.

This phenomenon, in which creative work in science-oriented industries tends to concentrate in centers where there is a strong focus on the intellectual environment, is apparent in many different places around the nation. New industrial parks are being established in the vicinity of universities, sometimes in actual formal cooperation with the university, sometimes as purely private ventures. In Dallas a group of community-minded industrialists has sponsored the formation of the Graduate Research Center of the Southwest, an educationally oriented nonprofit organization dedicated to raising the scientific and technological tone of industry and education in the entire area. At Ann Arbor a research community is evolving in the shadow of the University of Michigan. In Pittsburgh a $60 million science center is being developed in Panther Hollow, in what is now a useless gully immediately adjacent to Carnegie Institute of Technology and the University of Pittsburgh. Plans have been announced for two privately promoted industrial parks at Champaign, Illinois, near the University of Illinois. The Governor of Tennessee has advocated a $2 million University of Tennessee Graduate Space Institute near the Air Force's Arnold Engineering Center at Tullahoma, Tennessee. And so it goes.

The growing importance of industries based on science and technology has given the university a new role in national life. While this is touched on above, it can well stand further examination. Increasingly, each significant center of growth industry finds need for educational facilities at the university level. In turn, every university with a sound program in engineering and science, including at least some graduate work of merit, is a potential center for growth industries if it is not already one.

Universities are thus rapidly developing into more than mere places for learning. They are becoming major economic influences in the nation's industrial life, affecting the location of industry, population growth, and the character of communities. Universities are in brief a natural resource just as are raw materials, transportation, climate, etc. James R. Killian, former president of Massachu-

setts Institute of Technology, has described the university originated common market of ideas that has resulted from MIT, Harvard, etc., as the principal economic force in the present economy and prosperity of New England. Again, Clark Kerr, president of the far-flung University of California with its many campuses, has repeatedly presented the view that engineering programs must be established on new campuses in order that the University of California may adequately serve the industrial needs of a growing California.

The need that growth industries have for a university becomes apparent when one examines what is happening in areas where growth industries have been established in the absence of a nearby university. In some such situations isolated locations have been dictated by the nature of the work being done: Examples are the atomic energy installation at Hanford, Washington, the missile base at Huntsville, Alabama, and the Naval Ordnance Test Station at Inyokern, California. At each of these locations, and at many other similar installations, on-premise degree level educational programs are now being provided under sponsorship of the state university.

Again, when growth companies do creative work in cities that do not have an adequate local university, major efforts are often made to remedy this lack. Such efforts take several forms. At Hartford, Connecticut, companies have banded together under the leadership of United Aircraft to support a graduate campus of Rensselaer Polytechnic Institute, whose home base is Troy, New York. On Long Island, the Brooklyn Polytechnic Institute has established a branch campus adjacent to the plant of Republic Aviation, on land supplied by that company. Growth companies in Phoenix, Arizona, persuaded the state to establish undergraduate and graduate level programs in applied science at Arizona State College, formerly a teachers college. Even the Bell Telephone Laboratories, which has the largest research laboratory in the country and would appear to be self-sufficient, has an arrangement with New York University to provide graduate level degree programs of instruction on the Bell Laboratory premises at Murray Hill, New Jersey.

This situation is very different from that which existed even a quarter of a century ago. Then, most engineering schools operated in splendid isolation; their ivory towers were sullied by the world around only if the institution happened to be located in the center of a large city, which most institutions were not. Students came to these schools eager to learn, and after their four years left to work in factories around the country as graduate engineers. Most universities were then little worlds largely isolated from the hurly-burly of everyday life.

Those days are now gone, and my own beloved Stanford, on whose campus I have lived for over 51 years, has changed. Once known as the "Farm" because of its rural setting on a 9,000-acre campus, Stanford is not what it used to be. It is now the center of a major industrial activity. The students sit at the feet of professors who have important ties with the world outside of the university. In seminars the students see and hear a series of men from industry who are doing interesting, impressive, and important things. The lives of these students are far richer and more stimulating than the lives of their fathers who went to Stanford. Moreover, when the students obtain their degrees, now commonly a master's or doctor's degree instead of just a bachelor's degree, they do not need to go off a thousand or more miles to work

in some plant. Rather, a substantial fraction of them take jobs in a local company, stay on in the Stanford community, and keep coming back to the university to tell their old professors what they are doing, or to attend seminars; some will even give seminar talks to the next generation of students.

The lively university of today no longer means the same thing to the engineering student or to its faculty members that it did a quarter of a century ago.

In these modern communities of scholars there is a continuous ferment which makes these locations intellectually stimulating for those having the creative qualities that are so important to the growth industries. A university is first and foremost a center for brains. Its faculty members are highly trained and knowledgeable experts. It brings bright students in from all over the country to interact with each other and with the local intellectual environment. Upon completion of their college work these young people become available for employment and represent the most important raw material that goes into the growth industries.

As I have already indicated, the faculty members of a university that is part of such a modern community of technical scholars live in no ivory towers. They have numerous contacts with stimulating, highly creative individuals in industry. They typically do some consulting with one or more adjacent growth companies on subjects in which they have professional expertness, and often they sit on a board of directors. For example, members of the faculty of the Electrical Engineering Department at Stanford between them hold some 15 directorships in profit-making corporations, more than are held by faculty members of our large and highly regarded Graduate School of

Business. Moreover, a few of these professors are well on the way to becoming millionaires as a result of stock holdings in companies founded by their students —holdings acquired early when the company was very small and often received in return for consulting services before the stock was available to the public.

Many professors of engineering and science serve on government advisory committees concerned with highly technical problems of national defense, space, etc., and they sometimes even get involved in international diplomacy. Thus, several years ago a faculty member from Stanford (a physicist) was chairman of a five-man team—included in which was also a Stanford electrical engineering professor—which spent a summer at Geneva representing our Department of State, negotiating with the Russians in an attempt to reach an agreement on methods and procedures for detecting clandestine atomic bomb tests in outer space. They could not get the Russians to agree on anything, even on the technical facts involved.

As a result of varied experiences such as these that I have been enumerating, many present-day professors bring to the classroom a broad background because they are truly men of affairs.

In the modern community of technical scholars the people in industry in turn develop many close contacts with the academic activities in the community. The creative individuals who are doing interesting work in local companies frequently appear before seminar classes at the university. Here, they are both on exhibition to the students and also are subjected to critical questioning by the students. Junior employees of local companies in many cases will enroll in classes at the university; some of these will even do doctoral research at the university on subjects that are of interest

both to their employer and to the university faculty member with whom they are associated.

Original ideas, coming out of the research activities of the university, which have practical possibilities will be picked up and exploited by the local industry. In turn, the activities carried on by local industry react back on the research work being done in the universities, contributing to its progress and in some cases influencing the direction in which it goes. Thesis projects, by students, which have industrial implications are often moved from the university, at the completion of the doctor's degree, into a local company and modified to become part of a commercial development.

Such an environment is stimulating, is conducive to the development of new ideas, and in general maintains intellectual activity at a high tempo both in the university and in industry. It is in such an environment that new companies are born and older companies, if well managed, grow rapidly. This is the 20th and 21st century form of the honored and ancient community of scholars. It is a new and distinctive force in our society. Of particular importance is the fact that it is becoming one of the great economic forces for the future development of our national economy.

Growth companies are attractive to communities that are interested in growing or in strengthening their economic base. Such companies are characterized by the high average educational level of their employees, by the high average income resulting from the emphasis on intellectual abilities of the white-collar workers, and upon high levels of skills on the part of the blue-collar workers. Moreover, employment in such companies tends to be stable; in particular, it does not follow the "hire, lay-off, and fire" patterns typical of mass-production industries.

Again, growth companies generally occupy attractively landscaped plants with modern architecture, differing greatly from the old-fashioned and depressing factory. These companies are in competition for the best brains, and the people they want can be and are choosey about the surroundings in which they work.

As the attractive features of these growth companies have become generally appreciated, towns and cities all over the country have sought to induce such companies to settle down within their own boundaries, and to create for themselves a small or large community of technical scholars, as the case may be, depending on the size of local ambition. Private promoters, politicians, Chambers of Commerce, and even non-profit organizations are all in the act.

How does one get a community of technical scholars started? Alternatively, when the beginnings of such a community already exist, there is the question as to how one can best nourish and feed it so that it will grow and become stronger with time. In either case, the key is the availability of a strong educational program in engineering and science. When this exists, one has a foundation on which a sound future can be built.

If an adequate educational base does not exist, then, even if industries are induced to build factories in the community and the government is coaxed to place contracts with them that produce employment, the results will be disappointing. Without a strong educational base the community will lack the vital intellectual force that is characteristic of a true center of technical scholars, and one ends up with a high-grade factory

town, not a successful center of growth industry.

In developing the possibilities of an existing embryo center of technical scholars, or in attempting to bring into being a new center, one is involved in a highly competitive situation. Many others are trying to do the same thing; in addition, one must also compete against centers that are already well-established and going operations. The most important element contributing to success in this competition is to have something of quality to offer. Inducements in the form of tax concessions or low-priced land beautifully located, or high-pressure lobbying in Washington, are less important than being able to offer real intellectual quality, and the results desired will not be forthcoming if the quality is lacking. This is true even when a community is successful in securing government contracts, because, without a suitable intellectual base, the government-supported activity is sterile in comparison with what it could be. Quality education provides a leverage for which there is no substitute. At the same time, government contracts and grants are an important factor in every center of technical scholars. This is because the government supports more than half of the research and development carried on in this country by industry and supports practically all of the research work performed in our universities in engineering and science.

There is, however, a widespread lack of understanding of the basic factors that determine how this government money is allocated, particularly the research portion that is so important to graduate work in universities. In general, the government agencies concerned with supporting research and development, such as the Navy, Army, and Air Force, the Atomic Energy Commission, the National Institutes of Health, the National

Aeronautics and Space Administration, and even to some extent the National Science Foundation, are mission oriented. That is to say their research and development dollars are being spent to carry out the mission of the agency.

Thus, the military services are concerned with developing and maintaining the strongest possible military posture. The Atomic Energy Commission devotes its energies to developing atomic weapons and nuclear power. The Space Agency is striving to strengthen our position in space as compared with that of the Russians. The National Institutes of Health are dedicated to improving public health through research. All of these agencies accordingly prefer to spend their money in ways, and at places, that will bring the greatest return. Even though much of the basic research work that these agencies support is carried on in universities, the *primary motive is not to aid education* but rather to accomplish their mission of meeting the national need represented by their mission.

The universities come into the picture because it has been found that they are the most effective places that we have to carry on fundamental research. True, the agencies sponsoring research in universities are usually rather considerate of the welfare of the universities with which they work and attempt to handle their relations with them in such a way as to strengthen the universities rather than weaken them. However, this attitude comes about not primarily because the sponsoring agencies are trying to run a do-gooder program for universities but rather because the universities can contribute much more to the missions of these agencies if the universities are strong than if they are weak.

A natural result of this situation is that government money tends to flow to universities and to those parts of universities that possess strength. If the Office of Naval Research feels that it is in the interests of national defense to do more research on matters that relate to the transistor, they want first-class faculty members carrying on this research. It serves no purpose for the Navy to have the research done by third- or fourth-rate men if first-rate faculty men, interested in doing such research, can be found in some college, large or small. The use of a third-rate man at a third-rate institution might very well be good for both the man and the school, with the result that such a use of his bit of government money might very well make a useful contribution to education, but it wouldn't help the Navy.

Thus, the government funds for research in our universities are available for the primary purpose of getting research results that are important and useful to the nation and are not primarily for the purpose of strengthening education. *Don't ever forget this,* and don't ignore the fact that as a consequence government money flows more naturally and easily to the man and to the institution that can repay the government with a quality performance. This emphasis on quality in distributing research money is likely to continue for some time, irrespective of the efforts of all that pressure groups can do to inject pork into the distribution of such funds. We are in a major competition with Russia in weapon development and in the scientific and technological aspects of industry, and this nation can't afford to come in second to Russia in such a competition by frittering away our money in ways that fail to produce the results we could have obtained. . . .

I have developed the theme that communities of technical scholars are the coming thing in the growth industries, and that in communities of this type the most important component making for success is a strong educational operation which places an emphasis on quality.

Now, what is it that makes for quality in an educational institution in science and technology? Quality is not produced by magnificent buildings nor is it assured by huge enrollments. It is not even based upon beautiful laboratories with expensive equipment. What counts is the quality of the faculty or, more precisely, the quality of those few members of the faculty who combine leadership in education with research qualifications in engineering and science. An outstanding faculty member will attract outstanding students who, under his influence, will be trained to make important contributions. An outstanding faculty member will carry on, with the aid of his students, significant research activities that bring prestige to his institution and help it create the kind of environment that is essential for the existence of a community of technical scholars. The outstanding faculty man in science and technology will be able to obtain from the government the support that is required to carry on his research and will train young people in the ways of science and technology. On the other hand, no amount of government dollars flowing through an institution will produce very much that is worthwhile if spent on faculty members and students whose talents are mediocre—i.e., on those who are five-minute milers. Under such conditions, the government lacks leverage, and what you are getting is a modest payroll rather than the key that opens up the opportunity to develop an important and growing community of technical scholars.

3. Two Views of Automation, 1966

San Francisco Chronicle

No technological problem of the years since World War II has raised more alarm and perhaps less understanding than has automation. We cannot even agree on the definition of the word. For some it means the complete elimination of man from the productive process; for others it merely means a new process that uses significantly fewer men than did the preceding process. In general, management has minimized its significance, while unions have worried about its implications for labor.

Cartoon by Bastian, in the *San Francisco Chronicle*, September 5, 1966. Reprinted by permission of the *San Francisco Chronicle*.

"Bite? Why, it's a man's best friend!"

4. A Chart for Future Progress, 1966

Technology and the American Economy

The growing concern and uncertainty over the nature and probable results of automation led President Lyndon B. Johnson to appoint a National Commission on Technology, Automation, and Economic Progress. After spending many months collecting testimony and statistical data, the Commission issued its report in February 1966. Although the membership was balanced and on the whole conservative—the president of IBM, the head of AF of L-CIO, and similar responsible spokesmen for the nation's major economic interests—the recommendations made were considered too advanced, and the report was not given wide publicity. Nevertheless it reflects the conventional wisdom on the subject and, barring more radical solutions, will undoubtedly be the chart for future national policy. The Introduction was written by the chairman of the Commission, Howard R. Bowen, at the request of the Commission, but was not considered an official part of the report.

From *Technology and the American Economy*, Report of the National Commission on Technology, Automation, and Economic Progress, I (February 1966), *passim.*

439

INTRODUCTION

Future historians will probably describe
our time as an age of conscious social
change. The change we are witnessing
includes the rapid growth of population, the massive flow of peoples from
rural areas to the cities, the steady
growth of national wealth and income,
the rise of oppressed and submerged
peoples, the spread of mass education,
the extension of leisure, the venture
into space, and the frightening increase
in the destructiveness of military weapons. Change is worldwide in scope. Not
all nations or regions are participating
to the same degree or have reached the
same stage, but almost no part of the
world has been left untouched.

It is easy to oversimplify the course
of history; yet if there is one predomi-
nant factor underlying current social
change, it is surely the advancement of
technology. Technological change includes new methods of production, new
designs of products and services, and
new products and new services. Technological change is exemplified by the
automation of a machine tool, reorganization of an assembly line, substitution
of plastics for metals, introduction of a
supersonic transport, discovery of a
new method of heart surgery, teaching
of foreign languages by electronic machines, introduction of self-service into
retailing, communications by satellite,
bookkeeping by electronic computer,
generation of electricity from nuclear
energy, introduction of frozen foods and
air conditioning, and the development
of space vehicles and nuclear weapons.

As men have learned the power of
applying thought and experiment to the
attainment of human ends and have
systematically exploited the possibilities
of pure science and technology, a steady

flow of new methods, new designs, and
new products has resulted.

There has been widespread public
recognition of the deep influence of
technology upon our way of life. Everywhere there is speculation about the
future possibilities for human life, and
much public attention is directed toward scientific and technical trends.
The vast majority of people quite rightly
have accepted technological change as
beneficial. They recognize that it has
led to better working conditions by
eliminating many, perhaps most, dirty,
menial, and servile jobs; that it has made
possible the shortening of working hours
and the increase in leisure; that it has
provided a growing abundance of
goods and a continuous flow of improved and new products; that it has
provided new interests and new experiences for people and thus added to
the zest for life.

On the other hand, technological
progress has at various times in history,
one of them in recent years, raised
fears and concerns which have led to
some questioning of its benefits. One
of these concerns has been the fear of
annihilation by "the bomb." Another
concern has been the apparently harmful influences of modern technology on
the physical and community environment—leading to such problems as air
and water pollution, inadequate water
supply, unsatisfactory solid waste disposal, urban congestion and blight, de-
terioration of natural beauty, and the
rapid depletion of natural resources. Another concern has been the apparently
harmful influence of urban, industrial,
and technical civilization upon the personality of individual human beings—
leading to rootlessness, anonymity, insecurity, monotony, and mental dis-
order. Still another concern, perhaps the

one most responsible for the establishment of the Commission, has arisen from the belief that technological change is a major source of unemployment. This concern has been fostered by the substantial and persistent unemployment during the period 1954-65. The fear has even been expressed by some that technological change would in the near future not only cause increasing unemployment, but that eventually it would eliminate all but a few jobs, with the major portion of what we now call work being performed automatically by machine.

As a nation we have willingly accepted technological change because of its many benefits, but we have never been fully successful in dealing with its problems, even when the pace of technological advance and the growth of the labor force were less rapid than today.

The relatively high postwar labor productivity, much of it due to technological change, combined with the current and future high rate of labor force growth increases dramatically the number of jobs which must be created continually to achieve and maintain full employment. During the period since 1947 output per man-hour in the private economy has increased at the rate of about 3 percent a year as compared to 2 percent a year in the previous 35 years. It is possible that this higher rate of productivity growth will continue, and it may even accelerate in the decade ahead. Moreover, in the next 5 years, the labor force will increase by approximately 1.9 percent a year, and the increase beyond that time will be almost as fast. This figure compares with 1.5 percent a year in the last half of the 1950's.

The social costs and dislocations flowing from past technological changes underscore the need to prepare for the changes that lie ahead. For instance:

Modern farm technology—ranging from the cottonpicker and huge harvesting combines to chemical fertilizers and insecticides—has resulted in rapid migration of workers to the cities and has contributed to serious urban problems.

The technological revolution in agriculture has compounded the difficulties of a large section of our Negro population. Pushed out of rural areas, many of them have migrated to cities in search of livelihood. But they have arrived just when deficient economic growth rates have increased the competition for available jobs, and when advancing technology has been reducing the numbers of the semiskilled and unskilled manufacturing jobs for which they could qualify. Despite improvements in the past 2 years, there are 700,000 fewer factory production and maintenance jobs than at the close of the Korean war.

The closing of obsolete plants and facilities as a result of technological and economic changes has thrown some whole communities—particularly one-industry communities—into economic distress. The fact that coal mining employment fell by 46 percent in 7 years between 1947 and 1954 illustrates the problem. Appalachia is evidence of our failure to cope with it.

Technological change has upset the delicate balances of our environment. Pollution of air and water bedevil our metropolitan areas in which 70 percent of our population lives, while the growing urban population has intensified problems of urban transportation, housing, education, health, and public services.

Despite the great wealth that technology enables us to produce, in 1963 nearly 35 million Americans were still below the poverty level (7.2 million families and 1.8 million persons living alone). Approximately half of these people lived in family units whose breadwinners were employed full-time.

Technology is not a vessel into which people are to be poured and to which they must be molded. It is something to be adapted to the needs of man and to the furtherance of human ends, including the enrichment of personality and environment.

Technology has, on balance, surely been a great blessing to mankind—despite the fact that some of the benefits have been offset by costs. There should be no thought of deliberately slowing down the rate of technological advancement or hampering the freedom of discovery. The task for the decades ahead is to direct technology to the fulfillment of important human purposes. Much of this technology will be derived from the social sciences and the humanities as well as the physical and biological sciences. It will be concerned with such values as individuality, diversity, and decentralization rather than conformity, massive organization, and concentration. It will be directed toward human, environmental, and resource development rather than the proliferation of conventional consumer goods. It will seek to make work more meaningful rather than merely more productive.

In the new technology, machines and automated processes will do the routine and mechanical work. Human resources will be released and available for new activities beyond those that are required for mere subsistence. The great need is to discover the nature of this new kind of work, to plan it, and to do it. In the longer run, significant changes may be needed in our society—in education, for example—to help people find constructive and rewarding ways to use increasing leisure.

Our problem is to marshall the needed technologies, some of which are known and some not yet known. If we are to clean up our environment, enhance human personality, enrich leisure time, make work humanly creative, and restore our natural resources, we shall need inventiveness in the democratic decision making process as well as in the needed technologies. We shall also need to find creative combinations of public and private initiative, as some of the goals of the future may not be achievable through private initiative; leadership will be required by government—Federal, State, and local—with important roles to be played by universities and nonprofit institutions.

It was in the setting of the considerations outlined above that the legislation establishing the Commission was enacted in August 1964. Since that time, conditions have changed and public concerns have been modified. As a result of the tax cuts and other fiscal policies adopted beginning in early 1964, unemployment has been reduced from 5.4 percent to about 4 percent at present. With the intensification of the war in Vietnam, the prospects are for still further cuts in unemployment, and concern is expressed about inflation. However, despite the recent improvement in the employment situation, the basic issues which the Commission was asked to consider are just as relevant and urgent as they were a year ago; and they will continue to be relevant and urgent for many years. The Commission's basic recommendations have not been altered by the turn of recent events.

In the legislative charge (as expressed in Public Law 88-444 creating the Commission), the Congress gave the Commission the following mandate:

(a) To identify and assess the past effects and the current and prospective role and pace of technological change;
(b) To identify and describe the impact of technological and economic change on production and employment, including new job requirements and the major types

of worker displacement, both technological and economic, which are likely to occur during the next 10 years; the specific industries, occupations, and geographic areas which are most likely to be involved; and the social and economic effects of these developments on the Nation's economy, manpower, communities, families, social structure, and human values;

(c) To define those areas of unmet community and human needs toward which application of new technologies might most effectively be directed, encompassing an examination of technological developments that have occurred in recent years, including those resulting from the Federal Government's research and development programs;

(d) To assess the most effective means for channeling new technologies into promising directions, including civilian industries where accelerated technological advancements will yield general benefits, and assess the proper relationship between governmental and private investment in the application of new technologies to large-scale human and community needs;

(e) To recommend, in addition to those actions which are the responsibility of management and labor, specific administrative and legislative steps which it believes should be taken by the Federal, State, and local governments in meeting their responsibilities (1) to support and promote technological change in the interest of continued economic growth and improved well-being of our people, (2) to continue and adopt measures which will facilitate occupational adjustment and geographical mobility, and (3) to share the costs and help prevent and alleviate the adverse impact of change on displaced workers.

The Commission was asked to concern itself with only the next decade. It has not attempted to deal with the distant future. Nevertheless, the scope of the mandate was wide and the issues both complex and difficult. But the Commission has attempted, within the limits of its 1-year life, to answer the questions raised and to offer recommendations as requested.

SUMMARY OF MAJOR CONCLUSIONS AND RECOMMENDATIONS

The issues discussed in this report are complex and diverse. A brief summary of major conclusions cannot do justice to the report and is certainly not a substitute for the full text with its supporting evidence and argument. Once the text has been read, however, a summary may serve a useful purpose in crystallizing the major points and pointing up the recommendations which have been made. The principal conclusions and recommendations follow:

1. There has been some increase in the pace of technological change. The most useful measure of this increase for policy purposes is the annual growth of output per man-hour in the private economy. If 1947 is chosen as a dividing point, the trend rate of increase from 1909 to that date was 2 percent per year; from 1947 to 1965 it was 3.2 percent per year. This is a substantial increase, but there has not been and there is no evidence that there will be in the decade ahead an acceleration in technological change more rapid than the growth of demand can offset, given adequate public policies.

2. The excessive unemployment following the Korean war, only now beginning to abate, was the result of an economic growth rate too slow to offset the combined impact of productivity increase (measured in output per man-hour) and a growing labor force.

3. Since productivity is the primary source of our high standard of living and opportunity must be provided to those of the population who choose to enter the labor force, the growth of demand must assume the blame for and provide the answer to unemployment. But it must be realized that the growth

rate required to match rising productivity and labor force growth rates is unprecedented in our history, though not in the history of other industrial economies. There will be a continuing need for aggressive fiscal and monetary policies to stimulate growth.

4. To say that technological change does not bear major responsibility for the general level of unemployment is not to deny the role of technological change in the unemployment of particular persons in particular occupations, industries, and locations. Economic and technological changes have caused and will continue to cause displacement throughout the economy. Technological change, along with other changes, determines who will be displaced. The rate at which output grows in the total economy determines the total level of unemployment and how long those who become unemployed remain unemployed, as well as how difficult it is for new entrants to the labor force to find employment.

5. Unemployment tends to be concentrated among those workers with little education, not primarily because technology developments are changing the nature of jobs, but because the uneducated are at the "back of the line" in the competition for jobs. Education, in part, determines the employability and productivity of the individual, the adaptability of the labor force, the growth and vitality of the economy, and the quality of the society. But we need not await the slow process of education to solve the problem of unemployment.

6. The outlook for employment and adjustment to change in the next decade depends upon the policies followed. Uneven growth and decline of occupations and industries could, but need not, cause serious difficulties for the economy as a whole. The number of un-

skilled jobs will not decline, though unskilled jobs will continue to as a proportion of all jobs. Growth patterns in both the economy and the labor force provide an important warning: Unless Negroes and, to a lesser degree, youth, are able to penetrate growing occupations and industries at a more rapid rate than in the past, their high unemployment rates will continue or even rise. Our society must do a far better job than it has in the past of assuring that the burdens of changes beneficial to society as a whole are not borne disproportionately by some individuals.

7. The more adequate fiscal policies of the past 2 years have proven their ability to lower unemployment despite continued technological change and labor force growth. Economic policy must continue, watchfully but resolutely, to reduce the general unemployment rate. We must never again present the spectacle of wartime prosperity and peacetime unemployment. The needs of our society are such that we should give major attention in our fiscal policies to public investment expenditures.

8. With the best of fiscal and monetary policies, there will always be those handicapped in the competition for jobs by lack of education, skill, or experience or because of discrimination. The needs of our society provide ample opportunities to fulfill the promise of the Employment Act of 1946: "a job for all those able, willing, and seeking to work." We recommend a program of public service employment, providing, in effect, that the Government be an employer of last resort, providing work for the "hard-core unemployed" in useful community enterprises.

9. Technological change and productivity are primary sources of our unprecedented wealth, but many persons have not shared in that abundance. We

recommend that economic security be guaranteed by a floor under family income. That floor should include both improvements in wage-related benefits and a broader system of income maintenance for those families unable to provide for themselves.

10. To facilitate adjustment to change as well as to improve the quality of life, adequate educational opportunity should be available to all. We recommend compensatory education for those from disadvantaged environments, improvements in the general quality of education, universal high school education and opportunity for 14 years of free public education, elimination of financial obstacles to higher education, lifetime opportunities for education, training, and retraining, and special attention to the handicaps of adults with deficient basic education.

11. Adjustment to change requires information concerning present and future job opportunities. We recommend the creation of a national computerized job-man matching system which would provide more adequate information on employment opportunities and available workers on a local, regional, and national scale. In addition to speeding job search, such a service would provide better information for vocational choice and alert the public and policymakers to impending changes.

12. The public employment service is a key instrument in adjustment to technological and economic changes. But it is presently handicapped by administrative obstacles and inadequate resources. We recommend the now federally financed but State-administered employment services be made wholly Federal. This would bring them into harmony with modern labor market conditions. Then they must be provided with the resources, both in manpower

and funds, necessary to fulfill their crucial role.

13. We recommend that present experimentation with relocation assistance to workers and their families stranded in declining areas be developed into a permanent program.

14. Displacement, technological and otherwise, has been particularly painful to those blocked from new opportunity by barriers of discrimination. The Commission wishes to add its voice to others demanding elimination of all social barriers to employment and advocating special programs to compensate for centuries of systematic denial.

15. Technological and economic changes have differential geographic impacts requiring concerted regional efforts to take advantage of opportunities and avoid dislocation. We recommend that each Federal Reserve bank provide the leadership for economic development activities in its region. The development program in each Federal Reserve District should include: (1) A regular program of economic analysis; (2) an advisory council for economic growth composed of representatives from each of the major interested groups within the district; (3) a capital bank to provide venture capital and long-term financing for new and growing companies; (4) regional technical institutes to serve as centers for disseminating scientific and technical knowledge relevant to the region's development and (5) a Federal executive in each district to provide regional coordination of the various Federal programs related to economic development.

16. The responsibility of Government is to foster an environment of opportunity in which satisfactory adjustment to change can occur. But the adjustments themselves must occur primarily in the private employment rela-

tionship. The genius of the private adjustment process is the flexibility with which it accommodates to individual circumstances. Our report suggests areas for consideration by private and public employers, employees, and unions. We also recommend study of a reinsurance fund to protect pension rights and modifications of the investment tax credit to encourage employers to provide appropriate adjustment assistance. We also advocate a positive program by employers and unions to provide compensatory opportunities to the victims of past discrimination and stronger enforcement provisions in civil rights legislation relating to employment. Federal, State, and local governments are encouraged to conduct themselves as model employers in the development of new adjustment techniques.

17. Technology enlarges the capacities of man and extends his control over ·his environment. The benefits of increased productivity can and should be applied to combinations of higher living standards and increased leisure, improvements in the work environment, increased investment in meeting human and community needs, and assistance to less advantaged nations.

18. As examples of possible applications of new technologies to unmet human and community needs, we recommend improvements in health care, transportation, control of air and water pollution, and housing.

(1) To improve health care, we recommend: (a) Fuller access to diagnostic and patient care facilities by all groups in the population; (b) broader and bolder use of the computer and other new health technologies; (c) increased spread and use of health statistics, information, and indexes; and (d) new programs for training health manpower.

(2) To aid the development of an efficient transportation system we recommend: Federal support of a systems research program directed toward (a) the problems of particular multistate regions, (b) the determination of national transportation requirements, and (c) the evaluation of alternative programs.

(3) For air pollution control, we recommend: (a) Enlargement of research efforts to learn and understand the effects of various pollutants on living organisms; and (b) assignment of pollution costs to the sources of pollutants.

(4) To control water pollution, we recommend: The establishment of effective, amply empowered river basin authorities.

(5) To encourage improvement in housing technology, we recommend: (a) Federal stimulation of research; (b) use of federally supported public housing to provide initial markets for new housing technologies; (c) promulgation of a national model building code by making available Federal support and insurance of housing and other construction only in those communities which put their building codes in harmony with the national code; and (d) provision of adjustment assistance to any building crafts destroyed by technical change.

19. We also recommend (1) increased use of systems analysis in resolving social and environmental problems, (2) the use of Federal procurement as a stimulus to technological innovation through purchasing by performance criteria rather than product specification, (3) provision of Federal funds to universities and other organizations for the improvement of research techniques and their experimental application to urban problems, (4) the formation of

university institutes integrated with the educational function which would serve as laboratories for urban problem analysis and resources for local communities wanting their advice and services, and (5) increased efforts to make available for non-government use results of Government performed or funded research.

20. Finally, we recommend: (1) Efforts by employers to "humanize" the work environment by (a) adapting work to human needs, (b) increasing the flexibility of the lifespan of work, and (c) eliminating the distinction in the mode of payment between hourly workers and salaried employers; (2) exploration of a system of social accounts to make possible assessment of the relative costs and benefits of alternative policy decisions; and (3) continuous study of national goals and evaluation of our national performance in relation to such goals.

5. Predicting Effects, 1967

EMILIO Q. DADDARIO, *Technology Assessment*

Even though the National Commission on Technology, Automation, and Economic Progress tended to play down the revolutionary implications of automation, this and other technological forces have continued to intrude on the deliberations of those concerned with establishing national policy. It is universally conceded that technological change leads in many cases to broader social change as well. Often, however, these effects are but dimly seen, and even when accurately predicted they are not always provided for.

As the major promoter of technological (and therefore social) change in the nation today, the federal government is groping toward some definition of its responsibility for predicting and solving the problems raised by its own encouragement of innovation. One persistent and knowledgeable congressional critic of technological irresponsibility has been Representative Emilio Q. Daddario. He has suggested that the Congress should establish a board to assess the implications of new technologies.

On March 7, 1967 I introduced H.R. 6698 "to provide a method for identifying, assessing, publicizing, and dealing with the implications and effects of applied research and technology" by establishing a Technology Assessment Board. The bill recognized both the need for "identifying the potentials of applied research and technology and promoting ways and means to accom-

From U.S. Congress, House Committee on Science and Astronautics, Subcommittee on Science, Research, and Development, *Technology Assessment*, Statement by Emilio Q. Daddario, Chairman. 90th Cong., 1st sess. (Washington, D.C., 1967), pp. 3-15.

plish their transfer into practical use, and identifying the undesirable byproducts and side effects of such applied research and technology in advance of their crystallization and informing the public of their potential in order that appropriate steps may be taken to eliminate or minimize them."

This bill was introduced, not as a piece of perfected legislation, but as a stimulant to discussion. I have received many thoughtful comments, criticisms, and suggestions on the Technology Assessment Board concept. The discussions of the past few months have led to the decision that much more should be learned about the "how" of Technology Assessment before any permanent mechanism or organization was proposed. Therefore we on the Science committee are planning to undertake a long-range study of the concept of Technology Assessment. The subcommittee's intention is to employ a variety of information and advisory resources for the development of an optimum system.

A Technology Assessment capability for the legislative branch of our Government will enable us to deploy the finite scientific and engineering resources of money, facilities, and skilled manpower to take fullest advantage of the gains offered to society. At the same time, Technology Assessment can anticipate and minimize the unwanted side effects which so often accompany innovations. The purpose of the subcommittee study is to strengthen the role of the Congress in making judgments among alternatives for putting science to work for human benefit.

A capability for Technology Assessment is needed now in a new, different, and insistent way as compared to former times. Virtually all civilized activities are highly dependent on technology. A

progressive society is venturesome—willing to take risks in order to achieve potential benefits. New applications of science and engineering continually present attractive solutions to social, economic, and political problems.

Economic growth is a major U.S. national goal which increasingly is accomplished through technological change. The marketplace acts to magnify and dramatize the economic benefits of new technology. Easily quantifiable social effects (unemployment, health statistics, education factors, hourly productivity, etc.) are also efficiently appraised by society. Other results are not so easily calculated into the risk-benefit equations.

Technological change produces numerous and diverse effects—some recognizable before the fact, others not until later; some good and others bad; some never clearly established in a cause-and-effect relationship.

To maximize the standard of living, society needs to know as much as possible about the consequences of technological change. (This holds regardless of any disagreements as to what constitutes "progress" or what the collective tastes of a nation or region may set as standards.) Two new factors have made the assessment of technological alternatives more critical.

First, the increased worldwide population density (a result of technological advancements in itself) means that any activity is likely to affect a great many human beings. There is less uninhabited area in which to conduct risky ventures. There is less virgin land to move into if an activity deteriorates presently settled territory. Thus, the large, widespread world population has made the maintenance of environmental quality much more important today.

Second, the forces for change which

are at the disposal of mankind, are very powerful. Biological, chemical, radiation, and energy effects are now available which can literally upset the so-called balance of the natural world. This means that unforeseen consequences are less likely to be confined locally, or detected under restricted conditions, where lessons can be learned before significant damage is done. On the constructive side, it means that society has opportunities for human betterment which can alleviate the very basic problems of the world—war, hunger, disease, and poverty.

Technology Assessment could easily become a stifling influence on progress if the dangers are emphasized rather than the potentials for good. There is an innate conservatism in our culture which makes innovation difficult at the very best. History presents many familiar examples of the entrepreneur being ridiculed and frustrated by a society which clung to the status quo. Lack of imagination for the future is the general rule. It is all too easy to bring up reasons why a novel procedure or idea is not worthwhile or would bring dire results. The inventor is usually quite alone with his vision.

On the other hand, those who propose radical ventures are often blinded by their enthusiasm to the risks involved. Or if they foresee a dark side of technology, they are loath to point it out, knowing too well how precarious acceptance of their scheme may be; and having a confidence that somehow the hazards will be minimized and the benefits realized.

A characteristic of America in the past century has been the love of the new, a boldness to try something different, the courage to take risks in applying the fruits of science. This attitude has been responsible for a great portion of our material welfare and strength among nations.

But now, with the immensity of consequences and the irreversible nature of many technological changes, the propensity for risk taking must be coupled with a deeper assessment of both deficits and benefits. We must continue to advance, but *mere change is not equivalent to progress.* We must not discourage the entrepreneur, the idea man, or the engineer. Indeed we must encourage the greatest degree of imagination in order to meet the problems of life and political existence. This imagination must be extended to include the full assessment of all consequences without the fear that a reactionary society will seize on the risks and deficits as an excuse for stagnation.

Science and technology have become so much a part of everything that we do as individuals, businesses, or nations that old attitudes are gone forever. No more is science taken on faith, and technology accepted in awe. A major reason for the demise of these attitudes is the enormous financial investment in research and development. It is not difficult to engender interest and stimulate technical literacy in citizens, stockholders, and the electorate when the funding of science and engineering reaches the present level of $24 billion annually. In just the last decade, public and private funds for R. & D. have totaled $157 billion.

Thus, technology costs a lot of money, brings up perplexing problems of hazard and benefit, and beckons to an ever more complex future. This is the substance of the need for Technology Assessment in the Congress.

There is, of course, an alternative new attitude: the call for a moratorium on science until society gains the wisdom to use technology safely. We are warned that mankind can know too much for his own good. A catchup period is proposed—so that mores and rational conduct can develop which are equal to the choices forced by science. In the meantime, so goes the familiar argument, a renaissance of art, literature, and the humanities should be force fed to redress the imbalance in our culture which has been brought about by 20 years of unprecedented support for research and development. I do not believe this line of reasoning appeals to many of us. Certainly not to those who have observed the pain of disease, the tragedy of starvation abroad, or the raw force of Communist subversion. Surely, what is needed is more science, more knowledge of natural laws, and more prescience of what can and should result from the wise use of our resources. Science is concerned with truth, and, regardless of the shortcomings of our civilization, we cannot be hurt by knowing more, much more, of what we are about.

Progress is being redefined as something much more sophisticated and intricate than mere change. There is a strong element of renewal present in today's planning. Lessons of the past have shown what is to be discarded and what is to be restored, retained, and enhanced in individual lives, in corporations, in cities, in transportation systems, in agriculture, and in environments. Personal renewal is evidenced in the continuous reeducation which all of us undergo here in the legislative branch of Government.

The renewal of our institutions is part and parcel of the democratic process. A capability for Technology Assessment is a keystone for improved institutions and, most importantly, for the Congress. In the past 3 years we have taken several important steps to raise the level of understanding of science and technology within the Congress. The Science Policy Research Division of the Legislative Reference Service in the Library of Congress has been established. Incidentally, the dependence which the Congress is beginning to place on this skilled organization makes its expansion in the near future a virtual necessity.

The staffs of certain committees which deal substantially in technical matters have been strengthened. The National Academy of Sciences has worked through a direct contract with the Science and Astronautics Committee for a series of significant reports on basic and applied research. The sources of advice and testimony have been broadened from the traditional Federal agencies and special-interest groups to include advisory panels, professional society representatives, and men of stature from universities, independent research institutes, and industry. Technical issues which might be fragmented by our committee structure have been discussed and informally coordinated by meetings of key committee chairmen and senior members. The pending Congressional Reorganization Act could carry these valuable tools for legislative understanding of science even further.

But it does appear that a special effort may be necessary to bring Technology Assessment to a useful and timely status. Existing mechanisms may be modified or extended. New special arrangements for the Congress may be necessary. Our investigation has no preconceptions as to the final result. I would point out that Technology Assessment has been the concern of our Government for many years. But we have not yet felt the urgency to perfect and employ methods of appraisal, arbitration, planning, forecasting, and extrapolation to their fullest degree.

Let me quote a most pertinent viewpoint of the need for Technology Assessment. I believe its origin may surprise you:

The most important general conclusion to be drawn from these studies is the continuing growth of the already high and rapidly developing technology in the social structure of the Nation, and hence the hazard of any planning that does not take this fact into consideration. * * * In view of the findings regarding the importance of technology and applied science, it is recommended that the Federal government develop appropriate agencies for continuous study of them; and more specifically that there be set up in the respective departments science committees with the definite function of investigating and reporting at regular periods on the progress and trends of science and invention and the possible and economic effects flowing therefrom as they affect the work of the departments and of the agencies to whom they render service.

The sentences just quoted came from House Document 360, "Technological Trends and National Policy," a report of the Subcommittee on Technology to the National Resources Committee, which was submitted in the first session of the 75th Congress, in June 1937. So we see that 30 years ago, the need for systematic Government-wide Technology Assessment was recognized. Unfortunately the recommendations went largely unheeded.

But assessment has been carried out from time to time and is being carried out today on an ad hoc basis. Historically, assessment has usually occurred well after the technology was introduced and when undesirable consequences had reached serious proportions. For example, the intensive cultivation of grasslands in the Great Plains precipitated the duststorms and erosion during the drought of the 1930's. As a result, studies showed the way to corrective action

of windbreaks and other soil conservation measures—too late to prevent hardships to the farmers involved.

Frequently, the call for assessment has come from inspired social critics and writers. Such was the case in environmental and human health hazards from pesticides. Rachel Carson's "Silent Spring" brought the realization of how quickly we had accepted the pest control properties of certain chemicals without questioning what the consequences of their widespread dissemination might do to valuable insects, fish, and wildlife.

Countless times a radical change was made to a locality or region prior to any assessment of all potential consequences. Invariably, some adverse condition arose which took time and effort to combat. The opening of the St. Lawrence Seaway allowed certain predatory oceanic eels to enter into the Great Lakes, much to the detriment of commercial and sport fishing. The rabbit in Australia and the giant African snail in the Pacific Islands are other poignant reminders of what happens when biological control mechanisms are bypassed or upended. On the positive side, sufficient knowledge of local conditions has and will continue to open the way for more fruitful changes. Deliberate transfer of a plant or animal can be rewarding. The thought of a flowering plain where desert once stood is not a utopian hope. Imported plants have flourished in new homes when prior research and assessment were adequate. For example, mesquite trees of Southwest United States are growing naturally in the Egyptian desert.

The most dramatic example of drastic change is the extinction of a species. The Great Auk and the nearly extinct blue whale and the whooping crane have served to focus attention on a deadly trend—man's sacrifice of long range objectives for short term gains. Many animals which have survived as fitting in the environment are near extinction because of man-induced changes today. Their annihilation would be more than an esthetic and scientific loss. Life cycles could be disrupted and adverse side effects within the natural environment would carry over into the social and economic spheres of human beings.

Our current fight for air quality is an after-the-fact realization that the atmosphere could not be used as a convenient and inexpensive dumping place for gaseous and particulate wastes.

Many unwanted consequences have been labeled as the price of progress. But even in a nation as affluent as ours, these prices all at once seem too high. And at the same time, mature reflection suggests that the price need not have been paid at all if a thorough understanding had been gained of what was happening in the ecological system at an earlier date.

Technology Assessment has been haphazard in the United States because we have never fixed the responsibility for the total results of technology. The market place is an institution for assessing technology. Beyond mere competitive performance of goods and services, there is a realization by commercial interests that "caveat emptor" is an unworkable doctrine. Legal recourse and public opinion as well as enlightened self-interest underlie the large amount of safety testing and prevention of hazards in normal usage which goes on in every manufacturing concern.

In some cases, such as acceptability of drugs, food additives, and agricultural chemicals, or the safe design and construction of automobiles, the Government is assigning assessment functions to its agencies. For example, the Federal responsibility for assessment of nuclear technology is well established. A recent event illuminates the need for full recognition of this responsibility. Again, a Middle East crisis has demonstrated vividly that the supply of oil to the industrialized world sometimes flows at an uneven rate. Political and military conflict can even sever supply lines, producing economic and political repercussions throughout the Western World. Indirectly these confrontations add to the possibilities of abating air pollution from fossil fuel combustion to propel us faster into the age of nuclear power production. We are aware that atomic energy could be available as an endless source of efficient power. We are taking great strides to bring this about. But at the same time programs lag in devising a long term satisfactory disposal of reactor wastes. And the safety of central city location for nuclear electric power stations has yet to be confidently demonstrated.

These complex pros and cons are not sorted out by conventional appraisal processes. The marketplace does not take into account all the important values to society as a whole. There is a tendency to accept short term gains for both the supplier and purchaser. And a Federal agency may have too narrow a mission assignment to provide adequate assessment of an entire technological system. For example, the environmental pollution problem is fragmented among many agencies with the result that abatement of a contamination of one type may simply shift the pollutant load to another part of the ecosystem.

In the case of automation, we have been aware for at least a century that technology was bent on displacing man from labor. As long as there was more work to be done than skills were available to do it, then machines and automation caused only temporary dislocations. But today cybernation promises to eliminate all repetitive physical and mental tasks performed by human beings. No existing market or government function is able to assess the impact of this revolutionary application of technology.

These deficiencies in current institutions and procedures are becoming the subject of discussion in the Congress, in universities, in professional technical societies, and in public policy foundations. . . .

On the whole, the Congress can strengthen its ability to assess and judge technological programs without radical change. I take this view because, simply stated, Technology Assessment is a form of policy research which provides a balanced appraisal to the policymaker. Ideally, it is a system to ask the right question and obtain correct and timely answers. It identifies policy issues, assesses the impact of alternative courses of action and presents findings. It is a method of analysis that systematically appraises the nature, significance, status, and merit of a technological program. The method may well vary from case to case. For example, assessment of birth control devices undoubtedly will proceed somewhat differently from that of pollution abatement.

Technology Assessment is designed to uncover three types of consequences —desirable, undesirable, and uncertain. The benefits that accrue from technology are naturally the driving force for its application. Economic growth is fostered by more convenient and efficient services or by new and less expensive goods. Society benefits when technology is fashioned around some value or goal, consistent with democracy. Promotion of the general welfare, through medical research and services, or the

use of technology in education, are institutionalized social goals.

Undesirable consequences, sometimes played down by calling them harmful side effects, can be expected with most innovations. Technology means change —change to the natural environment, change in personal habits and behavior, change in social and economic patterns, and not infrequently change in the legal and the political processes. While many of these changes are beneficial, many are disruptive and dislocative. They change situations more rapidly than the pace at which individuals can adjust. The well-known cultural lag finds its logical beginnings in this phenomenon. Assessment of the risks is a necessary concomitant to assessment of the benefits.

Uncertain consequences are the third type to be identified and assessed. Available information may point out only that an effect will occur and can give no idea of the degree of impact. When the severity of impact is not known further research is often warranted. For example, new discoveries in disease control and prevention have to go through a prolonged trial period so that harmful effects are discovered before widespread use is sanctioned. In general, experimentation and pilot projects are required to determine what proscriptions might be necessary before the technology is able to safely diffuse through society.

If assessment is a method of policy research that identifies the amount and type of change for alternative courses of action and provides a balanced appraisal of each alternative, then what is the scope of technology assessment? What will it try to measure? What time frame will it consider? What yardsticks will be used? How does assessment differ from other methods of analysis?

Answers to these questions will more concisely define Technology Assessment and more clearly show its relationship to the policymaking process.

Technology Assessment for the Congress will deal for the most part with applications in the United States. It is worth noting, though, that the entire world, and even outer space, is the system with which we are concerned. Some of the technologies which must be assessed in a broader sense are nuclear blast effects, climate and weather modification, famine and disease epidemics, and oceanography. The international aspects of Technology Assessment will become more important as the power and ubiquity of man-made forces continue to increase.

Another division of viewpoint for assessment efforts is the difference between technology for the rich nations as opposed to that for the emerging countries. A risk which the Western world might avoid would perhaps be acceptable to a nation struggling with starvation. For example, the ecological hazards of chemical pesticides might be sufficient to restrict their use in the United States. But in India or Southeast Asia with the threat of malaria coupled to a severe nutritional problem, the use of a broad gage insecticide would be justified. On the other hand, the mistakes in applying transportation technology which have knotted many American and European cities can be avoided by better planning as new population centers are built elsewhere in the world. In either case, the full knowledge of good and bad consequences can be of great value to either the "have" or "have-not" cultures.

To assess technology one has to establish cause and effect relationships from the action or project source to the locale of consequences.

A direct or immediate effect is easy to spot and assess. The direct effects in turn will cause other consequences—indirect or derivative effects. As the scope of assessment moves outward in time the derivative effects become the result of many causes and not of one specific technological change.

Looking into the future we know birth control devices will have a profound impact on the world. There will be a change in the birth rate (a downward trend in the United States is already apparent). Following this will be a consequent shift in hospital facilities, various economic changes and, ultimately, changes in sexual behaviour, morals, and perhaps even religious beliefs. The function of technology assessment is to identify all of these—both short-term and long range. The emphasis, though, will be on the short-term impacts that can be measured by natural science parameters. That is, the focus of Technology Assessment will be on those consequences that can be predicted with a useful degree of probability.

Possible changes in values, attitudes or institutions are important but not easily predicted. These changes are usually long term and fall beyond the primary focus of Technology Assessment. Therefore, because of their slow evolution, present human values and political institutions will serve as the frame of reference for purposes of measurement and appraisal.

Assessment is a form of policy research and is not technological forecasting or program planning. It is a balanced analysis of how a technological program could proceed with the benefits and risks of each policy alternative carefully described. It incorporates prediction and planning but only to expose the potential consequences of the program.

Assessment is an aid to, and not a substitute for, judgment. Technology Assessment provides the decisionmaker with a list of future courses of action backed up by systematic analysis of the consequences. In this sense it is an analytical study that could be prepared by anyone. Its utility would be enhanced if it was undertaken for a policymaking group that could sketch in the nature of the problem for the study team beforehand. In a broader sense assessment is part of the legislative process. Our subcommittee will gather and assess information before we can make any judgments. Part of this information will be actual assessment studies prepared for the subcommittee by the scientific community and the Science Policy Research Division. When viewed as either a method of research or a part of the legislative process, Technology Assessment serves to provide information tailored to the constraints and needs of the policymaking process.

6. The Urban Challenge, 1967

ROBERT C. WOOD, "Challenge to Science and Engineering"

As we have already seen, the recognition of urban technological problems is not new to this generation. Only now, however, is the public being seriously challenged to support a broad program of urban rebuilding. Recent civil disorders have focused attention on the plight of the nation's cities, and once again technology is seen as a possible solution to their decay. The technological elements in the problem cannot be overlooked—over half the land mass of Los Angeles is today used by automobiles—for streets, freeway interchanges, parking lots, service stations, and so forth.

Even so, once again the resort to technological solutions threatens to obscure the social and economic roots of our problems. At a meeting of scientists and engineers concerned with urban problems, a spokesman for the federal Department of Housing and Urban Development pointed out some of the drawbacks and advantages of technical cures.

It is a special pleasure to see the engineering and scientific communities getting involved in the problems of cities and city-building. Both technically and politically this is a time of particular ripeness for applying scientific techniques to the discontinuities of urban life. Fresh public interest, promising

From Robert C. Wood, "Challenge to Science and Engineering," *Science, Engineering, and the City*, A Symposium sponsored by the National Academy of Sciences and National Academy of Engineering, April 1967. NAS Pub. No. 1498 (Washington, D.C., 1967), pp. 11-16.

new legislation, and the development of multivariant analysis and other new technical tools, have come together to make urban innovation, experimentation, and change a real possibility.

The Department of Housing and Urban Development and the Office of Science and Technology cosponsored a 3-week study on science and urban development at Woods Hole during the summer of 1966. Some very interesting things emerged from this, including the alacrity with which humanists, bureaucrats, and scientists adopt each other's jargon. Within a few days, sociologists were talking about "parameters" and "interface" and mathematicians about "social needs" and "urban texture." Not always precisely, of course, but fluently.

I want to discuss not the glorious promise of applying science to urban design but the difficulties of doing so. I want to discuss not the admirable scientific and engineering capacity that America has now but the additional capacity, the additional sophistication, that we need.

I do not do so to discourage the involvement of scientists and engineers in the urgent and historic task of building urban America. Such involvement is critical to our success. I think, however, that we must not lose sight of what a complicated, arduous, adventurous, and expensive job it is we have before us.

There are four facts of urban life which must be confronted as we endeavor to apply reason and analysis to our present and future cities:

First, the city is the most complicated system known to man. I am sure it is tempting for those best acquainted with the design demands involved to feel that nothing could be more complicated than getting a man to the moon—and back. Such is not the case.

Second, the city is and will remain the focus of intense conflicts. Different ethnic groups and economic groups do not agree on the values or the ground rules which should guide the system.

Third, any pure cost–benefit approach to urban programs will be doomed by their inevitable inconsistency.

Fourth, in future urban planning we are dealing with entirely new orders of magnitude. Every urban physical and social pattern must be prepared to respond to explosive growth.

I would like to deal briefly with each of these four limitations and the problems they pose for those of us who would like to see urban development become more manageable, more predictable, and more amenable to the hopes and needs of mankind.

COMPLEXITY

The city owes its very being to the fact that it serves as an intersection for a great many interrelated systems: health systems, educational systems, employment systems, transportation systems. The interaction and overlapping which this entails greatly increase the complexity of the city "system" as a whole.

In 1960 Raymond Vernon edited a pioneering series of studies on the New York metropolitan area which tried to determine what the forces were behind the growth and redistribution of the region's jobs and population and to use this information to project future patterns.

On close study, the metropolis turned out to be an enormously complicated entity. Many considerations of space, transportation, labor availability and cost, and relative taxes affected the decisions of businesses and industries in deciding whether and where to move in the rapidly expanding metropolis. Certain heavy industries determined residential patterns by their location, as workers moved within walking or rapid transit distance. Others tended to follow as consumers led.

Technological improvements in transportation, such as the truck, the subway, and the George Washington Bridge, had important effects on job distribution and residential patterns. And these patterns are always changing. "Each area of the region," Vernon pointed out, "is forever being tested and retested for its most efficient economic use." Wholesale areas of downtown Manhattan, once so accessible to port traffic, have faded out as the railroad and truck have suggested a new pattern of location.

Another complicating factor in the economic and population pattern was—if you will pardon the commercial—the 1,400 governments that exist in the region. Each of these entities—counties, towns, villages, school boards, special water districts, and so forth—has the capacity to raise and spend money and to provide services. These governments provide jobs, buy goods and services, provide services that affect industry, and exercise regulatory powers—for example, through zoning—that directly affect the region's development.

So, gradually, one could see the difficulty of isolating any single subsystem of the city, even its most fundamental one. In what it is now fashionable to call an ecological manner, every piece of the system was related, and pressures at one point were reflected at another.

In the effort to project these economic patterns to 1985, Vernon and his colleagues—of whom I was one—used mathematical models and the best computer technology then available. We assembled a mass of data and analyses and threw in some hunches as well. Yet we were still stuck with what Vernon called "an oversimplified concept of the future," which necessarily excluded war, depressions, great unforeseen changes in technology analogous to the invention of the automobile, and massive shifts in public policy such as accompanied the New Deal. We had no way of slotting in the effect of electing Mayor Lindsay or the impact of "instant rehabilitation" techniques applied on a substantial basis.

Caution, then, is indicated when we talk glibly about building mathematical models or about viewing the city as a system.

CONFLICT

The first step in systems analysis is to make your goals clear. In urban affairs this is a very difficult matter. The suburban commuter, the small downtown businessman, the low-income resident, the real estate developer all have quite different goals and often different values as well.

As we are beginning to see, not only in our low-income urban ghettos but on our college campuses as well, there is a growing disinclination on the part of the less powerful segments of the community to accept passively the judgments of those accustomed to running things. Conflicts over the allocation of community resources which previously might have been quietly confined to people's hearts or their front stoops are now breaking out noisily on the streets, in city council chambers, and across the pages of the daily newspapers. This is not a bad thing. Conflict and confrontation are often the necessary prelude to growth and change. It is only when conflict is carried on in a closed arena, with no possibility for accommodation or change, that it becomes truly destructive.

Our urban designs must provide for change and accommodation. They must provide ways for people to participate at the neighborhood level in decisions which intimately affect them. Everyone deeply needs a sense of having some control over his environment, some influence in determining his own destiny.

PROGRAM CONSISTENCY

These same kinds of problems—of differences between the beneficiaries of services and those who finance them, between those to whom the city is a market and those to whom it must be home—affect our efforts to evaluate rationally the urban programs we now have. Cost-benefit analysis is, of course, a very useful way of arraying the implications of various alternative approaches or programs. But how can cost be measured fairly, and whose benefit are we talking about?

Highways are evaluated in terms of dollar outlays versus time saved by drivers; renewal outlays are measured in dollar outlays versus additions to local tax (property) rolls. The problem is to relate redevelopment to travel patterns and new urban highways to demands for auto-auxiliary facilities (parking spaces) and to the concurrent reduction in tax rolls.

The cost of clearing land is obviously not the only one involved in urban renewal. What is the "cost" of uprooting families from their established life and neighborhood? On the other hand what are the costs—in poor health, crime, and destructive family patterns—of leaving substandard housing untouched? Highway users are a different group from highway impactees. Whose benefit is paramount?

Again no simple answers are possible. As Leonard Fein of MIT observed:

. . . the political problem is always how to spend the scarce resources of the society, whether to build roads or schools, airports or hospitals, jails or gardens. These are very properly matters for intense debate, and no computerized operation can ever make the final choice except as our programs specify our values.

As the community itself begins to assess its problems and to establish priorities, *then* cost–benefit techniques can play an important—if circumscribed—role. We hope that the Model Cities program will give us some experience on how this can happen.

NEW ORDERS OF MAGNITUDE

A final factor complicating our efforts to find new answers to urban problems is the sheer size of the undertaking. In 1889, the United States was a nation of 62 million persons, two out of three of whom lived in rural communities. By 1967, we were 180 million, three fourths of whom lived in cities or metropolitan areas. By the year 2000, there will be almost 312 million Americans, with 187 million living in the nation's fourteen major urban regions alone.

These people must be housed, educated, employed, and transported. We must provide for their health, recreational, and cultural needs. We stand on the verge of a period of sustained urban growth so unprecedented that only the inscrutable and dispassionate Budget Bureau, perhaps, has begun to grapple with its implications.

We need not fear this growth. But we must respond to its challenge. The coming urban flood will tend to course down existing stream beds. We have just a few years in which to cut new channels and determine their worth.

In the past, problems of urban design were handled largely through intuition. Now we have new tools with which to work. But even the elegance of newer mathematical models, electronic semi-conductors, and third-generation computers is not enough. Further advances in scientific and engineering sophistication are needed. We must find ways to understand considerations of individual personality, group and neighborhood identity, mobility, and aspirations.

This is the challenge of urban science as it is the challenge of urban government.

7. A General's Warning, 1961

DWIGHT D. EISENHOWER, "Farewell Radio and Television Address to the American People"

It can be argued that the technological problems we face today are more than simply the result of a myriad of discrete decisions, related by interlocking results but not by original design. Indeed, there has been a lack of public planning; yet this should not blind us to the fact that there is a great deal of private planning which is carried on as a matter of course in the industrial sector of our economy, and that this planning is related to our national goals and policies. Ironically, one of the earliest warnings that this was so came not from any noted social critic, but rather from a retiring President, Dwight D. Eisenhower.

This controversial speech has been variously interpreted—both his friends and his enemies have tended to discount it because it seems to contradict the otherwise obvious and simple thrust of his beliefs and career. Whatever his motives and degree of understanding, it remains a clear formulation of what may be the single most serious technological problem of our time.

My fellow Americans:

Three days from now, after half a century in the service of our country, I shall lay down the responsibilities of office as, in traditional and solemn cere-mony, the authority of the Presidency is vested in my successor.

This evening I come to you with a message of leave-taking and farewell, and to share a few final thoughts with you, my countrymen.

From Dwight D. Eisenhower, "Farewell Radio and Television Address to the American People, January 17, 1961," *Public Papers of the Presidents of the United States, Dwight D. Eisenhower, 1960-61* (Washington, D.C., 1961), pp. 1035-40.

Like every other citizen, I wish the new President, and all who will labor with him, Godspeed. I pray that the coming years will be blessed with peace and prosperity for all.

Our people expect their President and the Congress to find essential agreement on issues of great moment, the wise resolution of which will better shape the future of the Nation.

My own relations with the Congress, which began on a remote and tenuous basis when, long ago, a member of the Senate appointed me to West Point, have since ranged to the intimate during the war and immediate post-war period, and, finally, to the mutually interdependent during these past eight years.

In this final relationship, the Congress and the Administration have, on most vital issues, cooperated well, to serve the national good rather than mere partisanship, and so have assured that the business of the Nation should go forward. So, my official relationship with the Congress ends in a feeling, on my part, of gratitude that we have been able to do so much together.

II.

We now stand ten years past the midpoint of a century that has witnessed four major wars among great nations. Three of these involved our own country. Despite these holocausts America is today the strongest, the most influential and most productive nation in the world. Understandably proud of this pre-eminence, we yet realize that America's leadership and prestige depend, not merely upon our unmatched material progress, riches and military strength, but on how we use our power in the interests of world peace and human betterment.

III.

Throughout America's adventure in free government, our basic purposes have been to keep the peace; to foster progress in human achievement, and to enhance liberty, dignity and integrity among people and among nations. To strive for less would be unworthy of a free and religious people. Any failure traceable to arrogance, or our lack of comprehension or readiness to sacrifice would inflict upon us grievous hurt both at home and abroad.

Progress toward these noble goals is persistently threatened by the conflict now engulfing the world. It commands our whole attention, absorbs our very beings. We face a hostile ideology—global in scope, atheistic in character, ruthless in purpose, and insidious in method. Unhappily the danger it poses promises to be of indefinite duration. To meet it successfully, there is called for, not so much the emotional and transitory sacrifices of crisis, but rather those which enable us to carry forward steadily, surely, and without complaint the burdens of a prolonged and complex struggle—with liberty the stake. Only thus shall we remain, despite every provocation, on our charted course toward permanent peace and human betterment.

Crises there will continue to be. In meeting them, whether foreign or domestic, great or small, there is a recurring temptation to feel that some spectacular and costly action could become the miraculous solution to all current difficulties. A huge increase in newer elements of our defense; development of unrealistic programs to cure every ill in agriculture; a dramatic expansion in basic and applied research—these and many other possibilities, each possibly promising in itself, may be suggested as the only way to the road we wish to travel.

But each proposal must be weighed in the light of a broader consideration: the need to maintain balance in and among national programs—balance between the private and public economy, balance between cost and hoped for advantage— balance between the clearly necessary and the comfortably desirable; balance between our essential requirements as a nation and the duties imposed by the nation upon the individual; balance between actions of the moment and the national welfare of the future. Good judgment seeks balance and progress; lack of it eventually finds imbalance and frustration.

The record of many decades stands as proof that our people and their government have, in the main, understood these truths and have responded to them well, in the face of stress and threat. But threats, new in kind or degree, constantly arise. I mention two only.

IV.

A vital element in keeping the peace is our military establishment. Our arms must be mighty, ready for instant action, so that no potential aggressor may be tempted to risk his own destruction.

Our military organization today bears little relation to that known by any of my predecessors in peacetime, or indeed by the fighting men of World War II or Korea.

Until the latest of our world conflicts, the United States had no armaments industry. American makers of plowshares could, with time and as required, make swords as well. But now we can no longer risk emergency improvisation of national defense; we have been compelled to create a permanent armaments industry of vast proportions. Added to

this, three and a half million men and women are directly engaged in the defense establishment. We annually spend on military security more than the net income of all United States corporations.

This conjunction of an immense military establishment and a large arms industry is new in the American experience. The total influence—economic, political, even spiritual—is felt in every city, every State house, every office of the Federal Government. We recognize the imperative need for this development. Yet we must not fail to comprehend its grave implications. Our toil, resources and livelihood are all involved; so is the very structure of our society.

In the councils of government, we must guard against the acquisition of unwarranted influence, whether sought or unsought, by the military-industrial complex. The potential for the disastrous rise of misplaced power exists and will persist.

We must never let the weight of this combination endanger our liberties or democratic processes. We should take nothing for granted. Only an alert and knowledgeable citizenry can compel the proper meshing of the huge industrial and military machinery of defense with our peaceful methods and goals, so that security and liberty may prosper together.

Akin to, and largely responsible for the sweeping changes in our industrial-military posture, has been the technological revolution during recent decades.

In this revolution, research has become central; it also becomes more formalized, complex, and costly. A steadily increasing share is conducted for, by, or at the direction of, the Federal government.

Today, the solitary inventor, tinkering in his shop, has been overshadowed by task forces of scientists in laboratories and testing fields. In the same fashion, the free university, historically the fountainhead of free ideas and scientific discovery, has experienced a revolution in the conduct of research. Partly because of the huge costs involved, a government contract becomes virtually a substitute for intellectual curiosity. For every old blackboard there are now hundreds of new electronic computers.

The prospect of domination of the nation's scholars by Federal employment, project allocations, and the power of money is ever present—and is gravely to be regarded.

Yet, in holding scientific research and discovery in respect, as we should, we must also be alert to the equal and opposite danger that public policy could itself become the captive of a scientific-technological elite.

It is the task of statesmanship to mold, to balance, and to integrate these and other forces, new and old, within the principles of our democratic system— ever aiming toward the supreme goals of our free society.

V.

Another factor in maintaining balance involves the element of time. As we peer into society's future, we—you and I, and our government—must avoid the impulse to live only for today, plundering, for our own ease and convenience, the precious resources of tomorrow. We cannot mortgage the material assets of our grandchildren without risking the loss also of their political and spiritual heritage. We want democracy to survive for all generations to come, not to become the insolvent phantom of tomorrow.

VI.

Down the long lane of history yet to be written America knows that this world of ours, ever growing smaller, must avoid becoming a community of dreadful fear and hate, and be, instead, a proud confederation of mutual trust and respect.

Such a confederation must be one of equals. The weakest must come to the conference table with the same confidence as do we, protected as we are by our moral, economic, and military strength. That table, though scarred by many past frustrations, cannot be abandoned for the certain agony of the battlefield.

Disarmament, with mutual honor and confidence, is a continuing imperative. Together we must learn how to compose differences, not with arms, but with intellect and decent purpose. Because this need is so sharp and apparent I confess that I lay down my official responsibilities in this field with a definite sense of disappointment. As one who has witnessed the horror and the lingering sadness of war—as one who knows that another war could utterly destroy this civilization which has been so slowly and painfully built over thousands of years— I wish I could say tonight that a lasting peace is in sight.

Happily, I can say that war has been avoided. Steady progress toward our ultimate goal has been made. But, so much remains to be done. As a private citizen, I shall never cease to do what little I can to help the world advance along that road.

VII.

So—in this my last good night to you as your President—I thank you for the many opportunities you have given me for public service in war and peace. I trust that in that service you find some things worthy; as for the rest of it, I know you will find ways to improve performance in the future.

You and I—my fellow citizens—need to be strong in our faith that all nations, under God, will reach the goal of peace with justice. May we be ever unswerving in devotion to principle, confident but humble with power, diligent in pursuit of the Nation's great goals.

To all the peoples of the world, I once more give expression to America's prayerful and continuing aspiration:

We pray that peoples of all faiths, all races, all nations, may have their great human needs satisfied; that those now denied opportunity shall come to enjoy it to the full; that all who yearn for freedom may experience its spiritual blessings; that those who have freedom will understand, also, its heavy responsibilities; that all who are insensitive to the needs of others will learn charity; that the scourges of poverty, disease and ignorance will be made to disappear from the earth, and that, in the goodness of time, all peoples will come to live together in a peace guaranteed by the binding force of mutual respect and love.

For Further Reading

The literature dealing with the history of technology in the United States is vast. The student who ventures into this field should first consult an attempt at synthesis such as Melvin Kranzberg and Carroll W. Pursell, Jr., eds., *Technology in Western Civilization* (2 vols., New York, 1967). The first volume of that work discusses the growth of technology to 1900. The second volume deals only with the twentieth century and concentrates on American developments. Both volumes contain extensive annotated bibliographies. Another source, giving both narrative and bibliography, is David D. Van Tassel and Michael G. Hall, eds., *Science and Society in the United States* (Homewood, Ill., 1966),* which has separate chapters on agricultural, industrial, military, and other uses of applied science. A book-length study of American technology, with an exciting interpretation, is presented in John A. Kouwenhoven, *Made in America: The Arts in Modern Civilization* (New York, 1948). Shorter interpretations are provided by Eugene S. Ferguson, "On the Origin and Development of American Mechanical 'Know-How,'" *Midcontinent American Studies Journal,* III (Fall, 1962), 3-16, and John B. Rae, "The 'Know-How' Tradition: Technology in American History," *Technology and Culture,* I (Spring 1960), 139-50. Articles of a more specific nature may be found in such excellent journals as *Technology and Culture, Agricultural History, Journal of Economic History, Business History Review,* and *ISIS*.

* Titles marked with an asterisk are available in paperback.

Colonial Technology: Any study of early American technology should begin with Brooke Hindle, *Technology in Early America: Needs and Opportunities for Study* (Chapel Hill, 1966),* which contains both an enlightening essay on the subject and an extensive bibliography. Colonial agriculture is best approached through the two classics, Percy W. Bidwell and John I. Falconer, *History of Agriculture in the Northern United States, 1620-1860* (Washington, D.C., 1925), and Lewis C. Gray, *History of Agriculture in the Southern United States to 1860* (Washington, D.C., 1933). Colonial crafts are the subject of a short book by Carl Bridenbaugh, entitled *The Colonial Craftsman* (New York, 1950).* The best book on colonial ironworks is Arthur Cecil Bining, *Pennsylvania Iron Manufacture in the Eighteenth Century* (Harrisburg, 1938). A close study of one early and ambitious ironworks is provided by Edward N. Hartley, *Ironworks on the Saugus* (Norman, 1957).

The Industrial Revolution: Hindle, *Technology in Early America*, is also the starting point for understanding the coming of the Industrial Revolution to America. Not surprisingly, the literature on this aspect of our technological history is the most abundant. The best survey on transportation is George Rogers Taylor, *The Transportation Revolution, 1815-1860* (New York, 1951).* For a survey on steamboats see Louis C. Hunter, *Steamboats on the Western Rivers: An Economic and Technological History* (Cambridge, 1949). One particularly important canal is described in

Ralph D. Gray, *The National Waterway: A History of the Chesapeake and Delaware Canal, 1769-1965* (Urbana, 1967). Turnpikes are treated by Robert F. Hunter, "Turnpike Construction in Antebellum Virginia," *Technology and Culture*, IV (Spring 1963), 177-200. The role of army engineers in developing all these forms of transportation is told in Forest G. Hill, *Roads, Rails & Waterways: The Army Engineers and Early Transportation* (Norman, 1957).

Early American manufacturing is covered in many different studies. An economic investigation of labor costs is made in H. J. Habakkuk, *American and British Technology in the Nineteenth Century: The Search for Labour-Saving Inventions* (New York, 1962). An economic study of the iron industry is provided by Peter Temin, *Iron and Steel in Nineteenth-Century America: An Economic Inquiry* (Cambridge, 1964). The classic study of toolmakers is Joseph W. Roe, *English and American Tool Builders* (New Haven, 1916). An intimate portrait of Philadelphia and British machine makers is provided by Eugene S. Ferguson, ed., *Early Engineering Reminiscences (1815-40) of George Escol Sellers*, U.S. National Museum, *Bulletin No. 238* (Washington, D.C., 1965). A detailed but still unsatisfactory biography of early America's greatest inventor is Greville and Dorothy Bathe, *Oliver Evans: A Chronicle of Early American Engineering* (Philadelphia, 1935). New insight into the origins of the American System of manufacture is provided by Robert S. Woodbury, "The Legend of Eli Whitney and Interchangeable Parts," *Technology and Culture*, I (Summer 1960), 235-53. The reaction of foreigners to the American experience is told by Marvin Fisher, *Workshops in the Wilderness: The European Response to American Industrialization, 1830-60* (New York, 1967).

A good beginning has been made toward understanding the special way in which Americans regarded technology, and how they related it to their sense of mission. The most important book on this subject is Leo Marx, *The Machine in the Garden: Technology and the Pastoral Ideal in America* (New York, 1964).* A study based upon more recent American literature is Thomas Reed West, *Flesh of Steel: Literature and the Machine in American Culture* (Nashville, 1967). Two shorter but equally excellent surveys are given in Hugo A. Meier, "Technology and Democracy, 1800-1860, "*Mississippi Valley Historical Review*, XLIII (March 1957), 618-40, and "American Technology and the Nineteenth-Century World," *American Quarterly*, X (Summer 1958), 116-30, by the same author.

Agriculture: Bidwell and Falconer, and Gray, cited above in Colonial Technology, cover this period of agricultural development. A good one-volume summary is Paul W. Gates, *The Farmer's Age: Agriculture, 1815-1860* (New York, 1960).* Still of considerable value (and recently reprinted) is Leo Rogin, *The Introduction of Farm Machinery in its Relation to the Productivity of Labor in the Agriculture of the United States During the Nineteenth Century* (Berkeley, 1931). Good studies of various aspects of agricultural technology include William T. Hutchinson, *Cyrus Hall McCormick: Seed-Time, 1809-1856* (New York, 1930); Earle D. Ross, "Retardation in Farm Technology Before the Power Age," *Agricultural History*, XXX (January 1956), 11-18; Clarence H. Danhof, "Gathering the Grass," *Agricultural History*, XXX (October 1956),

169-73; and Edward C. Kendall, "John Deere's Steel Plow," U.S. National Museum, *Bulletin No. 218* (Washington, D.C., 1959), 15-25.

Expansion: Comparatively little attention has been paid to the problem of American technological expansion during the nineteenth century. D. L. Burn, "The Genesis of American Engineering Competition, 1850-1870," *Economic History*, II (January 1931), 292-311, gives data on this crucial period, when American industry began to overtake the British. One of the few biographies of an engineer who exported his talent is Albert Parry, *Whistler's Father* (Indianapolis, 1939). The elder Whistler was an army engineer who resigned his commission and went to Russia to help build railroads for the Czar. Some early American interests overseas are described in Merle Curti and Kendall Birr, *Prelude to Point Four: American Technical Missions Overseas, 1838-1938* (Madison, 1954).

New Industries: There is no satisfactory history of the steel industry, but the interested student may consult Temin, *Iron and Steel in Nineteenth-Century America* (cited above in Industrial Revolution), and the very revealing *The Autobiography of John Fritz* (New York, 1912). The chemical industry is surveyed in L. F. Haber, *The Chemical Industry During the Nineteenth Century: A Study of the Economic Aspects of Applied Chemistry in Europe and North America* (London, 1958). Matthew Josephson, *Edison* (New York, 1959)* is the best biography of an American technologist. For a study of the electrical industry as a whole, see Harold C. Passer, *The Electrical Manufacturers, 1875-1900: A Study in Com-*

petition, Entrepreneurship, Technical Change, and Economic Growth (Cambridge, 1953). A fine work which covers a broader range is W. Paul Strassmann, *Risk and Technological Innovation: American Manufacturing Methods during the Nineteenth Century* (Ithaca, 1959). The petroleum industry is treated in great detail in Harold F. Williamson *et al.*, *The American Petroleum Industry: The Age of Illumination, 1859-1899* (Evanston, 1959), and *The American Petroleum Industry: The Age of Energy, 1899-1959* (Evanston, 1963).

The West: The new but already standard study of scientific exploration in the West is William H. Goetzmann, *Exploration and Empire: The Explorer and the Scientist in the Winning of the American West* (New York, 1966). Mining is best handled by Rodman Wilson Paul, *Mining Frontiers of the Far West, 1848-1880* (New York, 1963). Agriculture is well covered by Fred A. Shannon, *The Farmer's Last Frontier: Agriculture, 1860-1897* (New York, 1945).* Reynold M. Wik, *Steam Power on the American Farm* (Philadelphia, 1953) discusses traction engines, and Henry D. and Frances T. McCallum, *The Wire That Fenced the West* (Norman, 1965), covers the invention and use of barbed wire.

Professionalization: Two authors have attempted to deal with the growing professionalization of engineers during the nineteenth century: Daniel Hovey Calhoun, *The American Civil Engineer: Origins and Conflict* (Cambridge, 1960), and Monte A. Calvert, *The Mechanical Engineer in America, 1830-1910* (Baltimore, 1967). No similar

study of engineering education is available, but the reader might begin with the biography, by William Frederick Durand, of one of the leading educators, *Robert Henry Thurston: A Biography. The Record of a Life of Achievement as Engineer, Educator, and Author* (New York, 1929). A generation later, another educator, Dexter S. Kimball, left his autobiography, *I Remember* (New York, 1953). A charming book of recollections by a man who started in the shop and became a leading journalist in the field is Fred H. Colvin, *60 Years With Men and Machines: An Autobiography* (New York, 1947). The beginning of a broad study is reported in John J. Beer and W. David Lewis, "Aspects of the Professionalization of Science," *Daedalus*, XCII (Fall 1963), 764-84.

The Cities: A useful general work, with an especially thorough bibliography, is Oscar Handlin and John E. Burchard, eds., *The Historian and the City* (Cambridge, 1963).* Western cities during the early nineteenth century are covered by Richard C. Wade, *The Urban Frontier* (Chicago, 1959).* One aspect of urban technology is discussed in Nelson Manfred Blake, *Water for the Cities: A History of the Urban Water Supply Problem In the United States* (Syracuse, 1956). Two books by Carl W. Condit, *American Building Art: The Nineteenth Century* (New York, 1960), and *American Building Art: The Twentieth Century* (New York, 1961), deal with buildings in an urban setting. The leading Progressive engineer to make a career of urban technology is examined in Kenneth E. Trombley, *The Life and Times of a Happy Liberal: A Biography of Morris Llewellyn Cooke* (New York, 1954).

The Progressive Era: A first-rate study of the intellectual content of the efficiency craze is given in Samuel Haber, *Efficiency and Uplift: Scientific Management in the Progressive Era, 1890-1920* (Chicago, 1964). Two studies by Samuel P. Hays give the best insight into urban and conservation problems: his article, "The Politics of Reform in Municipal Government in the Progressive Era," *Pacific Northwest Quarterly,* LV (October 1964), 157-69, links technology to urban reform, and his book, *Conservation and The Gospel of Efficiency: The Progressive Conservation Movement, 1890-1920* (Cambridge, 1959), is the standard work on that subject. The conservation story in the 1920's is best told in Donald C. Swain, *Federal Conservation Policy, 1921-1933* (Berkeley, 1963). One of the landmarks of the period is Thorstein Veblen, *The Engineers and the Price System*, originally published in 1921 but now available in a new edition with an excellent introduction by Daniel Bell (New York, 1963).*

World War I: America's role in World War I has not attracted the historical attention it deserves. The best survey is still Frederic L. Paxson, *America at War, 1917-1918* (Boston, 1939). An old but detailed description of America's war technology is Frank Parker Stockbridge, *Yankee Ingenuity in the War* (New York, 1920). One good recent study, which concentrates on aircraft, is I. B. Holley, *Ideas and Weapons* (New Haven, 1953). A history of one of the most active technical committees of the war is Lloyd N. Scott, *Naval Consulting Board of the United States* (Washington, D. C., 1920). A key scientist in the mobilization of American technology is the subject of a

recent biography by Helen Wright, *Explorer of the Universe: A Biography of George Ellery Hale* (New York, 1966).

The 1920's: The best survey of the rise of industrial research in this country is Howard R. Bartlett, "The Development of Industrial Research in the United States," *Research—A National Resource: II.—Industrial Research,* National Resources Committee (Washington, D.C., 1941), 19-77. A detailed description of the most important laboratory is provided by Kendall Birr, *Pioneering in Industrial Research: The Story of the General Electric Research Laboratory* (Washington, D.C., 1957). The whole problem of research and invention, with many case studies, is discussed in John Jewkes, David Sawers, and Richard Stillerman, *The Sources of Invention* (London, 1961). One important industry that was established during these years is covered in W. Rupert Maclaurin, *Invention and Innovation in the Radio Industry* (New York, 1949). An excellent survey of the automobile industry is John B. Rae, *The American Automobile* (Chicago, 1965).* The turning of industry to techniques of personnel control is covered in Loren Baritz, *The Servants of Power: A History of Social Science in American Industry* (Middletown, 1960).* One of the key government research bureaus concerned with industrial technology is the subject of Rexmond C. Cochrane, *Measures for Progress: A History of the National Bureau of Standards* (Washington, D. C., 1966).

The Depression: Strangely, the science and technology of the 1930's have been largely neglected. Two articles which touch upon aspects of the problem, both by Carroll W. Pursell, Jr., are

"The Anatomy of a Failure: The Science Advisory Board, 1933-1935," *Proceedings of the American Philosophical Society,* cix (December 10, 1965), 342-51, and "A Preface to Government Support of Research and Development: Research Legislation and the National Bureau of Standards, 1935-41," *Technology and Culture,* ix (April 1968), 145-64. A sociological study of one dissenting group is presented by Henry Elsner, Jr., *The Technocrats: Prophets of Automation* (Syracuse, 1967). Another study, dealing with a reform group that emphasizes science and technology, and written by a supporter, is Christy Borth, *Pioneers of Plenty: The Story of Chemurgy* (Indianapolis, 1939). Harry Jerome, *Mechanization in Industry* (New York, 1934) is a contemporary analysis of that problem.

World War II: The large number of works dealing with World War II tend to emphasize either combat or the diplomatic aspects of the struggle. For weapons and medical research one should begin with Irvin Stewart, *Organizing Scientific Research for War: The Administrative History of the Office of Scientific Research and Development* (Boston, 1948). Of the vast literature on the atomic bomb, the best history is that sponsored by the Atomic Energy Commission, Richard G. Hewlett and Oscar E. Anderson, *The New World 1939/1946. Volume I: A History of the United States Atomic Energy Commission* (University Park, 1962). Many of the problems of technology on the home front are vividly and accurately described in Bruce Catton, *The War Lords of Washington* (New York, 1948). Some of the important documents covering the war and postwar period are collected in James L. Penick,

Jr., Carroll W. Pursell, Jr., Morgan B. Sherwood, and Donald C. Swain, eds., *The Politics of American Science: 1939 to the Present* (Chicago, 1965).*

Postwar Problems: There are an enormous number of books dealing with the technological problems and opportunities of our own time, only a small number of which are, strictly speaking, historical. A brief survey is provided by J. Stefan Dupre and Sanford A. Lakoff, *Science and the Nation: Policy and Politics* (Englewood Cliffs, 1962).* A study of policy-making for war research within the government is Thomas A. Sturm, *The USAF Scientific Advisory Board: Its First Twenty Years, 1944-1964* (Washington, D. C., 1967), while the most famous of the research organizations is treated in Bruce L. R. Smith, *The RAND Corporation: Case Study of a Nonprofit Advisory Corporation* (Cambridge, 1966). Automation is the

subject of many studies, among the best of which is Ben B. Seligman, *Most Notorious Victory: Man in an Age of Automation* (New York, 1966). Other aspects of technological development are treated with varying degrees of insight in Eugene B. Skolnikoff, *Science, Technology, and American Foreign Policy* (Cambridge, 1967), Donald A. Schon, *Technology and Change: The New Heraclitus* (New York, 1967),* and Editors of *Scientific American, Technology and Economic Development* (New York, 1963).* A thoughtful series of essays on current problems is provided by Elting E. Morison, *Men, Machines, and Modern Times* (Cambridge, 1966).* Finally, an extremely influential philosophical criticism of our technological society is Herbert Marcuse, *One Dimensional Man: Studies in the Ideology of Advanced Industrial Society* (Boston, 1964).*